A SELECTION OF IMPORTANT PAPERS IN HEREDITARY ANGIOEDEMA

Contents

A SELECTION OF IMPORTANT PAPERS IN HEREDITARY ANGIOEDEMA

A SELECTION OF IMPORTANT PAPERS IN HEREDITARY ANGIOEDEMA

A SELECTION OF IMPORTANT PAPERS IN HEREDITARY ANGIOEDEMA

EDITORS

Bruce L. Zuraw, MD
University of California, San Diego
La Jolla, California

Michael M. Frank, MD
Duke University Medical Center
Durham, North Carolina

PLANNING COMMITTEE

Cindy H. Jablonowski, MA, *Director, Custom Publishing*

Vanessa Fendt, *Editorial Project Manager*

Editorial Office

685 Route 202/206
Bridgewater, NJ 08807

Release Date: November 2009.   ISBN: 978-1-4377-6731-5

A SELECTION OF IMPORTANT PAPERS IN HEREDITARY ANGIOEDEMA

DISCLOSURES

It is the policy of Excerpta Medica Inc. to require the disclosure of anyone who is in a position to control the content of a publication. All relevant financial relationships with any commercial interests and/or manufacturers must be disclosed to readers. The contributors to this publication disclose the following:

Contributor	Corporation/Manufacturer	Relationship
Bruce L. Zuraw, MD	Lev Pharmaceuticals, Inc.; Pharming	Clinical Trial Support
	Byax Corporation; CSL Behring; Jerini/Shire;	Consultant
	Lev; Pharming	
Michael M. Frank, MD	Byax; CSL Behring; Shire;	Consultant
	ViroPharma	

UNAPPROVED/OFF-LABEL USE DISCLOSURE

Excerpta Medica Inc. requires contributors to disclose to readers:

1. When products or procedures being discussed are off-label, unlabeled, experimental, and/or investigational (not US Food and Drug Administration [FDA] approved); and

2. Any limitations on the information that is presented, such as data that are preliminary or that represent ongoing research; interim analyses; and/or unsupported opinion.

Contributors may discuss information about pharmaceutical agents that is outside of FDA-approved labeling. This information is intended solely for discussion and is not intended to promote off-label use of these medications. If you have questions, contact the medical affairs department of the manufacturer for the most recent prescribing information.

FINANCIAL SUPPORT

The activity is supported by an educational grant from ViroPharma Incorporated.

Introduction

Under the many pressures of clinical practice, physicians are understandably focused on the here and now. Before us is a patient with symptoms and a history; our job is to diagnose and treat the problem as quickly and efficiently as possible so as to reduce the patient's suffering and resolve the illness. As we carry out these familiar but demanding tasks, we rarely reflect on the long history of scientific investigation and discovery to which our clinical knowledge and skills owe their origin. The immediate needs of the patient leave us little time for historical perspective. But each of us, whether we are conscious of it or not, is the repository of hundreds of years of investigation and thought, the gifts of the students of medicine who have preceded us. Like Isaac Newton, we see far by standing on the shoulders of giants.

Given the debt we owe to the great teachers of medicine, it is appropriate that occasionally we reflect upon how far we have come in our study. The purpose of this publication is to prompt that reflection with regard to a specific clinical syndrome, angioedema, a condition that has engaged some of the great minds of medicine since the 19th century. Here, some of the papers that have contributed to our current understanding and which serve as signposts in the history of our understanding of this disorder are compiled.

Angioedema was described over 100 years ago by J.L. Milton in the *Edinburgh Medical Journal*, where he wrote of a patient upon whom lay "across the face from temple to temple an oblong tumor almost closing both eyes," a disorder he termed "giant urticaria."[1] In 1882, Heinrich Quincke described "acute localized dropsy" and identified many characteristics of the condition, including "edematous tumidities of the skin and hypoderma" occurring most often on the face and extremities and sometimes involving the respiratory and gastrointestinal systems.[2] Quincke also noted the recurrent nature of the disorder and some of the stimuli that may trigger an episode, and proposed the term "angioneurotic edema" because he believed that angioedema arose from an abnormality of the nervous supply of the blood vessels that promoted plasma leakage. In Europe, angioedema is termed "Quincke's Disease" to this day.

Six years after Quincke's paper, William Osler established the hereditary nature of the disease we now know of as hereditary angioedema (HAE) or C1-inhibitor deficiency when he described 5 generations of a family affected by the disorder.[3] Osler is considered one of America's greatest clinicians and his extraordinary insight is evident in this paper. Not only did he touch upon almost all of the major clinical findings, even though he had access to only a few patients with the syndrome, but he also cautioned physicians to pay little attention to discussions of etiology until a greater understanding of pathophysiology was available. Subsequent clinical descriptions of HAE have confirmed Osler's description and highlighted the wide spectrum of clinical severity seen among affected patients.[4–6]

Seventy-five years following Osler's work, the biochemical abnormalities underlying HAE were identified in 2 landmark publications. First, Landerman et al[7] reported that plasma from HAE patients failed to inhibit serum globulin permeability factor (activated Hageman factor) or plasma kallikrein. The following year, Donaldson and Evans[8] reported the absence of C1-esterase inhibitor in patients with the disease. Since that time, steady progress has been made in the understanding of the pathophysiology of HAE. The availability of a biochemical marker for the disease rapidly led to the recognition of 2 distinct HAE phenotypes based on differences in C1-inhibitor antigenic and functional levels by Rosen et al.[9] Cloning of the gene encoding C1-inhibitor led to the recognition that HAE resulted from mutations in the gene and provided a mechanistic explanation for the 2 hereditary forms of C1-inhibitor deficiency.[10] Work in multiple laboratories established that the primary mediator of swelling in angioedema was bradykinin.[11] Most recently, a third form of HAE has been described that does not involve C1-inhibitor deficiency but in some instances appear to result from a gain in function mutation in coagulation factor XII (Hageman factor).[12]

Introduction

In 1972, Michael Frank and Albert Sheffer each demonstrated favorable results in double-blind studies of antifibrinolytic therapy as treatment of HAE.[13,14] Four years later, attenuated androgens were demonstrated to be effective in preventing HAE.[15] Subsequently, purified C1-inhibitor replacement therapy was shown to be effective in controlling attacks of HAE. The development of C1-inhibitor replacement therapy is chronicled in this publication in papers by Agostoni et al,[16] Gadek et al,[17] Bergamaschini et al,[18] and Bork and Witzke,[19] and extensive experience with this treatment is reported by Farkas et al.[20] The state of knowledge regarding angioedema was ably summarized by Nzeako et al[21] in 2001 and by Bork et al[22] in 2006. Recently completed clinical trials have suggested that bradykinin-directed therapy, using either a plasma kallikrein inhibitor or a β_2 bradykinin receptor antagonist, may have substantial efficacy in treating HAE.[23]

Taken together, these papers tell the remarkable story of more than a century of scientific accomplishment in the study of this persistent and sometimes life-threatening condition. We hope you enjoy seeing them gathered here and take inspiration from the efforts of the many dedicated physicians who tried to see just a bit further than the giants who preceded them.

REFERENCES

1. Milton JL. On giant urticaria. *Edinb Med J*. 1876;22:513.
2. Quincke H. Ueb er akutes umschriebenes Hautoedem. *Monatsschr Praht Dermatol*. 1882;1:129–131.
3. Osler W. Hereditary angio-neurotic oedema. *Am J Med Sci*. 1888;95:362–367.
4. Frank MM, Gelfand JA, Atkinson JP. Hereditary angioedema: The clinical syndrome and its management. *Ann Intern Med*. 1976; 84:580–593.
5. Frank MM. Hereditary angioedema: The clinical syndrome and its management in the United States. *Immunol Allergy Clin North Am*. 2006;23:653–668.
6. Frank MM. Hereditary angioedema. *J Allergy Clin Immunol*. 2008;121(Suppl 2):S398–S401.
7. Landerman NS, Webster ME, Becker EL, Ratcliffe HE. Hereditary angioneurotic edema. II. Deficiency of inhibitor for serum globulin permeability factor and/or plasma kallikrein. *J Allergy*. 1962;33:330–341.
8. Donaldson VH, Evans RR. A biochemical abnormality in hereditary angioneurotic edema: Absence of serum inhibitor of C1-esterase. *Am J Med*. 1963;35:37–44.
9. Rosen FS, Charache P, Pensky J, Donaldson V. Hereditary angioneurotic edema: Two genetic variants. *Science*. 1965;148:957–958.
10. Davis AE III. C1 inhibitor and hereditary angioneurotic edema. *Annu Rev Immunol*. 1988;6:595–628.
11. Davis AE III. Mechanism of angioedema in first complement component inhibitor deficiency. *Immunol Allergy Clin North Am*. 2006; 26:633–651.
12. Cichon S, Martin L, Hennies HC, et al. Increased activity of coagulation factor XII (Hageman factor) causes hereditary angioedema type III. *Am J Hum Genet*. 2006;79:1098–1104.
13. Sheffer AL, Austen KF, Rosen FS. Tranexamic acid therapy in hereditary angioneurotic edema. *N Engl J Med*. 1972;287:452–454.
14. Frank MM, Sergent JS, Kane MA, et al. Epsilon aminocaproic acid therapy of hereditary angioneurotic edema. A double-blind study. *N Engl J Med*. 1972;15:808–812.
15. Gelfand JA, Sherins RJ, Alling DW, Frank MM. Treatment of hereditary angioedema with danazol. Reversal of clinical and biochemical abnormalities. *N Engl J Med*. 1976;26:1444–1448.
16. Agostoni A, Bergamaschini L, Martignoni G, et al. Treatment of acute attacks of hereditary angioedema with C1-inhibitor concentrate. *Ann Allergy*. 1980;44:299–301.
17. Gadek JE, Hosea SW, Gelfand JA, et al. Replacement therapy in hereditary angioedema: Successful treatment of acute episodes of angioedema with partly purified C1 inhibitor. *N Engl J Med*. 1980;302:542–546.
18. Bergamaschini L, Cicardi M, Tucci A, et al. C1 INH concentrate in the therapy of hereditary angioedema. *Allergy*. 1983;38:81–84.
19. Bork K, Witzke G. Long-term prophylaxis with C1-inhibitor (C1 INH) concentrate in patients with recurrent angioedema caused by hereditary and acquired C1-inhibitor deficiency. *J Allergy Clin Immunol*. 1989;83:677–682.
20. Farkas H, Jakab L, Temesszentandrási G, et al. Hereditary angioedema: A decade of human C1-inhibitor concentrate therapy. *J Allergy Clin Immunol*. 2007;120:941–947.
21. Nzeako UC, Frigas E, Tremaine WJ. Hereditary angioedema: A broad review for clinicians. *Arch Intern Med*. 2001;161:2417–2429.
22. Bork K, Meng G, Staubach P, Hardt J. Hereditary angioedema: New findings concerning symptoms, affected organs, and course. *Am J Med*. 2006;119:267–274.
23. Zuraw BL. Hereditary angioedema. *N Engl J Med*. 2008;359:1027–1036.

Zwölf Hefte bilden einen Band, dem Sach- u. Namen-Register u. system. Über-sicht beigegeben wird.

Monatshefte
für
Praktische Dermatologie

redigiert von

Dr. H. v. Hebra
Wien.

Dr. O. Lassar
Berlin.

Dr. P. G. Unna
Hamburg.

Der Preis ist halbjährlich 6 Mark. — Zu beziehen durch alle Buchhandlungen und Postanstalten.

Band I.   No. 5.   Juli 1882.

A. Original-Mitteilungen.

Über akutes umschriebenes Hautödem

von

H. Quincke.

Mit dem in der Überschrift genannten Namen möchte ich eine Hauterkrankung bezeichnen, die nicht so ganz selten zu sein scheint, von der aber nur wenige Fälle, mehr als Curiosa, beschrieben sind. Dr. E. Dinkelacker hat in seiner Dissertation: *Über akutes Ödem.* Kiel 1882, nach mehrern von uns beobachteten und nach den bisher beschriebenen Fällen ein Bild der Krankheit entworfen.

Dieselbe manifestiert sich in dem Auftreten ödematöser Schwellung der Haut und des Unterhautzellgewebes an umschriebenen Stellen von 2—10 und mehr Zentimeter Durchmesser. Diese Schwellungen finden sich am häufigsten an den Extremitäten, besonders in der Umgebung der Gelenke, aber auch am Rumpf und im Gesicht, hier besonders an den Lippen und den Augenlidern. Die geschwollenen Hautpartien sind nicht scharf gegen die Umgebung abgegrenzt, auch an Farbe der letztern gleich oder sogar blaß und durchscheinend, seltener etwas gerötet. Gewöhnlich empfinden die Kranken darin nur etwas Spannungsgefühl, selten Jucken. — Von ähnlichen Schwellungen können gleichzeitig auch die Schleimhäute befallen werden, so namentlich die der Lippen, des Gaumensegels, des Pharynx und Larynxeinganges, sogar bis zu solchem Grade, daß erhebliche Atemnot entsteht. Auch auf Magen- und Darmschleimhaut dürften, nach den in einem Falle anfallsweise auftretenden gastrischen und intestinalen Symptomen zu schließen, solche umschriebenen Schwellungen vorkommen. — In einem Falle traten auch wiederholte seröse Ergüsse in den Gelenken auf.

Diese Schwellungen treten nun plötzlich, gewöhnlich an mehrern Stellen zugleich auf, erreichen in einer bis einigen Stunden ihr Maximum, um eben so schnell zu verschwinden, nachdem sie mehrere

The
Applied Dermatology
Monthly

Edited by

DR. H. VON HEBRA   **DR. O. LASSAR**   **DR. P. G. UNNA**
Vienna   *Berlin*   *Hamburg*

VOLUME I   **NO. 5**   **JULY 1882**

A. ORIGINAL REPORTS

On Acute Localized Cutaneous Dropsy

by

H. Quincke

As indicated in the title, this report refers to a skin disease that does not appear to be very rare, even though only few cases have been described, and mostly as oddity at that. Following several cases we have observed and reported to date, Dr. E. Dinkelacker, in his dissertation titled *On Acute Edema*, Kiel 1882, mapped out the pattern of this disease.

This disease is manifested by the occurrence of edematous tumidities of the skin and of the hypoderma in locally defined regions, having a diameter of 2 to 10 or more centimeters. These swellings occur most often at the extremities, especially in the area of the joints, but also on the torso and on the face, especially on the lips and eyelids. The cutaneous tumidities are not sharply contrasted against their surroundings, but have the same color as the latter or are pale and pellucid, and only in some cases are slightly reddened. The patients usually feel only a certain tautness and rarely, an itching sensation. – At the same time, similar swellings can also affect the mucous membranes, especially for instance, the lips, the soft palate, the pharynx, and the laryngeal passage, to the degree that they can cause major dyspnea. As one case suggests, based on episodes of gastric and intestinal symptoms, such local swellings can even affect the mucosa of the stomach and of the intestines. – One case showed repeated serous effusions in the joints.

These tumidities occur suddenly, usually in several places at the same time, reaching their maximum within one to several hours, and then disappearing just as rapidly after having persisted from several hours to a day. Even as one disappears, new ones often erupt at some other remote point, so that this disorder can drag out for several days and even weeks.

The person's general condition usually remains unaffected. In some cases, apart from a premonitory subjective indisposition, the eruption was accompanied by a general feeling of illness, lightheadedness, thirst, and reduced uropoiesis. An elevated temperature has never been observed.

Once an individual has had an acute edema, it may easily recur as new episodes, usually with a predilection for the points of earlier occurrences. This recurrence may be at irregular or regular intervals over a span of years, for instance, in weekly cycles.

At times the cause triggering it may be found in a cooling of the skin, a cold infection, or physical stress.

This disorder appears to afflict men more often than women. The persons afflicted were otherwise healthy, some perhaps slightly irritable. In the case of one patient whose episodes occurred at fairly regular intervals, the disorder was hereditarily transmitted to his son who showed symptoms in the very first year of his life.

In terms of its appearance as well as the manner of its incidence, acute local dropsy to a certain degree resembles Hebra's disease as well as hives, and transitional forms have also been observed.

However, apart from frequently affecting the mucous membranes, the pure cases differ in that there is less reddening and a more pronounced swelling that also extends to the hypodermis, often with different points of predilection and (usually) in the absence of any itching. In contrast to Hebra's disease, there is also a tendency toward a spotty (rather than areal) distribution. Again, compared to erysipelas, a final point to be considered is the greater fugacity of the eruption and the absence of any significant fever.

Erythema nodosum differs from acute localized dropsy by favoring the lower extremities and by the far longer persistence of the individual tumidity.

Based on the overall nature of its incidence, acute localized cutaneous and mucosal dropsy should perhaps be viewed as vasoneurosis. To be sure, it probably cannot be explained by (the absence of) purely motor effects on the vascular muscles, but may be assumed to be associated with a neurally engendered change in the transudability of the vascular wall, whereby the incidence appears more closely related to the actual inflammation. I tend to view as an analogue to the acute localized cutaneous dropsy the less rare menstrual edema, the intermittent edemas after a malaria fever, and the so-called typical arthrophyma.

In some cases, controlling the lifestyle and especially the diet proved to offer prophylactic benefits in treating this disorder, which is especially unpleasant when it recurs frequently. It has been possible to shorten individual episodes by resting, footbaths, and intestinal elimination. Atropine appears to work well too. In several cases an edema in the laryngeal passage required scarifications.

HEREDITARY ANGIO-NEUROTIC ŒDEMA.[1]

BY WILLIAM OSLER, M.D.,

PROFESSOR OF CLINICAL MEDICINE IN THE UNIVERSITY OF PENNSYLVANIA, PHYSICIAN TO THE UNIVERSITY HOSPITAL, TO THE PHILADELPHIA HOSPITAL, AND TO THE INFIRMARY FOR NERVOUS DISEASES.

UNDER the terms *acute local, acute circumscribed* or *angio-neurotic* œdema, a disease has been described, characterized by the sudden onset in various regions of œdematous swellings, more or less limited in extent, and of transient duration. Although not referred to at any length in text-books or cyclopedias, the affection is evidently not very uncommon, as Dinkelaker,[2] a pupil of Quincke, has collected a number of cases from the literature. Quincke has himself referred to the subject in *Monatshefte für practische Dermatologie*, 1882. Jamieson,[3] of Edinburgh, has written on the subject and Graham[4] has given a good account of the disease. Riehl[5], Falcone,[6] Strübing,[7] Matas,[8] have recently reported cases.

In three instances the disease appeared in succeeding generations, and it is this hereditary aspect which gives special interest to the following report:

Briefly summarized, the affection in the family which I have studied has the following characteristics:

1. The occurrence of local swellings in various parts of the body, face, hands, arms, legs, genitals, buttocks, and throat. In one instance, possibly in two, death resulted from a sudden *œdema glottidis*.

2. Associated with the œdema, there is almost invariably gastro-intestinal disturbance: colic, nausea, vomiting, and sometimes diarrhœa.

3. A strongly marked hereditary disposition, the disease having affected members of the family in five generations.

A member of the family, Mrs., H., aged twenty-four years, was admitted to the Infirmary for Nervous Diseases, September 20, 1887, and the following notes were taken by Dr. Burr, the house physician:

Medium sized, well-nourished brunette, admitted with neurasthenic symptoms. Has been married two years, no children. Has had good deal of back pain and menstruation is irregular and painful; was healthy as a child, and as a young woman. As long as she can remember, she has been subject to attacks of transient swelling in various parts—hands or fingers, knee-caps, elbows, buttocks, arm or thigh in fleshy parts, face, or more often the lips alone. The fingers have been so swollen that it was impossible to move them, and once the ring-finger was so greatly enlarged that the ring had to be filed off to prevent gan-

1 Read before the Philadelphia Neurological Society.
2 Dinkelaker: Ueber acutes Œdem. Inaug. Dissertation. Kiel, 1882.
3 Edinburgh Medical Journal, June, 1883.   4 Canadian Practitioner, 1885,
5 Riehl: Abstract in London Med. Record, Dec. 1887.
6 Falcone: Gazzetta degli Ospitali, Feb. 24, 1886.   7 Strübing, quoted by Matas.
8 Matas: New Orleans Medical Journal, Oct. 1887.

Reprinted with permission from *Am J Med Sci.* 1888;95:362–367.

grene. The underlip has been swollen to such a degree that the mouth could not be opened, and milk had to be poured in from above. A slight redness and itching of the part is first noticed, or a sensation of heat; the redness is not always present. The effusion may take place with great rapidity. She often has red spots on various parts of the skin, or irregular lines of redness without any swelling. The duration varies from one to four days. There is not much itching, particularly when the swelling is great, but a sense of distention and stiffness. When fully *out* it does not pit, but does so when going down. The attacks may come on when she is feeling quite well or there may be slight indisposition. In all the severer ones there is abdominal pain, described as colic, with nausea, and often vomiting. There is sometimes headache; no fever. The attacks have no relation to the menstrual flow. She rarely passes two weeks without an attack. She does not think that food has any influence on her case. She remained in the hospital three weeks, during which time there was no severe attack, but she had numerous wheal-like eruptions on the chest and sides of the thighs, with very slight swelling, and the day before she left there was a large spot of local œdema on the inner aspect of the left thigh. Dr. Morton dilated a very narrow cervix, and she went home much improved. She had not passed three weeks without a severe attack for a long time. I saw her again on January 16th. She had four or five bad attacks on the hands, feet, and thighs, since leaving the hospital.

From Mr. T., my patient's grandfather, a venerable old patriarch of ninety-two, with unimpaired vigor of mind and body, I was able to obtain a tolerably clear history of the affection as it has existed in his family.

FIRST GENERATION.—The disease first appeared in his mother, *Margaret A.*, b. 1762, d. 1834. He thinks it began with her, and feels sure that had it been in her father's or mother's family she would have known of the fact and mentioned it. She was twice married and had two children by the first husband, and three by the second. She had the attacks from an early age in the hands, feet, face, and neck. He had frequently seen her in them, and on one occasion she nearly died in an attack of shortness of breath. She had colic with them. After the age of forty-five or fifty years she was not so much troubled, but her constitution was much weakened by the strong medicines which she had taken. She had evidently, from the account, been badly salivated. She sought advice everywhere, but in vain, and, according to my patient's mother, was brought to Philadelphia, to the Pennsylvania Hospital, to see Dr. Rush or Dr. Physick. She died at the age of seventy-two.

SECOND GENERATION.—Of the children, all boys, four grew up; Samuel, Stacy, John M., and Allan.

Samuel was not affected, but his children have the attacks, and one of them, John, died of the disease in Salem, Mass. Particulars could not be obtained.

Stacy was never attacked.

John M. suffered from his youth, and had frequent attacks on the hands and privates. He has four children living, of whom only one is affected.

Allan, aged ninety-two years, a hale, vigorous man, with perfect faculties, and still able to walk five or six miles a day. He was healthy as a child. Remembers that the attacks began while he was an apprentice, at the age of eighteen or nineteen. They have recurred at intervals of a month or six weeks. A few years ago they became less frequent. The last attack was two weeks ago. The swelling is usually the first symptom, and in his case the hands and privates are the parts commonly affected, less often the trunk, and never the face. Sometimes itching precedes the onset. The œdema comes on rapidly, and the fingers in an attack are so thick and stiff that it is impossible to move them, the condition lasting some hours, or an entire day. Colicky pains are felt in the abdomen and become so intense that vomiting follows, usually with relief. The ejecta are yellowish, and, as he expressed it, "the bile had to come up before the pain got better." The swelling generally goes down before the sickness. Vomiting is not a constant feature of an attack. The entire duration is from one to three days. He never has headache, and very exceptionally diarrhœa. Very hard work, exposure to cold, and indiscretion in diet were the only circumstances which he thinks determine the attacks, but they as often come on without any apparent cause.

He has been married twice and has had fourteen children, of whom only three, one son by the first marriage and two daughters by the second wife, are affected.

THIRD GENERATION.—*George* began to "swell," as they term it, about the age of twenty and had very many bad attacks. He died, aged sixty, of Bright's disease. Of his nine children all with one exception are affected.

Sallie, married, no children, has very severe attacks in which Dr. Shipps has repeatedly attended her and given hypodermatics of morphia for the colic.

Emma began at the age of ten or twelve. Has attacks every few weeks. Face, hands, and sometimes the feet swell; less often on the body. Has to be very careful in her diet, cannot eat apples and certain vegetables.

FOURTH GENERATION.—George, the son of Allan, had nine children, of whom eight have been attacked. I am indebted to his widow for the following facts about the affection in this family.

1. *Hamilton.* Always suffered with attacks of cramps in the stomach and of late has very often swollen.

2. *Rebecca* began to "swell" when she was four or five years old, and the attacks became much more frequent after she was married. She had three children, one at seventh month, dead; a second at seventh month and now living (is seventeen and has recently had her first attack); a third at eighth month, living. In each instance the labor was prematurely brought on by the complaint. She died in an attack at 5 A.M., evidently a sudden œdema of the larynx. The late Dr. Van Dyke, of New Brunswick, was called, and before her regular physician, Dr. Williamson, arrived, she was dead.

3. *Almira*, who has never had it.

4. *Mary* has always had the cramps but "swelled" for the first time this winter.

5. *Julia*, "who always has swollen ever since she was a small child."

6. *Kate* has it, but "swells" less frequently than the others.

7. *Edwin* within the past few years has had bad spells of both cramps and swelling.

8. *Maggie* (case of Mrs. H. who came to Infirmary).

9. *George* has always had bad spells of the cramps, and last summer "swelled" for the first time.

The mother writes that none of her children has ever had chilblains, but all suffer with cold feet.

FIFTH GENERATION.—*Lizzie*, daughter of Hamilton, has had some very bad attacks. She was married in February, 1887, and has had six bad spells since. Once her face "swelled out of all shape."

A son of H., also has bad attacks.

A daughter of Rebecca, now seventeen years of age, "swelled" for the first time this winter.

GENEALOGICAL TABLE SHOWING ANGIO-NEUROTIC ŒDEMA IN THE FAMILY OF T.

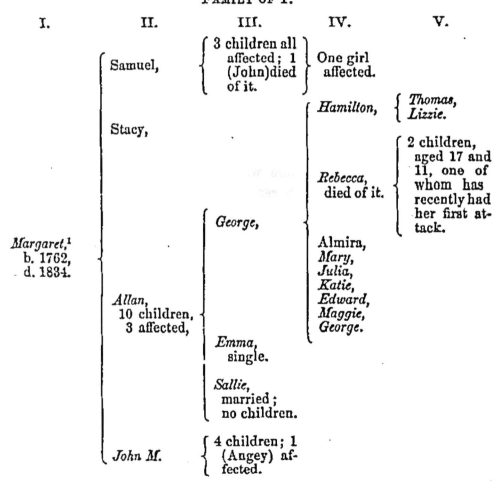

The general characters of the œdema may be gathered from the description given of the cases of Mrs. H. and her grandfather. A review of the literature shows that all of the cases in this respect are very similar. In some, the swelling is more constant in one locality, as

1 Those in italics have suffered with the disease.

eyelid or lip; but, as a rule, various parts are affected. The hands, face, and genitals, are most frequently attacked. Itching, heat, and redness, often precede the outbreak. In many cases the patient also had urticaria.

A special interest pertains to the occurrence of œdema about the throat and larynx, as sudden and extreme involvement of these parts may prove fatal. In Case I. of Quincke[1] and Dinkelaker,[2] the patient, a man aged twenty-two, had repeated attacks of suffocation, often with cyanosis, in association with local œdema about the joints, and colicky pains. The mucous membrane of the larynx was greatly swollen, and scarification had to be performed. There was no difficulty in swallowing.

In a case of Goltz,[3] male, aged thirty, there was œdema of the uvula and pharynx, in association with swelling of sides of arms and scrotum. Laudon[4] had in his own case swelling of the pharynx. Cuntz[5] describes a case in which the patient awoke one night with great dyspnœa and a sense of suffocation, which passed off in a few hours.

In one of Riehl's cases the patient had three attacks of angina, with difficulty of swallowing, and great breathlessness. In his second case also, the man is said to have had inflammation of the vocal cords, which had produced symptoms of suffocation.

In several of the cases there was a remarkable regularity in the sequence of the attacks which recurred on the seventh, fourteenth, or twelfth day. In Matas's case, this periodicity was very striking, the attack coming on every day at 11 or 12 A. M.

The hereditary aspect of the disease, which is so well illustrated in the family which I have studied, has been noticed by three observers. In Quincke's[6] first case the man had two children, one of whom, the son, aged one year, had had, from the age of three months, attacks of local œdema, often preceded by a red and marbled condition of the skin of the breast.

One of Strübing's[7] cases, a man aged seventy, had a son who suffered with the attacks of œdema.

In Falcone's case,[8] a lad of seven years, with well-marked attacks, the father had not been affected, but the grandfather had been afflicted in the same way.

The intestinal trouble, which forms so striking a feature of the attack, is of the nature of colic, and is really the most distressing symptom, usually requiring morphia for its relief. It is interesting to note that

---

[1] Loc. cit.

[2] Deutsche med. Wochenschrift, 1880, No. 17.

[4] Laudon : Berliner klin. Wochenschrift, 1880.

[6] Loc. cit. [7] Loc. cit.

[3] Loc. cit.

[5] Archiv der Heilkunde, Bd. xv.

[8] Loc. cit.

there is a disease in children characterized by painful œdomatous swellings about the joints, a purpuric or urticarial eruption, and most intense colic. There may be hemorrhage from the bowels, but the skin affection and the colic are the prominent features. The attacks may be repeated at intervals for many months. Couty[1] has given the only full account of the disease. Henoch[2] has also reported four cases. I have recently had an opportunity of seeing a typical case of the kind with Dr. Dunton, of Germantown. A boy aged six, has had, during the past ten weeks, three attacks, each one extending over many days, of purpura, with urticuria, swellings about the ankles, and intolerable colic. He has also passed blood in the stools, and the urine contains blood, albumen, and tube casts.

So far as I can gather, none of the members of the T. family has had purpura, nor have there been *painful* swelling of the joints. Some of them have had urticaria, and Mrs. H., while in the Infirmary, had very characteristic wheals on the chest and thighs.

The colic is, in all probability, due to œdema of local regions of the intestinal wall interfering with the regular and uniform progress of peristalsis. The colic of horses is, in most cases, the result of hemorrhagic œdema—infarction—of a limited portion of the intestine, due to embolism in association with the common verminous aneurisms of the mesenteric arteries.

Quincke has termed this condition *angio-neurotic œdema*, and regards it as a vasomotor neurosis, under the influence of which the permeability of the vessels is suddenly increased. That it has close relationship with urticaria, a skin disease of unquestioned neurotic origin, is shown by the frequency with which in the reported cases we find mention of the affection preceding or accompanying the local œdema. The condition resembles in some points urticaria tuberosa, and Juler[3] in a very able article, describes a case of u. porcellana which evidently belongs to the affection under discussion. In our present state of ignorance of the factors which regulate transudation, it seems useless to enter upon a theoretical discussion on the subject of nervous œdema, and we may conclude with Cohnheim,[4] "that we have to do here with clinical facts and observations which urgently call for scientific solution, and that we possess at present but extremely scanty material for an adequate explanation regarding neurotic œdema."

[1] Gazette Hebdomadaire, 1876.
[2] Henoch : Berliner klin. Wochenschrift, 1874.
[3] Cincinnati Lancet and Observer, 1878.
[4] Allgemeine Pathologie, Bd. 1, p. 500.

Assay and Properties of Serum Inhibitor of C'1-Esterase*   (25034)

Lawrence R. Levy[†] and Irwin H. Lepow[‡]

Institute of Pathology, Western Reserve University, Cleveland

Evidence has been presented that the first component of human and guinea pig complement (C'1) exists in serum as a proenzyme which may be activated by antigen-antibody complexes(1-5). Human C'1 was also activated by plasmin(1,6) and, in a partially purified state, by autocatalysis(6,7). Two activities were demonstrable for human "activated C'1" (C'1-esterase): hydrolysis of certain synthetic amino acid esters, of which N-acetyl-L-tyrosine ethyl ester (ALTEe) was most susceptible(6-8); and inactivation of the second and fourth components (C'2 and C'4) of human complement(3,7). Both activation of C'1 and enzymatic activity of C'1-esterase were inhibited by a property of fresh human serum which was non-dialyzable, heat-labile (56°-30 min.), and unrelated to any of the 4

recognized components of complement(6,8). However, the precise relationship of the serum inhibitor of activation and of esterolysis could not be defined in the absence of purification studies. The present investigation was undertaken to provide information for subsequent purification of the serum inhibitor of C'1-esterase. The assay and properties of this inhibitor in normal serum are described and a comparison is given of levels of inhibitor in various mammalian sera.

Materials and methods. *C'1-esterase*—Partially purified human C'1 was prepared by published procedures(7) and activated autocatalytically by adjustment of physico-chemical conditions (pH 7.4, ionic strength 0.15, 37°, 15 min)(6,7). Rabbit C'1 and C'1-esterase were prepared from normal rabbit serum by identical procedures. *ALTEe*—N-acetyl-L-tyrosine ethyl ester, synthesized in the Dept. of Chemistry of Western Reserve Univ., was used as a substrate for C'1-esterase. The ester was dissolved in 2-methoxy-ethanol (methyl cellosolve) to a stock concen-

---

* Supported by research grant, National Inst. of Allergy and Infect. Dis., U.S.P.H.S.

† Work carried out in partial fulfillment of requirements for M.D. degree, and performed in part during tenure of Lederle Medical Student Research Fellowship.

‡ Research Fellow, Cleveland Area Heart Soc.

tration of 1.6 M. *Mammalian Sera.* Blood was drawn without anticoagulant, clotted at room temperature for about 1 hr, and held overnight at 1-5°. Serum was separated by centrifugation in the cold and either maintained at 0° for use within 24 hr or frozen at –45°. Blood was obtained from healthy human donors by venipuncture; from rats and guinea pigs by exsanguination from the carotid artery; and from mice, rabbits and monkeys by cardiac puncture. Mouse serum represented a pool from 16 CF-1, female white mice anesthetized intraperitoneally with Nembutal® (25-35 mg/kg) and bled by cardiac puncture after thoracotomy. Monkey (rhesus) serum was obtained through the courtesy of Dr. F. C. Robbins, Cleveland Metropolitan General Hospital, and bovine, porcine, and ovine sera through the courtesy of Swift and Co., Cleveland. *Assay of C'1-esterase* (6,8). Esterase activity was measured by microformol titration of the acid liberated from ALTEe during 15 min. incubation with enzyme at 37°, pH 7.4, ionic strength 0.15, and a final substrate concentration of 0.08 M. Typically, 1.88 ml of pH 7.4 phosphate buffer of ionic strength 0.15 and 0.5 ml of an appropriate dilution of esterase were preincubated at 37° and 0.125 ml of ALTEe at 37° was then added. One ml aliquots were withdrawn at 0 time and at 15 min. and added immediately to one ml of neutralized (phenolphthalein) 37% formaldehyde. Each sample was microtitrated with a one ml microsyringe (Micrometric Instrument Co., Cleveland) using 0.05 N NaOH and one drop of 1% alcoholic phenolphthalein as indicator. Esterase activity was expressed in units based on the difference between the 15 min. and 0 time titrations. One unit was defined as that amount of enzyme which hydrolyzed an amount of ALTEe equivalent to a net titration of 0.01 ml of 0.05 N NaOH.

Results. 1) Assay of serum inhibitor of C'1-esterase. The studies to be described were confined entirely to inhibition of esterolytic activity of C'1-esterase. Accordingly, the assay for serum inhibitor was a modification of the assay for esterase activity(8). Various volumes of human serum, taken to 0.5 ml with 0.15 M NaCl, were preincubated

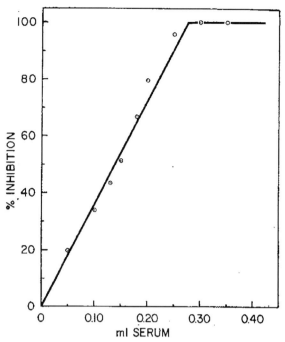

FIG. 1. Proportionality curve for inhibition of human C'1-esterase (38 units/ml) by normal human serum.

at 37° with a constant amount of human C'1-esterase and phosphate buffer at a final pH of 7.4 ± 0.4 and ionic strength of 0.15. ALTEe was added, the amount of residual free enzyme measured by microformol titration, and the amount of esterase inhibited calculated. The assay was found to be linear over the entire range of inhibition (Fig. 1). The effect of varying length of preincubation time of esterase and inhibitor was studied by reacting enzyme, buffer, and serum at 37° in the absence of ALTEe. At intervals of 1, 10, 20, 30, 60, and 120 min., aliquots were withdrawn, substrate added, and esterase inhibition determined. Maximal inhibition was found within 1 min. and was unaffected by further incubation(8). The effect of varying the concentration of esterase was also studied. In every case, a given amount of serum inhibited the same *number* of units of esterase regardless of initial concentration of enzyme, indicating that inhibition was stoichiometric (Table I). One unit of inhibitor was defined as that volume of serum which inhibited 10 units of esterase, as measured by micro-formol titration.

On the basis of these studies, the following assay procedure was adopted: 1.38 ml of pH

TABLE I. Stoichiometry of Interaction of Serum Inhibitor with C'1-Esterase: Various Concentrations of Esterase with Constant Serum Inhibitor.*

Esterase added, units/ml	Esterase inhibited, units/ml
16.4	11.4
23.8	10.8
32.8	10.7
36.9	10.8
41.0	12.6

* 0.1 ml of human serum, taken to 0.5 ml with 0.15 M NaCl.

7.4 phosphate buffer at ionic strength 0.15 was preincubated at 37° with 0.5 ml of human C'1-esterase at a concentration of 40 ± 2 units/ml and various volumes of the serum to be assayed for inhibitor, taken to 0.5 ml with 0.15 M NaCl. After 5-10 min., 0.125 ml of 1.6 M ALTEe at 37° was added, the mixtures were incubated at 37° for 15 min., and the residual free enzyme was determined by titration in the usual manner. Number of units of inhibitor in the unknown serum could then be calculated. For example, if 0.25 ml of serum inhibited 15 units of enzyme, the serum contained 1.5 units of inhibitor in 0.25 ml or 6 units/ml. Since the enzyme-inhibitor interaction was stoichiometric, inhibitor levels could be determined at any point on the inhibition curve. An enzyme control in the presence of substrate and absence of inhibitor was always included to reestablish the potency of the enzyme.

The precision of the assay was determined by 10 measurements of the inhibitory activity of a single human serum at each of 3 concentrations (0.10, 0.15 and 0.20 ml of serum). The mean of the 30 determinations was 7.2 units/ml with a range of 6.3-8.1 and a standard deviation of ± 0.42. 2) Some properties of serum inhibitor of C'1-Esterase. a) Time-temperature stability. The inhibitor in human serum was stable for at least 24 hr at 0°, 21° and 37° and for at least 4 months at −45°. It was unaffected by freezing and thawing 2 times. During incubation for 30 min, 20% of the inhibitor was inactivated at 52°, 90% at 56°, and 100% at 60°. b) pH stability. Aliquots of human serum were adjusted to various pH values with 0.15 N HCl or 0.15 N NaOH, brought to constant volume with 0.15 M NaCl, and allowed to stand overnight at 0°. Each sample was then readjusted to neutrality and assayed. The inhibitor was stable under these conditions between pH 6 and 10 but progressive inactivation occurred at pH values below 6. Complete inactivation was observed at pH 3.6; 65% inactivation at pH 4.8. c) Effect of alcohols and ammonium sulfate. The inhibitor was increasingly labile to methanol concentrations greater than 15% at −5°. Similarly, as reported previously(8), the inhibitor did not survive fractionation of human serum with ethanol by procedures of Cohn et al.(9). However, essentially all of the inhibitory activity of human serum could be recovered from the supernatant fraction resulting from precipitation with 40% ammonium sulfate. 3) Comparative levels of serum inhibitor of C'1-Esterase in various mammalian sera. Serum from 4 of the 9 species tested contained demonstrable inhibitor of human C'1-esterase (Table II). Human, monkey and guinea pig sera had comparable and relatively high titers of inhibitor, while rabbit serum was only about one-third as active. Rat and mouse sera contained spontaneous esterase activity and therefore no measurable inhibitor. Bovine, porcine and ovine sera demonstrated neither spontaneous esterase nor inhibitory activity. The inhibitor in rabbit and guinea pig serum had the same thermal lability as in human serum. Monkey serum was not tested.

Since human C'1-esterase was used in these experiments, the possibility existed that the variation in inhibitor levels among different species was a reflection of species specificity. A partial answer to this problem was provided by preparing and activating partially purified

TABLE II. Serum Inhibitor of Human C'1-Esterase in Various Mammalian Sera.

Serum	Avg. inhibitor titer, units/ml
Human (6 pools of 25)	6.4 (5.6-7.2)
Monkey (2)	5.0
Guinea pig (3)	5.2
Rabbit (3)	1.8
Rat (3)	0
Mouse (pool of 16)	0
Bovine (1)	0
Porcine (1)	0
Ovine (1)	0

TABLE III. Species Specificity of Rabbit and Human Sera as Sources of Inhibitor vs C′ 1-Esterase Prepared from Rabbit or Human Serum.*

Inhibitor source	C′ 1-Esterase source	Inhibitor titer, units/ml
Rabbit serum	Rabbit	2.0
,, ,,	Human	3.0
Human ,,	Rabbit	5.0
,, ,,	Human	7.7

* Each serum was assayed against equivalent amounts of rabbit and human C′ 1-esterase under the usual conditions.

rabbit C′1 by the same procedure used for human C′1(6,7). The inhibitory activity of rabbit and human sera vs. rabbit and human C′1-esterase was then compared (Table III). Rabbit serum was again found to have a lower titer of inhibitor than human serum even when tested against rabbit esterase. It was concluded, therefore, that at least with respect to these two species, no marked species specificity existed in the interaction of C′1-esterase and serum inhibitor.

Discussion and Summary. An assay is described for measurement of a serum inhibitor of an esterase derived from preparations of the first component of complement (C′1-esterase). Esterolysis of N-acetyl-L-tyrosine ethyl ester by C′1-esterase is inhibited instantaneously and stoichiometrically by fresh human serum. Units of C′1-esterase and of serum inhibitor are defined. The inhibitor in human serum is stable at −45° for at least 4 months, at 37° for at least 24 hr, and at 48° for at least 30 min. It is completely inactivated during 30 min. incubation at 60° and is labile at 0° at pH values below 6. The inhibitor is inactivated at −5° in the presence of methanol concentrations of 15% or greater but is recovered quantitatively in a 40% ammonium sulfate supernatant fraction. These data are being applied to purification of the inhibitor from human serum. Purification procedures and properties of the purified inhibitor will be reported elsewhere.

Monkey and guinea pig sera inhibit human C′1-esterase to about the same extent as human serum, while rabbit serum is about one-third as active. No marked species specificity exists in the interaction of inhibitor in human or rabbit serum with human or rabbit C′1-esterase. These observations are being employed on possible role of inhibitor in experimental hypersensitivity.

1. Lepow, I. H., Wurz, L., Ratnoff, O. D., Pillemer, L., *J. Immunol.,* 1954, v73, 146.

2. Lepow, I. H., Pillemer, L., *ibid.,* 1955, v75, 63.

3. Lepow, I. H., Ratnoff, O. D., Pillemer, L., PROC. SOC. EXP. BIOL. AND MED., 1956, v92, 111.

4. Becker, E. L., *J. Immunol.,* 1956, v77, 462.

5. ——, *ibid.,* 1956, v77, 469.

6. Lepow, I. H., Ratnoff, O. D., Levy, L. R., *J. Exp. Med.,* 1958, v107, 451.

7. Lepow, I. H., Ratnoff, O. D., Rosen, F. S., Pillemer, L., PROC. SOC. EXP. BIOL. AND MED., 1956, v92, 32.

8. Ratnoff, O. D., Lepow, I. H., *J. Exp. Med.,* 1957, v106, 327.

9. Cohn, E. J., Strong, L. E., Hughes, W. L., Jr., Mulford, D. J., Ashworth, J. N., Melin, M., Taylor, H. L., *J.A.C.S.,* 1946, v68, 459.

Received May 22, 1959.   P.S.E.B.M., 1959, v101.

HEREDITARY ANGIONEUROTIC EDEMA

II. Deficiency of Inhibitor for Serum Globulin Permeability Factor and/or Plasma Kallikrein

Nathaniel S. Landerman, Major, MC, USA,* Marion E. Webster, Ph.D.,** Elmer L. Becker, Ph.D., M.D.,*** and Harold E. Ratcliffe, Colonel, MC, USA,**** Washington, D. C., and Bethesda, Md.

THE etiology of hereditary angioneurotic edema has been unknown since the disease was first reported by Quincke[1] in 1882, who suggested the acute edema was primarily due to an "angioneurosis," i.e., nerve influence on the transudative ability of the vascular wall. In 1904, Fairbanks[2] postulated a neurotic etiology in the modern sense of psychologic abnormality. Cockayne,[3] in 1933, suggested an inherited hypersensitiveness to some foreign protein in the diet, perhaps one specific substance in each family. Sheldon[4] disproved this hypothesis when he reported an acute attack occurring in a patient on a completely synthetic diet. In most reports in the literature,[5] local trauma or pressure has been noted to be a fairly consistent precipitator of acute edema, which raises the possibility of physical allergy. Other types of allergic mechanisms have been searched for, and allergen skin tests have been positive in several patients, but without correlation with the clinical picture.

The inheritance of the disease as a mendelian dominant is more in keeping with an inherited specific biochemical defect.[6] The attacks of acute edema are of a noninflammatory type, which suggested a disordered vascular permeability as the cause. In recent years, there has been a rapid increase in knowledge about endogenous factors which increase capillary permeability.[7] Our approach to a study of this disease was to search for a possible abnormality related to one of these factors. We previously reported[8, 9] that the serum globulin permeability factor (PF) of Miles, Wilhelm, and their colleagues appeared to be altered in cases of hereditary angioneurotic edema, in that increased PF activity was obtained when the patient's own diluted serum was injected into the patient. However, neither the patient's diluted serum injected into normal controls nor the diluted serum from the normal controls injected into the patient gave an increased response. From these experimental data, we postulated that the

Presented at the Annual Meeting of the American Academy of Allergy, February, 1961, Washington, D. C.

Received for publication March 16, 1962.

*From the Department of Medicine, Walter Reed General Hospital, Washington, D. C. Present address: Valley Forge General Hospital, Phoenixville, Pa.

**From the Laboratory of Cardiovascular Physiology, National Heart Institute, Bethesda, Md.

***From the Department of Immunology, Walter Reed Army Institute of Research, Washington, D. C.

****From the Department of Medicine, Walter Reed General Hospital, Washington, D. C.

disordered vascular permeability in hereditary angioneurotic edema is an inherited hyperresponsiveness of the skin and other tissues to an autologus serum factor which, upon activation in vivo by an unknown stimulus, increases the permeability of capillaries. We have now extended and confirmed these findings and are presenting evidence to show that the inherited hyperresponsiveness of the skin is due rather to a deficiency of an inhibitor to a capillary permeability-increasing enzyme (PF and/or plasma kallikrein).

METHODS AND MATERIALS

Our subjects in this study were members of a family affected with hereditary angioneurotic edema through four generations.[5] Most of the experiments were concerned with a 33-year-old Caucasian woman affected by this disease since the age of 2, who will hereafter be referred to as the patient. Less extensively studied were her older son, 10 years of age, affected since the age of 4, and her younger son, 8 years of age, only questionably affected by the disease. Healthy adult men and women without a personal history of allergic disease were used as control subjects.

For studies on reactions to endogenous substances which increase capillary permeability, all subjects were given 0.5 mg. per kilogram of Evans blue dye, intravenously, 5 to 10 min. before intradermal injection of 0.1 ml. of the test solution. These permeability substances induce a blue wheal at the injection site, due to the passage of dye-stained plasma albumin into the tissue spaces.[10] Intradermal injections with short bevel No. 26 needles and tuberculin syringes were made in the skin of the back in the following area: inferior to the angle of the scapulae, superior to the posterior iliac crests, medial to the posterior axillary line, and omitting the skin for 2.5 cm. lateral to the spinous processes. Blue wheal diameter was measured with vernier scale calipers, and the figures given are the average of the long and short diameters. Intensity was estimated visually, and recorded as follows: no blue, 0; faint blue, ±; light blue, +; deep blue, ++.

Serum, or plasma (0.2 ml. of 1 per cent heparin sodium USP per 10 ml. of blood), was taken by venipuncture with a two-syringe technique. Plasma was separated after centrifugation at 3,000 r. p. m. for 10 min. Serum was prepared by allowing the blood to clot at room temperature for one hour, the margin of the clot was reamed with a glass rod; and the mixture was centrifuged at 10,000 r. p. m. for 15 min. at 5° C. Glassware was chilled before use and, in experiments with serum, all glass surfaces were silicone treated to prevent glass activation of the permeability factor. For intradermal tests, serial dilutions of serum or plasma in physiologic saline were allowed to stand at room temperature for one hour. Duplicate injections of test substances were made in most instances.

In several experiments, serum was diluted in saline containing the following substances: epsilon-aminocaproic acid*; crystalline chymotrypsin†; cortico-

---

*Supplied by Dr. N. Schimmel, Merck, Sharp and Dohme Research Laboratory, West Point, Pa.

†Worthington Biochemical Corporation, Freehold, N. J.

tropin injection USP; cyproheptadine; diphenhydramine hydrochloride USP; edathamil calcium-disodium (EDTA); heparin sodium USP; mepyramine maleate USP; neostigmine methylsulfate USP; ovomucoid trypsin inhibitor*; promethazine hydrochloride USP; sodium salicylate USP; crystalline soy bean trypsin inhibitor*; and crystalline trypsin.* Intradermal responses were also studied to the following test substances: acetylcholine, hyaluronidase for injection USP; heparin sodium USP; histamine acid phosphate USP; and serotonin as 5-hydroxytryptamine creatinine sulfate.

The authors are indebted to Dr. M. J. Davis, Dr. J. Barbaro, and Mr. J. Eichelberger, Walter Reed Army Institute of Research, who kindly conducted blood, plasma and/or serum levels of acetylcholine esterase; histamine; thromboelastograms, plasma fibrinogen levels, 24-hour whole blood clot lysis determinations, and plasma clotting times, respectively. All tests were done by standard techniques, including serum potassium, whole blood serotonin, and 24-hour urinary excretion of 5-hydroxyindole acetic acid.

Kallikrein in the serum was activated by the addition of 20 per cent acetone to the serum and allowing the solution to stand at room temperature for several hours. The vasodilator activity in the preparation, a measure of kallikrein activity, was determined by measuring the increase in blood flow following its injection into the dog.[11] The ability of serum to inhibit plasma kallikrein in the dog bioassay was determined by incubating 1.0 ml. of 1:50 to 1:200 dilutions of serum in 0.5 ml. M tris (hydroxymethyl) aminomethane buffer, pH 7.5, with 0.5 ml. of human plasma kallikrein dissolved in dialyzed proteose peptone at 1.5 Frey units per milliliter at 37° C. for 2 hours. The residual kallikrein was determined in the dog bioassay. In vitro measurement of inhibitor level was determined by utilizing p-toluenesulfonyl-L-arginine methyl ester as the substrate as previously described.[12] To 1.0 ml. of plasma or serum diluted 1:2 to 1:32 in water was added 1.0 ml. of 2.0 mg. per milliliter of plasma kallikrein, 2.0 Frey units per milligram in 0.75 M tris (hydroxymethyl) aminomethane buffer, pH 7.5. The mixture was incubated at 37° C. for exactly 30 min. and the enzymatic reaction initiated by the addition of 1.0 ml. of 0.06 M ester dissolved in water. Exactly one hour later, the reaction was stopped by the addition of the trichloroacetic acid.[12] Blanks were run substituting buffer for the plasma kallikrein and corrections were made for any significant digestion. Values were calculated for the amount of plasma kallikrein inhibited and 1.0 inhibitor unit was arbitrarily assigned to that amount of kallikrein inhibited by a normal control. A 1:4 dilution of experimental plasma or serum was suitable for determining the magnitude of the differences involved. Only the patient and her older son gave significant digestion in the blank determinations. Plasmin, purified by the Kline procedure, at 0.5 mg. per milliliter, was utilized as the proteinase in similar determinations with the serum of the patient and that of a normal control.

Human plasma kallikrein, 0.3 Frey units per milligram, was prepared by adsorption of inactive proteins on diethylaminoethyl cellulose and adsorption of the kallikrein on carboxymethyl cellulose as previously described.[12] The more

---

*Worthington Biochemical Corporation, Freehold, N. J.

highly purified kallikrein, 2 Frey units per milligram, was obtained by a modification of this procedure involving adsorption of plasma kallikrein on XE-64 (IRC-50). Details of this method will be described elsewhere.

RESULTS

Tables I and II present in greater detail than described previously[9] our experience with the increased cutaneous response of the patient to diluted autologous plasma or serum. As is shown in Table I, the patient gave a significantly greater bluing response to diluted autologous plasma, considering area and intensity of bluing, than any of the controls, even when measurements were

TABLE I. INTRADERMAL RESPONSE TO AUTOLOGOUS PLASMA*

| | BLUING RESPONSE† | | | |
| | PATIENT | | CONTROL | |
DILUTION	AVERAGE	RANGE	AVERAGE	RANGE
None	12.7 (+)	11.8-13.5	10.1 (±)	9.2-11.0
1:12.5	14.5 (++)	12.0-17.0	11.1 (+)	10.4-11.8
1:25	15.7 (++)	14.0-17.1	11.3 (+)	10.0-12.5
1:50	14.5 (++)	13.9-15.0	11.2 (+)	9.9-12.5
1:100	14.0 (++)	11.5-16.4	10.4 (+)	7.5-12.0
1:200	12.8 (++)	11.0-14.5	10.2 (±)	6.7-11.7
1:400	10.7 (+)	8.8-12.0	9.9 (±)	8.3-11.4
1:800	10.2 (+)	10.0-10.3	9.7 (±)	6.3-11.3

*Intradermal response of patient and 11 control subjects, 6 of whom were females.
†Bluing response noted 30 min. after injection and given as diameter in millimeters, and intensity of blue dye measured as follows: faint blue, ±; light blue, +; and deep blue, ++.

TABLE II. INTRADERMAL RESPONSE TO AUTOLOGOUS AND HOMOLOGOUS SERUM

| | | BLUING RESPONSE* | | |
| | | DILUTION | | |
RECIPIENT	DONOR	1:25	1:100	1:400
Patient	Patient	10.2 (++)	14.2 (++)	10.8 (+)
	A	6.2 (±)	9.9 (+)	10.1 (±)
	B	9.3 (+)	11.0 (+)	10.6 (±)
	C	9.9 (+)	12.0 (+)	10.0 (±)
Control A	A	11.2 (+)	8.8 (±)	8.4 (±)
	Patient	9.3 (+)	9.3 (+)	9.5 (+)
	B	12.3 (++)	10.5 (+)	9.3 (+)
	C	9.8 (+)	9.0 (+)	11.5 (+)
Control B	B	12.0 (±)	11.1 (±)	9.8 (±)
	Patient	11.8 (+)	10.2 (+)	10.6 (±)
	A	11.4 (±)	11.7 (+)	12.3 (±)
	C	8.7 (±)	11.4 (±)	6.9 (±)
Control C	C	11.2 (+)	10.6 (+)	8.7 (+)
	Patient	12.2 (+)	12.2 (+)	11.7 (±)
	A	12.2 (+)	12.4 (+)	12.4 (±)
	B	12.2 (+)	8.8 (+)	10.7 (±)

*See Table I.

made 30 min. after injection. In several experiments where wheal size was measured for 3 hours at 30 minute intervals after injection, it was noted that the patient's wheal size continued to increase during the 3 hours, whereas the controls reached a peak response 30 min. after injection and their wheals then decreased in size. From three further experiments comparing the response of the patient and 4 normal controls to diluted autologous and homologous serum which had been taken in silicone-coated tubes, it became apparent that the patient's increased reactivity was only to her own diluted serum. Table II shows the results of one of these experiments.

Studies in the patient's sons (Table III) revealed that the older son, 10 years of age and affected by the disease since the age of 4, showed the same increased response to the injection of a 1:12.5 dilution of his own plasma. The younger son, 8 years of age and only questionably affected by the disease, showed a range no different from that in the controls (Table I). Both sons, however, appeared to show a greater response to their own plasma than to that of the normal control used in these studies.

TABLE III. INTRADERMAL RESPONSE OF PATIENT'S SONS TO AUTOLOGOUS AND HOMOLOGOUS PLASMA

| | | BLUING RESPONSE* | | |
| | | DILUTION | | |
RECIPIENT	DONOR	NONE	1:12.5	1:100
Older son	Older son	9.6 (+)	12.8 (++)	11.7 (+)
	Younger son	8.3 (±)	10.7 (+)	11.0 (±)
	Control	7.1 (±)	6.9 (+)	11.0 (±)
Younger son	Younger son	9.7 (±)	11.0 (+)	9.1 (+)
	Older son	9.9 (+)	11.0 (+)	9.1 (+)
	Control	8.2 (+)	8.7 (±)	7.8 (±)

*See Table 1.

Differentiation of PF From Other Permeability Factors in Serum Except Kallikrein.—The nature of the factor causing increased bluing on dilution of the patient's serum was identified by demonstrating in the patient some of the salient characteristics of PF. Undiluted autologous serum taken in silicone-coated tubes caused no bluing response until it was contacted with glass or diluted in physiologic saline. As shown in Table IV, serum heated at 65° C. for 30 min. could no longer be activated by dilution or glass contact. The bluing response was also completely inhibited by diluting the patient's serum in physiologic saline containing soy bean trypsin inhibitor, but it was not inhibited when the serum was diluted in ovomucoid trypsin inhibitor. These characteristics are all similar to those reported by Mill and his associates[13] for human PF. Nevertheless, additional experiments were performed in order to exclude other known permeability factors[7] (Table IV). *Serotonin* has been reported to have a negligible capillary permeability increasing activity in human skin[14] and this activity is partially inhibited by cyproheptadine. However, cyproheptadine did not alter the patient's intradermal response. *Peptides* such as kallidin, bradykinin, substance U or Z, substance P, pepsitensin, pepsitocin, and angiotensin are all readily destroyed by chymotrypsin, and this proteinase added to the saline used to dilute the patient's serum failed to inhibit the patient's intradermal response. Peptides such as exudin have been reported to be inhibited by ACTH, and leukotaxine by soy bean trypsin inhibitor and cortisone.[16]

The patient's intradermal response to 0.1 ml. of 1:10,000 acetylcholine, 1.5 USP units of hyaluronidase, 1:100 heparin, 1:10,000 histamine, and 1:10,000 serotonin (5-hydroxytryptamine creatinine sulfate) showed no difference from that given by control subjects. Intradermal injection of *acetylcholine* exhibited no satellite whealing and neostigmine did not inhibit the patient's response to diluted autologous serum. *Hyaluronidase* and *heparin* at the concentrations tested caused no bluing response in the patient. Also as part of the blue wheal response to diluted serum in both the patient and the controls, the blue dye remains sharply confined to the wheal. Similarly, the patient's serum activity was not altered in the presence of heparin. *Histamine* causes itching and flare reaction and these responses were not noted with diluted autologous plasma or serum. The patient's response to diluted autologous serum was not inhibited by the antihistaminics mepyramine maleate, diphenhydramine hydrochloride, or promethazine hydrochloride. During angioneurotic edema attacks and edema-free periods, the patient's serum levels of acetylcholine esterase, blood levels of histamine and serotonin, and the glass and silicone clotting times were normal, as was the 24-hour urinary excretion of 5-hydroxyindole acetic acid.

TABLE IV. INTRADERMAL RESPONSE OF PATIENT TO 1:25 DILUTION OF TREATED AUTOLOGOUS SERUM

TREATMENT	BLUING RESPONSE*
None	12.3 (+)
Heated 56° C., 30 min.	13.5 (+)
65° C., 30 min.	0
Diluted in saline containing†:	
ACTH	11.1 (+)
Epsilon-aminocaproic acid	8.0 (+)
Albumin	11.4 (+)
Chymotrypsin	15.2 (++)
Cyproheptadine	14.6 (++)
Diphenhydramine	11.8 (+)
Edathamil calcium-disodium	13.2 (+)
Heparin	12.0 (+)
Hydrocortisone	12.9 (+)
Mepyramine maleate	12.5 (+)
Neostigmine methylsulfate	13.5 (+)
Norepinephrine	0
Ovomucoid trypsin inhibitor	12.6 (+)
Promethazine	12.1 (+)
Sodium salicylate	12.9 (+)
Soy bean trypsin inhibitor	0
Trypsin	18.3 (++)

*See Table I.

†Substances were at 0.1 mg. per milliliter except epsilon-aminocaproic acid, 0.25 mg. per milliliter, and sodium salicylate, 0.2 mg. per milliliter.

Potassium could not be the factor involved since the concentration of K+ present in cell-free serum is too small to cause the increase in capillary permeability seen with highly diluted serum. *Anaphylatoxin* has been formed only in rat and guinea pig serum and its action in the guinea pig appears to depend largely on its release of histamine. Therefore, it is difficult to assess the possible role of this toxin in the human. Two proteolytic enzymes, however, *plasmin* and *trypsin,* would appear to be more likely candidates since they are both capable of causing increase in permeability. As shown, trypsin at 0.1 mg. per milliliter gave a marked intradermal response. However, ovomucoid trypsin inhibitor did not alter the patient's intradermal response to diluted autologous serum. Plasmin has been reported to show permeability factor activity in the guinea pig.[13] However, during angioneurotic edema episodes and edema-free periods, the patient exhibited no significant lysis of 24-hour whole blood clots, and no abnormality in fibrinogen levels or on the thromboelastogram. Epsilon-aminocaproic acid (EACA) therapy, 10 Gm. given intravenously over a one hour period during several attacks of angioneurotic edema, caused no definite clinical improvement.[5] The patient's serum diluted in the presence of EACA (0.25 mg. per milliliter) and injected into the patient seemed to give a lesser bluing response than serum diluted in the absence of EACA, but no such inhibition occurred if the autologous serum was diluted in physiologic saline, allowed to stand at room temperature for 30 min., and then diluted in EACA to a final concentration of 0.5 mg. per milliliter.[9] Other factors studied as possible inhibitors were *albumin, EDTA, sodium salicylate,* and *norepinephrine.* Of these factors, only norepinephrine was capable of altering the response to PF. This compound apparently acts antagonistically as a vasoconstrictor to prevent the vasodilatation furnished by PF. It has previously been shown that the blood pressure lowering effect of kallikrein can be completely blocked by the addition of the appropriate concentrations of norepinephrine or epinephrine.[17]

Close Relationship of PF and Plasma Kallikrein.—In recent years, several authors have suggested a close relationship between PF and plasma kallikrein.[7, 18] Both factors are present in human plasma as inactive precursors (kallikreinogen, pro-PF). The precursor, upon activation by dilution, forms free PF and, by the addition of 20 per cent acetone,[11] forms plasma kallikrein. Both factors are inhibited by plasma, diisopropyl fluorophosphate (DFP), soy bean trypsin inhibitor, and are not inhibited by ovomucoid trypsin inhibitor. Present evidence[12, 19] suggests that both factors are proteolytic enzymes, and their inactivation by DFP is prevented by synthetic arginine ester substrates. Hageman factor is essential for the activation of both factors.[20, 21] It has recently been reported[22] that serum kallikrein (the source of the serum was not stated) is a very effective agent in increasing capillary permeability in the guinea pig, and that salivary kallikrein[23] produced a wheal without flare reaction after intracutaneous injection in human skin.

With this background of information, it appeared desirable to investigate the various components of the kallikrein system in the patient, her two sons, and three normal controls. Serum taken in silicone-coated tubes was first investigated for its kallikreinogen content, i.e., its ability to be activated by acetone to form kallikrein. As shown in Table V, serum from the patient and her older son, both of whom were affected with the disease, did have slightly lower levels of kallikrein than did the normal controls. Certainly, however, no deficiency in kallikrein could be claimed since their serum still contained around 4.5 Frey units per milliliter.

Identification of Biochemical Lesion in Hereditary Angioneurotic Edema as Deficiency of Serum Inhibitor.—The patient and five normal controls were next investigated for their cutaneous response to partially purified human plasma

TABLE V. LEVELS OF SERUM KALLIKREIN AND ITS INHIBITOR(S)

SUBJECT	SERUM KALLIKREIN* (FREY UNITS/ML.)	INHIBITOR† (UNITS/ML.)
Patient	4.6	75
Older son	4.7	75
Younger son	8.5	150
Control A	8.1	150
Control B	6.2	200
Control C	7.4	200

*Frey units per milliliter of serum kallikrein activity formed on acetone activation of serum.

†Reciprocal of serum dilution necessary to cause 50 per cent inhibition of plasma kallikrein as measured in dog bioassay.

kallikrein. The preparation utilized for these studies contained 0.3 Frey units per milligram. As shown in Table VI, the injection of as little as 0.03 Frey units in 0.1 ml. volume furnished a response in the control subjects which was probably better than that furnished by 1:100 dilution of plasma (Table I). The controls had a peak bluing response 30 min. after injection, with an average wheal diameter of 12.7 mm. The patient, on the other hand (Table VI), had a peak bluing response of 23.5 mm. approximately 14 hours after injection. In a repetition of this experiment at a later day, the patient had a 40 mm. peak bluing response 12 hours after injection. These data clearly suggested that the deficiency in this disease was an absence of serum inhibitor to plasma kallikrein.

TABLE VI. INTRADERMAL RESPONSE TO HUMAN PLASMA KALLIKREIN*

RECIPIENT	BLUING RESPONSE†				
	TIME AFTER INJECTION (HR.)				
	0.5	3.5	5.5	14	18
Patient	8.1 (+)	9.9 (++)	16.2 (++)	23.5 (++)	19.9 (++)
Control A	9.3 (+)	0.0‡			
Control B	15.5 (+)	0.0			
Control C	13.8 (+)	0.0			
Control D	12.8 (+)	0.0			
Control E	12.3 (+)	0.0			

*The response to the injection of 0.1 ml. of 1 mg. per milliliter of solution of partially purified human plasma kallikrein, 0.3 Frey units per milligram. After 0.5 hr. all control subjects were negative.

†See Table I.

‡Blue color absent.

The inhibitor levels to plasma kallikrein were measured as previously described.[11] In these experiments, 0.5 Frey units per milliliter of plasma kallikrein was added to increasing dilutions of the serum and the mixture incubated for 2 hours at 37° C. The plasma kallikrein remaining after this treatment was determined by measuring the increase in blood flow in the dog bioassay. As shown in Table V, the inhibitor levels of the patient and her older son were definitely lower than those for the controls. These data had additional significance in that, in our experience, we had never previously had a normal serum which contained less than 150 inhibitor units. However, as measured by this technique, there appeared to be no absence of serum inhibitor.

Norman,[24] however, has reported the presence in human plasma of two inhibitors to plasmin, i.e., an "immediate" inhibitor and a "slow" inhibitor, and Werle[25] has reported that certain kallikreins are reversibly inactivated by plasma and others irreversibly. It appeared possible that, after 2 hours of incubation at 37° C., we were measuring the total of two or more inhibitors. Since it was known[12] that p-toluenesulfonyl-L-arginine methyl ester (TAMe) could compete successfully with the reversible inhibitor, it was thought that measurement of the inhibitor utilizing TAMe as a substrate in vitro might clarify the situation. In these experiments, kallikrein at 2 Frey units per milligram was inhibited by various dilutions of serum and 1 unit of inhibitor was arbitrarily defined as the amount of inhibitor found in 1.0 ml. of a particular normal serum. As is shown in Table VII, this method of measuring the inhibitor was

TABLE VII. INHIBITOR LEVELS TO SERUM KALLIKREIN UTILIZING TAMe* AS SUBSTRATE

SUBJECT	INHIBITOR UNITS†
Patient	0.16
Older son	0.13
Younger son	1.3
Control A	1.0
Control B	2.0

*TAMe, p-toluenesulfonyl-L-arginine methyl ester.
†Inhibitor units per milliliter of serum where 1 unit is approximately that found in 1.0 ml. of human serum. Values are corrected for micromoles of TAMe digested by serum.

effective in demonstrating the deficiency of the ability of the serum to inhibit plasma kallikrein. Both the serum from the patient and her older son who had inherited the disease furnished only 0.13 to 0.16 units of inhibitor per milliliter whereas the younger son and the normal controls ranged from 1.0 to 2.0 units of inhibitor per milliliter.

DISCUSSION

The discovery of a deficiency of inhibitor to a capillary permeability increasing proteinase in hereditary angioneurotic edema parallels abnormalities found in other diseases previously characterized as "inborn errors of metabolism," i.e., genetically transmitted biochemical defects ordinarily are deficiencies of enzymes necessary to normal metabolism.[6]

The serum inhibitor of the permeability factor (IPF) and the presumably identical inhibitor to plasma kallikrein has been found to be associated with the albumin and alpha-1 globulin fractions.[13] Similarly, the "slow" inhibitor for plasmin has been associated with this fraction of plasma.[24] Measurement of the patient's inhibitor level to plasmin purified by the Kline procedure utilizing TAMe as the substrate revealed a 50 per cent reduction. It seems likely that the two proteinases share an inhibitor in plasma.[11]

In the guinea pig, IPF has been demonstrated in the tissue fluid of skin as well as in serum.[26] A deficiency of inhibitor in both skin and serum in patients with hereditary angioneurotic edema explains all our experimental findings. The increased intradermal response of the patient to her own diluted serum and to plasma kallikrein is due to inhibitor deficiency in her serum and skin. Her normal intradermal response to diluted normal serum is attributable to the presence of normal amounts of inhibitor in the normal serum. The normal intradermal response of control subjects to the patient's diluted serum is due to normal levels of inhibitor in normal skin.

Deficiency of inhibitor in serum, skin, and, presumably, mucous membrane explains the pathogenesis of episodic edema in hereditary angioneurotic edema. Trauma or pressure is the only known fairly consistent precipitator of skin and mucosal edema in this disease.[5] Local injury apparently activates kallikreinogen or pro-PF, possibly via the activation of Hageman factor,[20, 21] and the active proteinase (PF or plasma kallikrein) is then freed to exert its capillary permeability effect. In a normal individual, normal amounts of inhibitor prevent edema from occurring, unless the injury is severe. In patients with hereditary angioneurotic edema, the activated permeability enzyme is present in a high concentration relative to the deficient inhibitor, and significant edema occurs locally in the area of injury. The edema then spreads until the relative concentration of inhibitor, or the reversible inhibitor, becomes sufficient to overcome the action of progressively decreasing amounts of proteinase in the periphery of the advancing edematous area.

The precise way in which PF increases capillary permeability is unknown. It has been suggested that PF may act directly on the capillary wall by depolymerizing the endothelial cement substance, and thus allows larger molecules to pass through. Another possibility is the formation of a small-molecular basic polypeptide intermediate between the proteinase and the capillary wall.[27] In view of the known ability of plasma kallikrein to act on an alpha-2 globulin, called kallidinogen, to release a polypeptide, kallidin,[28, 29] it is possible that the increased permeability is mediated through such a mechanism.

Logical treatment of these patients would be with replacement therapy of the inhibitor to the proteinase or by an inhibtor to the proposed polypeptide. However, the serum inhibitor to the proteinase has only been partially purified and no suitable inhibitors of the polypeptide are known.[28, 29] Soy bean trypsin inhibitor was considered because of its known inhibitory effect on the proteinase and its previous use in humans.[30] It was not used, however, when we learned that it had a dangerous pyrogenic effect when approximately 6 mg. per kilogram of body weight was given intravenously to patients not in shock.[31] Promethazine therapy has been reported to be of some benefit in the disease[32] but its mechanism of action is not known. Similarly, testosterone therapy[33] has been reported to be highly beneficial to some patients, but, again, the mechanism for its protective action is unknown. Future studies may reveal the nature of these protective mechanisms and provide new agents for specific therapy of these patients.

SUMMARY

Studies of a 33-year-old Caucasian woman with hereditary angioneurotic edema and her two sons, of whom only one is definitely affected with the disease, have revealed that the inborn biochemical lesion is likely an inherited deficiency of serum inhibitor to plasma kallikrein and/or serum globulin permeability factor. The patient showed a significantly greater bluing response to intradermal injections of diluted autologous serum or to plasma kallikrein than did the normal controls and this response, unlike that of the control subjects, continued to increase for a period of hours. By use of an enzymatic determination utilizing p-toluenesulfonyl-L-arginine methyl ester as the substrate, it is possible to demonstrate a deficiency in both patients to an inhibitor of plasma kallikrein. A variety of other known permeability factors have been excluded as the potential agent involved.

REFERENCES

1. Quincke, H.: Über akutes unschriebenes Hautodem, Monatsh. prakt. Dermat. **1:** 129, 1882.
2. Fairbanks, A. W.: Hereditary Oedema, Am. J. M. Sc. **127:** 877, 1904.
3. Cockayne, E. A.: Inherited Abnormalities of the Skin and Its Appendages, London, 1933, Oxford University Press, pp. 371-375.
4. Sheldon, J. M., Schreiber, E. O., and Lovell, R. G.: Hereditary Angioneurotic Edema With a Case Report, J. Lab. & Clin. Med. **34:** 524, 1949.
5. Landerman, N. S.: Hereditary Angioneurotic Edema. I. Case Reports and Review of the Literature, J. ALLERGY **33:** 316, 1962.
6. Garrod, A. E.: The Croonian Lectures on Inborn Errors of Metabolism, Lancet **2:** 1, 1908.
7. Spector, W. G.: Substances Which Affect Capillary Permeability, Pharmacol. Rev. **10:** 475, 1958.
8. Landerman, N. S., Becker, E. L., Ratcliffe, H. E., Davis, M. J., and Kamin, E. J.: Increased Activity of the Plasma Permeability Factor in Familial Hereditary Angioedema, Clin. Res. **7:** 139, 1959.
9. Landerman, N. S., Becker, E. L., and Ratcliffe, H. E.: Increased Cutaneous Response to Diluted Autologous Serum in Hereditary Angio-edema, Lancet **1:** 1053, 1960.
10. Stewart, P. B., and Bliss, J. Q.: The Permeability-Increasing Factor in Diluted Human Plasma, Brit. J. Exper. Path. **38:** 462, 1957.
11. Webster, M. E., and Pierce, J. V.: Studies on Plasma Kallikrein and Its Relationship to Plasmin, J. Pharmacol. Exper. Therap. **130:** 484, 1960.
12. Webster, M. E., and Pierce, J. V.: The Action of the Kallikreins on Synthetic Ester Substrates, Proc. Soc. Exper. Biol. & Med. **107:** 186, 1961.
13. Mill, P. J., Elder, J. M., Miles, A. A., and Wilhelm, D. L.: Enzyme-like Globulins From Serum Reproducing the Vascular Phenomena of Inflammation. VI. Isolation and Properties of Permeability Factor and Its Inhibitor in Human Plasma, Brit. J. Exper. Path. **39:** 343, 1958.
14. Demis, D. J., Davis, M. J., and Lawler, J. C.: A Study of the Cutaneous Effects of Serotonin, J. Invest. Dermat. **34:** 43, 1960.
15. Menkin, V.: Biochemical Mechanisms in Inflammation, Springfield, Ill., 1956, Charles C Thomas, Publishers, pp. 11 and 353-354.
16. Wilhelm, D. L., Miles, A. A., and Mackay, M. E.: Enzyme-like Globulins From Serum Reproducing the Vascular Phenomena of Inflammation. II. Isolation and Properties of the Permeability Factor and Its Inhibitor, Brit. J. Exper. Path. **36:** 82, 1955.
17. Frey, E. K., Kraut, H., and Werle, E.: Kallikrein (Padutin), Stuttgart, 1950, Enke.
18. Ungar, G., and Hayashi, H.: Enzymatic Mechanisms in Allergy, Ann. Allergy **16:** 542, 1958.
19. Becker, E. L., Wilhelm, D. L., and Miles, A. A.: Enzymatic Nature of the Serum Globulin Permeability Factor, Nature **183:** 1264, 1959.
20. Margolis, J.: Hageman Factor and Capillary Permeability, Australian J. Exper. Biol. **37:** 239, 1959.
21. Webster, M. E., and Ratnoff, O. D.: The Role of Hageman Factor in the Activation of Vasodilator Activity in Human Plasma, Nature **192:** 180, 1961.
22. Bhoola, K. D., Calle, J. D., and Schachter, M.: The Effect of Bradykinin, Serum Kallikrein and Other Endogenous Substances on Capillary Permeability in the Guinea Pig, J. Physiol. **152:** 75, 1960.
23. Herxheimer, A., and Schachter, M.: Wheal and Flare in Human Skin Produced by Histamine and Other Substances, J. Physiol. **145:** 34P, 1959.
24. Norman, P. S., and Hill, B. M.: Studies of the Plasmin System. III. Physical Properties of the Two Plasmin Inhibitors in Plasma, J. Exper. Med. **108:** 639, 1958.
25. Werle, E., and Maier, L.: Über die Chemische und Pharmakalogische untersheidung von kallikrein verschiedener herkunft, Biochem. Ztschr. **323:** 279, 1952.

26. Miles, A. A., and Wilhelm, D. W.: Distribution of Globulin Permeability Factor and Its Inhibitor in the Tissue Fluid and Lymph of the Guinea Pig, Nature **181**: 96, 1958.

27. Miles, A. A.: Are We Too Trigger-happy? Table-talk About Some Initiators of the Inflammatory Response, Henry Ford Hospital International Symposium, Mechanisms of Hypersensitivity, Boston, 1959, Little, Brown & Company, pp. 735-747.

28. Lewis, G. P.: Active Polypeptides Derived From Plasma Proteins, Physiol. Rev. **40**: 647, 1960.

29. Huggins, C. G., and Walaszek, E. J.: Depressor Polypeptides, Am. Heart J. **60**: 976, 1960.

30. Heuson, J. C., Peers, W., and Tagnon, H. J.: A New Diagnostic and Therapeutic Approach to Fibrinolysis and Hemorrhage, Blood **13**: 874, 1958.

31. Tagnon, H. J.: Personal communication, March, 1960.

32. Landerman, N. S., Ratcliffe, H. E., and Becker, E. L.: Familial Hereditary Angio-oedema Treated With Promethazine, Lancet **2**: 183, 1959.

33. Spaulding, W. B.: Methyltestosterone Therapy for Hereditary Episodic Edema (Hereditary Angioneurotic Edema), Ann. Int. Med. **53**: 739, 1960.

A Biochemical Abnormality in Hereditary Angioneurotic Edema*

Absence of Serum Inhibitor of C'1-Esterase

VIRGINIA H. DONALDSON, M.D.† *and* RICHARD R. EVANS, M.D.

Cleveland, Ohio

HEREDITARY angioneurotic edema is a rare disease characterized by episodes of localized swelling often of life-threatening severity. As noted by Osler [1] the predisposition to these attacks is transmitted as an autosomal dominant trait [2–6]. Generally, no specific agent is identifiable as the cause of the attacks. Unlike allergic angioneurotic edema, the hereditary form in most instances is not associated with convincing evidence of hypersensitivity to foods or environmental allergens [3]. In addition, the results of skin tests are usually negative, and various types of antiallergic therapy do not relieve symptoms [3,6,7].

Attacks of swelling occur at varying intervals. Although they may be mild, death from respiratory tract obstruction has frequently been reported [6,8]. Severe abdominal pain from gastrointestinal edema may lead to unnecessary surgery, particularly when the clue of superficial swelling is absent [9]. Often, trauma to the part affected, strenuous exercise, emotional excitement or anxiety may precede an attack [2,7,10]. Edema may repeatedly form in the same area [2]. Persons with this disease are relatively free of other organic ailments and may have long lives if they survive repeated episodes.

Landerman and associates [11,12] recently reported that a woman with hereditary angioneurotic edema had a decreased amount of the serum inhibitor of a globulin permeability factor (kallikrein). They suggested that this deficiency might permit exaggeration of the effect of a vascular permeability increasing property of serum [12].

The present report presents evidence that persons with hereditary angioneurotic edema lack the serum inhibitor directed against the esterase derived from the first component of complement (C'1-esterase). This absence appears to be inherited.

Recent evidence indicates that the first component of complement, known as C'1, exists in serum as a proesterase [13–16]. Following contact with antigen-antibody complexes [13,17] or plasmin [18,19], serum fractions containing C'1 rapidly hydrolyze N-acetyl-L-tyrosine ethyl ester and several other synthetic amino acid esters. Partially purified preparations of C'1 have similar esterolytic properties upon appropriate adjustment of salt and hydrogen ion concentrations [14,19], and serum treated with ether can provide a fraction rich in this activity [16]. In each instance, C'1 is required for development of this esterolytic property. It differs from plasmin, which does not hydrolyze N-acetyl-L-tyrosine ethyl ester [13].

As C'1-esterase evolves, the hemolytic activity of C'1 is lost, and the capacity to inactivate the fourth and second components of complement (C'4 and C'2) appears [14]. Although direct evidence to identify C'1 as this proesterase necessarily awaits its further purification, studies of highly purified preparations of C'1 provide data consistent with this concept [20].

* From the Research Division and Department of Allergy, Cleveland Clinic Foundation and the Department of Medicine, Western Reserve University School of Medicine, Cleveland, Ohio. This work was presented in part to the Thirty-Fourth Annual Meeting of the Central Society for Clinical Research, Chicago, Illinois, November 3, 1961. These studies were supported by grant No. H-5126 from the National Institutes of Health. Manuscript received September 4, 1962.
† Present address: Research Division, St. Vincent Charity Hospital, Cleveland, Ohio.

Normal human serum inhibits both esterolytic and complement inactivating functions of C′1-esterase [21,22]. Inhibition is provided by a specific alpha globulin which reacts stoichiometrically with the enzyme [22,23]. The role of this serum inhibitor *in vivo* is unknown, but it can impair complement action *in vitro* [24–26]. In our experience, over 500 serum specimens from persons in various states of health and disease have all contained inhibitor [27]. Only serum specimens from persons with hereditary angioneurotic edema lacked this property. The observations to be described implicate a hereditary abnormality related to the function of the complement system in hereditary angioneurotic edema.

CASE REPORT

A twenty-two year old white married woman (R. G., Cleveland Clinic Hospital No. 903086) was admitted to the Cleveland Clinic Hospital on February 8, 1961, for investigation of attacks of swelling and colic-like abdominal pain recurrent since the age of two years. Other members of her family were known to have a similar condition. During childhood these episodes occurred once or twice a year, but in recent years both the frequency and severity of symptoms had increased. At times she was free of symptoms for only a few days. She recognized no single factor as causing attacks but believed emotional upsets were often related to onset of symptoms. Physical trauma might sometimes play a part. For example, her hand and forearm became involved after she had used a hand stapler for several hours. She indicted no environmental allergens or foods as causing attacks. She had been relatively free of symptoms during her two pregnancies, two and three years prior to admission, but believed an attack would usually occur with menstruation.

Localized swelling was ordinarily the first symptom of an attack, occurring most often on the face, the neck, an extremity, the throat or the abdominal wall. External areas were so uncomfortable when tense with edema that the patient was often unable to use the involved part. Swelling of the throat was most frequent at night and was accompanied by fear of imminent suffocation. Symptoms usually subsided in two or three days.

Treatment with adrenaline injections, throat sprays and cortisone injections had not been clearly helpful. During periods of hospitalization elsewhere, her abdominal pain, distention and tenderness had at times prompted consideration of surgical exploration. Morphine and Demerol® therapy relieved abdominal pain.

The patient had had no other illnesses of unusual severity or frequency. She had not had repeated infections, eczema, asthma, hay fever or renal disease. She had never had any hemorrhagic symptoms, and attacks of edema were unassociated with ecchymoses.

Characteristic attacks had occurred on the paternal side of the family in the grandfather, uncle, father and a half brother. Her mother, full brother, half sister and two young sons have never had these symptoms. (Fig. 1, Family A.)

Not shown in Figure 1 is another branch of Family A, which was not available for study. From the history provided by the family, all twelve known members of this branch, comprising four generations, were affected. Three appeared to have died of respiratory tract obstruction during an attack, and one was thought to have had meningitis during a terminal episode. However, laboratory findings to support this diagnosis are not available.

Upon physical examination on admission to the hospital, the patient appeared well except for a mild upper respiratory tract infection with pharyngeal inflammation. There was no evidence of other acute or chronic disease.

Laboratory findings on admission revealed the following: hemoglobin 15.2 gm. per cent, hematocrit 46 per cent and leukocytes 11,800 per cu. mm. with 75 per cent polymorphonuclear leukocytes, 6 per cent band forms, 4 per cent eosinophils, 10 per cent lymphocytes and 5 per cent mononuclear cells. Platelets appeared normal on stained smear. The urine was clear with a pH of 7.5 and a specific gravity of 1.005 with no cells, sugar or albumin. Serum electrolyte concentrations, blood urea and blood sugar were normal. Serum proteins determined by paper electrophoresis were normal.

Coagulation studies revealed no evidence of a hemostatic defect. Clotting, prothrombin and bleeding times were all normal. There was no evidence of increased blood fibrinolytic activity during the attack of edema; clots formed of her blood remained unlysed for a week at 37°C.

Skin test results for a variety of food and environmental allergens were entirely negative.

On the day following admission, the patient experienced swelling of the left foot where her slipper fitted tightly. Within hours, edema of the left forearm appeared. During that night, a sense of fullness of the throat developed, and she became alarmingly apprehensive. The pharynx and uvula were diffusely involved with boggy translucent edema. She did not have respiratory signs suggesting impaired ventilation but commenced to have severe episodic abdominal pain which was at first described as both crampy and steady. The abdominal wall was not swollen, but her entire abdomen was slightly tender without spasm. Bowel sounds were present and at times hyperactive; no enlarged organs were felt.

Treatment with tripelennamine, phenobarbital, subcutaneous injections of adrenaline, intravenously administered methylprednisolone, diphenhydramine, phenothiazine and prochlorperazine had no apparent effect on her symptoms. Demerol therapy provided some relief from abdominal pain.

For two days the patient remained in bed alternating between a slumberous state, probably due to sedation, and episodes of agonizing abdominal pain. The external edema then became less tense so that it could be pitted, and her other symptoms gradually subsided. She had one episode of nonbloody diarrhea as her abdominal pain, distention and tenderness subsided. After further investigations, she was discharged on February 14, 1961, in apparent good health. Treatment with 10 mg. per day of methyl testosterone was prescribed as suggested by Spaulding [28]. While receiving this treatment during the succeeding eighteen months, the patient has had only one mild attack of edema.

SPECIAL LABORATORY STUDIES

Further investigations related to some *in vitro* functions of the complement system and serum inhibition directed against plasmin and trypsin. In addition to the index case, some of the patient's relatives and members of two other families known to have hereditary angioneurotic edema were studied. (Fig. 1, Families A, B and C.)

Complement is a group of substances in fresh serum, probably proteins, which may participate in antigen-antibody reactions but is not increased by immunization. The four originally described components of complement are referred to by number denoting the chronologic order of their discovery and are designated $C'1$, $C'2$, $C'3$ and $C'4$ [29]. An enzyme, $C'1$-esterase, is thought to be derived from $C'1$. For these studies, a partially purified preparation of this enzyme was fractionated from normal human serum as has been described [14] and used in a concentration of 40 ± 4 units per ml. [22].

The naturally occurring inhibition directed against $C'1$-esterase in human serum was measured by the method of Levy and Lepow [22]. In essence, this determines the amount of inhibition of a standardized preparation of $C'1$-esterase provided by variable volumes of serum. Two different volumes of serum were incubated with approximately 20 units of $C'1$-esterase, and residual capacity to hydrolyze N-acetyl-L-tyrosine ethyl ester* was determined. Ester hydrolysis was measured by a microformol titration using 0.05 N sodium hydroxide to determine the amount of acid liberated in fifteen minutes. The amount of inhibitor, in units per milliliter, represents the mean value provided by two volumes of serum [22]. This will be referred to as the amount of serum inhibitor of $C'1$-esterase, even though it was not fractionated from serum prior to assay.

* Prepared in the laboratories of the Department of Organic Chemistry, Western Reserve University, Cleveland, Ohio.

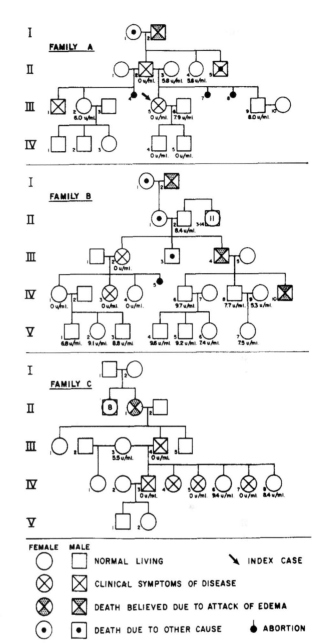

FIG. 1. Levels of serum inhibitor of $C'1$-esterase in families with hereditary angioneurotic edema. Generations of three families are designated by Roman numerals to the left; individual members are designated by Arabic numerals at the lower left corner of each figure. The family members in each pedigree are described according to the key. Levels of serum inhibitor of $C'1$-esterase (units per milliliter of serum) are shown beneath figures representing family members upon whom this determination could be made. Of those whose deaths were "believed due to an attack," evidence of pulmonary edema was found at autopsy in IV-10, Family B. Only historic evidence of this cause of death was available in the others in this category. In Family B, IV-5 represents a therapeutic abortion performed during an attack of swelling, without evidence of toxemia. All other abortions were spontaneous. In generation II of both Families B and C combined figures represent normal subjects, the numbers of whom are described within the figures.

Hydrolysis of N-acetyl-L-tyrosine ethyl ester by serum alone was measured to determine C'1-esterase-like activity therein. Details of assay have been described [22].

To test the effect of a patient's serum on the inhibitor of C'1-esterase in normal serum, equal volumes of each were incubated together for one hour at 37°c. Residual inhibition was then measured as described. Control mixtures consisted of normal serum and patient's serum incubated separately but concurrently for the same period, chilled and combined in equal volumes just prior to assay for residual inhibition.

Upon its conversion to an esterase, a preparation of C'1 simultaneously has the ability to inactivate or inhibit C'4 and C'2. Levels of the four components of complement in serum specimens were determined in hemolytic assays by published methods [13,30,31]. Reagents markedly deficient in the component in question fulfilled previously described criteria for each [13,17,30,31]. Reagents used to measure C'1, C'2, C'3 and C'4 are called R-1, R-2, R-3 and R-4, respectively.

Inhibition of casein hydrolysis by trypsin or plasmin by serum specimens of affected and unaffected members of families with hereditary angioneurotic edema was compared. Chloroform-activated bovine plasmin (Fibrinolysin,® Parke Davis Co., Detroit, Michigan) in a concentration of 2.8 Loomis units [32] per ml. was used to determine antiplasmin activity; crystalline trypsin (Worthington Biochemical Corp., Freehold, New Jersey) in a concentration of 0.001 mg. per ml. was employed in assays for antitryptic activity. Both were dissolved in solutions of "Tris buffer," 0.15 M, pH 7.5, which was prepared with "Tris" (2-amino-2-(hydroxy methyl) 1,3-propanediol) and hydrochloric acid. A 5 per cent solution of casein (Hammerstan Quality, Nutritional Biochemicals, Cleveland, Ohio) was prepared as Norman [33] described and then dialyzed against Tris buffer for use as substrate in assays for proteolysis.

Mixtures of 0.35 ml. of enzyme and 0.35 ml. of serum diluted in Tris buffer (1 to 4 and 1 to 16) were warmed at 37°c. for ten minutes and 1.9 ml. of warmed casein solution added. After incubation for four hours at 37°c., 2.0 ml. from each mixture was added to 2.0 ml. of 0.3 N trichloracetic acid. For the control experiments, mixtures of enzyme and serum were incubated apart from casein for the same period and combined just prior to precipitation in acid. Acid-soluble tyrosine-like materials liberated during incubation were measured by a minor modification of the method of Folin and Ciocalteu [34]. Comparison of amounts of these products of hydrolysis in mixtures containing serum with those containing buffer instead permitted estimation of relative amounts of inhibition of either enzyme.

Blood from members of Families A and B were drawn into glass syringes, allowed to clot and kept at 4°c. overnight. Serum was separated by centrifugation at 0°c. in an International PR-2 centrifuge at 2,500 r.p.m. for fifteen minutes and tested for inhibitor of C'1-esterase immediately and again after storage at −25°c. for as long as two months. Serum specimens obtained from members of Family C had been stored at −70°c. for two weeks and then shipped by air. These serum specimens, in sealed ampules, had thawed during transit. They were all tested for inhibitor of C'1-esterase upon arrival and then stored at −70°c. Portions used in assays for components of complement were stored at −70°c. for as long as two months prior to assay.

RESULTS

The serum of the index patient, R. G., was completely lacking in inhibitor of C'1-esterase during the attack described, after its conclusion and again when she had been well for a six month period. Normally, human serum contains 5.8 (±1.8) units of this inhibitor per ml., as determined in the esterolytic assay described [22,35].

Available members of this patient's family were studied. Her father, who has had numerous attacks of edema, and her two young sons, as yet asymptomatic, also lacked serum inhibitor of C'1-esterase, whereas other unaffected relatives had normal or somewhat increased amounts. (Fig. 1, Family A.)

Another Caucasian family with this disease (Fig. 1, Family B) living in the same city but apparently unrelated to family A was studied. A woman (III-2) had had severe attacks, often with abdominal pain, since the age of twenty-five years. Her serum lacked inhibitor of C'1-esterase (Fig. 1) as did serum specimens from each of her three daughters, only one of whom has had symptoms. Their surviving cousins (Fig. 1, IV-6 and 8) have not been subject to characteristic attacks, and all had somewhat increased amounts of this inhibitor. One clinically affected member of this generation (IV-10) died recently during an attack of edema with respiratory distress. He had had intermittent attacks of swelling from the age of two years until his death at twenty years.

Serum specimens from some members of a Negro family (Fig. 1, Family C), which has been observed elsewhere, were subsequently tested. All affected members lacked serum inhibitor of C'1-esterase. (Fig. 1.)

The amount of serum inhibitor of C'1-esterase in serum specimens of persons with

TABLE I

LEVELS OF SERUM INHIBITOR OF C'1-ESTERASE
IN ANGIONEUROTIC EDEMA

Source of Serum	No. Tested	Inhibitor of C'1-Esterase* (units/ml.)
Normal adults and children...	165	5.8 ± 1.8
Patients with hereditary angioneurotic edema............	12†	0
Unaffected relatives of those with hereditary angioneurotic edema.................	19	7.7 ± 1.4
Patients with nonhereditary angioneurotic edema.......	15	9.2 ± 2.6

* Mean value obtained when each of 2 vol. of serum was tested in the esterolytic assay described.

† There were twelve subjects in these families who lacked serum inhibitor of C'1-esterase. Although some have not yet had symptoms, they are designated as having hereditary angioneurotic edema.

acute or chronic urticaria and extensive angioneurotic edema of nonfamilial types, was measured. With one exception, these persons had greater than normal amounts. None was completely lacking. (Table I.)

C'1-Esterase may have some as yet undefined proteolytic function. It is conceivable, therefore, that absence of its inhibitor might reflect a more general deficiency of serum inhibitors of proteolytic enzymes. However, serum of affected and unaffected members of all three families impaired casein hydrolysis by trypsin to similar degrees. A 1 to 16 dilution of serum specimens from affected and unaffected members of Families A and B provided 100 per cent inhibition of plasmin. Antiplasmin was found in serum specimens of members of Family C when tested elsewhere [36].

If some destructive process were responsible for the absence of serum inhibitor of C'1-esterase in hereditary angioneurotic edema, its effect should be demonstrable upon the inhibitor in normal serum. To test this possibility, serum samples from patients lacking this inhibitor were incubated with those from normal persons. When the amount of inhibition remaining was measured, no loss from normal serum could be demonstrated. (Table II.)

C'1-Esterase may evolve from its inactive precursor through an autocatalytic mechanism [19]. Activity attributable to this esterase might develop in serum samples which lacked its

TABLE II

EFFECT OF HEREDITARY ANGIONEUROTIC EDEMA SERUM
ON INHIBITOR OF C'1-ESTERASE IN NORMAL SERUM

Incubation Mixture*	Residual Inhibitor in Normal Serum † (units/ml.)
Normal and patient's serum:	
Incubated together.................	8.6
Incubated separately...............	7.6

* This patient's serum specimen did not contain C'1-esterase-like activity. It is difficult to quantify inhibitor in the presence of serum having this esterolytic property, as further activation can occur during assay if there is C'1 which has not yet been converted to C'1-esterase.

† Equal volumes of patient's serum and normal serum were incubated for one hour at 37°C. and the residual inhibitor of C'1-esterase tested in the standard assay. In the control experiment, the two serum samples were incubated separately but concurrently and combined in equal volumes just prior to assay.

TABLE III

DATA FROM A FAMILY (FAMILY C) WITH HEREDITARY
ANGIONEUROTIC EDEMA

Subject	Serum Inhibitor of C'1-Esterase (units/ml.)	C'1-Esterase-Like Activity (units/ml.)	Components of Complement (units/ml. of serum)			
			C'1	C'2	C'3	C'4
II-1	5.5	0	2,560	40	≥640	2,560
II-2	0	16.5	480	<20	480	<20
IV-3	0	19.4	<20	<20	≥640	<20
IV-5	0	17.4	<20	<20	480	<20
IV-6	9.4	0	3,840	120	240	1,280
IV-7	0	11.2	<20	<20	480	<20
IV-8	8.4	0	2,560	30	≥640	2,560

NOTE: Serum inhibitor of C'1-esterase was measured in the esterolytic assay described using N-acetyl-L-tyrosine ethyl ester as substrate. C'1-esterase-like activity reflected the amount of this ester hydrolyzed by 0.5 ml. of each serum in the standard assay. Units of components of complement were calculated from the volume of each serum which induced 50 per cent hemolysis of sensitized sheep red cells when incubated with a reagent markedly deficient in the component in question (R-1, R-2, R-3 or R-4).

inhibitor. However, none of the serum specimens from members of Families A and B contained significant amounts of N-acetyl-L-tyrosine ethyl esterase activity whether or not inhibitor was present. On the other hand, serum specimens from members of Family C lacking inhibitor clearly contained esterase activity; serum samples containing inhibitor had none of this esterolytic property. (Table III.)

Partially purified preparations of C'1-esterase

readily inactivate C'4 in normal serum; C'2 is inactivated less rapidly [14]. Small amounts of C'1-esterase activity may be more accurately detected by measuring its effect on C'4 than on N-acetyl-L-tyrosine ethyl ester, as titration error in the latter assay may obscure limited hydrolysis [16].

The amounts of hemolytic C'4 remaining in serum specimens from members of Family A were all within normal limits, and no esterolytic activity was found. However, three of the four inhibitor-free serum samples from Family B lacked C'4 and also C'2, although originally free of detectable N-acetyl-L-tyrosine ethyl esterase activity. Hemolytic C'1 was undetectable in only one of these serum specimens. When serum samples from members of Family C were tested, each sample lacking inhibitor of C'1-esterase also lacked C'4 and C'2. (Table III.)

COMMENTS

Persons with hereditary angioneurotic edema completely lacked serum inhibitor of C'1-esterase which is normally present in human serum. None of over 500 healthy or sick persons who was not a candidate for this disease lacked this inhibitor [27].

Of three families studied, some members who are not yet clinically affected also lacked this inhibitor. Inasmuch as the age of initial appearance of symptoms can be as late as the fourth decade, these younger persons may eventually become symptomatic [1,2]. It is likely that this finding provides evidence of this inherited disorder in an affected person not yet clinically identifiable.

This serum defect cannot be ascribed to environmental effects studied. Attacks of angioneurotic edema were not the cause, for those with nonhereditary types or urticaria not only had this serum inhibitor, but also all save one had greater than normal amounts. This indicated a relationship between hereditary angioneurotic edema and absence of serum inhibitor of C'1-esterase. In addition, absence of this inhibitor was not a manifestation of a general lack of serum antiproteolytic activity, for antiplasmin and antitrypsin were present.

It was also possible that this finding could be explained by some property which inactivated or destroyed normally occurring inhibitor. However, when a patient's serum lacking inhibitor was incubated with serum containing a normal amount, no loss could be demonstrated.

Absence of inhibitor of C'1-esterase in hereditary angioneurotic edema is probably an inherited defect. The tendency for members of affected families to have characteristic attacks of edema is transmitted as an autosomal dominant trait [1–6]. Incidence of this serum defect in these families is also consistent with the expression of an autosomal dominant trait.

Four serum specimens lacking inhibitor of C'1-esterase (Family C) readily hydrolyzed N-acetyl-L-tyrosine ethyl ester, a substrate for this enzyme. They had also lost hemolytic activity of C'2 and C'4, both of which are inactivated by C'1-esterase. In contrast, serum specimens containing inhibitor had no evidence of either function of the esterase. Thus, in the absence of inhibitor, some or all of the C'1 had apparently been converted to C'1-esterase, which in turn had inactivated C'2 and C'4. Comparable samples from Families A and B contained none of this esterolytic property and had inconstant evidence of C'4 or C'2 inactivation. It was suspected that C'1 activation in the serum samples from Family C had occurred during shipment, as they were not frozen throughout this time. We were unable to explain the mechanism of this apparent activation.

Symptoms of this disease cannot be ascribed to absence of inhibitor of C'1-esterase alone, for although swellings occur sporadically, inhibitor seems always to be missing. Immediate causes of attacks in these people are not clear and probably vary even for one person. In most instances no convincing evidence of hypersensitivity can be obtained [3,5,6,37]. It has been emphasized that physical trauma so minor as to reveal no abnormality in an unaffected relative, may induce symptoms in the affected person [4,10,38]. Several described patients with this disease [2,3,10] and some of the members of the families in this study are aware that emotional upsets constitute a most important factor in initiating an attack. Possible roles of fear, anger and pleasurable excitement have received comment [2,4,10]. Still others are unable to identify any associated circumstances. A heterogeneity of factors may initiate the events ultimately leading to local increases in vascular permeability.

One of the subjects in the present series (III-2, Family B) stated that forced exercise (for the purpose of weight reduction) and taking amphetamine would often initiate characteristic attacks of edema or abdominal pain. Trauma of minor degree, as tight clothing, often seemed causative. She believed that "emotional upsets" bore the most predictable relationship to the beginning of an attack. Some of these situations are reminiscent of those which Macfarlane et al. found associated with enhanced fibrinolytic activity in the blood [39,40]. In vitro studies have shown that streptokinase activated plasmin can in some way convert C'1 to an esterase [18,19]. Perhaps an in vivo mechanism providing enhanced fibrinolytic activity can similarly affect C'1; however, we had no evidence for this in our index case. A clot formed of our patient's blood remained unlysed for a week. This sample was not obtained at the time of onset of symptoms but nearly thirty-six hours later. We have not had the opportunity to observe the blood of a patient at the beginning of an attack.

It is tempting to speculate that in the absence of serum inhibitor of C'1-esterase, such a series of events might proceed without the usual physiologic brake provided by this property of blood. Even so, symptoms are inadequately explained, for edema is circumscribed rather than generalized. As aptly described by the Crowders, some attacks of swelling repeat themselves with "photographic correctness" [2]. Thus, local tissue factors appear to be involved.

Perhaps C'1-esterase can function to increase vascular permeability [41]. Landerman and associates reported that a woman with hereditary angioneurotic edema was deficient in serum inhibitor of kallikrein [12]. When we tested serum from their patient, we found that it completely lacked inhibitor of C'1-esterase. Therefore, there may be some relationship between the actions of serum inhibitors of C'1-esterase and of kallikrein.

SUMMARY

Affected persons in three families with hereditary angioneurotic edema completely lack naturally occurring serum inhibitor of C'1-esterase. This inhibitor is also absent from some younger relatives who have not yet had typical attacks of swelling. Its absence is characteristic of the hereditary form of angioneurotic edema, for those with nonhereditary types have normal or increased amounts of the inhibitor. Of 500 persons tested, no others completely lacked this inhibitor.

This deficiency did not result from a destruc-tive property in these serum specimens, for normal serum lost no inhibitor during its incubation with that from a patient. In addition, lack of this inhibitor did not reflect a generalized absence of antiproteolytic activity, for antiplasmin and antitrypsin were present.

This evidence suggests that absence of serum inhibitor of C'1-esterase is an inherited abnormality in those with the familial type of angioneurotic edema. This does not explain the sporadic occurrence of localized swellings; tissue mechanisms are implicated. This determination may permit identification of young family members who will have attacks of swelling later in life.

Acknowledgment: It is a pleasure for us to thank the many people who have aided in these studies. Drs. Glynn Rivers of Muncie, Indiana and John Battle of the Cleveland Clinic referred the index case to one of us (R. R. E.). Dr. Atys Q. DaSilva, now of Austin Texas, brought Family B to our attention and Drs. Kemper Venis, Lall Montgomery and Arthur Morse of Muncie, Indiana and Miss Antoinette Ianetta of Cleveland assisted in studies of Families A and B. Dr. Philip S. Norman, Department of Medicine, the Johns Hopkins Hospital and Mr. H. S. Shin, then a fourth year medical student, provided us with serum specimens and historical material on Family C.

Mr. William Bennett provided expert technical assistance throughout these studies. Mr. Earl Todd, Institute of Pathology, Western Reserve University, Cleveland, performed assays for hemolytic complement. Bovine fibrinolysin was generously provided by Dr. M. F. Fahey, Research Department, Parke Davis Co., Detroit, Michigan.

Drs. Irvine H. Page and Arthur G. Steinberg have lent valuable criticisms and suggestions during the preparation of this manuscript. Lastly, the willing cooperation of members of these families deserves continuing thanks.

REFERENCES

1. OSLER, W. Hereditary angioneurotic edema. Am. J. M. Sc., 95: 362, 1888.
2. CROWDER, J. R. and CROWDER, T. R. Five generations of angioneurotic edema. Arch. Int. Med., 20: 840, 1917.
3. COCKAYNE, E. A. Inherited Abnormalities of the Skin and Its Appendages, p. 364. London, 1933. Oxford University Press.
4. HAGY, G. W. and DANHOF, I. Genetic and physiological aspects of a family with chronic hereditary

lymphedema (Nonne-Milroy-Meige's disease) and hereditary angioneurotic edema. *Am. J. Human Genet.*, 10: 141, 1958.

5. FINEMAN, A. H. Hereditary angioneurotic edema. *Ann. Int. Med.*, 14: 916, 1940.

6. TRIGG, J. W. Hereditary angioneurotic edema. Report of a case with gastrointestinal manifestations. *New England J. Med.*, 264: 761, 1961.

7. CASSIRER, R. Vasomotorische Trophischen Neurosen, p. 242. Berlin, 1901. S. Karger.

8. BULLOCH, W. Hereditary angioneurotic edema. In: The Treasury of Human Inheritance, p. 38. London, 1909. Cambridge University Press.

9. OSLER, W. On the surgical importance of the visceral crises in the erythema group of skin diseases. *Am. J. M. Sc.*, 127: 751, 1904.

10. SPAULDING, W. B. Hereditary angioneurotic edema in two families. *Canad. M. A. J.*, 73: 181, 1955.

11. LANDERMAN, N. S., BECKER, E. L. and RATCLIFFE, H. E. Increased cutaneous response to diluted autologous serum in hereditary angio-edema. *Lancet*, 2: 1053, 1960.

12. LANDERMAN, N. S., WEBSTER, M. E., BECKER, E. L. and RATCLIFFE, H. E. Hereditary angioneurotic edema. II. Deficiency of inhibitor for serum globulin permeability factor and/or plasma kallikrein. *J. Allergy*, 33: 330, 1962.

13. LEPOW, I. H., WURZ, L., RATNOFF, O. D. and PILLEMER, L. Studies on the mechanism of inactivation of human complement by plasmin and by antigen-antibody aggregates. I. The requirement for a factor resembling C'1 and the role of Ca^{++}. *J. Immunol.*, 73: 146, 1954.

14. LEPOW, I. H., RATNOFF, O. D., ROSEN, F. S. and PILLEMER, L. Observations on a proesterase associated with partially purified first component of complement (C'1). *Proc. Soc. Exper. Biol. & Med.*, 92: 32, 1956.

15. BECKER, E. L. Concerning the mechanism of complement action. II. The nature of the first component of guinea pig complement. *J. Immunol.*, 77: 469, 1956.

16. DONALDSON, V. H. Studies on the activation of a serum esterase with ether and its relationship to C'1-esterase. *J. Clin. Invest.*, 40: 673, 1961.

17. LEPOW, I. H. and PILLEMER, L. Studies on the mechanism of inactivation of human complement by plasmin and by antigen-antibody aggregates. II. Demonstration of two distinct reaction stages in complement fixation. *J. Immunol.*, 75: 63, 1955.

18. PILLEMER, L., RATNOFF, O. D., BLUM, L. and LEPOW, I. H. The inactivation of complement and its components by plasmin. *J. Exper. Med.*, 97: 573, 1953.

19. LEPOW, I. H., RATNOFF, O. D. and LEVY, L. R. Studies on the activation of a proesterase associated with partially purified first component of human complement. *J. Exper. Med.*, 107: 451, 1958.

20. HAINES, A. L. and LEPOW, I. H. Purification and properties of human C'1-esterase. (Abstract.) *Fed. Proc.*, 21: 17, 1962.

21. RATNOFF, O. D. and LEPOW, I. H. Some properties of an esterase derived from preparations of the first component of complement. *J. Exper. Med.*, 106: 327, 1957.

22. LEVY, L. R. and LEPOW, I. H. Assay and properties of serum inhibitor of C'1-esterase. *Proc. Soc. Exper. Biol. & Med.*, 101: 608, 1959.

23. PENSKY, J., LEVY, L. R. and LEPOW, I. H. Partial purification of a serum inhibitor of C'1-esterase. *J. Biol. Chem.*, 236: 1674, 1961.

24. LEPOW, I. H. and ROSS, A. Studies on immune cellular injury. II. Functional role of C'1-esterase in immune cytotoxicity. *J. Exper. Med.*, 112: 1107, 1960.

25. HINZ, C. F., JR., PICKEN, M. E. and LEPOW, I. H. Studies on immune human hemolysis. II. The Donath-Landsteiner reaction as a model system for studying the mechanism of action of complement and the role of C'1 and C'1-esterase. *J. Exper. Med.*, 113: 193, 1961.

26. LEPOW, I. H. and LEON, M. A. Interaction of a serum inhibitor of C'1-esterase with intermediate complexes of the immune haemolytic system. I. Specificity of inhibition of C'1-activity associated with intermediate complexes. *J. Immunol.*, 5: 222, 1962.

27. DONALDSON, V. H. Unpublished observations.

28. SPAULDING, W. B. Methyltestosterone therapy for hereditary episodic edema (hereditary angioneurotic edema). *Ann. Int. Med.*, 53: 739, 1960.

29. PILLEMER, L. and ECKER, E. E. The terminology of the components of complement. *Science*, 94: 437, 1941.

30. BIER, O. G., LEYTON, G., MAYER, M. M. and HEIDELBERGER, M. A comparison of human and guinea pig complements and their component fractions. *J. Exper. Med.*, 81: 449, 1945.

31. KABAT, E. A. and MAYER, M. M. Experimental Immunochemistry. Springfield, Ill., 1948. Charles C Thomas.

32. LOOMIS, E. C., GEORGE, C., JR. and RYDER, A. Fibrinolysin: nomenclature, unit, assay, preparation and properties. *Arch. Biochem.*, 12: 1, 1947.

33. NORMAN, P. S. Studies of the plasmin system. I. Measurement of human and animal plasminogen. Measurement of an activator in human serum. *J. Exper. Med.*, 106: 423, 1957.

34. FOLIN, O. and CIOCALTEU, V. On tyrosine and tryptophane determinations in proteins. *J. Biol. Chem.*, 73: 627, 1929.

35. DONALDSON, V. H. and EVANS, R. R. Absence of an enzyme inhibitor in hereditary angioneurotic edema. (Abstract.) *J. Lab. & Clin. Med.*, 58: 812, 1961.

36. NORMAN, P. S. Personal communication.

37. SHELDON, J. M., SCHREIBER, M. D. and LOVELL, R. G. Hereditary angioneurotic edema with a case report. *J. Lab. & Clin. Med.*, 34: 524, 1949.

38. CASSIRER, R. In: Lewandowsky's Handbuch der Neurologie, vol. 5, p. 256. Berlin, 1914. Springer-Verlag.

39. MACFARLANE, R. G. and BIGGS, R. Observations of fibrinolysis. Spontaneous activity associated with surgery, trauma, etc. *Lancet*, 2: 862, 1946.

40. BIGGS, R., MACFARLANE, R. G. and PILLING, J. Observations on fibrinolysis. Experimental activity produced by exercise or adrenaline. *Lancet*, 1: 402, 1947.

41. LEPOW, I. H. and RATNOFF, O. D. Personal communication.

Hereditary Angioneurotic Edema:
Two Genetic Variants

Abstract. Serums of patients with hereditary angioneurotic edema lack inhibitory activity against the esterase derived from the first component of complement. In one group of patients this lack appears to result from failure to synthesize the esterase inhibitor of the first component of complement, whereas in another group of patients an abnormal, nonfunctional protein is synthesized.

The serums of patients with hereditary angioneurotic edema (HANE) are unique in that they do not inhibit the hydrolysis of N-acetyl-L-tyrosine ethyl ester by the esterase derived from the first component of complement (C'1) (*1*). This observation led to the conclusion that serums of such patients lack the C'1 esterase inhibitor (EI). Further support for this observation was obtained from the demonstration that the titer of the fourth component of complement is decreased in vivo in the blood of these patients and that the free esterolytic activity in their serum or plasma has similar ultracentrifugal characteristics to C'1 esterase (*1*).

The C'1 esterase inhibitor has been isolated in a highly purified state; it is an acid labile α_2 globulin (*2*). In order to estimate the amount of this inhibitor in normal serums and in the serums of patients with hereditary angioneurotic edema by immunochemical means, two rabbits were repeatedly injected in the foot pads during the course of 1 year with a total of 4 mg of the purified inhibitor in complete adjuvant. Upon immunoelectrophoresis, the rabbit antiserum formed three bands of precipitation with normal human serum. This antiserum could be made specific for the inhibitor without diminution in its potency, and two contaminating bands could be eliminated by mixing 20 parts of the rabbit antiserum with 1 part of the serum from a patient whose serum contained only trace amounts of the inhibitor. The antiserum was titrated by agar-gel diffusion (*3*) against a highly purified preparation of the inhibitor freed of contaminating protein as measured by immunologic criteria. The concentration of the inhibitor in normal serum was 2.4 ± 0.4 mg per 100 ml.

The serums of 25 patients from ten kindreds with hereditary angioneurotic edema contained 0.16 to 0.64 mg of EI per 100 ml. Upon immunoelectrophore-

sis, these 25 serums formed only faint bands of precipitation with antiserum against EI. The serums of the "normal" relatives of the 25 patients contained normal concentrations of the inhibitor. In contrast, the serums of nine patients in two additional affected kindreds contained normal amounts of inhibitor as estimated by immunochemical means, even though these serums had no inhibitory activity in the esterolytic assay. The rabbit antibody to the inhibitor prepared from a pool of normal human serums gave a reaction of complete identity with the nonfunctional inhibitor of these nine patients, an indication that the abnormal protein was not deficient in antigenic determinants (Fig. 1). Upon immunoelectrophoretic analysis in barbital buffer at pH 8.2 (ionic-strength 0.05), no difference could be discerned between the bands of precipitation formed with EI in normal serums or with the nonfunctional inhibitor in the serums of patients. However, immunoelectrophoresis in the presence of calcium lactate, as outlined by Hirschfeld (*4*), showed a clear differ-

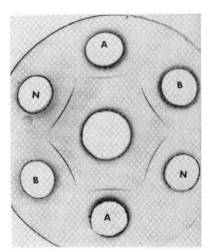

Fig. 1. Agar double diffusion of serum from normal humans (*N*), serum deficient in EI from patients with hereditary angioneurotic edema (*A*), and serum from patients synthesizing nonfunctional EI (*B*) against rabbit antiserum to EI.

Fig. 2. Immunoelectrophoresis of serum from normal humans (*N*) and serum with nonfunctional EI from a patient with hereditary angioneurotic edema (*B*) against rabbit antiserum to EI. The anode is to the right.

From *Science*. 1965;148:957–958. Reprinted with permission from the American Association for the Advancement of Science.

ence between the normal and abnormal serums in that a characteristic double-arc "gull-wing" band of precipitation was formed by the inhibitor in normal serum, whereas that in the abnormal serum formed only a single component which corresponded to the fast portion of the normal "gull-wing" pattern (Fig. 2). These differences could not be attributed to the effect of concentration or pH and were believed to result from a structural alteration in the nonfunctional protein. Inasmuch as the reaction of identity was found on Ouchterlony analysis, the altered immunoelectrophoretic pattern implies a structural alteration in the nonfunctional inhibitor without deleting antigenic determinants.

Hereditary angioneurotic edema is transmitted as an autosomal dominant characteristic, and studies of pedigrees indicate that patients with the disease are heterozygotes. However, the serums of patients in 10 of the 12 kindreds studied contained only 6 to 25 percent of the normal amount of inhibitor. The deficiency of antigenic inhibitor in these serums results from a defect in synthesis of EI since a study of I^{131}-labeled inhibitor showed that the rate of catabolism of the inhibitor in the patients did not differ from that in the normal subjects (5). In the two other kindreds a normal amount of nonfunctional, structurally altered inhibitor is synthesized. The two genetic variants of hereditary angioneurotic edema may be analagous to the two types of tryptophane synthetase mutants of *Neurospora crassa*: one type lacks the enzyme, and, in the other type, enzymatically inactive protein is synthesized and this inactive protein is antigenically cross-reacting (6). Possibly synthesis by a heterozygous individual of a nonfunctional, abnormal protein might suppress the regulatory mechanism for the synthesis of normal, functional protein (7). Further study of the genetic variant in which a nonfunctional protein is synthesized may confirm the hypothesis.

FRED S. ROSEN
PATRICIA CHARACHE
Children's Hospital and *Department of Pediatrics, Harvard Medical School, Boston, Massachusetts*

JACK PENSKY
Institute of Pathology, Western Reserve University, Cleveland, Ohio

VIRGINIA DONALDSON
St. Vincent's Charity Hospital and *Department of Medicine, Western Reserve University, Cleveland, Ohio*

References and Notes

1. V. Donaldson and R. Evans, *Am. J. Med.* **35**, 37 (1963); V. Donaldson and F. S. Rosen, *J. Clin. Invest.* **95**, 362 (1964).
2. J. Pensky, L. R. Levy, I. H. Lepow, *J. Biol. Chem.* **236**, 1674 (1961); J. Pensky, *Federation Proc.* **19**, 76 (1960).
3. O. Ouchterlony, *Arkiv Kemi* **1**, 43 (1949); J. G. Feinberg, *Immunology* **2**, 346 (1959).
4. J. Hirschfeld, *Nature* **185**, 931 (1960).
5. F. S. Rosen, J. Pensky, P. Fireman, in preparation.
6. S. R. Suskind, C. Yanofsky, D. M. Bonner, *Proc. Natl. Acad. Sci.* **41**, 577 (1955).
7. H. E. Sutton, in *The Metabolic Basis of Inherited Disease*, J. B. Stanbury, J. B. Wyngaarden, D. S. Fredrickson, Eds. (McGraw-Hill, New York, 1960), p. 46.
8. Supported in part by grants from the PHS (AI-0587701 and AI-0125508), the Cleveland Area Heart Society, and the National Hemophilia Foundation. J.P. and F.S.R. are recipients of PHS career development awards. Presented at the 56th annual meeting of the American Society for Clinical Investigation, 4 May 1964.

10 March 1965

TRANEXAMIC ACID THERAPY IN HEREDITARY ANGIONEUROTIC EDEMA

Albert L. Sheffer, M.D.,

K. Frank Austen, M.D.,

and Fred S. Rosen, M.D.

HEREDITARY angioneurotic edema results from an inborn error in the biosynthesis of a serum alpha-2 globulin that inhibits the enzymatic activity of the first component of complement and is thus designated the C1 inhibitor (C$\bar{1}$ INH).[1] As a consequence of this defect, there is unopposed action of the first component of complement (C1) in the plasma of affected patients and consequent consumption of the second and fourth components of complement (C4 and C2).[2,3] It appears that the episodic activation of C1 is pathogenetically related to attacks of angioedema. Thus, a potential strategy for the suppression of attacks of angioedema might involve prevention of C1 activation. In addition to antigen-antibody interactions, plasmin is also known to activate C1.[4] The plasmin inhibitor epsilon aminocaproic acid (EACA) and its analogue, trans 4-aminomethylcyclohexane-1-carboxylic acid (tranexamic acid), have been shown in preliminary studies to prevent attacks of edema in patients with hereditary angioneurotic edema.[5] The present study was undertaken to evaluate the efficacy of tranexamic acid in this regard.

MATERIALS AND METHODS

Eighteen patients with hereditary angioneurotic edema were admitted to the study. The age range of the patients was 12 to 72 years. Of the 18, 11 were females and seven males. In each case, the diagnosis was established by immunochemical or functional estimation of the serum C$\bar{1}$ INH concentration.[6,7] Only one of the 18 patients had the rare form of the disease characterized by an abnormal C$\bar{1}$ INH molecule, which is present in serum in normal immunochemical quantity but is not functional. The serum of the 17 other patients contained less than 30 per cent of the normal C$\bar{1}$ INH level.[6]

Serum C$\bar{1}$ INH, C4, and C2 levels were assayed as previously described.[7] Five milliliters of blood was collected in iced tubes containing 0.5 ml of 3.7

From the departments of Medicine and Pediatrics, Harvard Medical School, the Children's Hospital Medical Center and the Robert B. Brigham Hospital (address reprint requests to Dr. Rosen at 300 Longwood Ave., Boston, Mass. 02115).

Supported by grants (AI-05877, RR-128, and 1-P15-AI-10356) from the U.S. Public Health Service and by a grant from Lederle Laboratories (Dr. Rosen is the recipient of a career-development award [AM-19,650] from the U.S. Public Health Service).

Presented at the annual meeting of the American Academy of Allergy, San Francisco, Cal., Feb 5-9, 1972.

per cent sodium citrate. Five thousand units of streptokinase were added to 1 ml of recalcified plasma to assay streptokinase-induced lysis of plasma clots.[8]

Tranexamic acid tablets were supplied in coded bottles. Patients were instructed to take two 0.5-g pills of placebo or drug thrice daily and to maintain a daily log of symptoms. Presence or absence of gastrointestinal symtpoms, subcutaneous edema, and oropharyngeal edema or hoarseness was annotated daily in a diary supplied to the patient. The efficacy of the therapy was evaluated at monthly intervals by one of us, who remained uninformed of the key to the code until the end of the study period. Each patient remained on the coded drug or placebo regimen for two successive periods of three months each. In some cases, the study period was less than six months.

Serial studies were performed to assess hepatic and renal function. Repeated leukocyte, platelet, and red-cell counts were obtained on peripheral blood. Thirty milliliters of blood was obtained to assay prothrombin time, activated partial thromboplastin time, fibrinogen, factor V, factor VIII, and serial thrombin time. Plasma was examined for fibrinogen split products and euglobulin clot-lysis time.

RESULTS

Seven of the 18 patients admitted to the study sustained a complete or almost complete cessation of attacks of angioedema during the drug-trial period, whereas the episodes of angioedema continued with unabated frequency during the placebo trial period. Four more patients had some attenuation in the frequency but a marked reduction in the severity of their angioedema while taking the drug as compared with the placebo period. In one patient, the tranexamic acid was ineffective, and the number of attacks of angioedema on the drug or placebo was the same. Six other patients received either placebo or drug but failed to enter the crossover period of drug or placebo. The results are summarized in Table 1. The significance of the difference between frequency of attacks on drug or placebo was tested by a paired t-test. The calculated value for t was 4.9 yielding a p value of less than 0.005.

No significant alteration was noted in any of the coagulation studies, except for the streptokinase-induced plasma clot-lysis time. The mean clot-lysis time in plasma of patients on the placebo was 12 minutes (normal range, five to 30 minutes). Ingestion of tranexamic acid lengthened the lysis time to greater than 180 minutes. This assay was useful in confirming that the patients were indeed taking the prescribed pills on schedule. It was found that a 0.5-g tablet would prolong the lysis time to greater than 180 minutes, two hours after its ingestion. The effect remained maximal for eight hours.

Urinalysis, blood counts and liver and renal-function tests revealed no abnormality during the drug-trial period. No significant differences by hemolytic or immunochemical estimation were noted in serum C1̄ INH, C4, and C2 titers during the drug-trial period as compared with the placebo period.

Table 1. Comparison of Frequency of Attacks of Angioedema in Patients Taking Tranexamic Acid or Placebo.

CASE No.	DRUG		PLACEBO	
	DURATION OF TREATMENT (MO)	ATTACKS	DURATION OF TREATMENT (MO)	ATTACKS
Excellent response:				
1	9	2	5	4
2	11	2	4	5
3	4	0	9	6
4	13	0	3	3
5	1	0	4	6
6	4	0	7	10
7	13	0	3	3
Totals	55	4	35	37
Moderate response:				
8	13	5	3	3
9	11	5	3	4
10	4	1	11	9
11	5	5	1	4
Totals	33	16	18	20
No response:				
12	6	12	4	6

Side effects from the tranexamic acid ingestion were minimal. One patient complained of pruritis ani, and four noted mild abdominal discomfort and diarrhea. The patients volunteered the information that the abdominal symptoms were readily distinguishable from symptoms of angioedema. All patients, except for the one treatment failure, continued to ingest the tranexamic acid upon completion of the trial period at a reduced daily dose of 1.0 g. They continued to have an abatement of their symptoms without noticeable side effects at this dose.

DISCUSSION

The plasminogen inhibitors, epsilon amino caproic acid (EACA) and trans 4-amino-methylcyclohexane-1-carboxylic acid (tranexamic acid), have both been observed to attenuate symptoms in patients with hereditary angioneurotic edema.[5] Tranexamic acid is known to be at least 10 times more effective as an inhibitor of plasminogen activation and thus offers the advantage of achieving therapeutic efficacy at a much lower dose than that required of EACA.[9] One gram of tranexamic acid daily in this study was as effective as 18 to 20 g of EACA, the dose used in other studies. The side effects of EACA at the effective dose range seriously compromise its use. They include profound muscle weakness, nasal congestion, and syncopal attacks from hypotension. Effective amounts of tranexamic acid induce no discernible side effects.

The attenuation of symptoms in patients with hereditary angioneurotic edema by plasminogen inhibitors suggests that the activation of plasminogen is an important factor in the pathophysiology of angioedema. Plasmin is known to activate C1. Tranexamic acid blocks not only the action of plasmin but also the streptokinase-induced plasminogen activator.[10] Activated Hageman factor not only initiates the clotting sequence of human plasma by conversion of pro-PTA to PTA but also interacts with one or more cofactors termed Hageman-factor cofactor[11] or plasminogen proactivator,[12] or both, to initiate fibrinolysis by conversion of plasminogen to plasmin. $C\bar{1}$ INH is known to inhibit the capacity of active Hageman factor or its fragments to initiate clotting or plasminogen activation, as well as to inhibit $C\bar{1}$, plasmin, kallikrein, or PTA. Spontaneous attacks of angioedema, and especially attacks provoked by trauma, may reflect activation of Hageman factor, with subsequent conversion of plasminogen to plasmin, which could then activate C1. Alternative pathways of C1 activation, such as antigen-antibody reactions and activation of kallikrein, could also participate in the pathogenesis of angioedema and explain why tranexamic acid is not uniformly effective in abating symptoms.

We are indebted to Miss Nobuko Sugimoto, Miss Maria Seavey, and Dr. Shaun Ruddy for assistance.

REFERENCES

1. Donaldson VH, Evans RR: A biochemical abnormality in hereditary angioneurotic edema: absence of serum inhibitor of $C'1$-esterase. Am J Med 35:37-44, 1963
2. Donaldson VH, Rosen FS: Action of complement in hereditary angioneurotic edema: the role of $C'1$-esterase. J Clin Invest 43:2204-2213, 1964
3. Carpenter CB, Ruddy S, Shehadeh IH, et al: Complement metabolism in man: hypercatabolism of the fourth (C4) and third (C3) components in patients with renal allograft rejection and hereditary angioedema (HAE). J Clin Invest 48:1495-1505, 1969
4. Ratnoff OD, Naff GB: The conversion of $C'1s$ to $C'1$ esterase by plasmin and trypsin. J Exp Med 125:337-358, 1967
5. Lundh B, Laurell AB, Wetterqvist H, et al: A case of hereditary angioneurotic oedema successfully treated with ε-aminocaproic acid: studies on $C'1$ esterase inhibitor, $C'1$ activation, plasminogen level and histamine metabolism. Clin Exp Immunol 3:733-745, 1968
6. Rosen FS, Alper CA, Pensky J, et al: Genetically determined heterogeneity of the C1 esterase inhibitor in patients with hereditary angioneurotic edema. J Clin Invest 50:2143-2149, 1971
7. Gigli I, Ruddy S, Austen KF: The stoichiometric measurement of the serum inhibitor of the first component of complement by the inhibition of immune hemolysis. J Immunol 100:1154-1164, 1968
8. Johnson AJ, Fletcher AP, McCarty WR, et al: The intravascular use of streptokinase. Ann NY Acad Sci 68:201-208, 1957
9. Okamoto S, Okamoto U: Amino-methyl-cyclohexane-carboxylic acid: AMCHA: a new potent inhibitor of the fibrinolysis. Keio J Med 11:105-115, 1962
10. Dubber AHC, McNicol GP, Douglas AS, et al: Some properties of the antifibrinolytically active isomer of amino-methylcyclohexane carboxylic acid. Lancet 2:1317-1319, 1964
11. Ogston D, Ogston CM, Ratnoff OD, et al: Studies on a complex mechanism for the activation of plasminogen by kaolin and by chloroform: the participation of Hageman factor and additional cofactors. J Clin Invest 48:1786-1801, 1969
12. Kaplan AP, Schreiber AD, Austen KF: Isolation and reaction mechanism of human plasma plasminogen activator and its precursor. Fed Proc 31:624, 1972

TREATMENT OF HEREDITARY ANGIOEDEMA WITH DANAZOL

Reversal of Clinical and Biochemical Abnormalities

Jeffrey A. Gelfand, M.D., Richard J. Sherins, M.D., David W. Alling, M.D., Ph.D., and Michael M. Frank, M.D.

Abstract Danazol, an androgen derivative, was evaluated for its effectiveness in preventing attacks of hereditary angioedema in a double-blind study with nine patients. Of 47 placebo courses, 44 ended with attacks, but during 46 danazol courses only one attack occurred. Side effects were minimal, and virilization was not observed in the women studied. C1 esterase inhibitor levels increased three to four times, and levels of the fourth component of complement (C4) increased 15 times. These changes began during the first day of therapy and were maximal by one to two weeks. After therapy was stopped, C1 esterase inhibitor and C4 levels rapidly decreased. Danazol effectively prevents attacks in hereditary angioedema and acts to correct the underlying biochemical abnormality. (N Engl J Med 295:1444-1448, 1976)

HEREDITARY angioedema is characterized by episodic swelling of the extremities, face, abdominal viscera or airway.[1-3] In some patients with this disorder minor trauma may lead to the development of extensive subcutaneous edema; anxiety and emotional stress are also associated with an increased frequency of attacks.[2-4] However, many attacks occur without obvious provocation. The disease is thought to be due to deficient activity of the inhibitor of the activated first component of complement (C1 esterase).[5] This deficiency of C1 esterase inhibitor activity in serum may be due to diminished levels of the protein in plasma (presumably because of decreased synthesis) or to production of a functionally deficient protein.[6] Both these types of C1 esterase inhibitor deficiency result in a similar clinical picture, and in both, the deficiency is inherited as an autosomal dominant trait.[1,2,3,6] Mortality from this disease has been reported as high as 30 per cent, death usually being caused by airway obstruction.[1-4] There is as yet no reproducibly effective way of stopping attacks of angioedema while they are under way.[2-4] The mainstay of therapy is prevention: the avoidance of provocative factors (trauma); plasma transfusion before predictable trauma (tonsillectomy, dental extraction); and the long-term administration of drugs.[4]

Two classes of drugs can be used for the prophylaxis of attacks of hereditary angioedema. The antifibrinolytic agents, such as epsilon aminocaproic acid (EACA), have been shown to be effective.[7-10] Their usefulness is limited by their side effects, of which an increased predisposition to thrombosis and phlebitis may be the most serious. In addition, reversible, dose-related myositis has been described with EACA, and muscle fatigue is common at higher dose levels.[8] The second group of therapeutic agents are the androgens, first introduced in the treatment of hereditary angioedema in 1960 by Spaulding, who demonstrated the effectiveness of methyltestosterone in a double-blind study of six members of a single family.[11] Later, fluoxymesterone and oxymetholone, less masculinizing androgens, were reported to be effective in a study that used the patient's previous experience before therapy as a comparison.[12] Despite the usefulness of these agents, they still have serious limitations. Even the less potent androgens may produce virilization after many months of therapy, and drug-induced hepatotoxicity may be a problem, especially with methyltestosterone.[13] We therefore set out to test the therapeutic effectiveness of a synthetic androgen, danazol, for the prophylaxis of attacks of hereditary angioedema. Danazol, a derivative of ethinyltestosterone, is mildly myogenic (anabolic), but has markedly attenuated androgenic potential (an "impeded" androgen). It produces dose-dependent reduction of serum gonadotropins, resulting in a concomitant decrease of the primary sex hormone. The drug is currently undergoing clinical evaluation for use in men and women as a contraceptive, as well as extensive testing as an agent for the treatment of endometriosis. Observed side effects in these and other studies have been minimal.[14-19]

A double-blind study design was thought to be necessary because of the variable clinical activity of hereditary angioedema. The attack rate is influenced by the patient's emotional state[4] and, hence, potentially by placebo effect.

MATERIALS AND METHODS

Patients

Five women (25 to 38 years of age) and four men (28 to 63 years of age) with hereditary angioedema were selected for the study. Each patient had an attack frequency of one or more per month. The diagnosis was established in each subject on the basis of characteristic clinical history, low serum levels of the fourth component of complement (C4) and low C1 esterase inhibitor (C1EI) activity. Eight of the patients had low serum levels of C1EI protein, and one patient had normal serum levels of a functionally deficient inhibitor protein.

Study Design

Clinical trial. The study design was that of a controlled double-blind trial. Each patient received a numbered, randomized sequence of courses of drug or placebo. The randomization scheme

From the Laboratory of Clinical Investigation, National Institute of Allergy and Infectious Diseases, and the Reproduction Research Branch, National Institute of Child Health and Human Development, National Institutes of Health (address reprint requests to Dr. Frank at Room 11-B-12, Bldg. 10, National Institutes of Health, Bethesda, MD 20014).

Presented at the national meeting of the American Society for Clinical Investigation, Atlantic City, NJ, May 2, 1976.

yielded approximately equal numbers of each agent for any given number of assignments.[20] Either danazol,* 200 mg, or placebo, in identical capsules, was taken by mouth three times daily. A course was terminated whenever an attack occurred; if there was no attack a course lasted for 28 days. A new course was begun either after a successful 28-day course was completed or after an attack subsided.

An attack was defined as peripheral, consisting of an area of peripheral swelling ≥5 cm in diameter, or abdominal, consisting of crampy abdominal pain with nausea or vomiting (or both) lasting for 12 or more hours, in the absence of fever or another obvious cause. Attacks were counted only if they occurred 48 hours or more after a course began. The outcome of each course, whether terminated by an attack or after 28 attack-free days, was reported to a data monitor, who recorded the course results. The monitor did not interact with patients or enter into clinical decisions, except to notify the clinician that a particular patient's study was terminated when the appropriate criteria were met. The study was classified a "drug success" if the patient experienced five attacks on placebo and none on drug therapy or seven attacks on placebo and one attack on drug therapy. The combined probability of these events, assuming the null hypothesis that there is no therapeutic difference between drug and placebo, is at most 0.051.[8] A patient's study was classified a "drug failure" if two attacks occurred on the drug. With this study design, the number of attacks that a patient would experience was minimized.

Danazol and placebo were not distinguishable by physical appearance, taste or immediate effects. During a random sequence of courses of varying length, the presence or absence of menses provided no clue to the nature of the course.

Laboratory studies. Serum was obtained for assays of C1EI protein levels, C1EI functional levels, and C4 levels (C4, a substrate of C1 esterase, is low because of deficient C1EI activity). In addition, serum protein electrophoresis was performed, and total protein, albumin, C3, α-2 macroglobulin, transaminases, alkaline phosphatase, bilirubin, serum electrolytes and complete blood count were determined periodically during the course of the study. Samples for C1EI and C4 levels were obtained before the study, at random during the double-blind period and at the termination of the protocol. These samples were obtained by clotting of blood at room temperature for 30 minutes, followed by centrifugation. Serum was immediately stored at −40 to −70°C for later assay. C1EI levels were determined by radial immunodiffusion, using monospecific antibody kindly supplied by Dr. John Robbins, of the Bureau of Biologies, FDA. Functional assays of C1EI were performed by the method of Gigli et al.,[21] which measures the ability of serum to inhibit C1 esterase-dependent hemolysis. Hemolytic assays of C4 were performed by the method of Gaither and Frank.[22] Levels of C3, albumin and α-2 macroglobulin were determined by commercial radial immunodiffusion plates (Behring Diagnostics, Somerville, New Jersey). In two subjects, serum samples had to be shipped to our laboratory. In some cases, the serum specimens thawed and were excluded from our analysis.

RESULTS

Clinical Trial

Nine patients completed a total of 93 courses, of which 47 were placebo and 46 were danazol (Table 1). Attacks occurred in 44 of the 47 placebo courses (93.6 per cent) but in only one of the 46 danazol courses (2.2 per cent). The difference in the rate of attacks on drug and placebo was highly significant (P<0.001). The first seven of the nine patients completed their studies as drug successes. Patients 8 and 9 did not complete their series of treatment courses because the main study was terminated. The duration of

*Kindly supplied by the Sterling–Winthrop Research Institute, Rensselaer, NY. The drug is now available as Danocrine from Winthrop Laboratories.

Table 1. Results of Study.

PATIENT NO.	SEX	AGE (YR)	COURSES WITH DANAZOL		COURSES WITH PLACEBO		TOTALS
			ATTACKS	ATTACK-FREE	ATTACKS	ATTACK-FREE	
1	F	25	0	5	5	0	10
2	M	34	0	5	5	0	10
3	F	38	0	4	5	0	9
4	F	28	1	6	7	1	15
5	F	36	0	6	5	2	13
6	F	33	0	4	5	0	9
7	M*	28	0	5	5	0	10
8	M	29	0	5	3	0	8†
9	M	63	0	5	4	0	9†
Totals			1	45	44	3	93
% Courses with attacks‡			1/46 = 2.2%		44/47 = 93.6%		

*Patient with abnormal C1EI protein.
†Study terminated.
‡Chi-square = 77.8; P<0.001.

study for the individual patients varied from six to 11 months.

During the course of the study, only minor side effects were noted. Virilization was not observed in any woman, and no changes in potency were noted by the men. All nine patients gained weight. Mean weight gain in the five women was 2.7 kg (range, 1.3 to 4.5 kg) and in the men 2.5 kg (range, 1.3 to 4.1 kg). Each of the women noted menstrual irregularity during the first three months of the study, and four of the five ceased menstruating after the third month. Because of continued menstrual spotting in one woman with a history of chronic menometrorrhagia (Patient 4), an endometrial biopsy was performed, and proliferative endometrium was demonstrated.

Laboratory Findings

The levels of C1EI obtained at random during the courses are shown in Figure 1. The mean C1EI level increased threefold on drug therapy as compared to the patient's own control. In four patients it reached normal or near normal levels (95 per cent confidence interval). Serum C4 levels measured on the same samples showed a 15-fold rise on drug therapy (Fig. 2), again frequently rising to the normal range. When pretreatment C1EI levels were compared to levels obtained after a minimum of two weeks of danazol treatment the C1EI level was increased 4.5 times. Levels of albumin, C3 and α-2 macroglobulin showed no statistically significant changes associated with danazol therapy, and there was no increase in the total serum protein.

In some cases, serum samples were obtained less than four days into a new course or were received by mail, having been improperly handled. Patient 7, with very high levels of an abnormal C1EI protein, was excluded from the analysis of C1EI protein levels. Thus, Patients 6 and 7 were not included in Figure 1, and Patients 5 and 6 were omitted from Figure 2.

It is interesting that Patient 4, the only one to have an attack while receiving the drug, had the smallest

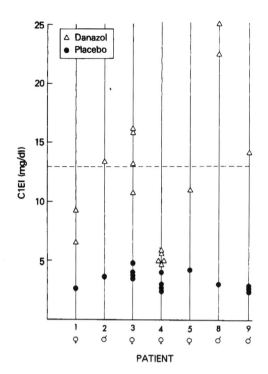

Figure 1. C1 Esterase Inhibitor (C1EI) Levels Measured at Random during the Course of the Double-Blind Study.

All points represent samples obtained at least four days after the beginning of a new course. Patient 7, with the abnormal inhibitor protein, was excluded. The dotted line indicates the lower limit of the normal range.

It is important to note that when danazol was added to serum in vitro at levels achievable in the plasma in vivo (1 to 2 μg per milliliter), the drug did not itself function to inhibit C1.

Time Course of Drug Effects

The biochemical response in one subject was followed during the first five days of danazol therapy (Fig. 3). By the fifth day, C1EI levels were nearly normal, and C4 levels were rising towards normal. Data were also obtained on the persistence of the danazol effect after therapy in a second subject (Fig. 4). Pretreatment C1EI levels were noted. At the end of the double-blind study (first day) the patient was given danazol, 600 mg per day, for 60 days. On the 55th day, her C1EI level was normal. After the 60th day, danazol was discontinued, and she remained off the drug for 12 days. During this period, C1EI levels fell to near pretreatment levels. On resumption of danazol therapy, C1EI levels rapidly rose to normal.

Analysis of the danazol effect during the double-blind study showed that attacks occurred later in the course of placebo if the preceding course was danazol (mean of 14 days) than if the preceding course was placebo (mean of 9 days; $P<0.05$).

increments of both C1EI and C4 levels, suggesting that she continued to have active circulating C1. However, her C1EI levels doubled (mean on placebo, 2.5, and on drug therapy, 5.1), and presumably this increase was enough to reduce, though not entirely to eliminate, the activity of her disease. This effect is reflected by the increase of her C4 titer from a mean of <10 on placebo to a mean of 21,700 on therapy. We have no ready explanation for the variability of the response demonstrated to the drug.

Functional assays of C1EI activity showed statistically significant increases, with four of the five patients' serum samples studied demonstrating normal inhibitor activity after two weeks of treatment with danazol. It is of interest that the patient with the abnormally functioning inhibitor protein had 9 per cent of normal inhibitor activity before therapy and 100 per cent of normal activity after therapy.

To assess the effect of danazol on C1EI levels in normal persons, serum was obtained from five normal women before and during the administration of danazol in a contraceptive trial (this serum was kindly supplied by Dr. Anne C. Wentz, of the Johns Hopkins Hospital). The mean C1EI level rose from 24 before to 35.9 mg per deciliter after one month of danazol therapy ($P<0.05$).

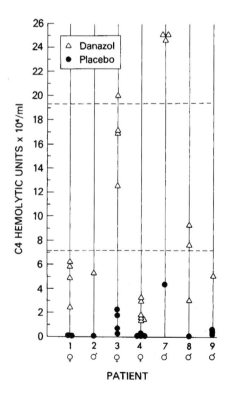

Figure 2. Serum C4 Hemolytic Titers Measured at Random during the Course of the Double-Blind Study.

All points represent samples obtained at least four days after the beginning of a new course. The dotted lines show the normal range.

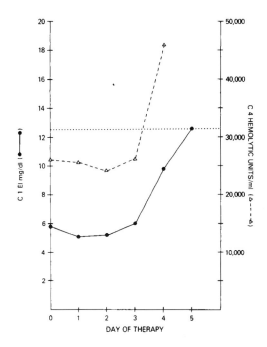

Figure 3. C1EI Levels and C4 Titers of a Patient after the Initiation of Danazol Therapy.
The dotted line represents the lower limit of the normal range for C1EI. The lower limit of normal for the C4 titer is 70,000 units per milliliter.

DISCUSSION

At present, the treatment of hereditary angioedema is largely prophylactic; there is no widely accepted method for treating or reversing attacks once they have begun. Prophylactic therapy has included the avoidance of instigating factors, plasma transfusion and drug therapy with antifibrinolytic agents or androgens.[4] The thrombotic potential of the antifibrinolytic agents has limited our use of them, particularly in older patients. Androgens, although effective in reducing the frequency of attacks,[11,12,24] may produce unacceptable virilization in women when used chronically. Accordingly, danazol, an androgen derivative whose virilizing side effects are markedly attenuated,[14-19] appeared to offer several advantages over previous therapies.

In the present study, danazol proved highly effective in the prevention of attacks in patients of both sexes. The therapeutic effect, in terms of correction of the underlying biochemical abnormality, appeared to be greater than that reported for any other agent.[8,9,11,12,24] Most striking were the effects on C1EI levels and activity, which increased three to 4.5 times, frequently to normal levels, and on C4 levels, which increased 15 times on drug therapy.

Side effects noted during the course of the study were minimal. Virilization has not been seen during one year of study, and weight gain was only 1.3 to 4.5 kg. Amenorrhea occurred in four of the five women studied, but each subject considered this effect pref-

erable to having attacks. As the study progressed, patients did find that they could distinguish drug from placebo because of the total absence of any of the symptoms of hereditary angioedema. Obviously, this observation does not detract from the study and might be expected with any highly successful therapeutic agent in a controlled trial. Since termination of the double-blind study, all nine patients have chosen to remain on danazol therapy, some as long as six months without further toxicity. During this period, the dosage has been reduced. Thus far, four of four patients are attack free on danazol therapy, 400 mg per day, and three of three are free of attacks on 300 mg per day. Although one man has noted an actual increase in libido with a dose of 300 mg per day, he had not identified diminished libido as a problem while he was on the higher dosage. The other three men have noted no change in their potency. Nonetheless, decreased libido in men and secondary hypoestrogenism in women, with its attendant symptoms, might be anticipated as possible side effects with long-term use.[14-19] It is hoped that lower dosages will offset these possible side effects. The use of danazol in children may be precluded by its possible interference with normal sexual maturation.[17] Likewise, its unknown effects on the fetus might contraindicate the use of danazol in pregnant patients with hereditary angioedema.

Danazol appears to mediate its effect on activity of the disease by increasing levels of C1EI, an effect also noted in normal women. Whether danazol acts to increase C1EI production or C1EI release into serum, or to reduce its catabolism, is unknown at present. The first hypothesis appears to be the most attractive. Dr. Wendell Rosse and his associates have noted considerable elevations of C1EI levels during the

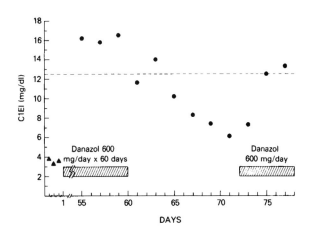

Figure 4. C1EI Levels of a Patient on and off Danazol Therapy.
Pretreatment levels are indicated by triangles. After the double-blind study, the patient was given danazol, 600 mg per day, for 60 days. Therapy was discontinued for 12 days, and then reinstituted. The dotted line represents the lower limit of the normal range for C1EI.

treatment of patients with fluoxymesterone or oxymetholone, and suggested that androgens act by increasing the levels of C1EI activity.[24,25] How this effect might occur at a cellular level is purely speculative. It is not likely to be a nonspecific steroid effect on hepatic protein synthesis, since prednisone and medroxyprogesterone acetate do not produce these changes.[4] Furthermore, no generalized increase in serum protein was noted with the drug, including several proteins synthesized in the liver, the presumed site of synthesis of C1EI.[26] The effects of C1EI levels occur rapidly. After one week of therapy, near normal C1EI levels were noted, and C1EI levels fell rapidly after the drug was discontinued.

We have shown in a double-blind study that the "impeded" androgen danazol was strikingly effective in controlling activity of the disease. The drug corrects the underlying deficiency of C1EI. It offers several advantages over existing therapies, and broadens the physician's armamentarium in his dealing with this disease. Study of the actions of this drug in hereditary angioedema may provide a greater understanding of the underlying factors controlling and modifying this, and possibly other, genetic diseases.

We are indebted to Dr. William P. Blackmore, of Sterling–Winthrop Laboratories, Mr. Paul Hiranaka of the NIH Pharmaceutical Development Service, Mr. Robert Reinhart and Ms. Thelma Gaither and Drs. Jerry O. Weaver, of Cedartown, Georgia, and William W. Levis III, of Swansboro, North Carolina, for assistance.

REFERENCES

1. Osler W: Hereditary angio-neurotic oedema. Am J Med Sci 95:362-367, 1888
2. Landerman NS: Hereditary angioneurotic edema. I. Case reports with a review of the literature. J Allergy 33:316-329, 1962
3. Donaldson VH, Rosen FS: Hereditary angioneurotic edema: a clinical survey. Pediatrics 37:1017-1027, 1966
4. Frank MM, Gelfand JA, Atkinson JP: Hereditary angioedema: the clinical syndrome and its management. Ann Intern Med 84:580-593, 1976
5. Donaldson VH, Evans RR: A biochemical abnormality in hereditary angioneurotic edema: absence of serum inhibitor of C1-esterase. Am J Med 35:37-44, 1963
6. Rosen FS, Charache P, Pensky J, et al: Hereditary angioneurotic edema: two genetic variants. Science 148:957-958, 1965
7. Nilsson IM, Andersson L, Björkman SE: Epsilon-aminocaproic acid (E-ACA) as a therapeutic agent based on 5 years' clinical experience. Acta Med Scand [Suppl] 448:1-46, 1966
8. Frank MM, Sergent JS, Kane MA, et al: Epsilon aminocaproic acid therapy of hereditary angioneurotic edema: a double blind study. N Engl J Med 286:808-812, 1972
9. Sheffer AL, Austen KF, Rosen FS: Tranexamic acid therapy in hereditary angioneurotic edema. N Engl J Med 287:452-454, 1972
10. Blohmé G: Treatment of hereditary angioneurotic oedema with tranexemic acid: a random double-blind cross-over study. Acta Med Scand 192:293-298, 1972
11. Spaulding WB: Methyltestosterone therapy for hereditary episodic edema (hereditary angioneurotic edema). Ann Intern Med 53:739-745, 1960
12. Davis PJ, Davis FB, Charache P: Long-term therapy of hereditary angioedema (HAE): preventive management with fluoxymesterone and oxymetholone in severely affected males and females. Johns Hopkins Med J 135:391-398, 1974
13. Boyer JL, Preisig R, Zbinden G, et al: Guidelines for assessment of potential hepatotoxic effects of synthetic androgens, anabolic agents and progestagens in their use in males as antifertility agents. Contraception 13:461-468, 1976
14. Sherins RJ, Gandy HM, Thorslund TW, et al: Pituitary and testicular function studies. I. Experience with a new gonadal inhibitor, 17α-pregn-4-en-20-yno-(2,3-d) isoxazol-17-ol (Danazol). J Clin Endocrinol Metab 32:522-531, 1971
15. Greenblatt RB, Dmowski WP, Mahesh VB, et al: Clinical studies with an antigonadotropin — Danazol. Fertil Steril 22:102-112, 1971
16. Wood GP, Wu CH, Flickinger GL, et al: Hormonal changes associated with Danazol therapy. Obstet Gynecol 45:302-304, 1975
17. Lee PA, Thompson RG, Migeon CJ, et al: The effect of Danazol in sexual precocity. Johns Hopkins Med J 137:265-269, 1975
18. Andrews MC, Wentz AC: The effects of Danazol on gonadotropins and steroid blood levels in normal and anovulatory women. Am J Obstet Gynecol 121:817-828, 1975
19. Wentz AC, Jones GS, Sapp KC: Investigation of Danazol as a contraceptive agent. Contraception 13:619-621, 1976
20. Efron B: Forcing a sequential experiment to be balanced. Biometrika 58:403-417, 1971
21. Gigli I, Ruddy S, Austen KF: The stoichiometric measurement of the serum inhibitor of the first component of complement by the inhibition of immune hemolysis. J Immunol 100:1154-1164, 1968
22. Gaither TA, Alling DW, Frank MM: A new one-step method for the functional assay of the fourth component (C4) of human and guinea pig complement. J Immunol 113:574-583, 1974
23. Laurell A-B, Martensson U: C1 inactivator protein complexed with albumin in plasma from a patient with angioneurotic edema. Eur J Immunol 1:146-149, 1971
24. Rosse WF, Logue GL, Silberman HR: The effect of synthetic androgens on the clinical course and C1 esterase inhibitor (C1 INH) levels in hereditary angioneurotic edema (HANE). Clin Res 24:482A, 1976
25. Rosse WF, Logue GL, Silberman HR, et al: The effect of synthetic androgens in hereditary angioneurotic edema: alteration of C1 inhibitor and C4 levels. Trans Assoc Am Physicians (in press)
26. Johnson AM, Alper CA, Rosen FS, et al: C1 inhibitor: evidence for decreased hepatic synthesis in hereditary angioneurotic edema. Science 173:553-554, 1971

a communication from Italy

TREATMENT OF ACUTE ATTACKS OF HEREDITARY ANGIOEDEMA WITH C1-INHIBITOR CONCENTRATE

ANGELO AGOSTONI, M.D., LUIGI BERGAMASCHINI, M.D.,
GIANCARLO MARTIGNONI, M.D., MARCO CICARDI, M.D.,
and BIANCA MARASINI, M.D.

Attacks of laryngeal edema in patients with hereditary angioedema (HAE) have been successfully treated with the infusion of C1-inhibitor (C1-INH) concentrate. No side effects were observed.

HEREDITARY ANGIOEDEMA (HAE) is a familial disease due to the absence or to the functional deficiency (variant HAE) of the inhibitor of the activated first component of complement (C1 INH). It is characterized by recurrent attacks of localized edema affecting skin and mucosal surfaces. Edema of the skin, though distressing, is not dangerous but edema affecting the gastrointestinal mucosa may mimic small bowel obstruction, while edema of the laryngeal mucosa is the cause of death in approximately 30% of all patients.

The paroxysmal attacks of swelling, characteristic of HAE, can be prophylactically treated with antifibrinolytic and hormonal agents.[1] In our series of 76 patients from 26 kindreds good results have been obtained with antifibrinolytic agents (tranexamic acid) in 70% of cases.[2] Better results have been obtained with testosterone derivatives,[3,4,5,6] particularly with danazol, a weak impeded androgen.[7,8,9,10] However, all these steroids are 17 α-alkylated[11] and the long-term use of these agents seems to be implicated in the development of cholestatic jaundice, peliosis hepatitis and liver tumors.[12,13,14] Moreover, such endocrine therapy is not recommended in pregnant women and growing children.[15] Thus there may be some patients not suitable for such a therapeutic endeavour and because antifibrinolytic and androgenic agents are of no value in the acute situation one must turn to some other treatment that may be used during attacks of life-threatening severity.[1,16]

We report here the results of treatment with infusion of purified C1 INH preparation during acute attacks of HAE.

Materials and Methods

Patients

C1 INH concentrate was infused in 13 HAE patients during 19 severe attacks early in their courses. Ten patients had low serum levels of C1 INH and C4 and three showed low serum levels of C4, normal concentration but low activity of C1 INH (variant HAE). On 13 occasions the paroxysmal attacks of swelling were located in mucous membranes (larynx, bowel), three in subcutaneous tissues (face, arm) and three in mucous membranes and subcutaneous tissue.

C1 INH Concentrate

C1 INH concentrate was supplied by The Netherland Red Cross Blood Transfusion Service, Amsterdam. This product contains 1,200 U/ml (12 mg/ml) of C1 INH, about 60 times the fresh normal plasma concentration.[17] C1 INH was given via a single, slow (10 minutes) infusion in a dosage varying from 12,000 to 36,000 U. No other form of treatment was used immediately before and during the study.

Laboratory Studies

In nine patients, directly treated in our hospital, blood samples were taken immediately before C1 INH concentrate infusion and at different intervals after

From the Department of Clinical Medicine, University of Milan, Italy.

completion of the infusion. C1 INH and C4 levels were determined by single radial immunodiffusion and C1 INH activity was tested according to Lachmann et al.[18]

Results

All patients treated with 24,000-36,000 U of C1 INH concentrate for acute attacks responded well to therapy (the infusion of 12,000 U was ineffective in one patient). Mucous edema began to reduce within 15-60 minutes consistent with the disappearance of abdominal pain or the subjective sensation of reduction of airway obstruction. Subcutaneous edema began to decrease in a longer time (1-3 hours) (Table I). No side effects were observed in any of the patients.

Pretreatment serum level and functional activity of C1 INH ranged from 10% to 35% and from 0% to 20% of normal human serum, respectively. There was no correlation between severity of clinical sysptoms and C1 INH levels. After infusion of 36,000 U of C1 INH preparation serum level and functional activity of C1 INH increased up to 60% and 50%, respectively, and

slowly returned towards preinfusion values within 48 hours (Table II). In one patient, with variant HAE, the infusion of 36,000 U induced a similar increase in C1 INH functional activity, while C1 INH serum concentration, starting from 126%, increased up to 200% of normal value (Table II). In all patients with HAE (variant form as well) C4 serum level, starting from 0% to 25%, began to increase 12 hours after completion of infusion; in some cases it was still at its highest level after 48 hours.

Discussion

When a patient with HAE is not suitable for preventive therapy with antifibrinolytic or hormonal agents it may be necessary to manage an acute attack, frequently of life-threatening severity.

An acute attack may be reversed by infusion of aprotinin (Trasylol) as well as replacement therapy with fresh frozen plasma or purified preparation of C1 INH.[15,16] Although our own experience with kallikrein inhibitor is satisfactory,[19] we do prefer to treat severe swelling with C1 INH concentrate because of more rapid improvement and absence of allergic reactions reported with kallikrein inhibitor. On the other hand the slowly increasing serum level of C4 protein after completion of infusion means that C1 INH concentrate is preferable to plasma transfusion, which provides C1-esterase substrates, C4 and C2, possible sources of kinin-like peptides of HAE.

Typically, attacks become increasingly severe in about 6-24 hours and then slowly resolve in 10-12 hours. In case of a patient having symptoms from 3-4 hours with partial airway obstruction, one would be concerned with the possibility that the swelling might lead to total obstruction. Eleven patients with laryngeal edema of rapidly increasing severity were treated with the infusion of C1 INH concentrate. Within 15-60 minutes after completion of infusion (36,000 U), laryngeal swelling, dysphagia and change in the tone of voice ceased and all patients reported a clear sensation of improvement. Emergency tracheostomy was never necessary. Rapid positive results were also obtained in episodes of diffuse

Table I. Clinical Effect of Intravenous Infusion of C1 INH Concentrate in Patients with Hereditary Angioedema.

Patient	Sex	Age (yrs)	Seat of edema	Dose of (U)	Beginning of regression of symptoms after infusion start (minutes)
Fr.G.	F	39	Arm	12,000	36 hours
F.M.	F	35	Larynx, bowel	24,000	60
C.L. *	M	5	Larynx, bowel	24,000	30
D.F.	F	13	Larynx	24,000	15
F.B.	F	45	Larynx	36,000	30
" "	"	"	Larynx	36,000	30
F.G.	F	20	Arm	36,000	180
P.G.	M	27	Larynx	36,000	30
B.R. *	M	40	Face, pharynx	36,000	60
S.G.	M	57	Larynx	36,000	30
" "	"	"	Bowel	36,000	30
" "	"	"	Bowel	24,000	15
" "	"	"	Larynx	36,000	15
" "	"	"	Face	24,000	12 hours
G.G.	M	44	Layrnx	24,000	60
F.F.	M	44	Bowel	36,000	60
B.C. *	F	55	Face, pharynx	36,000	60
" "	"	"	Face, pharynx	36,000	60
F.C.	M	43	Larynx	36,000	30

* Patients with variant HAE

Table II. Changes of C1 INH and C4 Concentrations and C1 INH Activity in Sera of Patients with Hereditary Angioedema Before and at Different Intervals after Completion of Infusion of C1 INH Concentrate. (The Values are expressed as Percentages of the Normal Means).

Patient	Dose of C1 INH (U.)	C1 INH (immunochemical assay)						C1 INH (enzymatic assay)						C4 (immunochemical assay)					
		Pre-treat-ment	15"	60"	12h	24h	48h	Pre-treat-ment	15"	60"	12h	24h	48h	Pre-treat-ment	15"	60"	12h	24h	48h
Fr.G.	12,000	14	14	22	14	13	14	-	-	-	-	-	-	0	0	0	25	25	21
F.G	36,000	10	41	44	49	29	24	-	-	-	-	-	-	12	12	12	21	31	33
F.B.	36,000	11	49	51	49	43	26	-	-	-	-	-	-	0	0	0	25	25	25
" "	36,000	10	65	65	65	56	34	0	50	45	20	15	1	9	9	9	31	31	31
B.R. *	36,000	126	200	200	200	200	200	17	55	58	58	58	58	10	10	10	36	63	80
P.G.	36,000	10	55	55	52	40	40	20	50	54	50	50	45	25	25	25	52	52	63
S.G.	36,000	28	28	60	26	24	27	15	57	54	25	16	10	0	0	0	20	20	0
" "	36,000	35	58	46	-	39	37	13	39	50	-	23	14	35	35	35	-	54	40
" "	36,000	26	43	42	19	15	17	16	48	39	16	12	15	0	0	0	16	13	12

* Patient with variant HAE

abdominal pain. By contrast, the effects on subcutaneous edema took a longer time. The infusion of a smaller dose of C1 INH concentrate (12,000 U) failed to improve the clinical symptoms and to increase C1 INH and C4 serum levels.

In conclusion, we believe that infusion of 36,000 U of C1 INH concentrate is the treatment of choice in life-threatening attacks of HAE, so much so that we suggest to our patients not being treated with androgens to keep at home in the refrigerator ampoules of this drug.

References

1. Atkinson JP: Diagnosis and management of hereditary angioedema (HAE). Ann Allerg 42: 348, 1979.
2. Agostoni A, Marasini B, Cicardi C, Martignoni GC, Uziel L and Pietrogrande M: Hepatic function and fibrinolysis in patients with hereditary angioedema undergoing long-term treatment with tranexamic acid. Allerg 33: 216, 1978.
3. Spaulding WB: Methyltestosterone therapy for hereditary episodic edema (hereditary angioneurotic edema). Ann Intern Med 53: 739, 1960.
4. Davis PJ, Davis FB and Charache P: Preventive management with fluoxymesterone and oxymetholone in severely affected males and females. Johns Hopkins Med J 135: 391, 1974.
5. Saihan EM and Warin RP: Treatment of hereditary angioneurotic oedema with methadienone. Br Med J 1: 367, 1978.
6. Agostoni A, Marasini B, Cicardi M and Martignoni GC: Intermittent therapy with danazol in hereditary angioedema. Lancet 1: 453, 1978.
7. Gould DJ, Cunliffe WJ and Smiddy FC: Anabolic steroids in hereditary angioedema. Lancet 1: 770, 1978.
8. Gelfand JA, Sherins RJ, Alling DW and Frank MM: Treatment of hereditary angioedema with danazol. Reversal of clinical and biochemical abnormalities. New Eng J Med 295: 1444, 1976.
9. Pitts JS, Donaldson VH, Forristal J and Wjatt RJ: Remission induced in hereditary angioneurotic edema with an attenuated androgen (danazol): correlation between concentrations of C1-inhibitor and the fourth and second components of complement. J Lab Cin Med 92: 501, 1978.
10. Rothbach C, Green R, Levine M and Fireman P: Prophylaxis of attacks of hereditary angioedema. Am J Med 66: 681, 1979.
11. Agostoni A, Cicardi M, Martignoni GC, Bergamaschini L and Marasini B: Danazol and stanazolol in long-term prophylactic treatment of hereditary angioedema. J Allerg & Clin Immunol 65: 75, 1980.
12. Westaby D, Ogle SJ, Paradinas FJ, Rondell JB and Murray-Lyon IM: Liver damage from long-term methyltestosterone. Lancet II: 261, 1977.
13. McDonald EC and Speicher CE: Peliosis hepatis associated with administration of oxymetholone. JAMA 240: 243, 1978.
14. Chopra S, Edelstein A, Koff RS, Zimilman AP, Lacson A and Neiman RS: Peliosis hepatis in hemathologic disease. JAMA 240: 1153, 1978.
15. Rosen FS and Austen KF: Androgen therapy in herediatry angioneurotic edema. New Eng J Med 295: 1476, 1976.
16. Frank MM, Gelfand JA and Atkinson JP: Hereditary angioedema: the clinical syndrome and its management. Ann Int Med 84: 580, 1976.
17. Vogelaar EF, Brummelhuis HGJ and Krunen HW: Contribution to the optimal use of human blood. Vox Sang 26: 118, 1974.
18. Lachmann PJ, Hobart MJ and Aston WP: Complement technology. In: Handbook of Experimental Immunology. (Ed.) Weir DM Oxford: Blackwell, 1973, pp. 1-17.
19. Marasini B, Cicardi M, Martignoni GC and Agostoni A: Treatment of hereditary angioedema. Klin Wschr 56: 819, 1978.

Requests for reprints should be addressed to:
Dr. Angelo Agostoni
Dept. of Clinical Medicine
University of Milan, Ospedale S. Paolo
20142 Milano, Italy

GOVERNMENT IN MEDICINE (1702-03)

"On the 27th of February, 1702-3, while hunting, the King (William III) fell from his horse, and broke his right clavicle near the acromium. This occurred in the neighborhood of Hampton Court; but the French surgeon Ronjat was at hand, and soon reduced the fracture. But when he wanted to bleed His Majesty, a new obstacle arose, for it was necessary not only to have the sanction of some one of the court physicians, but also the authority of the privy council for the performance of that operation."

William Macmichael
The Gold-Headed Cane

REPLACEMENT THERAPY IN HEREDITARY ANGIOEDEMA

Successful Treatment of Acute Episodes of Angioedema with Partly Purified C1 Inhibitor

James E. Gadek, M.D., Stephen W. Hosea, M.D., Jeffrey A. Gelfand, M.D., Maria Santaella, M.D., Milan Wickerhauser, Ph.D., D. C. Triantaphyllopoulos, M.D., and Michael M. Frank, M.D.

Abstract Although considerable progress has been made during the past two decades in the use of androgens to prevent attacks of hereditary angioedema, replacement of the deficient C1-inhibitor protein would provide a useful means of treatment once an attack has begun. We studied the clinical use of C1 inhibitor that was partly purified on a large scale from pooled plasma. The in vivo efficacy and safety of this protein concentrate were evaluated during 11 intravenous infusions in eight patients with hereditary angioedema. Three patients received the C1-inhibitor preparation during an asymptomatic period. Increases in serum C4 activity provided evidence of the biologic activity of the infused inhibitor. Intravenous administration of the concentrate during acute abdominal or laryngeal attacks of hereditary angioedema in five patients resulted in abatement of symptoms in addition to increased serum C4 activity. No untoward effects of the intravenous administration of the C1 inhibitor were observed in these eight patients. Thus, this C1-inhibitor preparation seems to offer the potential for safe, effective replacement therapy and may provide a means of controlling an attack of hereditary angioedema that is in progress. (N Engl J Med. 1980; 302:542-6.)

HEREDITARY angioedema is an autosomal-dominant disorder associated with serum deficiency of functionally active C1-inhibitor protein. Episodic swelling of the extremities, face, and bowel wall leads to severe morbidity in many patients.[1] Involvement of the upper airway, with resultant asphyxia, is a major source of mortality among these patients.

Within the past several years considerable progress has been made in the management of this potentially lethal genetic disorder. It has long been known that androgen therapy suppresses disease activity.[2] More recently, methyltestosterone and androgen derivatives with minimal masculinizing effects have been shown to control disease activity by increasing serum levels of the C1-inhibitor protein.[3-6] The most effective androgen, danazol, can induce a threefold to fivefold increase in serum C1 inhibitor in the majority of patients with hereditary angioedema.

In spite of these therapeutic advances, there is no effective means of interrupting an attack of angioedema once it has begun. In a patient with an attack that compromises the airway, danazol offers no proved benefit.[7] Moreover, long-term administration of a drug is undesirable in patients whose disease activity (less than one attack per month) does not justify the risk of continuous prophylactic therapy. In pregnancy and childhood as well, an alternative to androgenic or antifibrinolytic therapy[8,9] is needed. For these reasons we have examined the usefulness of C1-inhibitor replacement as an adjunct therapy to the drug management of hereditary angioedema.

From the Pulmonary Branch, National Heart, Lung, and Blood Institute, and the Laboratory of Clinical Investigation, National Institute of Allergy and Infectious Diseases, National Institutes of Health, Bethesda, Md.; the Blood Research Laboratory, the American National Red Cross, Bethesda, Md.; and the Department of Medicine, Tufts University Medical School, Boston (address reprint requests to Room 11N-232, Bldg. 10, NIAID, Bethesda, MD 20205).

biologic activity of the infused inhibitor. Intravenous administration of the concentrate during acute abdominal or laryngeal attacks of hereditary angioedema in five patients resulted in abatement of symptoms in addition to increased serum C4 activity. No untoward effects of the intravenous administration of the C1 inhibitor were observed in these eight patients. Thus, this C1-inhibitor preparation seems to offer the potential for safe, effective replacement therapy and may provide a means of controlling an attack of hereditary angioedema that is in progress. (N Engl J Med. 1980; 302:542-6.)

Replacement therapy is the mainstay of clinical control of several other inherited serum protein deficiencies, including hemophilia[10] and hypogammaglobulinemia.[11] Our group, as well as others, has evaluated the use of fresh frozen plasma as a source of C1 inhibitor.[12,13] In our studies the infusion of fresh frozen plasma prevented the life-threatening angioedema that often accompanies dental surgery in patients with hereditary angioedema. In this setting, the plasma infusion was not followed by symptoms of hereditary angioedema.

Unfortunately, there are several formidable objections to the use of plasma infusion for the control of an attack in progress. Well-controlled studies of replacement therapy during an attack have not been performed. Fresh plasma contains C2 and C4, the substrates of activated C1 esterase, whose enzymatic cleavage is reported to yield the kinin-like factor that induces the angioedema.[14] Thus, there is concern that replenishment of these components may increase the generation of this kinin activity, with resultant propagation of the attack. The use of fresh frozen plasma also carries the risk of transfusion hepatitis. These objections to the use of whole plasma have stimulated a search for a source of C1 inhibitor suitable for use during an acute attack of hereditary angioedema. A study using partly purified C1 inhibitor derived from plasma treated with ammonium sulfate was complicated by transfusion hepatitis and was performed in asymptomatic patients only.[15]

We describe a new method for the large-scale preparation of partly purified C1 inhibitor. The initial infusions of this preparation were performed in asymptomatic patients with hereditary angioedema to establish the activity of the C1 inhibitor in vivo and exclude potential deleterious side effects. This report presents the results of C1-inhibitor infusions in those asymptomatic patients in an attempt to determine whether the C1 inhibitor has a clearly demonstrable effect in vivo. In addition, this report describes preliminary studies documenting the functional activity of this C1-inhibitor preparation in vivo when infused during acute attacks of hereditary angioedema. In this preliminary work no attempt was made to perform a double-blind study. The serum biochemical response and the subjective clinical response were taken as an index of effectiveness.

METHODS

C1-Inhibitor Preparation

A partly purified C1-inhibitor preparation was obtained from pooled, citrated, human plasma that was initially treated with polyethylene glycol (20 per cent; Carbowax 4000, Fisher Scientific Co., Fairlawn, N.J.). The precipitate contained C1 esterase, C2, and C4; in addition, this precipitate would also have contained hepatitis B virus if it were present.[16] The plasma fraction containing C1 inhibitor was then chromatographed in sequence on diethylaminoethyl and carboxymethyl Sephadex (Pharmacia Fine Chemicals, Piscataway, N.J.) according to the method of Wickerhauser and Hao.[17] After concentration of the C1-inhibitor pool by means of lyophilization, the material was stored at 4°C in sterile 10-ml vials. The lyophilized product was devoid of C1 esterase and its natural substrates C4 and C2, which were discarded in the 20 per cent polyethylene glycol precipitate. The product contained neither IgG aggregates nor IgA. The material contained large amounts of albumin and trace amounts of other proteins with alpha mobility. Radioimmunoassay showed that the starting materials (pooled plasma) as well as the partly purified C1-inhibitor concentrates were free of hepatitis B virus. Each of these preparations of C1 inhibitor was determined to be sterile and free of pyrogen by means of in vivo testing in rabbits and in vitro assays with limulus lysate.

Patients

All patients under study were admitted to the National Institutes of Health Clinical Center. Each patient conformed to the accepted clinical and laboratory criteria for hereditary angioedema.[1] All patients had decreased function of serum C1 inhibitor, and each had frequent attacks that eventually required continuous drug prophylaxis. One patient (Patient 3) had normal or elevated levels of C1-inhibitor antigen that represented a functionless form of the protein. As a result of the reduced functional activity of serum C1 inhibitor, all patients had evidence of the unopposed action of C1 esterase reflected in diminished functional activity of serum C4.

Three patients (Patients 1 to 3) received the C1-inhibitor concentrate during an asymptomatic period. Five patients (Patients 4 to 8) received the C1-inhibitor concentrate during acute abdominal or laryngeal attacks of hereditary angioedema. Patient 4 received infusions of C1 inhibitor on three separate occasions for acute abdominal attacks. Most patients were receiving no therapy for hereditary angioedema at the time of the infusion since the frequency of their attacks was being studied to establish whether they needed long-term prophylaxis with danazol. However, Patient 4 was receiving 200 mg of danazol per day at the time of the second and third infusions. Patient 7 was also receiving 150 mg of danazol per day at the time of his infusion. Patient 6 had two infusions, one for a laryngeal attack and one for an abdominal attack.

C1-Inhibitor Levels

Antigenic determinations of serum C1 inhibitor were performed at several time intervals during the course of the study by means of radial immunodiffusion. Five lambda serum samples were added to wells in gel layers containing 0.75 per cent Agarose mixed with monospecific rabbit C1-inhibitor antibody. Rings of precipita-

tion were read after 48 hours of incubation. Normal levels of C1 inhibitor obtained in our laboratory were 13.5 to 24 mg per deciliter.

The functional activity of the purified preparations of C1 inhibitor was examined according to the method of Gigli et al.,[18] and that of Levy and Lepow.[19] The method of Gigli et al. assesses the activity of a preparation of C1-esterase inhibitor in destroying the functional C1 hemolytic site.

Functional-C4 Titrations

Serum C4 activity was assayed with the one-step method employing serum from C4-deficient guinea pigs as described previously.[20] The C4 activity for a given serum sample is expressed as the reciprocal of the dilution that produces one hemolytic C4 site per sheep erythrocyte (normal range, 70,000 to 180,000 units per milliliter) in an assay containing 1.5×10^8 antibody-sensitized sheep erythrocytes per milliliter of reaction mixture.

Infusion of C1-Inhibitor Concentrate

Each vial of C1-inhibitor concentrate was reconstituted with sterile distilled water to a final volume of 10 ml. For patients with acute attacks this was further diluted with 5 per cent dextrose in water to a final volume of 50 ml.

The contents of each vial were administered intravenously over a 10 to 45-minute period. Serum samples for measurement of C1 inhibitor and C4 activity were obtained before infusion and at intervals during the five days after administration of the inhibitor concentrate. Whole blood samples were allowed to clot at room temperature for 30 minutes. The cells were sedimented by centrifugation, and the serum removed and stored at −40°C until assayed. After infusions, patients were evaluated for the presence of antibody to C1 inhibitor by means of counterimmunoelectrophoresis.

RESULTS

All patients receiving the C1-inhibitor concentrate tolerated the infusion without incident. No patient had fever or evidence of a hypersensitivity reaction. In no patient was an attack of angioedema precipitated by the infusion. Patients 1 and 2 had fourfold and threefold increases, respectively, in the C1 inhibitor serum level after the infusion (Fig. 1). In these two patients the increase in hemolytic activity of C4 provides evidence of effective modulation of the action of C1 esterase on its substrate C4. C1-inhibitor levels were not measured in Patient 3 since this patient had an elevated serum level of functionless C1-inhibitor protein that obscured the antigenic analysis (Table 1). However, the in vivo activity of the infused inhibitor was reflected by the 75 per cent increase in serum C4 activity seen in this patient.

Infusion of C1 Inhibitor in Patients during Attacks of Hereditary Angioedema

Patient 4 provided the initial opportunity to assess the efficacy of this C1-inhibitor concentrate in the management of an attack in progress. Severe, colicky, abdominal pain associated with nausea and vomiting signaled the onset of an abdominal attack of angioedema 12 hours before the infusion. After a period of

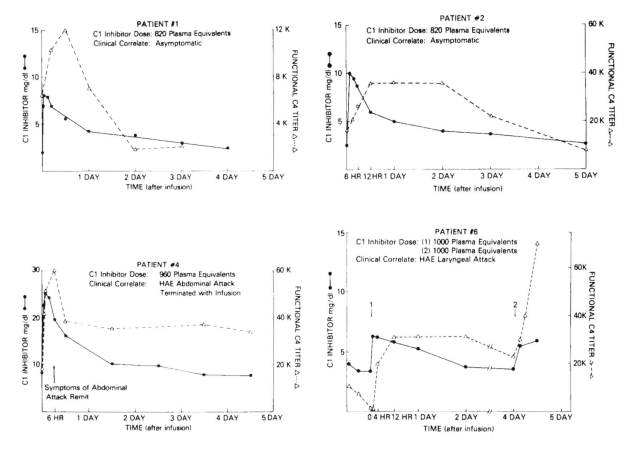

Figure 1. Results of Intravenous Administration of Partly Purified C1-Inhibitor Concentrate.
Values for serum concentration of C1 inhibitor (solid circles) and serum C4 functional activity (triangles) were determined immediately before infusion of the C1 inhibitor and then at intervals during the next five days in two asymptomatic patients with hereditary angioedema (HAE) (Patients 1 and 2) and two patients during an acute attack of angioedema. The kinetics of the serum C1 inhibitor and C4 response to the inhibitor infusion demonstrated in these four patients are closely representative of observations made in all the study patients.

observation, during which the patient's symptoms pursued a crescendo course, two vials of the C1-inhibitor concentrate were administered over a period of 10 minutes (Fig. 1). The abdominal symptoms resolved promptly during the six hours after infusion of the inhibitor preparation. The serum C4 activity followed a pattern consistent with the observed clinical effect (Fig. 1). Despite the prompt return of serum levels of C1 inhibitor toward pretreatment levels over the ensuing 36 hours, there was no return of the patient's symptoms. This patient subsequently received two additional infusions of C1 inhibitor for abdominal attacks and had a marked biochemical response and resolution of symptoms on each occasion (Table 1).

Four other patients received infusions of the C1-inhibitor concentrate during acute episodes of angioedema (Table 1). Each patient had successful clinical and biochemical control of disease activity after the infusion. Patient 6 had an attack of laryngeal edema while in the hospital and was given an infusion of C1

Table 1. Infusion of C1 Inhibitor in Patients with Hereditary Angioedema.

PATIENT NO.	CLINICAL STATUS	UNITS OF C1 INHIBITOR INFUSED	CLINICAL RESPONSE*	BIOCHEMICAL RESPONSE	
				C1 INHIBITOR	C4
				antigen†	function†
1	Asymptomatic	820	—	400	88
2	Asymptomatic	820	—	330	90
3	Asymptomatic	410	—	—‡	75
4	Abdominal attack	960	6	300	135
		1000	6	200	240
		1000	24	300	600
5	Abdominal attack	960	5	195	229
6	Laryngeal attack	1000	7	225	400
	Abdominal attack	1000	6	135	180
7	Abdominal attack	1000	6	230	—§
8	Laryngeal attack	1000	1	180	230

*Time (hours) from infusion to resolution of symptoms.

†Per cent increase compared with preinfusion values.

‡C1 inhibitor was not measured since the patient possessed a functionless inhibitor protein that obscured changes in C1-inhibitor antigen.

§C4 functional titer was undetectable before the infusion.

inhibitor within 30 minutes of the onset of the attack. The edema subsided totally within seven hours (Fig. 1). Four days later, the patient had similar symptoms, in addition to abdominal discomfort, and was again given the C1-inhibitor concentrate. Again, clinical and biochemical improvement was noted. Patient 8 had laryngeal edema with obvious swelling of the uvula and posterior pharynx after two to three days of peripheral angioedema. Although a dramatic decrease in edema occurred 30 minutes after infusion, the absolute magnitude of the increment in serum C4 titer was minimal (3000 to 6930) (Table 1).

There was a consistent lag between the infusion of the C1 inhibitor and the resultant peak of C4 activity. In all patients approximately six hours separated the inhibitor peak from the point at which the C4 activity was maximal. The C1-inhibitor antigenic peak merely served as a marker for the infusion time, and the subsequent fall in serum C1 inhibitor reflects dilution of the protein as it equilibrates from the intravascular space to the other compartments of the extracellular volume, binding of the infused inhibitor to the activated C1 esterase, and catabolism of the infused protein. The lag between C1 inhibitor and C4 peaks presumably reflects the rate of synthesis of new C4 protein. The infusion of functional C1-inhibitor protein results in an increase in serum C4 activity that may result from decreased C4 catabolism, permitting newly synthesized C4 to appear intact within the serum.

No acute untoward consequences of the infusion of C1 inhibitor were noted by any of the study patients. Neither clinical nor biochemical evidence of transfusion hepatitis was detected. Formation of antibodies against the missing protein is a potential hazard in the replacement therapy of any serum protein deficiency. However, hereditary angioedema is a disease expressed in the heterozygous state.[6] The presence of low levels of C1 inhibitor in patients with hereditary angioedema results in antigenic familiarity with the C1-inhibitor protein and seems to obviate this problem. No antibody to C1 inhibitor was detected by means of counterimmunoelectrophoresis, and no patient had untoward effects at the time of the second infusion.

On two occasions (Patients 2 and 3) typical attacks of hereditary angioedema occurred toward the end of the five-day study period. In both instances the serum levels of C1 inhibitor and C4 had returned to nearly the preinfusion levels. These two patients had attack frequencies approximating one every two weeks and were receiving no prophylactic drug therapy during the five-day infusion study. It is probable that these episodes of angioedema (upper extremity in Patient 1 and abdominal attack in Patient 3) were coincidental to the inhibitor infusions; however, it cannot be shown that they do not represent a "rebound" effect.

DISCUSSION

This paper presents a new method for the large-scale preparation of C1-inhibitor protein that may be suitable for use in the replacement therapy of hereditary angioedema. All patients receiving this inhibitor had an increment in the activity of functional C4. This finding provides evidence of the in vivo efficacy of the lyophilized material.

Comparison of these findings with the previously reported use of plasma as a source of C1 inhibitor suggests that the C1-inhibitor concentrate is likely to provide the same level of protection in those patients with hereditary angioedema who undergo oral surgery. The increments in C1-inhibitor levels obtained with this source of inhibitor protein exceed those of the plasma study. The infusion of two units of plasma in six patients resulted in a mean increase in serum C1 inhibitor of 2.5 mg per deciliter,[13] whereas the infusion of the C1-inhibitor concentrate produced a mean increment in C1 inhibitor of 7.2 mg per deciliter in the 10 studies in which C1-inhibitor antigen was measured. This difference occurs because the plasma functional equivalent of C1 inhibitor administered to all patients, except Patient 3, exceeded the amount of plasma administered in the former study, and because the administration of C1 inhibitor as a concentrate permits rapid intravenous administration and thereby reduces the dilution effect resulting from equilibration into the extravascular space. Of greater relevance was the fact that the use of this source of C1 inhibitor produced increases in the activity of functional C4 that approximated those achieved with plasma.

The use of such a lyophilized purified preparation of C1 inhibitor has several advantages over the use of whole plasma as a means of C1-inhibitor replacement. Treatment of the starting material with 20 per cent polyethylene glycol provides a desirable margin of safety as a result of the known precipitation of hepatitis B virus under these conditions.[16] In addition, the use of the lyophilized C1-inhibitor concentrate permits storage at 4°C and administration in more convenient volumes. However, the advantages of a partly purified preparation of C1 inhibitor over plasma are most apparent in replacement therapy during an attack of hereditary angioedema. The results of plasma infusion to date are equivocal, and strenuous objection has been raised to the use of whole plasma during an acute attack. It is clear that plasma administration has not proved a consistent, safe means of interrupting an attack. In contrast, the results in Patients 4 to 8 suggest that this C1-inhibitor concentrate provides a means of mitigating an attack that is under way. Prompt alleviation of clinical symptoms occurred in all patients studied during acute attacks. The occurrence of a second attack in Patient 6 four days after the first attack raises the possibility that continuing infusions of the inhibitor may be necessary in some patients. Interruption of the angioedema attacks was achieved with the infusion of approximately 1000 plasma equivalents of C1 inhibitor. Similar results have been obtained with the use of 2000 to 3000 plasma equivalents of C1 inhibitor in Europe.[21]

The current data suggest that this new C1-inhibitor preparation may be a suitable substitute for plasma in the prophylaxis of airway embarrassment resulting from oral surgery, and, more importantly, that it may provide a safe, definitive approach to the treatment of acute attacks of hereditary angioedema. This form of replacement has considerable advantages over plasma, owing to the reduced risk of transfusion hepatitis as well as convenience of storage and administration. In addition, despite the existence of effective prophylactic drug therapy, there remains a sizable subpopulation of patients with hereditary angioedema who are not receiving prophylactic therapy. This group includes pregnant women, children not having realized acceptable bone growth, patients with infrequent attacks (one every two to three months), and those who have adverse reactions to androgen therapy. For these patients a safe, effective means of acute replacement of C1 inhibitor would provide the physician with a means of controlling the incapacitating or life-threatening expressions of hereditary angioedema. Since the shelf life of the lyophilized C1-inhibitor concentrate exceeds 12 months at 4°C, clinics engaged in the therapy of patients with hereditary angioedema could anticipate the needs of these patients and maintain a stock of the inhibitor.

References

1. Frank MM, Gelfand JA, Atkinson JP. Hereditary angioedema: the clinical syndrome and its management. Ann Intern Med. 1976; 84:580-93.
2. Spaulding WB. Methyltestosterone therapy for hereditary episodic edema (hereditary angioneurotic edema). Ann Intern Med. 1960; 53:739-45.
3. Davis PJ, Davis FB, Charache P. Long-term therapy of hereditary angioedema (HAE): preventive management with fluoxymesterone and oxymetholone in severely affected males and females. Johns Hopkins Med J. 1974; 135:391-8.
4. Gelfand JA, Sherins RJ, Alling DW, Frank MM. Treatment of hereditary angioedema with danazol: reversal of clinical and biochemical abnormalities. N Engl J Med. 1976; 295:1444-8.
5. Rosse WF, Logue GL, Silberman HR, Frank MM. The effect of synthetic androgens in hereditary angioneurotic edema: alteration of C1 inhibitor and C4 levels. Trans Assoc Am Physicians. 1976; 89:122-32.
6. Gadek JE, Hosea SW, Gelfand JA, Frank MM. Response of variant hereditary angioedema phenotypes to danazol therapy: genetic implications. J Clin Invest. 1979; 64:280-6.
7. Frank MM, Gelfand JA, Sherins RJ, Gadek JE. The treatment of hereditary angioedema with danazol. In: Opferkuch W, Rother K, Schultz DR, eds. Clinical aspects of the complement system. Stuttgart: Georg Thieme, 1976:134-7.
8. Frank MM, Sergent JS, Kane MA, Alling DW. Epsilon aminocaproic acid therapy of hereditary angioneurotic edema: a double-blind study. N Engl J Med. 1972; 286:808-12.
9. Sheffer AL, Austen KF, Rosen FS. Tranexamic acid therapy in hereditary angioneurotic edema. N Engl J Med. 1972; 287:452-4.
10. Johnson AJ, Karpatkin MH, Newman J. Preparation of and clinical experience with antihemophilic factor concentrates. Thromb Diath Haemorrh [Suppl]. 1969; 35:49-59.
11. Janeway CA, Rosen FS. The gamma globulins. IV. Therapeutic uses of gamma globulin. N Engl J Med. 1966; 275:826-31.
12. Pickering RJ, Kelly JR, Good RA, Gewurz H. Replacement therapy in hereditary angioedema: successful treatment of two patients with fresh frozen plasma. Lancet. 1969; 1:326-30.
13. Jaffe CJ, Atkinson JP, Gelfand JA, Frank MM. Hereditary angioedema: the use of fresh frozen plasma for prophylaxis in patients undergoing oral surgery. J Allergy Clin Immunol. 1975; 55:386-93.
14. Donaldson VH, Merler E, Rosen FS, Kretschmer KW, Lepow IH. A polypeptide kinin in hereditary angioneurotic edema plasma: role of complement in its formation. J Lab Clin Med. 1970; 76:986. abstract.
15. Vogelaar EF, Brummelhuis HGJ, Krijnen HW. Contributions to the optimal use of human blood. III. Large-scale preparation of human C1 esterase inhibitor for clinical use. Vox Sang. 1974; 26:118-27.
16. Hao YL, Wickerhauser M. An integrated plasma fractionation system based on the use of polyethylene glycol. In: Sandberg HE, ed. Proceedings of the International Workshop on Technology for Protein Separation and Improvement of Blood Plasma Fractionation. Washington, D.C.: Government Printing Office, 1977:372-9. (DHEW Publication No. 781422).
17. Wickerhauser M, Hao YL, Mercer J. Method for large-scale preparation of C1 inhibitor concentrate for clinical studies (abstract). Presented at the Joint Congress of the International Societies of Hematology and Blood Transfusion. Paris, July 24-26, 1978.
18. Gigli I, Ruddy S, Austen KF. The stoichiometric measurement of the serum inhibitor of the first component of complement by the inhibition of immune hemolysis. J Immunol. 1968; 100:1154-64.
19. Levy LR, Lepow IH. Assay and properties of serum inhibitor of C'1-esterase. Proc Soc Exp Biol Med. 1959; 101:608-11.
20. Gaither TA, Alling DW, Frank MM. A new one-step method for the functional assay of the fourth component (C4) of human and guinea pig complement. J Immunol. 1974; 113:574-83.
21. Replacement therapy in hereditary angioedema. Agostoni A, Bergamaschini L, Martignoni G, Cicardi M, Marsini B. Presented at the First International Conference on Hereditary Angioedema. Milan, Italy, July, 1978.

Biochimica et Biophysica Acta, 612 (1980) 433—449
© Elsevier/North-Holland Biomedical Press

BBA 68940

KINETICS OF REACTION OF HUMAN C1-INHIBITOR WITH THE HUMAN COMPLEMENT SYSTEM PROTEASES C1r and C1s

ROBERT B. SIM *, GERARD J. ARLAUD and MAURICE G. COLOMB

DRF/Biochimie, Centre d'Etudes Nucleaires de Grenoble, 85 X, 38041 Frenoble Cedex and Universite Scientifique et Medicale de Grenoble, Grenoble (France)

(Received August 6th, 1979)

Key words: $C\bar{1}$-inhibitor; Complement protease; $C\bar{1}r$; $C\bar{1}s$; (Kinetics)

Summary

The interactions of the two classical serine proteases of the complement system with their natural inhibitor, C1-inhibitor, have been studied. $C\bar{1}r$ and $C\bar{1}s$ react with C1-inhibitor to form complexes which contain 1 mol of C1-inhibitor per mol of protease monomer. The complexes are not degraded in the presence of excess protease, and are not dissociated by strong denaturing agents. Rate constants and dissociation constants for these reactions fall within the normal range for protease-protease inhibitor interactions. The affinity of both proteases for C1-inhibitor is similar, but $C\bar{1}s$ reacts more rapidly than does $C\bar{1}r$. The presence of Ca^{2+} decreases the rate at which $C\bar{1}r$ complexes with C1-inhibitor, but does not affect the reactivity of $C\bar{1}s$. The $C\bar{1}r$-(C1-inhibitor) reaction is also inhibited by extremes of ionic strength, and has a more marked temperature-dependence than the $C\bar{1}s$-(C1-inhibitor) interaction.

Heparin stimulates the rate of the reaction of $C\bar{1}s$ with C1-inhibitor by a factor of 14—15. The $C\bar{1}r$-(C1-inhibitor) interaction is also accelerated by heparin, but the effect is much smaller than for $C\bar{1}s$. Neither protease is inhibited by heparin alone. In contrast to the effect of heparin, flufenamic acid was found to inhibit the action of C1-inhibitor.

The incorporation of $C\bar{1}r$ into C1 bound to immune complexes was found to increase the reactivity of $C\bar{1}r$ towards C1-inhibitor. $C\bar{1}s$ reactivity, however,

---

* Present address: MRC Immunochemistry Unit, Department of Biochemistry, University of Oxford, South Parks Road, Oxford OX1 3QU, U.K.
Abbreviations: DIP-$C\bar{1}s$, DIP-$C\bar{1}r$, respectively, $C\bar{1}s$ and $C\bar{1}r$ which have been totally inactivated with diisopropyl phosphorofluoridate; EDTA, ethylenediaminetetraacetic acid.
The nomenclature of the components of complement is that recommended by the World Health Organization [Bull. W.H.O. (1968) 39, 935—936]. An enzymically active component is indicated by a superscript bar, e.g. $C\bar{1}r$.

was not stimulated by this treatment. The enhancement of $C\bar{1}r$ activity by strong binding to antibody-antigen-C1q complexes and to $C\bar{1}s$, parallels earlier work (Dodds, A.W., Sim, R.B., Porter, R.R. and Kerr, M.A. (1978) Biochem. J. 175, 383—390) on the activation of the C1r proenzyme, and demonstrates that the other components of the antibody-antigen-C1 complex act as modifiers of the activities of both activated and proenzymic C1r.

Introduction

The humoral immune defence system, complement, is activated by a number of stimuli associated with entry of foreign material into the circulation. One mode of activation of complement, the interaction of the first component of complement, C1, with antibody-antigen complexes, is now relatively well understood [1]. $C\bar{1}$ is a glycoprotein complex consisting of three distinct types of subcomponent, C1q, C1r and C1s, bound together in the presence of Ca^{2+}. Binding of the C1q subunit in C1 to antibody in immune complexes leads to sequential proteolytic activation of the C1r and C1s subunits [2]. The activated forms of these subunits, $C\bar{1}r$ and $C\bar{1}s$, are both serine proteases [3], and $C\bar{1}s$ initiates the proteolytic activation of subsequent components in the complement reaction sequence [1].

Once activated, these two proteases, like other circulating plasma proteases, become subject to control by endogenous protease inhibitors. $C\bar{1}r$ and $C\bar{1}s$ are both inhibited by $C\bar{1}$-inhibitor [4,5], a well-characterised plasma protease inhibitor first isolated by Schultze et al. [6]. It has been shown that inhibition of $C\bar{1}r$ and $C\bar{1}s$ by $C\bar{1}$-inhibitor is accompanied by formation of a complex, containing 1 molecule of $C\bar{1}$-inhibitor per molecule of protease. The complexes formed do not dissociate in sodium dodecyl sulphate and urea [7—9]. Recent studies indicate that $C\bar{1}$-inhibitor is the only plasma protease inhibitor which reacts with $C\bar{1}r$ and $C\bar{1}s$ [10].

Qualitative studies of the formation of complexes between isolated $C\bar{1}s$ and $C\bar{1}$-inhibitor have been reported [8], but little further information is available on the reaction of isolated $C\bar{1}r$ with $C\bar{1}$-inhibitor. $C\bar{1}$-inhibitor may be regarded as a pseudo-substrate of $C\bar{1}r$ and $C\bar{1}s$, and although these two proteases are very similar in size, structure and mode of proteolytic activation [3,11,12] they are distinct in their proteolytic substrate specificities [11,12]. It is therefore likely that differences in their interaction with $C\bar{1}$-inhibitor will exist. The present study was undertaken to compare directly and quantitatively the characteristics of the reactions between each protease and $C\bar{1}$-inhibitor.

Materials and Methods

Materials

Human citrated plasma was obtained from the Centre de Transfusion Sanguine, Grenoble. Serum was prepared and stored as in Ref. 9. The sources of commercial products were as follows: $Na^{125}I$, The Radiochemical Centre, Amersham, Bucks, U.K.; lactoperoxidase (Grade B), Calbiochem, San Diego, CA, U.S.A.; materials for polyacrylamide gels, sodium dodecyl sulphate and iodoacetamide, Merck, Darmstadt, F.R.G.; N-α-carbobenzoxy-L-lysine p-nitrophenol ester, Interchim, Montluçon, France; heparin (sodium salt), Fluka A.G., Buchs, Switzerland; flufenamic acid (2-{[3-(trifluoromethyl)-phenyl]amino}-benzoic acid), Aldrich-Europe, Beerse, Belgium, hen ovalbumin, Sigma, St. Louis, MO, U.S.A. Other reagents and chemicals were from Merck or from Prolabo, Paris, France.

Proteins

$C\bar{1}r$ and $C\bar{1}s$ were isolated by either of two methods [3,13] which yield products equivalent in purity and activity. $C\bar{1}$-inhibitor was prepared by the method of Reboul et al. [7]. C1q was isolated as described in Ref. 13. $C\bar{1}r$ and $C\bar{1}s$, totally inactivated by diisopropyl phosphorofluoridate (DIP-$C\bar{1}r$, DIP-$C\bar{1}s$), were formed as in Ref. 2.

Immune complexes containing hen ovalbumin and rabbit-antihen ovalbumin IgG antibody were prepared as previously described [9,12].

Isolated proteins in solution were quantified from their specific absorbance at 280 nm [9]. Molecular weight estimates used to calculate molar concentrations were: C1q, 410 000 [1]; $C\bar{1}r$ or $C\bar{1}s$ monomer, 83 000 [3]; $C\bar{1}$-inhibitor, 100 000 [7] and rabbit IgG, 150 000.

Protein iodination

$C\bar{1}r$ and $C\bar{1}s$ were labelled with ^{125}I by lactoperoxidase catalysis [10] using an Na^{125}I solution diluted to a specific activity of 500 μCi/ml. This iodination method has been shown to be without effect on the enzymic activities of $C\bar{1}r$ and $C\bar{1}s$, and does not alter the rate at which they react with $C\bar{1}$-inhibitor [10].

Sodium dodecyl sulphate polyacrylamide gel electrophoresis

Electrophoresis in 5.6% (w/v) polyacrylamide gels in buffers containing sodium dodecyl sulphate was done as described by Fairbanks et al. [14]. Preparation of samples for electrophoresis, staining of gels with Coomassie blue, scanning of stained gels, and slicing of gels for determination of radioactivity were done as before [15].

Spectrophotometric assay of $C\bar{1}s$ and estimation of $C\bar{1}$-inhibitor activity

The N-α-carbobenzoxy-L-lysine p-nitrophenol esterase activity of $C\bar{1}s$ was determined at pH 6.0 [2,11] using a Beckman Acta III or Leres spectrophotometer, maintained at 37°C by means of a Huber Ministat water circulator. Linear increase in absorbance at 340 nm was measured continuously for 3 min.

To determine the inhibitory activity of $C\bar{1}$-inhibitor towards $C\bar{1}s$, samples of $C\bar{1}s$ were incubated with $C\bar{1}$-inhibitor in 5 mM triethanolamine-HCl, 145 mM NaCl, pH 7.4, containing 5 mM CaCl$_2$ or 5 mM EDTA. At various times a portion (50—100 μl) of the incubation mixture was withdrawn and diluted to 3.0 ml with 100 mM sodium phosphate, 100 mM NaCl, 15 mM EDTA, pH 6.0. The residual $C\bar{1}s$ esterase activity in the 3 ml sample was then measured as noted above. Dilution of the $C\bar{1}s$ + $C\bar{1}$-inhibitor mixture and lowering of the pH to 6.0 reduces the rate of the $C\bar{1}$-inhibitor-$C\bar{1}s$ interaction to negligible values, permitting an accurate measurement of the remaining $C\bar{1}s$ activity.

Measurement of the extent of complex formation between $C\bar{1}r$ or $C\bar{1}s$ and $C\bar{1}$-inhibitor

The extent of inhibition of $C\bar{1}s$ by $C\bar{1}$-inhibitor can be measured conveniently and rapidly by estimating $C\bar{1}s$ esterase activity, as described above. $C\bar{1}r$, however, has only very weak esterase activity [11,16,17] and no rapid, direct assay for $C\bar{1}r$ esterase activity is available. Therefore, in order to compare directly the rates of interaction of $C\bar{1}r$ and $C\bar{1}s$ with $C\bar{1}$-inhibitor, the rates of formation of the sodium dodecyl sulphate and urea-stable complexes between the two proteases and $C\bar{1}$-inhibitor were measured. The formation of such complexes has been shown to correlate with inhibition of the proteases [9] and so measurement of complex formation is essentially equivalent to measurement of inhibition.

Samples of ^{125}I-labelled $C\bar{1}r$ or of ^{125}I-labelled $C\bar{1}s$ were incubated with $C\bar{1}$-inhibitor in 5 mM triethanolamine-HCl, 145 mM NaCl, pH 7.4, containing 5 mM $CaCl_2$ or 5 mM EDTA. At various times, portions of 50 μl were withdrawn from the incubation mixture, and diluted immediately with 50 μl of 200 mM Tris-HCl, 8 M urea, 2% (w/v) sodium dodecyl sulphate, 40 mM iodoacetamide, pH 8.0, and incubated for 4 min at 100°C. The samples were then loaded onto sodium dodecyl sulphate polyacrylamide gels, and the complexes of radiolabelled $C1r$ or $C\bar{1}s$ with $C\bar{1}$-inhibitor were separated from free, unreacted $C\bar{1}r$, $C\bar{1}s$ and $C\bar{1}$-inhibitor by electrophoresis. Gels were stained with Coomassie blue, destained and sliced into 2 mm segments. Radioactivity in the slices was measured on an Intertechnique CG2000 gamma-counter. The progress of reaction between $C\bar{1}r$ or $C\bar{1}s$ and $C\bar{1}$-inhibitor was calculated from the proportion of the ^{125}I radioactivity associated with the $C\bar{1}r$-($C\bar{1}$-inhibitor) or $C\bar{1}s$-($C\bar{1}$-inhibitor) complexes at various incubation times, as described previously [10,15]. The specific radioactivity of the ^{125}I-labelled $C\bar{1}r$ or $C\bar{1}s$ was adjusted so that each polyacrylamide gel was loaded with 2500—3000 cpm.

Calculation of kinetic constants for the reaction of $C\bar{1}r$ or $C\bar{1}s$ with $C\bar{1}$-inhibitor

The overall rates of the reactions shown in Eqn. 1

$$C\bar{1}r + C\bar{1}\text{-inhibitor} \xrightarrow{k_1} C\bar{1}r\text{-}(C\bar{1}\text{-inhibitor})$$
$$C\bar{1}s + C\bar{1}\text{-inhibitor} \xrightarrow{k_1} C\bar{1}s\text{-}(C\bar{1}\text{-inhibitor})$$
(1)

were determined experimentally as described above, using ^{125}I-labelled $C\bar{1}r$ or $C\bar{1}s$, and examining complex formation by sodium dodecyl sulphate polyacrylamide gel electrophoresis. Rates of protease-protease-inhibitor complex formation were studied at pH 7.4 and 37°C in the presence of Ca^{2+} or of EDTA, by incubating mixtures of different concentrations of ^{125}I-labelled-$C\bar{1}r$ or $C\bar{1}s$ and $C\bar{1}$-inhibitor. The concentration ranges examined were: $C\bar{1}r$, 0.2—4.9 μM (16.6—407 μg/ml); $C\bar{1}s$, 0.2—4.4 μM (16.6—366 μg/ml) and $C\bar{1}$-inhibitor, 1.2—10.2 μM (120—1022 μg/ml). The progress of the reaction was found to conform to the second-order rate equation (Eqn. 2)

$$v = k_1 [P] [I]$$
(2)

where v is the reaction velocity and k_1 is the rate constant of association. [P] and [I] represent the concentrations of the protease and of C$\overline{1}$-inhibitor, respectively. The kinetic constant, k_1, was calculated by fitting data to the integrated rate equation as described in [18]. This equation is of the form

$$\log_{10} \frac{P_0(I_0 - C)}{I_0(P_0 - C)} = k_1 t \frac{I_0 - P_0}{2.303} \tag{3}$$

where P_0, I_0, represent the concentrations of protease or of C$\overline{1}$-inhibitor, repectively, at time zero, and C is the concentration of protease-(protease-inhibitor) complex at time t.

Calculation of the dissociation constant for the reaction of C$\overline{1}$r or C$\overline{1}$s with C$\overline{1}$-inhibitor

The dissociation constant, K_D, for the reaction between C$\overline{1}$r or C$\overline{1}$s and C$\overline{1}$-inhibitor was determined in a manner similar to that described by Wiman and Collen [19]. ^{125}I-labelled C$\overline{1}$r or C$\overline{1}$s (1.2 μM, 100 μg/ml) was incubated with an equivalent molar quantity of C$\overline{1}$-inhibitor, and also with a 2-, 4-, 8-, and 16-fold molar excess of C$\overline{1}$-inhibitor, for 1 h at 37°C. Incubations were done in 5 mM triethanolamine-HCl, 145 mM NaCl, pH 7.4, containing 5 mM CaCl$_2$ or 5 mM EDTA. The extent of formation of complexes was determined by electrophoresis, as described above. K_D was calculated from Eqn. 4,

$$K_D = \frac{P_e I_e}{C_e} \tag{4}$$

where P_e, I_e and C_e represent, respectively, the concentrations of protease, of C$\overline{1}$-inhibitor and of the protease-(C$\overline{1}$-inhibitor) complex at equilibrium.

Results

Formation of complexes between C$\overline{1}$r or C$\overline{1}$s and C$\overline{1}$-inhibitor

On incubation of C$\overline{1}$r and C$\overline{1}$s with C$\overline{1}$-inhibitor, complexes are formed which remain stable even under the strong denaturing conditions used in preparation of samples for sodium dodecyl sulphate polyacrylamide gel electrophoresis [7—9]. Scans of Coomassie blue-stained gels illustrating C$\overline{1}$r-(C$\overline{1}$-inhibitor) and C$\overline{1}$s-(C$\overline{1}$-inhibitor) complexes, formed in the presence either of excess protease or of excess C$\overline{1}$-inhibitor, are shown in Fig. 1.

Formation of complexes of similar stability between various protease-(protease-inhibitor) pairs has been reported, e.g., plasmin-(C$\overline{1}$-inhibitor) [8]; trypsin-α_2 antiplasmin; plasmin-α_2 antiplasmin [20]; thrombin-antithrombin III [21] and trypsin-α_1 antitrypsin [22]. In the majority of such cases, it has been shown that in the presence of an excess of the protease involved, the inhibitor, or the protease-(protease-inhibitor) complex itself undergoes proteolytic degradation [8,20—22]. As shown in Fig. 1, however, when C$\overline{1}$-inhibitor is incubated with a large excess of C$\overline{1}$r or C$\overline{1}$s, only one type of complex is formed, and no degradation of the complex by the excess of free protease is detected. Similarly, no degradation of free C$\overline{1}$-inhibitor is observed when C$\overline{1}$-inhibitor is in excess. Harpel and Cooper [8], examining C$\overline{1}$s-(C$\overline{1}$-inhibitor) interaction, also concluded that C$\overline{1}$s does not degrade C$\overline{1}$-inhibitor. Thus, the C$\overline{1}$r-(C$\overline{1}$-inhibitor) and C$\overline{1}$s-(C$\overline{1}$-inhibitor) complexes are stable both to dissocia-

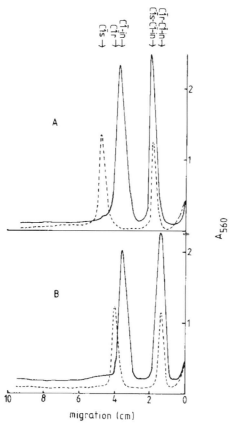

Fig. 1. Scans of sodium dodecyl sulphate polyacrylamide gels of mixtures of C$\bar{1}$r or C$\bar{1}$s and C$\bar{1}$-inhibitor. C$\bar{1}$s + C$\bar{1}$-inhibitor (A) or C$\bar{1}$r + C$\bar{1}$-inhibitor (B) were incubated for 1 h at 37°C, then run on sodium dodecyl sulphate polyacrylamide gels without reduction of disulphide bonds. ———, mixtures of 15 μg of protease with a 3-fold molar excess of C$\bar{1}$-inhibitor; ------, mixtures of 5 μg of C$\bar{1}$-inhibitor with a 3-fold molar excess of protease.

tion by denaturing agents and to proteolysis, and are therefore always readily separable from excess free C$\bar{1}$r or C$\bar{1}$s or free C$\bar{1}$-inhibitor by polyacrylamide gel electrophoresis in the presence of sodium dodecyl sulphate.

Kinetic and dissociation constants

Typical curves showing the rates of formation of complexes between C$\bar{1}$r or C$\bar{1}$s and C$\bar{1}$-inhibitor are shown in Fig. 2. The progress of the reaction was found to conform to the second-order rate equation (Eqn. 2), and the simplified integrated form of the equation (Eqn. 3) described the reaction up to about 70% completion. The fit of the reaction rate data to Eqn. 3 is shown in Fig. 2C. The reactions illustrated in Fig. 2 all reach completion in less than 1 h, justifying the use of a 1 h incubation to determine the dissociation constant, as described in Materials and Methods.

The calculated values for the kinetic constants of association, and the dissociation constants are shown in Table I. These results demonstrate that C$\bar{1}$r and C$\bar{1}$s have similar affinities for C$\bar{1}$-inhibitor, but that C$\bar{1}$r reacts with the inhibitor more slowly than does C$\bar{1}$s. The presence of Ca^{2+} does not affect the rate at which C$\bar{1}$s combines with C$\bar{1}$-inhibitor, but the rate of the C$\bar{1}$r-(C$\bar{1}$-inhibitor) reaction is slowed by a factor of two to three in the presence of Ca^{2+},

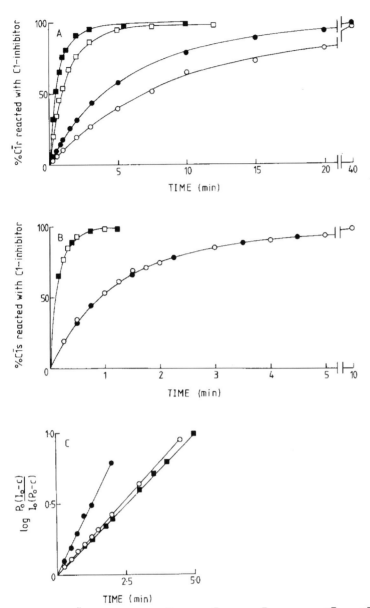

Fig. 2. Rates of reaction of $C\overline{1}r$ and $C\overline{1}s$ with $C\overline{1}$-inhibitor. $C\overline{1}r$ or $C\overline{1}s$ and $C\overline{1}$-inhibitor were incubated at $37°C$, and the extent of formation of $C\overline{1}r$-(C1-inhibitor) or $C\overline{1}s$-(C$\overline{1}$-inhibitor) complexes was estimated by the sodium dodecyl sulphate polyacrylamide gel electrophoresis method described in Materials and Methods. The curves shown are: (A) $C\overline{1}r$ (0.6 μM) + $C\overline{1}$-inhibitor (1.2 μM) in the presence of EDTA (●) or of Ca^{2+} (○); $C\overline{1}r$ (4.9 μM) + $C\overline{1}$-inhibitor (10.2 μM) in the presence of EDTA (■) or Ca^{2+} (□). (B) $C\overline{1}s$ (0.6 μM) + $C\overline{1}$-inhibitor (1.2 μM) in the presence of EDTA (●) or of Ca^{2+} (○); $C\overline{1}s$ (4.4 μM) + $C\overline{1}$-inhibitor (10.2 μM) in the presence of EDTA (■) or of Ca^{2+} (□). Results shown are means of two experiments at each concentration. (C), data from parts A and B have been fitted to the integrated second-order rate equation (see Eqn. 3 in text). For clarity, some time points are omitted. $C\overline{1}r$ (4.9 μM) + $C\overline{1}$-inhibitor (10.2 μM) in the presence of EDTA (●) or of Ca^{2+} (○); $C\overline{1}s$ (0.6 μM) + $C\overline{1}$-inhibitor (1.2 μM) in the presence of either EDTA or of Ca^{2+} (■).

compared with the rate seen in EDTA. The dissociation constants for both reactions are, however, unaffected by the presence or absence of Ca^{2+}, and the values shown in Table I are the means of values which include determinations in the presence of Ca^{2+} or of EDTA.

The lower velocity of the $C\overline{1}r$-(C$\overline{1}$-inhibitor) interaction supports previous

TABLE I

VALUES OF REACTION CONSTANTS FOR THE INTERACTION OF C$\bar{1}$r OR C$\bar{1}$s WITH C$\bar{1}$-INHIBITOR

k_1 and K_D (see text for definition) were calculated from results obtained at 37°C in the presence of 5 mM CaCl$_2$ or 5 mM EDTA. Values of k_1 and K_D are the means ± S.D. of 5—8 determinations. Values for the activation energy were calculated from the best straight line and standard deviation of two or three rate determinations at each temperature.

	C$\bar{1}$r + C$\bar{1}$-inhibitor	C$\bar{1}$s + C$\bar{1}$-inhibitor
k_1 (in Ca^{2+}) (M$^{-1} \cdot$ s^{-1})	$(1.53 \pm 0.3) \cdot 10^3$	$(1.25 \pm 0.2) \cdot 10^4$
k_1 (in EDTA) (M$^{-1} \cdot$ s^{-1})	$(2.84 \pm 0.2) \cdot 10^3$	$(1.20 \pm 0.15) \cdot 10^4$
K_D (Ca^{2+} or EDTA) (M)	$(1.21 \pm 0.2) \cdot 10^{-7}$	$(9.6 \pm 0.5) \cdot 10^{-8}$
Activation energy (kcal $\cdot$ mol^{-1})	44.3 ± 4.0	11.7 ± 0.5

observations [7] that C$\bar{1}$r in solution does not compete effectively with C$\bar{1}$s for C$\bar{1}$-inhibitor. The inhibitory effect of Ca^{2+} on the C$\bar{1}$r-(C$\bar{1}$-inhibitor) reaction confirms a previous suggestion by Laurell et al. [23]. Ca^{2+} also has an inhibitory effect on the proteolytic activity of C$\bar{1}$r [12,17]. The reactivity of C$\bar{1}$s with C$\bar{1}$-inhibitor, like the proteolytic and esterolytic activities of C$\bar{1}$s [12,24], is unaffected by Ca^{2+}.

Effect of temperature on reaction rates

The effect of temperature on the interaction of C$\bar{1}$r or C$\bar{1}$s with C$\bar{1}$-inhibitor was tested by determining the initial velocities of these reactions over the temperature range 15°—37°C. The rates determined were fitted to the Arrhenius equation. The Arrhenius plot, shown in Fig. 3, was found to be linear for both reactions over the temperature range tested. The slopes of the plots for the C$\bar{1}$r-(C$\bar{1}$-inhibitor) or C$\bar{1}$s-(C$\bar{1}$-inhibitor) reactions were not significantly altered when the reactants were incubated in the presence of Ca^{2+}. Values for the activation energies, calculated from the slope of the graph, are shown in Table I. The value obtained for the C$\bar{1}$s-(C$\bar{1}$-inhibitor) interaction, 11.7 kcal/mol, is in close agreement with that reported by Loos et al. [25] for the reaction between guinea-pig C$\bar{1}$s and C$\bar{1}$-inhibitor from the same species. Similar values have been calculated for various hydrolytic reactions of C$\bar{1}$s, e.g., hydrolysis of amino acid esters (10.4—12.0 kcal/mol) [24,26].

The decrease in reaction rate with falling temperature is much more marked for C$\bar{1}$r than for C$\bar{1}$s. The reaction of C$\bar{1}$r with C$\bar{1}$-inhibitor is very slow at 15°C and at 20°C. At these temperatures, incubation for several hours is required to obtain 50% complex formation in the presence of physiological concentrations of C$\bar{1}$r and C$\bar{1}$-inhibitor. This is reflected in the high value for the activation energy (Table I). The rate of proteolysis by C$\bar{1}$r of its physiological substrate, C1s, is also strongly temperature-dependent, with an activation energy of 30—32 kcal/mol [27,28].

Effect of ionic strength on reaction rates

The effect of varying the ionic strength of the incubation medium in the range of 40—775 mM on the reactions between C$\bar{1}$-inhibitor and the two proteases is shown in Fig. 4. The C$\bar{1}$r-(C$\bar{1}$-inhibitor) reaction occurs optimally

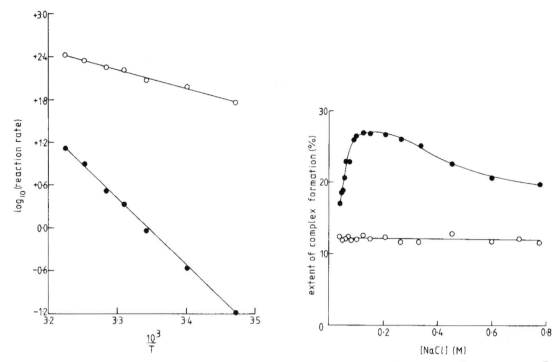

Fig. 3. Effect of temperature on the rate of reaction of C̄1r or C̄1s with C̄1-inhibitor. C̄1r (0.6 μM) or C̄1s (1.2 μM) were incubated with a 2-fold molar excess of C̄1-inhibitor at various temperatures between 15 and 37°C in the presence of 5 mM EDTA. The rate of uptake of C̄1r or C̄1s into complexes with C̄1-inhibitor was calculated at each temperature from graphs of the type shown in Fig. 2A, B. The logarithm of the initial reaction rate for C̄1r (●) and C̄1s (○) is shown as a function of the absolute temperature, T. Two or three determinations of initial reaction rate were performed at each temperature.

Fig. 4. The effect of ionic strength on the reaction between C̄1r or C̄1s and C̄1-inhibitor. C̄1r or C̄1s (final concentration 0.6 μM) was incubated at 37°C with a 2-fold molar excess of C̄1-inhibitor in 5 mM triethanolamine-HCl, 5 mM EDTA, pH 7.4, containing 45—775 mM NaCl. The percentage of C̄1r taken up into C̄1r-(C̄1-inhibitor) complexes was determined after 2 min (●) by sodium dodecyl sulphate polyacrylamide gel electrophoresis, as described in Materials and Methods. The percentage of C̄1s taken up in complexes was determined after 10 s (○).

between 110 and 300 mM. A sharp decrease in reaction rate is seen below 100 mM, and a more gradual decrease occurs above 300 mM. In contrast, variation in salt strength over this range has no significant effect on the C̄1s-(C̄1-inhibitor) interaction. The same pattern of results is obtained in the presence of Ca^{2+} or of EDTA. Preincubation (5 min, 37°C) either of the protease alone, or of C̄1-inhibitor alone, at the ionic strength used in each test did not alter the results obtained.

The inhibition of the C̄1r-(C̄1-inhibitor) interaction at high ionic strength is likely to be a direct effect on C̄1r itself, since similar effects are seen in the hydrolysis of amino acid esters by C̄1r [17] and in the cleavage of proenzymic C1s by C̄1r [28,29]. High ionic strength does not appear to affect the reactivity of C̄1-inhibitor, since its reaction with C̄1s (Fig. 4) is not inhibited at high ionic strength. The effect on the C̄1r-(C̄1-inhibitor) interaction at low ionic strength may reflect the low solubility of C̄1r [28], and possible inhibition of the reaction by formation of soluble C̄1r aggregates. No visible precipitation occurred during the time course of the reaction.

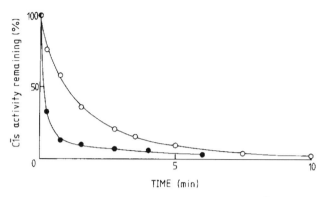

Fig. 5. The effect of heparin on inhibition of C$\overline{1}$s esterase activity by C$\overline{1}$-inhibitor. C$\overline{1}$s (1.6 µM) was incubated in 5 mM triethanolamine-HCl, 145 mM NaCl, pH 7.4, at 15°C with a 4-fold molar excess of C$\overline{1}$-inhibitor, in the absence of heparin (○) or with 5 µg/ml heparin (●). At various times, 50-µl samples of the mixture were withdrawn, and the remaining N-α-carbobenzoxy-L-lysine p-nitrophenol esterase activity of C$\overline{1}$s was measured as described in Materials and Methods.

Effect of heparin on reaction rates

Heparin has been shown to potentiate the inhibition of C$\overline{1}$ by C$\overline{1}$-inhibitor [30], and so tests were carried out to determine whether this action affected the inhibition of both C$\overline{1}$r and C$\overline{1}$s. Results obtained with C$\overline{1}$s using the spectrophotometric assay system described in Materials and Methods, demonstrated that heparin does greatly enhance the rate at which C$\overline{1}$s is inhibited by C$\overline{1}$-inhibitor (Fig. 5). Heparin alone, in agreement with previous findings [30,31] has no effect on the esterolytic activity of C$\overline{1}$s up to the highest concentration of heparin tested, 150 µg/ml.

Further studies on the effect of heparin on both C$\overline{1}$r-(C$\overline{1}$-inhibitor) and C$\overline{1}$s-(C$\overline{1}$-inhibitor) reactions were carried out using the sodium dodecyl sulphate polyacrylamide gel electrophoresis assay system. Results are shown in Fig. 6. The rate of reaction of C$\overline{1}$s with C$\overline{1}$-inhibitor increases linearly with heparin concentration up to about 15 µg/ml heparin, and then increases more slowly. The C$\overline{1}$r-(C$\overline{1}$-inhibitor) interaction is also accelerated in the presence of heparin, but the effect is much smaller than for C$\overline{1}$s. The maximum enhancement of reaction rate observed for C$\overline{1}$r is 2—2.5-fold, while for C$\overline{1}$s, the reaction rate can be increased by a factor of 14—15. As is the case for C$\overline{1}$s, the esterolytic activity of C$\overline{1}$r is not affected by heparin alone [17]. The enhancement of reaction rates observed was independent of the presence of Ca^{2+} or of EDTA.

Effect of flufenamic acid on C$\overline{1}$-inhibitor

Flufenamic acid, an in vitro fibrinolytic agent, has been suggested to promote plasmin action by decreasing the reactivity of various protease inhibitors which act on plasmin [32]. The effect of flufenamate on C$\overline{1}$-inhibitor was investigated in the C$\overline{1}$s-(C$\overline{1}$-inhibitor) system, and results are shown in Fig. 7. Concentrations of flufenamate between 1 mM and 3 mM were found to arrest almost completely the inhibition of C$\overline{1}$s by a 2-fold molar excess of C$\overline{1}$-inhibitor. Pre-incubation of C$\overline{1}$-inhibitor with flufenamate was necessary to obtain this effect. Flufenamic acid has an aromatic structure, and is known to inhibit chymotrypsin [33]. As shown in Fig. 7, flufenamate also inhibits C$\overline{1}$s activity,

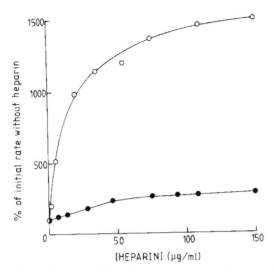
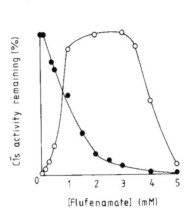

Fig. 6. Relationship of heparin concentration to the rate of reaction of C̄1r or C̄1s with C̄1-inhibitor. C̄1r (●) or C̄1s (○) at a final concentration of 0.6 μM was incubated at 37°C with a 2-fold molar excess of C̄1-inhibitor, in the presence of 5 mM EDTA and various concentrations of heparin. The time-course of formation of protease-(C̄1-inhibitor) complexes was followed by the sodium dodecyl sulphate polyacrylamide gel method as shown, e.g. in Fig. 2A, B. Initial rates of raction at each heparin concentration were calculated, and are shown relative to the initial rates in the absence of heparin which are taken as 100%.

Fig. 7. The effect of flufenamic acid on C̄1-inhibitor and on C̄1s. Curve 1 (●) shows the effect of flufenamic acid on C̄1s alone. C̄1s (0.6 μM) was incubated for 1 h at 37°C in 5 mM triethanolamine-HCl, 145 mM NaCl, pH 7.4, with various concentrations of flufenamic acid. The remaining N-α-carbobenzoxy-L-lysine p-nitrophenol esterase activity of C̄1s was then measured. Curve 2 (○) shows the effect of flufenamic acid on C̄1-inhibitor. C̄1-inhibitor (1.2 μM) was incubated for 1 h at 37°C with various concentrations of flufenamic acid in the same buffer. The remaining capacity of C̄1-inhibitor to inhibit C̄1s was then tested by adding C̄1s to the C̄1-inhibitor such that the final molar ratio C̄1s : C̄1-inhibitor was 1 : 2. Incubation was continued for 15 min at 37°C and the residual esterase activity of C̄1s was measured as above. Flufenamic acid was used as a stock 100 mM solution, adjusted to pH 7.4 with NaOH.

but inhibition of C̄1s occurs at a higher concentration of flufenamate than does the observed inactivation of C̄1-inhibitor. At concentrations greater than 3 mM, however, in this system, the direct effect of flufenamate on C̄1s become predominant. A previous report [34] documented an effect of flufenamate on the whole complement system which is consistent with the inhibition of C̄1s seen here.

These results demonstrate that flufenamate is a potent inhibitor of isolated C̄1-inhibitor, and confirm earlier indirect evidence of this phenomenon presented by Kluft [33].

Effect of uptake of C̄1r and C̄1s into C̄1 bound to immune complexes

In the blood, C1r and C1s exist predominantly as macromolecular C1, i.e., as a firm Ca²⁺-dependent complex of two C1r plus two C1s monomers, or four C1r plus four C1s monomers bound to one molecule of C1q [1]. On activation of macromolecular C1 by immune complexes, both C1r and C1s become cleaved and activated, but they remain together in the C̄1 complex, bound in the immune aggregates [1,2,15]. Thus in plasma, C̄1r and C̄1s are likely to become available for interaction with C̄1-inhibitor while they are incorporated into a large complex, rather than reacting as independent free proteases. The effect of the presence of an excess of various combinations of other C̄1 subcomponents, and of insoluble antibody-antigen complexes on the reactivities of $C\bar{1}r$ and $C\bar{1}s$ towards $C\bar{1}$-inhibitor was therefore studied. In these experiments, in mixtures in which both $C\bar{1}r$ and $C\bar{1}s$ were present, one of the two proteases was used in the form completely inactivated by diisopropyl phosphorofluoridate (DIP-$C\bar{1}r$, DIP-$C\bar{1}s$). These inactivated molecules do not react with $C\bar{1}$-inhibitor [9] but their ability to interact with other C1 subcomponents to form the C1 complex is unimpaired [2,15]. Use of these forms simplifies interpretation, by preventing competition of $C\bar{1}r$ and $C\bar{1}s$ for the $C\bar{1}$-inhibitor which is available.

Results are shown in Table II. In the presence of EDTA, which greatly weakens or prevents the binding of $C\bar{1}r$ or $C\bar{1}s$ to each other or to C1q, the rates of reaction of $C\bar{1}r$ or $C\bar{1}s$ with $C\bar{1}$-inhibitor are not significantly altered by the presence of other $C\bar{1}$ subcomponents or of immune complexes.

In the presence of Ca^{2+}, however, the following binding reactions occur [1,2,28,36]. (a) In the absence of immune aggregates, strong complexes between $C\bar{1}r$ and $C\bar{1}s$ are formed, which are likely to bind to C1q. $C\bar{1}r$ and $C\bar{1}s$ individually do not bind to C1q. (b) In the presence of immune aggregates, C1q binds to the aggregates, and $C\bar{1}r$ alone, or $C\bar{1}r$-$C\bar{1}s$ complexes bind strongly to the bound C1q. $C\bar{1}s$ alone does not bind to antibody-antigen-C1q complexes. $C\bar{1}r$, $C\bar{1}s$ and $C\bar{1}r$-$C\bar{1}s$ complexes do not interact with immune aggregates in the absence of C1q.

As shown in Table II, under conditions where $C\bar{1}r$ does not bind to the other

TABLE II

THE EFFECT OF IMMUNE COMPLEXES AND OTHER $C\bar{1}$ SUBCOMPONENTS ON THE REACTION OF $C\bar{1}r$ AND $C\bar{1}s$ WITH $C\bar{1}$-INHIBITOR

$C\bar{1}r$ or $C\bar{1}s$ was mixed with large excesses of other $C\bar{1}$ subcomponents or of immune complexes (IC), and incubated at 37°C with 2-fold molar excess of $C\bar{1}$-inhibitor. Incubation was done in a total volume of 0.1 ml of 5 mM triethanolamine-HCl, 145 mM NaCl, pH 7.4, containing 5 mM Ca^{2+} or 5 mM EDTA. Initial rates of formation or protease-($C\bar{1}$-inhibitor) complexes were calculated from graphs of the type shown in Fig. 2A, B. The rate observed with $C\bar{1}r$ in 5 mM Ca^{2+}, in the absence of other components, is expressed as 1.0, and other rates are shown relative to this value.

Sample No.	Components present (μg)						Initial rate of reaction of $C\bar{1}r$ or $C\bar{1}s$ with $C\bar{1}$-inhibitor	
	$C\bar{1}r$	$C\bar{1}s$	DIP-$C\bar{1}r$	DIP-$C\bar{1}s$	C1q	IC	Ca^{2+}	EDTA
1	5	—	—	—	—	—	1.0	1.9
2	5	—	—	20	—	—	0.8	2.0
3	5	—	—	—	20	—	1.0	2.0
4	5	—	—	—	—	200	1.0	2.0
5	5	—	—	20	20	—	0.7	1.8
6	5	—	—	20	—	200	0.8	2.0
7	5	—	—	—	20	200	0.9	1.8
8	5	—	—	20	20	200	3.7	1.9
9	—	5	—	—	—	—	8.1	7.9
10	—	5	20	—	—	—	7.9	8.1
11	—	5	—	—	20	—	8.3	8.0
12	—	5	—	—	—	200	8.0	8.1
13	—	5	20	—	20	—	7.7	7.9
14	—	5	20	—	—	200	8.0	8.0
15	—	5	—	—	20	200	7.8	8.3
16	—	5	20	—	20	200	7.3	8.1

components present (lines 3 and 4), its reactivity towards C1-inhibitor is identical to that observed with C1̄r alone in Ca²⁺. When binding of C1̄r to C1̄s or to C1q plus C1̄s is expected (lines 2, 5 and 6), a slight decrease in the rate of reaction with C1-inhibitor is observed. This may be due to some steric interference of the C1̄r active site by C1̄s binding as discussed in [15]. When C1̄r is bound to insoluble C1q-antibody-antigen complexes (Table II, line 7), a slight decrease in reactivity is again observed. Such a decrease may be due to insolubilization of C1̄r. However, when C1̄r is bound firmly both to C1̄s and to antibody-antigen-C1q complexes (Table II, line 8) a 4-fold increase in reactivity is seen.

To summarise, the reactivity of C1̄r towards C1-inhibitor in the various mixtures is decreased slightly by either of two influences: - (a) binding to C1̄s or (b) when it become insolubilized. When the whole C1̄ complex is assembled on immune aggregates, however, (line 8), a net increase in reactivity of C1̄r is observed, even though C1̄r is in this case both insolubilized and bound to C1̄s.

For C1̄s, binding to C1̄r (Table II. lines 10 and 14) or to C1̄r plus C1q (line 13) has no significant effect on the reactivity of C1̄s towards C1-inhibitor. Insolubilization of C1̄s occurs only when C1̄r, C1q and immune complexes are present (line 16) and this reduces slightly the reactivity of C1̄s. No enhancement of C1̄s reactivity is seen in any of the mixtures.

Previous work [7,9] has shown that while free isolated C1̄r does not compete effectively with C1̄s for C1-inhibitor, C1̄r bound to immune complexes does compete. The results presented here are consistent with this finding, and show that the alteration in relative reactivities is mainly an enhancement effect on C1̄r. To confirm the enhancing effect seen for C1̄r, titration experiments

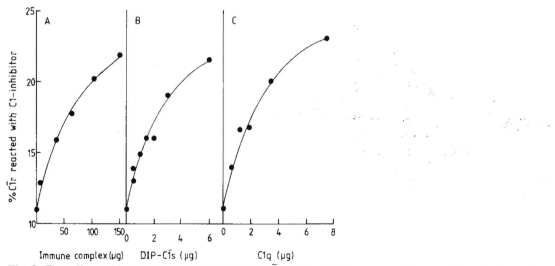

Fig. 8. The effect of increasing quantities of DIP-C1̄s, C1q and immune complexes on the rate of reaction of C1̄r with C1-inhibitor. C1̄r (5 µg) was incubated in 5 mM triethanolamine-HCl, 145 mM NaCl, 5 mM CaCl₂, pH 7.4, with a 2-fold molar excess of C1-inhibitor in the presence of: (A) DIP-C1̄s (5 µg) + C1q (5 µg) + increasing quantities of immune complexes. (B) C1q (5 µg) + immune complexes (100 µg) + increasing quantities of DIP-C1̄s. (C) DIP-C1̄s (5 µg) + immune complexes (100 µg) + increasing quantities of C1q. Total incubation volume was 0.1 ml. After 1 min incubation at 37°C, the proportion of C1̄r taken up into complexes with C1-inhibitor was estimated by sodium dodecyl sulphate polyacrylamide gel electrophoresis.

were carried out, varying the quantity of immune complexes, of C1q or of DIP-CĪs added to CĪr. The results which are shown in Fig. 8, demonstrate the absolute requirement for all components of the CĪ-immune complex assembly in inducing an increase in the rate of binding of CĪr to CĪ-inhibitor.

Discussion

Protease-(protease inhibitor) interactions are generally considered to occur by a two-step mechanism [19,37] consisting of a rapid second-order reaction to form a reversible complex, followed by a slower first-order rearrangement to a more stable or irreversible complex (Eqn. 5).

$$P + I \rightleftharpoons C^* \rightarrow C \tag{5}$$

Such a mechanism is likely to be applicable to the reactions of CĪr of CĪs with CĪ-inhibitor.

In the experiments described here, only the formation of the final product C was monitored. The rate constants determined (Table I) are therefore constants for the overall reaction. The dissociation constants, K_D, shown in Table I are an expression of the reversibility of the first part of the reaction.

Despite the probability of reaction intermediates being present, the overall reaction of CĪr of CĪs with CĪ-inhibitor follows second-order kinetics. This is a general finding for reactions of proteases with their inhibitors [37]. The rate constants found for the reactions of CĪr or CĪs with CĪ-inhibitor are in the range 10^{-3}—10^{-4} $M^{-1} \cdot s^{-1}$, and are comparable to other values reported for interactions of plasma proteases with plasma protease inhibitors, e.g. the reactions of thrombin with antithrombin III or α_2 macroglobulin [38] and of plasmin with α_1 antitrypsin [39]. Reactions of this type are however, much slower than those between trypsin and inhibitors of plant or tissue origin, e.g., soybean trypsin inhibitor or ovomucoids, for which velocity constants are typically in the range 10^{-5}—10^{-7} $M^{-1} \cdot s^{-1}$ [37].

With some exceptions, dissociation constants for protease-(protease inhibitor) interactions generally lie within the range 10^{-6}—10^{-9} M [19,37] and the constants shown in Table I lie in the higher part of this range.

The effects of temperature, Ca^{2+} and ionic strength on the reactivities of CĪr and CĪs with CĪ-inhibitor are similar to the effects produced by these variables on the proteolytic and esterolytic activities of the two enzymes. This justifies the treatment of CĪ-inhibitor as a pseudo-substrate. The very large difference in temperature coefficients of CĪr and CĪs (Table I) emphasises the need to study both enzymes at 37°C. Comparisons of the activities of CĪr or CĪs at temperatures lower than 37°C will lead to a considerable underestimate of the relative reactivity of CĪr.

Heparin, as shown in Figs. 5 and 6, enhances the rate at which CĪr and CĪs react with CĪ-inhibitor, although the effect is much greater for CĪs.

Heparin is well-known as an accelerator of the inhibition of thrombin by the protease inhibitor, antithrombin III. This plasma protease inhibitor reacts with most of the serine proteases of the blood coagulation and fibrinolysis systems. As discussed by Chan et al. [40], heparin accelerates inhibition of all these proteases by antithrombin III, but the degree of enhancement differs considerably for each protease, as is the case for the reactions of CĪ-inhibitor (Fig. 6).

The mechanism by which heparin enhances antithrombin III is not fully established. Rosenberg and Damus [41] have suggested that heparin binds directly to antithrombin III, inducing a change to a more active conformation. Griffith et al. [42], however, have determined by indirect methods that there may also be a requirement for heparin to bind directly to the protease involved in the reaction. The effect of heparin on CĪ-inhibitor interactions is at least superficially similar to the effect on antithrombin III in that the enhancement is not the same for each protease, and the two proteases studied here, CĪr and CĪs, are known to bind heparin [43] although they are not inhibited by heparin alone.

CĪ-inhibitor appears to be a major physiological inhibitor of the proteases involved in the initiation of coagulation and fibrinolysis (coagulation factors XIIa, XIa, factor XIIa fragments and kallikrein) [44]. It would be of great interest to determine the effect of heparin on the CĪ-inhibitor-mediated inhibition of these proteases. The anticoagulant action of heparin is generally regarded [45] as resulting from stimulation of antithrombin III, but it seems probable, in view of the results presented here, that CĪ-inhibitor may also contribute to this anticoagulant action. The effect of heparin in accelerating inhibition of CĪr and CĪs is only one of a number of inhibitory effects of heparin on the complement system [46].

An enhancement of reactivity of CĪr with CĪ-inhibitor is seen (Table II and Fig. 8) when CĪr is incorporated into CĪ bound to antibody-antigen complexes. Ratnoff and Naff [47] have reported that addition of C1q plus C1s to CĪr, in the presence of Ca^{2+}, caused an enhancement of the proteolytic activity of CĪr towards its substrate, C1s. In the present study, the reactivity of CĪr was enhanced only if antibody-antigen aggregates, as well as C1q plus CĪs, were present. Ratnoff and Naff, however, used impure preparations of C1q, C1r and C1s and it is probable that IgG aggregates were present in the C1q preparations. Such IgG aggregates would act in the same way as the antibody-antigen aggregates used in the present study. The increase in activity seen by Ratnoff and Naff was variable, further suggesting that it may have been caused by variable quantities of aggregated IgG.

The activation of proenzymic C1r has also been shown to occur only when C1r is incorporated into C1 bound to immune aggregates [2,28]. This effect may be interpreted as the enhancement of the inherent proteolytic activity of C1r proenzyme caused by binding to antibody-antigen-C1q complexes and to C1s. From the results shown in Table II and Fig. 8, and from the data of Ratnoff and Naff [47] it is evident that the activity of CĪr is also increased by the same binding reactions.

The demonstration that the activities of both CĪr and of proenzymic C1r are modified by strong binding of immune-complex-bound C1q and of C1s (or CĪs) further strenghthens the analogy between C1 activation and the activation of plasminogen by streptokinase. In the latter system, the activities of both plasmin and of its proenzyme, plasminogen, are modified by strong binding of streptokinase [48]. This phenomenon of induction of zymogen activation and modulation of protease activity by the same modifier proteins may prove to be a more general protease control mechanism.

Acknowledgements

This work was supported by the Centre National de la Recherche Scientifique (E.R.A. No. 695), I.N.S.E.R.M. (A.T. 487780), the Délégation Générale à la Recherche Scientifique (Contract Nos. 76.7.1194 and 76.7.1195) and the Fondation pour la Recherche Medicale. We thank Drs. A. Reboul and E. Sim for helpful advice and discussion. R.B.S. thanks the M.R.C. (U.K.) and I.N.S.E.R.M. for an exchange fellowship.

References

1 Reid, K.B.M. (1978) in Immunology 1978 (Gergely, J., Medgyesi, G.A. and Hollan, T., eds.), pp. 307—316, Hungarian Acad. Sciences, Budapest
2 Dodds, A.W., Sim, R.B., Porter, R.R. and Kerr, M.A. (1978) Biochem. J. 175, 383—390
3 Sim, R.B. and Porter, R.R. (1976) Biochem. Soc. Trans. 4, 127—129
4 Levy, L.R. and Lepow, I.H. (1959) Proc. Soc. Exp. Biol. Med. 101, 608—611
5 Ratnoff, O.D., Pensky, J., Ogston, D. and Naff, G.B. (1969) J. Exp. Med. 129, 315—331
6 Schultze, H.E., Heide, K. and Haupt, H. (1962) Klin. Wochenschr. 40, 427—429
7 Reboul, A., Arlaud, G.J., Sim, R.B. and Columb, M.G. (1976) FEBS Lett. 79, 45—51
8 Harpel, P.C. and Cooper, N.R. (1975) J. Clin. Invest. 55, 593—604
9 Arlaud, G.J., Reboul, A., Sim, R.B. and Colomb, M.G. (1979) Biochim. Biophys. Acta 576, 151—162
10 Sim, R.B., Arlaud, G.J., Reboul, A., Villiers, C.L. and Colomb, M.G. (1979) FEBS Lett. 97, 111—115
11 Sim, R.B., Porter, R.R., Reid, K.B.M. and Gigli, I. (1977) Biochem. J. 163, 219—227
12 Gigli, I., Porter, R.R. and Sim, R.B. (1976) Biochem. J. 157, 541—548
13 Arlaud, G.J., Sim, R.B., Duplaa, A.-M. and Colomb, M.G. (1979) Mol. Immunol. 16, 445—450
14 Fairbanks, G., Steck, T.L. and Wallach, D.F.H. (1971) Biochemistry 10, 2602—2617
15 Sim, R.B., Arlaud, G.J. and Colomb, M.G. (1979) Biochem. J. 179, 449—457
16 Volankis, J.E., Schrohenloher, R.E. and Stroud, R.M. (1977) J. Immunol. 119, 337—342
17 Naff, G.B. and Ratnoff, O.D. (1968) J. Exp. Med. 128, 571—593
18 Vincent, J.-P. and Lazdunski, M. (1972) Biochemistry 11, 2967—2977
19 Wiman, B. and Collen, D. (1978) Eur. J. Biochem. 84, 573—578
20 Moroi, M. and Aoki, N. (1976) J. Biol. Chem. 251, 5956—5965
21 Rosenberg, R.D. and Damus, P.S. (1973) J. Biol. Chem. 248, 6490—6505
22 Moroi, M. and Yamaski, M. (1974) Biochim. Biophys. Acta 359, 130—141
23 Laurell, A.-B., Mårtensson, U. and Sjoholm, A.G. (1976) Acta Path. Microbiol. Scand., Sect. C 84, 455—464.
24 Ratnoff, O.D. and Lepow, I.H. (1957) J. Exp. Med. 106, 327—343
25 Loos, M., Wolf, H.U. and Opferkuch, W. (1972) Immunochemistry 9, 151—459
26 Haines, A.L. and Lepow, I.H. (1964) J. Immunol. 92, 456—467
27 Lepow, I.H., Ratnoff, O.D. and Levy, L.R. (1958) J. Exp. Med. 107, 451—459
28 Sim, R.B. (1976) D. Phil. Thesis, University of Oxford
29 Arlaud, G.J., Reboul, A. and Colomb, M.G. (1977) Biochim. Biophys. Acta 485, 227—235
30 Rent, R., Myrrman, R., Fiedel, B.A. and Gewurz, H. (1976) Clin. Exp. Immunol. 23, 264—271
31 Ogston, D., Murray, J. and Crawford, G.P.M. (1976) Thromb. Res. 9, 217—222
32 Von Kaulla, K.N. (1968) Arzneimittel-Forsch. 18, 407—412
33 Kluft, C. (1977) Haemostasis, 6, 351—369
34 Harrity, T.W. and Goldlust, M.B. (1974) Biochem. Pharmacol. 23, 3107—3120
35 Lepow, I.H., Naff, G.B., Todd, E.W., Pensky, J. and Hinz, C.F., Jr. (1963) J. Exp. Med. 177, 983—1008
36 Ziccardi, R.J. and Cooper, N.R. (1977) J. Immunol. 118, 2047—2052
37 Laskowski, M., Jr. and Sealock, R.W. (1971) in The Enzymes (Boyer, P.D., ed.), 3rd edn., Vol. III, pp. 375—473, Academic Press, New York
38 Downing, M.R., Bloom, J.W. and Mann, K.G. (1978) Biochemistry 17, 2649—2653
39 Hercz, A. (1974) Eur. J. Biochem. 49, 287—292
40 Chan, J.Y.C., Burrowes, C.E., Habal, F.M. and Mowat, H.Z. (1977) Biochem. Biophys. Res. Commun. 74, 150—158
41 Rosenberg, R.D. and Damus, P.S. (1973) J. Biol. Chem. 248, 6490—6505
42 Griffith, M.J., Kingdon, H.S. and Lundblad, R.L. (1979) Biochem. Biophys. Res. Commun. 87, 686—692

43 Von Zeipel, G., Hanson, H.-S. and von Stedingk, L.-V. (1975) Acta Pathol. Microbiol. Scand., Sect. C 83, 241—243

44 Saito, H., Goldsmith, G.H., Moroi, M. and Aoki, N. (1979) Proc. Natl. Acad. Sci. U.S.A. 76, 2013—2017

45 Damus, P.S., Hicks, M. and Rosenberg, R.D. (1973) Nature 246, 355—357

46 Johnson, B.J. (1977) J. Pharm. Sci. 66, 1367—1377

47 Ratnoff, O.D. and Naff, G.B. (1969) J. Lab. Clin. Med. 74, 380—388

48 Castellino, F.J. (1979) Trends Biochem. Sci. 4, 1—5

C1 INH Concentrate in the Therapy of Hereditary Angioedema

L. Bergamaschini, M. Cicardi, A. Tucci, M. Gardinali, D. Frangi,
C. Valle and A. Agostoni

Dept. of Clinical Medicine, University of Milan, Italy

Ten acute attacks were managed in nine patients with hereditary angioedema by means of the infusion of a C1 INH concentrate produced on large scale. No side effects were observed.

Key words: C1 INH concentrate; hereditary angioedema.

Accepted for publication 14 September 1982

CLINICAL ASPECTS

Hereditary angioedema is a disorder characterized by deficiency of the C1 esterase inhibitor (C1 INH). The edema involves subcutaneous and/or mucous tissues. Laryngeal edema may cause the death of the patient by asphyxia. Antifibrinolytic agents and androgen-derivatives are useful in the prophylactic treatment of the disease. Acute attacks can be successfully managed with the infusion of C1 INH concentrate. Replacement therapy resolves mucous edema in 15–20 min.

The clinical signs of hereditary angioedema (HAE) were first recognized a century ago by Osler (4), but the biochemical abnormality was first defined by Donaldson & Evans in 1963 (6). The disease is related to the genetically transmitted absence or functional deficiency (CRM+ variant) of the inhibitor of C1-esterase (C1 INH). It is characterized by recurrent spontaneous attacks of subcutaneous and mucous swelling lasting 24–48 h. When edema involves the gastrointestinal tract, nausea, vomiting, diarrhea and abdominal pain may occur. If swelling involves the upper respiratory tract the patient may die of asphyxia as a result of laryngeal edema.

Although in many patients the edema occurs following a direct trauma (psychological or mechanical) about half of the attacks have no relation to a triggering event (5).

HAE patients can be prophylactically treated with antifibrinolytic agents (7) or androgen-derivatives (8). In our experience with 120

patients good results were obtained with tranexamic acid, which reduced the severity of the attacks in about 70% of treated subjects without serious side effects even in long-term therapy (3). Better results were obtained with 17α-alkylated androgen-derivatives (danazol, stanazolol) which induce clinical remission in patients by producing a 4–5-fold increase in serum C1 INH activity (2, 10). However, the 17α-alkylated androgens seem to be implicated in the development of liver tumors, cholestatic jaundice, and peliosis hepatis (5). Long-term administration of drugs is not recommended in patients whose disease activity does not justify continuous prophylactic treatment. In pregnant women and in children an alternative to androgen or antifibrinolytic therapy is needed. Moreover, neither androgen nor antifibrinolytic agents can be successfully used when edema formation has begun. For these reasons an alternative to prophylaxis is needed to manage the acute attacks of life-threatening severity. Good results have been obtained by our group using C1 INH concentrate prepared by The Netherlands Red Cross Blood Transfusion Service, Amsterdam, in 19 severe HAE attacks (1). Similar results were obtained by Gadek et al. (9) with the infusion of a different preparation in eight acute episodes of mucous and subcutaneous swelling. We have recently been supplied with a new C1 INH preparation, produced by Immuno AG, Vienna.

In this paper we report the *in vivo* efficacy and safety of this protein preparation in nine HAE patients during 10 acute attacks. In seven cases we were also able to evaluate the biochemical response determining the serum levels of C1 INH and C4 at several time intervals after the infusion.

MATERIAL AND METHODS

Patients

In each patient hereditary angioedema was diagnosed according to the accepted clinical and laboratory criteria (8). All patients had decreased functional activity of C1 INH, one patient (C.L.) had normal serum level of C1 INH representing the CRM+ variant. In all cases the C4 serum level was decreased. Three patients (V.Mo, V.Ma, C.L.) were children not suitable for long-term treatment with androgen or antifibrinolytic drugs, the remainder were not prophylactically treated because of limited disease activity (less than one attack per month).

C1 INH and C4 serum levels

Antigenic and functional determinations of C1 INH and antigenic C4 serum levels were performed immediately before the infusion and at several time intervals during the course of the study (15, 60, 120 min and 24 h). Antigenic determinations of C1 INH and C4 were performed by single-radial immunodiffusion on cellulose acetate strips (4). C1 INH functional activity was determined according to the Lachmann method (12).

C1 INH preparation

C1 INH preparation was supplied by Immuno AG, Vienna (Austria). The partially purified preparation was obtained by selective absorption of C1 INH from a cryoprecipitate of pooled human plasma. Radioimmunoassay showed that the starting material and C1 INH concentrate were hepatitis B surface antigen (HbsAg)-free. The concentrate was reconstituted with 10 ml of sterile distilled water. The final concentration (55 U/ml) was (v/v) 70-fold higher than fresh human plasma. The preparation was infused intravenously in about 10–15 min.

RESULTS

We treated nine patients for 10 acute attacks with 1,100–2,200 U. No side effects were observed in any of the subjects, particularly, there was no evidence of allergic reaction. 15–20 min after the infusion swelling ceased to increase, and within 30–60 min mucous edema began to subside as evidenced by the disappearance of abdominal pain or a subjective sensation of reduced airway obstruction. Subcutaneous edema began to subside after a longer time period (2–3 h). In each case patients could be discharged within 3–4 h of the infusion.

Pretreatment C1 INH activity ranged from 2 to 29% of the normal standard pool, 15 min after the infusion it increased up to 44–136% and slowly began to decrease after approx. 24 h. There was a consistent lag between infusion and the increment of C4 serum levels that results from decreased catabolism of this protein (Table 1). The different antigenic levels of C1 INH in serum of three HAE children (V.Mo, V.Ma, C.L.), with about the same body weight, after the infusion of 1,100 U of concentrate, probably reflects the equilibration time of the protein from the intravascular to the extravascular compartment.

During two severe attacks of laryngeal edema, patient G.A. was treated with 1,650 and 1,100 U of C1 INH concentrate, respectively, but both infusions gave the same clinical response.

Table 1

Biochemical and clinical effect of intravenous infusion of C1 INH concentrate in patients with hereditary angioedema.
(Values are expressed as percentage of normal mean)

Patient	Sex	Age (years)	Site of edema	Dose (U) of C1-INH	C1 INH (immunochem. assay)					C1 INH (enzymatic assay)					C4 (immunochem. assay)					Clinical response**
					0	15'	60'	120'	24h	0	15'	60'	120'	24h	0	15'	60'	120'	24h	
S.G.	F	43	Pharynx	2,200	10	74	126	120	58	10	75	94	90	55	22	22	24	30	58	20 min
G.A.	M	19	Larynx	1,650	16	45	41	41	36	29	63	63	60	54	24	27	25	28	33	15 min
G.A.	M	19	Larynx	1,100	10	38	40	40	35	7	44	37	35	39	24	22	22	25	67	20 min
V.Ma.	M	4	Face	1,100	19	198	182	180	150	20	122	140	140	105	13	11	12	12	15	3 h
V.Mo.	F	8	Bowel	1,100	28	226	182	168	130	25	136	112	123	80	18	20	19	19	38	15 min
C.L.*	M	6	Face	1,100	78	148	–	–	164	3	65	–	–	60	8	12	–	–	40	3 h
F.G.	F	40	Larynx	1,650	10	59	90	85	43	2	59	62	60	61	6	10	10	15	31	15 min
P.A.	F	18	Bowel	1,100	–	–	–	–	–	–	–	–	–	–	–	–	–	–	–	20 min
G.C.	M	43	Bowel	1,100	–	–	–	–	–	–	–	–	–	–	–	–	–	–	–	15 min
S.A.	M	48	Face	1,100	–	–	–	–	–	–	–	–	–	–	–	–	–	–	–	3–4 h

* Patient with variant HAE (CRM⁻).

** Beginning of symptom regression after start of infusion.

None of the treated patients suffered any untoward consequences from the infusions and there was no clinical or biochemical evidence of transfusion hepatitis.

DISCUSSION

The infusion of C1 INH concentrate is the treatment of choice in acute attacks of hereditary angioedema (1, 9).

Although the management of an attack with kallikrein inhibitor (Trasylol®) is satisfactory (12) we prefer replacement therapy with C1 INH concentrate because it gives a more rapid remission of clinical symptoms and avoids the risk of the allergic reaction reported with kallikrein inhibitor (15). On the other hand, transfusion of fresh plasma, in addition to being a less convenient volume to administer, provides C1-esterase substrates (C4, C2), a source of the kinin-like peptide of HAE (10).

In this study we report the clinical and biochemical results obtained with a large-scale preparation of C1 INH protein the storage of which, in same cases, exceeded 12 months at 4°C. A rapid positive clinical result was observed in all the patients treated for mucous edema, particularly those treated for laryngeal edema, who reported a clear improvement within 20–30 min of the infusion, and emergency tracheostomy was never necessary.

The patients receiving this C1 INH preparation showed a lag of the C4 serum increment providing in vivo evidence of the efficacy of this concentrate. Similar results have recently been reported with other C1 INH preparations (1, 9).

These current data suggest that a C1 INH preparation, even produced on a large-scale, provides a safe and definitive approach to the management of acute attacks of hereditary angioedema. Thus for patients not suitable for long-term prophylactic treatment a stock of the C1 INH preparation could be maintained and self-infusion authorized in order to reverse the incapacitating or life-threatening manifestations of hereditary angioedema.

REFERENCES

1. Agostoni, A., Bergamaschini, L., Martignoni, G. C., Cicardi, M. & Marasini, B.: Treatment of acute attacks of hereditary angioedema with C1 INH concentrate. Ann. Allergy 44, 299–301, 1980.

2. Agostoni, A., Cicardi, M., Martignoni, G. C., Bergamaschini, L. & Marasini, B.: Danazol and stanazolol in long-term prophylactic treatment of hereditary angioedema. J. Allergy Clin. Immunol. 65, 75–79, 1980.

3. Agostoni, A., Marasini, B., Cicardi, M., Martignoni, G. C., Uziel, L. & Pietrogrande, M.: Hepatic function and fibrinolysis in patients with hereditary angioedema undergoing long-term treatment with tranexamic acid. Allergy 33, 216–221, 1978.

4. Agostoni, A., Marasini, B., Cicardi, M., Martignoni, G.C. & Brenna, O.: Studio mediante dosaggio enzimatico e immunochimico dell'inibitore della C1-esterasi in 59 pazienti affetti da angioedema ereditario. Boll. Ist. Sieroter. Milanese 56, 22–28, 1977.

5. Cicardi, M., Bergamaschini, L., Marasini, B., Boccassini, G., Tucci, A. & Agostoni, A.: Hereditary angioedema: an appraisal of 104 cases. Am. J. Med. Sci. 284, 2–9, 1982.

6. Donaldson, V. H. & Evans, R. R.: A biochemical abnormality in hereditary angioedema: absence of serum inhibitor of C1-esterase. Am. J. Med. 35, 37–44, 1963.

7. Frank, M. M., Gelfand, J. A. & Alling, D. W.: Epsilon-aminocaproic acid for hereditary angioedema. N. Engl. J. Med. 296, 1235–1236, 1977.

8. Frank, M. M., Gelfand, J. A. & Atkinson, J. P.: Hereditary angioedema, the clinical syndrome and its management. Ann. Intern. Med. 84, 580–594, 1976.

9. Gadek, J. E., Hosea, S. W., Gelfand, J. A., Santaella, M., Wickerhauser, M., Triantaphyllopoulos, D. C. & Frank, M. M.: Replacement therapy in hereditary angioedema. Successful treatment of acute episodes of angioedema with partly purified C1 inhibitor. N. Engl. J. Med. 302, 542–546, 1980.

10. Gelfand, J. A., Sherins, R. J., Alling, D. W. & Frank, M. M.: Treatment of hereditary angioedema with danazol. Reversal of clinical and biochemical abnormalities. N. Engl. J. Med. 295, 1444–1449, 1976.

11. Kleperer, M. R., Rosen, F. S. & Donaldson, V. H.: A polypeptide derived from second component of complement (C'2) which increases vascular permeability. J. Clin. Invest. 47, 604–611, 1968.

12. Lachman, P. J., Hobart, M. J. & Astan, W. P.: Complement technology. In Weir, D. M. (ed.): Handbook of experimental immunology, pp. 1–17. Blackwell, Oxford, 1973.

13. Marasini, B., Cicardi, M., Martignoni, G. C., Agostoni, A. & Levi, L.: Treatment of hereditary angioedema. Klin. Wochenschr. 56, 819–823, 1976.

14. Osler, W.: Hereditary angioneurotic edema. Am. J. Med. Sci. 95, 362–367, 1888.

15. Proud, G. & Chamberlain, J.: Anaphylactic reaction to aprotinine. Lancet ii, 48–49, 1976.

16. Westaby, D., Ogle, S. T., Paradinas, F. J., Randell, J. B. & Murray-Lyon, I. M.: Liver damage from long-term methyltestosterone. Lancet ii, 261–263, 1977.

Adress:
Luigi Bergamaschini, M.D.
Clinica Medica VII
Ospedale San Paolo
via di Rudini 8
20142 Milano
Italy

Human C1̄ Inhibitor: Primary Structure, cDNA Cloning, and Chromosomal Localization[†]

Susan Clark Bock,*[,‡] Karen Skriver,[§] Egon Nielsen,[§] Hans-Christian Thøgersen,[§,‖] Björn Wiman,[⊥] Virginia H. Donaldson,[#] Roger L. Eddy,[▽] Jean Marrinan,[‡] Elzbieta Radziejewska,[‡] Robert Huber,[○] Thomas B. Shows,[▽] and Staffan Magnusson*[,§]

The Rockefeller University, New York, New York 10021, Department of Molecular Biology, University of Aarhus, DK-8000, Aarhus C, Denmark, Department of Clinical Chemistry, Karolinska Hospital, S-10401 Stockholm, Sweden, Children's Hospital Research Foundation, Cincinnati, Ohio 45229, Roswell Park Memorial Institute, Buffalo, New York 14263, and Max-Planck-Institut fuer Biochemie, 8033 Martinsried, FRG

Received April 11, 1986; Revised Manuscript Received May 8, 1986

ABSTRACT: The primary structure of human C1̄ inhibitor was determined by peptide and DNA sequencing. The single-chain polypeptide moiety of the intact inhibitor is 478 residues (52 869 Da), accounting for only 51% of the apparent molecular mass of the circulating protein (104 000 Da). The positions of six glucosamine-based and five galactosamine-based oligosaccharides were determined. Another nine threonine residues are probably also glycosylated. Most of the carbohydrate prosthetic groups (probably 17) are located at the amino-terminal end (residues 1–120) of the protein and are particularly concentrated in a region where the tetrapeptide sequence Glx-Pro-Thr-Thr, and variants thereof, is repeated 7 times. No phosphate was detected in C1̄ inhibitor. Two disulfide bridges connect cysteine-101 to cysteine-406 and cysteine-108 to cysteine-183. Comparison of the amino acid and cDNA sequences indicates that secretion is mediated by a 22-residue signal peptide and that further proteolytic processing does not occur. C1̄ inhibitor is a member of the large serine protease inhibitor (serpin) gene family. The homology concerns residues 120 through the C-terminus. The sequence was compared with those of nine other serpins, and conserved and nonconserved regions correlated with elements in the tertiary structure of α1-antitrypsin. The C1̄ inhibitor gene maps to chromosome 11, p11.2-q13. C1̄ inhibitor genes of patients from four hereditary angioneurotic edema kindreds do not have obvious deletions or rearrangements in the C1̄ inhibitor locus. A *Hgi*AI DNA polymorphism, identified following the observation of sequence variants, will be useful as a linkage marker in studies of mutant C1̄ inhibitor genes.

C1̄ inhibitor is a highly glycosylated 104 000-Da[1] plasma protease inhibitor that can inhibit components of the complement, coagulation, fibrinolytic, and kinin-releasing systems. It was first purified in 1961 (Pensky et al., 1961) and later (Pensky & Schwick, 1969) found to be immunologically identical with a previously characterized α2-neuraminoglycoprotein (Schultze et al., 1962). C1̄ inhibitor has been shown to inhibit macromolecular C1̄, the C1̄s and C1̄r sub-

components of the first component of complement (Ratnoff & Lepow, 1957; Levy & Lepow, 1959; Lepow & Leon, 1962; Gigli et al., 1968; Pensky et al., 1961; Ratnoff et al., 1969), factors XIIa and XIa (Forbes et al., 1970), plasma kallikrein (Ratnoff et al., 1969; Gigli et al., 1970), and plasmin (Ratnoff et al., 1969). Like other serine protease inhibitors [serpins (Carrell, 1984)] of the antithrombin III–α1-antitrypsin family (Petersen et al., 1979), C1̄ inhibitor reacts with target proteases to form proteolytically inactive, stoichiometric 1:1 complexes that are stable during NaDodSO₄–PAGE (Harpel & Cooper, 1975; Sim et al., 1979; Sim et al., 1980) under reducing conditions (Nilsson et al., 1983). To improve understanding of how C1̄ inhibitor regulates diverse plasma serine proteases, we have determined its sequence and covalent structure. To address questions concerning the evolution and structure of

[†] This work was supported by USPHS Grants HL-15690 (V.H.D.), HL-16238 (S.M.), HL-30712 (S.C.B.), and HD-05196 and GM-20454 (T.B.S.) and funds from the Danish Science and Medical Research Councils (S.M.), the Danish Cancer Society (S.M. and K.S.), and the American Heart Association (83-1202, S.C.B.).

* Correspondence should be addressed to these authors.
[‡] The Rockefeller University.
[§] University of Aarhus.
[‖] Present address: MRC Laboratory of Molecular Biology, Cambridge, England CB2 2QH.
[⊥] Karolinska Hospital.
[#] Children's Hospital Research Foundation.
[▽] Roswell Park Memorial Institute.
[○] Max-Planck-Institut fuer Biochemie.

[1] Abbreviations: bp, base pairs; kb, kilobase; Da, dalton; serpin, serine protease inhibitor; NaDodSO₄, sodium dodecyl sulfate; PAGE, polyacrylamide gel electrophoresis; HANE, hereditary angioneurotic edema; Å, angstrom; DNS, 5-(dimethylamino)naphthalenesulfonyl; RFLP, restriction fragment length polymorphism; HPLC, high-performance liquid chromatography; PTH, phenylthiohydantoin.

serpins, we compared the C̄1 inhibitor sequence with those of nine other family members.

C̄1 inhibitor deficiency is inherited as an autosomal dominant trait in hereditary angioneurotic edema (HANE) which is associated with bouts of localized, increased vascular permeability (Donaldson & Evans, 1963). Although all persons with HANE are deficient in C̄1 inhibitor function, the molecular defects are heterogeneous (Rosen et al., 1971; Donaldson et al., 1985). In order to understand the genetic lesions responsible for hereditary angioneurotic edema, we have isolated a full length C̄1 inhibitor cDNA, mapped the C̄1 inhibitor locus to human chromosome 11, p11.2-q13, and initiated studies on normal and abnormal C̄1 inhibitor genes.

Materials and Methods

Protein Purification. C̄1 inhibitor was isolated from human plasma by precipitation with poly(ethylene glycol), chromatography on DEAE-cellulose and hexyl-Sepharose (Nilsson & Wiman, 1982), and gel filtration in 0.1 M NH_4HCO_3, pH 8.3, on Sepharose 6B. The resulting single-chain material was fully active against C̄1s (Chapuis et al., 1977) and migrated with an apparent molecular mass of 105 000 Da in NaDod-SO_4-PAGE. Phosphate was determined by a modified Fiske–Subbarow method (Ames, 1966). The activation peptide was separated from the C̄1s–C̄1 inhibitor complex by gel filtration on Sephacryl S-300 in 40 mM sodium phosphate, 0.1 M NaCl, 0.1 M NaN_3, and 0.1% NaDodSO_4, pH 7.3.

Amino Acid Sequencing. C̄1 inhibitor was degraded chemically or enzymatically as indicated in Figure 1a. For digestion with pepsin, the protein was dissolved in 99% formic acid and then diluted to 5%; the enzyme/substrate ratio was 1/100 w/w, and the digest was incubated at room temperature for 3 h. Carbohydrate-rich peptides were treated with trifluoromethanesulfonic acid (Edge et al., 1981) or alkaline sodium borohydride (Spiro & Bhoyroe, 1974). Peptides were purified by an initial gel filtration on Sephadex G-50F or Sephacryl S-200, mostly in 0.1 M NH_4HCO_3, followed by ion-exchange chromatography on DEAE-Sephacel using a linear gradient of 0.01–1.0 M NH_4HCO_3. Final purification was achieved by reversed-phase HPLC on a Hewlett-Packard 1084B liquid chromatograph. Peptides were sequenced on an Applied Biosystems Model 470A (using the chemicals and the 02n vac program supplied by the manufacturer) or on a Beckman 890C sequenator. Amino acid analysis was performed on a Beckman 121MB instrument. In addition to the systems commonly used in our laboratory (Skorstengaard et al., 1982, 1984), columns of Vydac C4 (with elution gradients of 2-propanol and triethylamine, pH 5.2, in 0.1% CF_3COOH) were also employed for HPLC of peptides and glycopeptides.

Carbohydrate Determination. N-Glycosylated Asn residues were assigned when the PTH derivative was obtained in much less than normal yield and the presence of aspartic acid and a ninhydrin-positive glucosamine peak (eluting near isoleucine and leucine) was observed in the amino acid chromatogram. In addition, Asn residues 59, 216, and 231 were also identified as DNS-Asp in "full" yield when the DNS–Edman sequencing method was used (Gray, 1967). O-Glycosylated threonine or serine residues were assigned on the corresponding combined criteria of low yield (or no yield) of PTH derivatives and the presence of galactosamine and threonine or serine in the hydrolysate.

cDNA Clone Isolation. The initial positive clone, λ37, was isolated from a λgt11 (Young & Davis, 1983) human liver cDNA expression library kindly provided by Drs. S. L. C. Woo and T. Chandra. This library was screened with (1) goat anti-human C̄1 inhibitor serum preabsorbed with hereditary angioneurotic edema serum (which was essentially devoid of C̄1 inhibitor antigens) and (2) rabbit anti-human C̄1 inhibitor serum preabsorbed with human serum albumin. Positive phage were detected by using biotinylated second antibodies and ^{125}I-streptavidin. λ29a, λ13p, and λ10q (Figure 1c) were identified by hybridization with the 5′ λ37 EcoRI fragment and a pool of 96 17-base oligonucleotides encoding the hexapeptide Met-Leu-Phe-Val-Glu-Pro (Harrison, 1983). λ8q, λ2r, and λ4r were obtained by again screening the library, this time with the oligonucleotide dGTCAGCAGGGTCAGCC, which had been identified at the 5′ end of clone λ10q on the noncoding strand. Sequence analysis showed that λ8q, λ2r, and λ4r contain sequences at their 5′ ends (thick lines) that correspond to sequences from elsewhere in the C̄1 inhibitor cDNA and that are in inverted repeat orientation to them. This artifact of cDNA cloning occurs occasionally for full-length cDNAs (Weaver et al., 1981). The cDNA clone pK11 was obtained from a pUC expression library (Helfman et al., 1983) synthesized from HepG2 (Knowles et al., 1980) poly-(A)+ RNA and codes for a valine as residue 458.

DNA Sequencing Strategy. Fragments of the cDNA clones shown in Figure 1c were subcloned into pUC plasmids, and sequence was obtained from linearized double-stranded DNA by the dideoxy method (Sanger et al., 1977). Most of the cDNA was sequenced in both directions (Figure 1d); solid amino acid sequence data was available for regions where it was determined on only one strand.

Serpin Alignment. The alignment was obtained by visual inspection of the mature protein sequences with due consideration of already published comparisons (Petersen et al., 1979; Hunt & Dayhoff, 1980; Carrell et al., 1982; Doolittle, 1983, 1985; Hill et al., 1984; Hejgaard et al., 1985; Ragg, 1986).

Genomic DNA and Southern Blot Preparation. The methods that were used for extracting genomic DNA from peripheral blood samples of normals and HANE patients and for preparing Southern blots have been described previously (Bock et al., 1985a).

Chromosomal Localization. Southern blots containing BamHI-digested DNA from 41 different human–mouse hybrids were hybridized with the human C̄1 inhibitor cDNA probe and scored for the presence or absence of 4- and 6-kb bands present in the human C̄1 inhibitor gene. The cell hybrids were generated from 15 unrelated human cell lines and 4 mouse cell lines (Shows et al., 1982, 1984) and have been characterized by chromosome analysis and mapped enzyme markers and partly by mapped DNA probes (Shows et al., 1978, 1982; Shows, 1983).

Results

Primary Structure. The amino acid and cDNA sequences of human C̄1 inhibitor were determined. Figure 1 shows the sequences and the strategies by which they were obtained. Figure 2 shows the disulfide bridge pattern, known sites of oligosaccharide attachment, and the bond cleaved by C̄1s during complex formation.

Signal Peptide. C̄1 inhibitor is synthesized in the liver (Colten, 1972). Like many other secreted proteins (Jackson & Blobel, 1980), it has an N-terminal signal peptide that contains a basic residue near the N-terminus, a hydrophobic core region, and a small amino acid prior to the signal cleavage site. The absence of adjacent basic residues between the putative signal cleavage site and the N-terminus of the circulating glycoprotein suggests that a "pro" form of the protein does not occur as an intermediate in the maturation of C̄1 inhibitor.

a

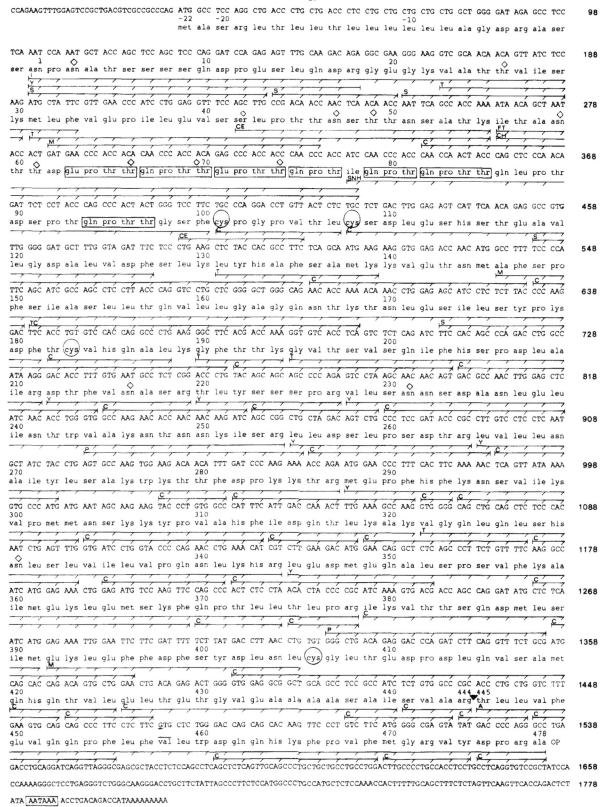

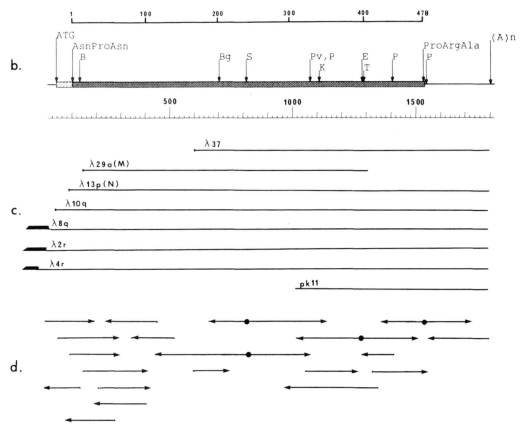

FIGURE 1: (a) Nucleotide sequence and amino acid sequence of C1̄ inhibitor; protein sequencing strategy. Numbers between the DNA and protein sequences indicate amino acid residue positions; nucleotide numbering appears in the right margin. Peptides for sequencing were generated by chemical degradation with cyanogen bromide (M) or enzymatic digestion with trypsin after citraconylation (Y) (Dixon & Perham, 1968) or chymotrypsin (C), elastase (E), pepsin (P), or thermolysin (H) digestion. Reduced carboxymethylated C1̄ inhibitor was used in all enzymatic digests except the peptic. Subdigests of a fragment corresponding to residues 1–211 (obtained by trypsin digestion after citraconylation) were prepared, after deblocking, with trypsin (T) and *Staphylococcus aureus* V8 protease (S). In some cases, carbohydrate-rich peptides were treated with trifluoromethanesulfonic acid (F) or alkaline sodium borohydride (N). A and I indicate sequencing of the activation peptide and intact inhibitor, respectively. Cysteine residues are circled. The reactive site is marked with an arrowhead (residues 444–445). Known carbohydrate attachment sites are shown by diamonds. Residues known from amino acid analysis are indicated by horizontal lines while diagonal markings indicate that the PTH derivative was identified by HPLC. Vertical lines indicate N- and C-terminal residues for which evidence is certain. Glx-Pro-Thr-Thr type repeats have been boxed, as has the polyadenylation signal. The nucleotide and amino acid residues involved in the valine-458–methionine polymorphism are underlined and overlined respectively. (b) Restriction map of full-length C1̄ inhibitor cDNA. Untranslated portions of the cDNA are shown as thin lines, while the thick slashed line represents the signal peptide encoding region and the thick shaded line represents the mature polypeptide encoding region with Asn-Pro-Asn and Pro-Arg-Ala as its N- and C-termini, respectively. The ruler above the map shows amino acid residue numbers for the mature inhibitor, while the ruler below the map indicates nucleotide numbering for the cDNA. The rulers and the map are aligned with the cDNA clone and sequencing information presented in parts c and d. Symbols: B, *Bam*HI; Bg, *Bgl*II; S, *Sst*I; Pv, *Pvu*II; P, *Pst*I; K, *Kpn*I; E, *Eco*RI; T, *Taq*I. (c) C1̄ inhibitor cDNA clones. (d) DNA sequencing strategy.

N- and O-Glycosylation. The present work implies that 49% of the total molecular mass of C1̄ inhibitor is added as a result of posttranslational modification. Of the 104 000-Da apparent molecular mass of the circulating inhibitor [determined by sedimentation equilibrium (Haupt et al., 1970)], the 478-residue protein moiety accounts for only 52 869 Da. A polypeptide of similar size (by NaDodSO$_4$–PAGE) was precipitated by antiserum against C1̄ inhibitor from rabbit reticulocyte cell-free translation reactions primed with Hep G2 (Knowles et al., 1980) poly(A)+ RNA (data not shown).

Sites of carbohydrate attachment to C1̄ inhibitor were determined during amino acid sequencing. Glucosamine-based oligosaccharide groups were found on all six of those asparagine residues that conform to the pattern Asn-X-Ser/Thr (Asn-3, -47, -59, -216, -231, -330). At least five serine and threonine residues (Ser-42 and Thr-26, -66, -70, -74) carry galactosamine-based oligosaccharides. For two other threonine residues (49 and 61), none of the usual PTH derivatives were observed, indicating that they are also posttranslationally

glycosylated. The sequence Glx-Pro-Thr-Thr, and minor variations of it, occurs 7 times between residues 63 and 97. The extent of O-glycosylation in this region is even greater than shown in Figures 1a and 2, but only three oligosaccharide positions have been unequivocally identified. Seven other threonine residues, Thr-77, -84, -85, -89, -93, -96, and -97, are probably also glycosylated.

Phosphorylation. No phosphate was detected in the C1̄ inhibitor at a level of less than 0.3 mol/mol of protein.

Reactive Site. The reactive site region of a serpin contains a substrate sequence for the respective target protease. The P1 residue of the reactive site (or a larger part of the structure) is recognized by the target protease, and its acyl bond is cleaved during complex formation. Complex formation between C1s and C1̄ inhibitor leads to exposure of a new N-terminal threonine residue (Nilsson et al., 1983). We isolated the M_r 4000 peptide released during this process and determined its complete sequence, which was identical with the last 34 res-

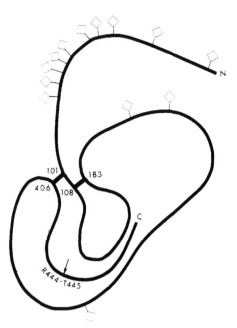

FIGURE 2: Schematic diagram of the mature, circulating, intact CĪ inhibitor. N and C indicate the N- and C-termini of the 478-residue polypeptide chain. The disulfide bridge pattern is shown with bars; residue numbers refer to participating half-cystines. Diamonds mark known sites of oligosaccharide attachment (Asn-3, -47, -59, -216, -231, and -330, Ser-42, Thr-26, -49, -61, -66, -70, and -74). The peptide bond cleaved by CĪs during complex formation is indicated with an arrow.

idues of the intact CĪ inhibitor. These data indicate that the P1 residue of CĪ inhibitor is Arg-444 and the P1' is Thr-445 and are in agreement with previously (Salvesen et al., 1985) identified residues P3–P9' at the reactive site and the specificity of CĪs for arginyl residues.

Disulfide Bridges. Two disulfide-bridged peptides (residues 39/40–107 bound to residues 403–410, and residues 108–111 bound to 181–190) were isolated from a pepsin digest of intact, denatured CĪ inhibitor. Sequence analysis of these peptides and of a smaller fragment (residues 99–105 bound to 404–408, obtained by subdigestion with elastase) showed that Cys-101 is connected to Cys-406 and Cys-108 is connected to Cys-183 (see Figure 2).

3' End of CĪ Inhibitor cDNA. The presence of a single stop codon directly following the triplet encoding the C-terminal alanine of CĪ inhibitor indicates that translation is terminated at this site. An unprocessed C-terminus appears to be the rule for the plasma serpins on which both protein and nucleotide sequence data are available (Petersen et al., 1979; Bock et al., 1982; Kurachi et al., 1981; Carrell et al., 1982; Ragg, 1986) and for ovalbumin (McReynolds et al., 1978). The polyadenylation signal AATAAA (Proudfoot & Brownlee, 1976) occurs 246 bases after the stop codon and is followed 15 nucleotides later by a poly(A) tail.

Homology of CĪ Inhibitor with Other Serine Protease Inhibitors. CĪ inhibitor can now be assigned to the serpin gene family (Carrell, 1984) on the basis of its mechanistic properties and sequence homology with other family members. This homology has also been noted by Davis and co-workers (Davis et al., 1986), who sequenced cyanogen bromide fragments of CĪ inhibitor and isolated and sequenced a cDNA clone encoding residues 219–436. The protein sequence generated from their partial cDNA clone differs from ours in two extended regions (of nine and six amino acid residues) and at three

isolated residues. The extended differences can be accounted for by shifts in reading frame; the three isolated substitutions may represent protein sequence variants.

Figure 3a shows an alignment of the amino acid sequence of CĪ inhibitor with those of human antithrombin III (Petersen et al., 1979; Bock et al., 1982), α1-antitrypsin (Kurachi et al., 1981; Carrell et al., 1982), α1-antichymotrypsin (Chandra et al., 1983), angiotensinogen (Kageyama et al., 1984), heparin cofactor II (Ragg, 1986), α2-antiplasmin (Lijnen et al., 1982), mouse contrapsin (Hill et al., 1984), chicken ovalbumin (McReynolds et al., 1978), and barley protein Z (Hejgaard et al., 1985). The homology between CĪ inhibitor and the other serine protease inhibitors is not limited to the reactive site region that interacts directly with the target protease during complex formation but extends over 80% of the polypeptide chain between approximately residue 120 and the C-terminus. This extensive homology shows that CĪ inhibitor and other members of the serpin gene family arose by divergent evolution from a common ancestral gene.

Further inspection of Figure 3a reveals that the N-terminal ends of CĪ inhibitor and other serpins are dissimilar with respect to both length and sequence and thus may represent separate domains evolved from different protein families. The nonhomologous, N-terminal region of CĪ inhibitor occurs between residues 1 and 120; it includes 3 of the 6 N-glycosylation sites, all of the 14 probable O-glycosylation sites, and the highly modified region in which the Glx-Pro-Thr-Thr type repeat occurs 7 times.

Homology and Tertiary Structure. Extensive amino acid sequence homology in a protein family often indicates an equal or even greater degree of tertiary structure homology (Birktoft & Blow, 1972; Sawyer et al., 1978; Marquart et al., 1983; James et al., 1978). At present, the only serpin tertiary structure that has been solved is that of α1-antitrypsin (Loebermann et al., 1984).

Examination of Figure 3a shows that the major part of CĪ inhibitor (residues 120–478) is homologous with the corresponding regions from other serpins. Although the area of homology spans a total of 358 amino acid residues, certain discrete stretches of stronger homology alternate with less homologous stretches. We marked the positions of defined helix and sheet strand elements from the α1-antitrypsin 3-Å crystallographic structure on the alignment shown in Figure 3a and observed a correspondence between clusters of conserved or nonconserved residues and certain structural elements. The conserved sequence stretches correspond to the B, F (its C-terminal end), G, H, and I helices, strands 3, 4 (its N-terminal end), 5, and 6 of the A sheet, the B sheet, and sheet strand 3C as shown in Figure 3b. The B sheet and helix B are internal in the crystal structure.

Conversely, the sequence stretches corresponding to helices A (its N-terminal end), C, D, and F (its N-terminal end), strands 1 and 2 of sheet C, strands 1, 2, and 4 (its C-terminal end) of sheet A (shaded areas in Figure 3B), and certain connecting strands (bold lines in Figure 3b) are not conserved among different serpins. These sequences map almost entirely to defined areas on the surface of the molecule. In addition to the identity of the P1 residue (which is Met-358 in α1-antitrypsin, Figure 3b) (Jörnvall et al., 1979; Owen et al., 1983; Scott et al., 1986), other surface residues in close proximity to P1 may well contribute to the definition of the exact protease specificity of the surface.

The disulfide bridge positions in CĪ inhibitor can be used to predict the disposition of its N-terminal, nonhomologous polypeptide chain. The four half-cystine residues of CĪ in-

a

```
   Clinh:                                                     NPNATSS
```

```
Clinh: SSQDPESLQDRGEGKVATTVISKMLFVEPILEVSSLPTTNSTTNSATKITANT
hcII:            GSKGPLDQLEKGGETAQSADPQWEQLNNKNLSMPLLPADFHKENTVT
AGTH:                                            DRVYIHPFHLVIH
```

```
                                                    1        10
Clinh: TDEPTTQPTTEPTTQPTIQPTQPTTQLPTDSPTQPTTGSFCPGPVTLCSDLES
A1AT:                                            EDPQGDAAQKTDTSHHDQD
ATIII:          HGSPVDICTAKPRDIPMNPMCIYRSPEKKATEDEGSEQKIPEAT
hcII:       NDWIPEGEEDDDYLLDLEKIFSEDDDYIDIVDSLSVSPTDSDVSAGNILQLFHG
A1ACT:                                            NSPLDEENLTQPENQDRG
AGTH:  NESTCEQLAKANAGKPKDPTFIPAPIQAKTSPVDEKALQDQLVLVAAKLDTED
```

```
       20        30        40        50   60
       <           helix A        >  <s6B>< helix B >
              *   **+ +*  +          +++ **-+* +++++- ***
Clinh: HSTEAVLGDALVDFSLKLYHAF-SAMKKVETNMAFSPFSIASLLSQVLLGA
A1AT:  HPTFNKITPNLAEFAFSLYRQLA--HQSNSTNIFFSPVSIATAFAMLSLGT
ATIII: NRRVWELSKANSRFATTFYQHLAD-SKNDNDNIFLSPVSISTAFAMTKLGA
hcII:  KSRIQRLNILNAKFAFNLYRVLKD-QVNTFDNIFIAPVGISTAMGMISLGL
A1ACT: THVDLGLASANVDFAFSLYKQLV--LKALDKNVIFSPLSISTALAFLSLGA
AGTH:  LDHTADRLQAILGVPWKDKNCTSRL-DAH--KVLSALQAVQGLLV
ova:        GSIGAASMEFCFDVFKELKVHHANENIFYCPIAIMSALAMVYLGA
```

```
       70        80        90        100
       < helix C  >           < helix D >
          *    -   + +              +
Clinh: GQNTKTNLESILSYPKDFTCVH------QALKGFTTKGVTSVSQ---
A1AT:  KADTHDEILEGLNFNLTEIPEA----QIHEGFQELLRTLNQPDSQ
ATIII: CNDTLQQLMEVFKFDTISEKTSD---QIHFFFAKLNC-RLYRKAN
hcII:  KGETHEQVHSILHFKDFVNASSKYEITTIHNLFRKLTHRLFRRNF
A1ACT: HNTTLTEILKASSSPHGDLLRQKFT-QSF--QHLRAPSISSSDEL
AGTH:  LDHTADRLQAILGVPWKDKNCTSRL-DAH--KVLSALQAVQGLLV
ova:   KDSTRTQINKVVRFDKLPGFGDSIE---AQCGTSVNVHSSLRDIL
```

```
       110       120       130       140
       <       sheet 2A        >   < helix E  ><sheet1A>
                          +*  * -  *   * *-    * *
Clinh: ------------------------IFHSPDLAIRDTFVNASRTLYSSSPR----V
A1AT:  LQLTTDGG----------LFLSEGLKLVDKFLEDVKKLYHSEAFTV--N
ATIII: KSSKLVSANR--------LFGDKSLTFNETYQDISELVYGAKLQPL--D
hcII:  GYTLRSVND----------LYIQKQFPILLDFKTKVREYYFAEAQIA--D
A1ACT: QLSMGNA----------MFVKEQLSLLDRFTEDAKRLYGSEAFAT--D
A2AP:                                            PVS
AGTH:  AQGRADSQAQLLLSTVVGVFTAPGLHLKQPFVQ-GLALYTPVVLPRSLD
ova:   NQITKPNDVYSFSLASR-LYAEERYPILPEYLQCVKELYRGGLEPI--N
```

```
       150       160       170       180       190
       <           helix F        >              < sheet 3A >
          * +   ** +* *  * *** + +    +  *  *****-+*****
Clinh: LSNNSDANLELINTWVAKNTNNKISRLL---DSLPSDTRLVLLNAIYLSAKW
A1AT:  FGDTEEAKKQ-INDYVEKGTQGKIVDLV--KELDRDTVFALVNYIFFKGKW
ATIII: FKENAEQSRAAINKWVSNKTEGRITDVIPSEAINELTVLVLVNTIYFKGLW
hcII:  FSDPAFISKT--NNHIMKLTKGLIKDAL--ENIDPATQMMILNCIYFKGSW
A1ACT: FQDSAAAKKL-INDYVKNGTRGKITDLI--KDPDSQTMMVLVNYIFFKAKW
A2AP:  LTGKQEDDLANINQWVKEATEGKIQEF
ctpsn:                                            VVLVNYINFKGKW
AGTH:  FTELDVAAEK-IDRFMQAVTGWKTGCSL--MGASVDSTLAFNTYVHFQGKY
ova:   FQTAADQARELINSWVESQTNGIIRNVLQPSSVDSQTAMVLVNAIVFKGLW
bpZ:   WVEQVTXGL-IXEILPP                          W
```

```
       200       210       220       230
                            < sheet 3C >   <sht1B>
       + *** +* + *  ++ ++++++  *++* - *
Clinh: KTTFDPKKTRMEPPHFKNS-VIKVPMMNSKKYPVAHFIDQT
A1AT:  ERPFEVKDTEEEDFHVDQVTTVKVPMMKRLGM-FNIQHCKK
ATIII: KSKFSPENTRKELFYKADGESCSASMMYQEG-KFR-YRRVA
hcII:  VNKFPVEMTHNHNFRLNEREVVKVSMMQTKG-NFLAANDQE
A1ACT: EMPFDPQDTHQSRFYLSKKKWVMVPMMSLHHLTIPYFRDEE
A2AP:  SLKFDPSLTQRDSFLHDEQFTVPVEMMQARVYP
ctpsn: KISFDPQDTFESEFYLDEKRSVKVPMMKMKLLTTRHFRDEE
AGTH:  K-GFSLLAEPQE-FWVDNSTSVSVPMLSGMG-TFQHWSDIQ
ova:   EKAFKDEDTQAMPFRVTEQESKPVQMMYQIGL-FRVASMAS
bpZ:   QK-FDEXN                          LTKKQYISSS
```

```
         240       250       260       270
         <sheet2B> < sheet 3B  >  < helix G> < helix H>
         *    ****** +++.....**-+**+   * +  +* * ** +   *
Clinh:  LKAKVGQLQLSHNL-----SLVILVPQNLKHRLEDMEQALSPSVFK--AIME
A1AT:   LSSWVLLMKYLGNA-----TAIFFLPDEGK--LQHLENELTHDIIT--KFLE
ATIII:  EGTQVLELPFKGDDI----TMVLILPKPEKS-LAKVEKELTPEVLQ--EWLD
hcII:   LDCDILQLEYVGGI-----SMLIVVPHKMSG-MKTLEAQLTPRVVE--RWQK
A1ACT:  LSCTVVELKYTGNA-----SALFILPDQDK--MEEVEAMLLPETLK--RWRD
ctpsn:  LSCSVLELKYTGNA-----SALLILPDQGR--MQQVEASLQPETLR--KWRK
AGTH:   DNFSVTQVPFTESA-----CLLLIQPHYASD-LDKVEGLTFQQNSL--NWMK
ova:    EKMKILELFASGTM-----SMLVLLPDEVSG-LEQLESIINFEKLT--EWTS
bpZ:    DNLKVLKLPYAKGHDKRQFSMYILLPGAQDG-LWSLAKRLSTEPEFIENHIP
```

```
         280       290       300
         <sheet 2C><sheet6A>< helix I>
         *      + **** * *  * .-* ++
Clinh:  KLEMSK-FQPTLLTLPRIKVTTSQDMLSIMEKL
A1AT:   NEDRRS--ASLHLPKLSITGTYDLKS-VLGQLG
ATIII:  ELEEMM--LVVHMPRFRIEDGFSLKE-QLQDMG
hcII:   SMTN--RTREVLLPKFLEKNYNLVE-SLKLMG
A1ACT:  SLEFR-EIGELYLPKFSISRDYNLND-ILLQLG
ctpsn:  TLFPSQ-IEELNLPKFSIASNYRLEEDVLFMNG
AGTH:   KLSP--RTIHLTMPQLVLQGSYDLQD-LLAQAE
ova:    SNVMEERKIKVYLPRMKMEEKYNLTS-VLMAMG
bpZ:    KQTVEV--GRFQLPKFKISYQFEASS-LLRALG
```

```
         310       320       330       340
                                       < sheet 5A >
         *   **  *+.****-    * **  *-+********+
Clinh:  EFFDFSYDLN-LCGLTEDPD--LQVSAMQHQTVLELTE
A1AT:   ITKVFSNGAD-LSGVTEEAP--LKLSKAVHKAVLIIDE
ATIII:  LVDLFSPEKSKLPGIVAEGRDDLYVSDAFHKAFLEVNE
hcII:   IRMLFDKNGNMA-GISDQRIAIDLFK---HQGTIITVNE
A1ACT:  IEEAFTSKAD-LSGITGARN--LSVSQVVHKKVVSDVFE
ctpsn:  IKEVFTEQAD-LSGIIETKK--LSVSQVVHKAVLDVAE
AGTH:   LPAILHTELN-LQKLSNDR---IRVGEVLNSIFFEL-E
ova:    ITDVFSSSAN-LSGISSAES--LKISQAVHAAHAEINE
bpZ:    LQLPFSEEAD-LSEMVDSSQG-LEISHVFHKSFVEVNE
```

```
         350       360       370       380       390 394
         <   sheet 4A  >  <sheet 1C  > <sheet4B> < sheet 5B>
         ***********+        * *     *  ***** +   --***** **
Clinh:  TGVEAAAASAISVA--RTLL-----VFEVQQPFLFMLWDQQHKFPVFMGRVYDPRA
A1AT:   KGTEAAGAMFLEAIP-MSIP-----PEVKFNKPFVFLMIEQNTKSPLFMGKVVNPTQK
ATIII:  EGSEAAASTAVV-IAGRSL--NPNRVTFKANRPFLVFIREVPLNTIIFMGRVANPCVK
hcII:   EGTQATTVTTVGFMP-LST-----QVRFTVDRPFLFLIYEHRTSCLLFMGRVANPSRS
A1ACT:  EGTEASAATAVK-ITLLSAL-VEIRIVRFNRPFLMIIVPTDTQNIFFMSKVTNPKQA
ctpsn:  TGTEAAAATGVIGGIRKAIL-----PAVHFNRPFLFVIYHTSAQSILFMAKVNNPK
AGTH:   ADEREPTESTQQLNK-PEV-----LEVTLNRPFLFAVYDQSATALHFLGRVANPLSTA
ova:    AGREVV-GSAEAGVDAASV-----SEEFRADHPFLFCIKHIATNAVLFFGRCVSP
bpZ:    EGTEAGAA-TVAMGVAMSMPLKVDLVDFYANHPFLFLIREDIAGVVVFVGHVTNPLISA
```

b

FIGURE 3: (a) Alignment of the protein sequence of CĪ inhibitor with those of nine other serpins. Human antithrombin III (ATIII), α1-antitrypsin (A1AT), α1-antichymotrypsin (A1ACT), angiotensinogen (AGTH), and chicken ovalbumin (ova) sequences were obtained from *Atlas of Protein Sequence and Structure* (1985) with the following qualifications: (1) the C-terminus of A1ACT was according to Hill et al. (1984) rather than *Atlas of Protein Sequence and Structure* (1985), and (2) a threonine (Kurachi et al., 1981; Carrell et al., 1982) was substituted for residue 249 of α1-antitrypsin [reported as asparagine in *Atlas of Protein Sequence and Structure* (1985)]. Mouse contrapsin (ctpsn), heparin cofactor II (hcII), α2-antiplasmin (A2AP), and barley protein Z (bpZ) sequences were obtained from Hill et al. (1984), Ragg (1986), Lijnen et al. (1982), and Hejgaard et al. (1985), respectively. A dash indicates a gap in the sequence. Spaces in A2AP and bpZ sequences indicate that no information is available for these regions. Arrowheads indicate P1–P1′ bond cleaved during complex formation with target proteases, or the putative reactive site. Degree of homology is indicated above aligned sequences as follows: *, identity in five or more proteins, +, identity in four or more proteins; −, chemically similar residues occurring in this position in the majority of the proteins. Dots mark aligned gaps in areas of homology; aligned gaps are not marked in nonhomologous regions. The positions of helices and sheet strands in the cleaved α1-antitrypsin structure (Loebermann et al., 1984) are indicated above the alignment. The numbering shown is that of α1-antitrypsin. Due to minor corrections, the beginning and ending residues of some structural elements differ slightly from those reported in Table 8 of Loebermann et al. (1984). (b) Tertiary structure of cleaved α1-antitrypsin with locations of nonconserved sequences indicated. Sheet strands are represented by arrows, helices by cylinders, and irregular segments by lines, and they are labeled as in Loebermann et al. (1984). The path of the α-carbon chain can be traced by following the amino acid residue numbers that appear at the ends of each helix and sheet strand. The identities of selected residues are indicated next to the numbers. Superimposed upon the structure is information from the sequence alignment shown in part a. Sequences in the elements that have been shaded or marked with bold lines are not conserved among different serpin family proteins. Large black arrows indicate the proposed unfolding scheme that occurs when the peptide bond between reactive site residues Met-358 (P1) and Ser-359 (P1′) is cleaved and the stressed, native inhibitor relaxes to form the nicked structure that has been crystallized.

Table I: Segregation of the CĪ Inhibitor Gene with Human Chromosomes in Human–Mouse Cell Hybrids[a]

HYBRID	C1 Inhibitor	1	2	3	4	5	6	7	8	9	10	11	12	13	14	15	16	17	18	19	20	21	22	X	Translocations
ATR-13	–	+	+	+	+	+	+	+	+	–	+	–	+	+	–	+	+	+	+	+	–	–	–	t	5/X
DUA-3BSAGA	–	–	+	–	–	+	–	–	+	+	–	–	+	–	–	+	–	–	+	–	–	+	–	–	
DUA-5BSAGA	+	–	–	+	–	+	–	–	+	–	–	+	–	–	+	–	–	+	–	+	–	–	–	–	
DUM-13	+	+	+	+	+	+	+	+	–	+	+	–	+	t	+	+	+	+	+	+	+	+	+	t	X/15 15/X
EXR-5CSAz	–	+	+	+	+	+	+	+	+	+	+	t	+	+	+	–	+	+	+	+	+	+	+	+	X/11
GAR-1	–	–	–	+	–	+	–	+	–	+	–	+	–	+	–	+	+	–	–	+	–	–	+		
ICL-15	–	–	–	–	–	–	–	+	–	+	–	+	–	+	–	–	+	–	+	+	–	–	+		
JSR-2	–	–	–	+	+	–	–	+	–	–	–	–	+	+	–	+	–	–	–	–	+	+		
JSR-14	–	+	+	+	+	+	+	–	–	–	+	–	–	+	–	+	–	1	–	+	+	+		
JWR-26C	+	t	+	+	+	+	+	+	–	+	+	+	+	–	+	+	+	+	+	–	+	+	–	+	1/2
NSL-9	–	–	–	–	–	–	+	t	+	–	+	–	+	+	–	+	+	–	+	+	+	–	17/9
NSL-16	–	–	–	+	–	–	–	+	t	+	–	+	+	–	+	+	–	+	+	+	–	17/9
REW-5	+	+	+	+	+	+	+	–	+	+	+	–	+	+	–	+	+	+	+		
REW-8D	–	–	–	–	+	+	+	–	–	–	–	+	+	–	+	+	+	+		
REW-11	+	+	+	+	+	+	+	–	+	+	+	–	+	–	+	+	+	+		
REX-11BSAgB	–	–	–	+	–	–	–	+	–	+	–	–	–	+	–	–	–	–		
REX-11BSHF	–	–	–	+	–	–	–	+	–	+	–	–	–	+	–	–	t	t	22/X
REX-26	+	+	+	+	–	+	–	+	+	+	+	–	+	–	+	+	–	t	t	22/X
SIR-8	+	+	+	+	+	+	–	+	+	+	+	+	+	+	+	–	+	+	+	+	
SIR-11	–	–	–	–	+	–	–	–	+	+	–	+	–	–	–	–	+	+	+	
TSL-1	+	–	+	+	–	+	–	+	+	+	–	+	–	+	–	+	+	–	–	
TSL-2	–	–	+	t	–	+	+	–	–	+	–	+	–	t	–	+	+	+	–	+	17/3 3/17
VTL-2	+	+	+	–	+	+	+	–	+	+	–	+	–	+	–	–	+	+	–	
VTL-8	–	–	–	–	–	–	+	–	+	–	+	–	+	–	–	+	+	–	+	
VTL-17	+	–	+	+	–	–	+	–	–	+	–	+	+	+	–	+	–	–	+	
WIL-1	–	–	–	+	–	–	+	–	–	+	–	+	–	+	–	+	+	–	+	
WIL-2	–	–	+	+	–	+	+	–	+	–	+	–	+	–	+	+	–	+	
WIL-5	–	–	–	–	+	+	–	+	+	–	+	+	–	+	–	–	+	–	+	
WIL-6	–	+	–	+	–	+	–	–	+	–	+	–	+	–	+	–	+	
WIL-7	+	+	–	+	–	+	+	–	–	+	–	+	+	+	–	+	–	–	+	
WIL-8	+	+	+	+	+	+	+	+	+	+	+	+	+	+	+	+	+	+	+	
WIL-8X	+	–	+	+	+	+	+	+	+	–	+	+	–	+	+	+	+	+	+	
WIL-8Y	+	–	+	+	–	+	+	+	–	+	+	–	+	+	–	+	+	+	+	
WIL-13	–	–	+	+	–	+	–	–	+	–	+	–	+	–	+	–	+	+	
WIL-14	–	–	+	+	–	+	+	–	–	+	+	–	+	–	+	+	–	+	
WIL-15	+	–	+	+	+	–	+	+	–	+	+	+	+	–	+	–	+	+	–	+	
XER-7	+	+	+	+	+	+	+	+	+	–	t	+	+	+	–	–	+	+	–	–	–	+	11/X X/11
XER-8	+	+	+	+	+	+	+	+	–	+	–	+	+	–	+	+	+	+	+	+	t	11/X X/11
XER-11	+	+	–	+	+	+	+	+	+	+	t	+	–	–	+	+	+	+	+	+	t	11/X X/11
XTR-11BSAGA	–	–	–	–	–	–	–	–	–	+	–	–	+	–	–	+	–	–	+	–	20p+
XTR-22	+	–	+	t	+	+	+	–	+	–	+	+	–	–	+	–	–	+	+	+	+	X/3

	Chromosome	1	2	3	4	5	6	7	8	9	10	11	12	13	14	15	16	17	18	19	20	21	22	X
		**
Concordant	(+/+)	8	13	15	14	14	15	16	14	7	17	18	12	11	18	17	18	12	14	19	18	12
# of hybrids	(–/–)	19	16	9	13	14	17	13	10	19	12	20	12	12	9	13	18	7	11	19	13	8	15	7
Discordant	(+/–)	11	7	4	6	6	7	4	6	13	3	0	8	10	4	8	18	3	4	8	6	1	9	4
# of hybrids	(–/+)	2	5	11	8	7	4	8	11	1	9	0	9	9	12	8	3	15	10	2	8	13	5	12
% Discordancy		32	29	38	34	32	27	29	41	35	29	0	41	46	39	40	32	40	34	24	34	54	38	46

[a] "t" indicates a translocated piece of the chromosome, but no intact chromosome, is present.

hibitor correspond to residues 7, 319, 14, and 88 of α1-antitrypsin (see Figure 3a). Of these residues, only 319 and 88 are defined in the α1-antitrypsin crystal structure. Our chemical evidence shows that the disulfide bridge pattern of CĪ inhibitor is 1–4, 2–3, and thus implies that the nonhomologous, N-terminal end of the polypeptide chain runs close to the strand that connects helix I with sheet strand 5A (and contains residue 319) and near to the beginning of helix D (which contains residue 88) (see Figure 3b).

All of the CĪ inhibitor O-glycosylation sites and three of the N-glycosylation sites are located in the N-terminal region of the polypeptide chain, which is not homologous to sequences from other serpin family members. However, the positions of the three remaining N-glycosylation sites can be predicted from the α1-antitrypsin model structure. Asn-216 corresponds to residue 132 of α1-antitrypsin, which is residue 5 of helix E. Asn-231 corresponds to residue 149 and is at the beginning of helix F, in a surface turn (the third residue of the turn). Asn-330 corresponds to residue 247, which is located on the turn between strands 2 and 3 of sheet B. All three of these N-glycosylation sites are external and on the far side of the drawing shown in Figure 3b; they are found in the same general area, 27–30 Å apart.

Chromosomal Localization. The CĪ inhibitor gene was mapped to subregion p11.2-q13 of human chromosome 11 by analyzing segregation of CĪ inhibitor gene containing DNA fragments and human chromosomes on Southern blots of

DNA from human–mouse cell hybrids (Table I). Concordant hybrids have either retained or not retained CĪ inhibitor together with a specific human chromosome (+/+ and –/–, respectively). Discordant hybrids either retained the gene, but not a specific chromosome (+/–), or the reverse (–/+). Percent discordance indicates the degree of discordant segregation for CĪ inhibitor and a chromosome. A 0% discordance is the basis for assignment of the CĪ inhibitor gene to chromosome 11. The hybrids XER-7 and EXR-5CSAz with two different 11/X and X/11 translocations localize the CĪ inhibitor gene to the p11.2-q13 region of chromosome 11. XER-7 is positive for CĪ inhibitor and retains the translocation chromosome 11qter-11p11.2::Xq11-Xqter. EXR-5CSAz is negative for CĪ inhibitor and retains the translocation chromosome Xpter-Xq22::11q13-11qter.

Polymorphisms. A polymorphism was identified in the CĪ inhibitor gene by comparison of our protein and cDNA data. Amino acid sequencing of CĪ inhibitor isolated from pooled plasma yielded a valine at residue 458, while nucleotide sequencing of the originally isolated cDNA clone revealed a methionine (ATG) at this position. A cDNA clone from another allele (pK11, Figure 1c) was subsequently obtained and sequenced, and it showed a valine-encoding GTG for residue 458. Examination of the nucleotide sequence around residue 458 indicated that a *Hgi*AI recognition sequence (GTGCTC) is present in the valine variant, but not in the methionine variant. A *Hgi*AI restriction fragment length polymorphism (RFLP) (Botstein et al., 1980) was observed when a Southern blot prepared from *Hgi*AI-digested genomic DNAs was hybridized with the C$\bar{1}$ inhibitor cDNA probe. This polymorphism has two alleles, which produce 0.7- and 0.4-kb hybridizing bands, and displays Mendelian inheritance. The frequencies of the alleles in a sample of 34 chromosomes from 17 unrelated individuals were 0.32 and 0.68, respectively.

In order to identify additional RFLPs that could be useful for genetic linkage studies on HANE pedigrees, genomic DNA from 7–10 unrelated individuals was screened on Southern blots by using the C$\bar{1}$ inhibitor cDNA probe. No further RFLPs were found in a screen of 21 different restriction enzymes (*Apa*I, *Bam*HI, *Ban*II, *Bcl*I, *Bgl*II, *Bst*EII, *Bst*NI, *Dra*I, *Eco*RI, *Hinc*II, *Hin*dIII, *Msp*I, *Pst*I, *Pvu*II, *Rsa*I, *Sca*I, *Sst*I, *Stu*I, *Sty*I, *Taq*I, and *Xba*I). However, from comparison of the fragment number and length data generated in this screen and the restriction map of the cDNA, it can be inferred that the C$\bar{1}$ inhibitor gene contains at least seven introns and spans at least 16 kb.

Hereditary Angioneurotic Edema. The C$\bar{1}$ inhibitor cDNA probe was used to examine C$\bar{1}$ inhibitor genes from one HANE kindred with type I deficiency (reduced activity and antigen levels) and three with type II deficiencies (reduced activity levels in the presence of normal or elevated antigen levels). DNA samples were digested with 7–12 different restriction enzymes. At the resolution of Southern blot analysis, hybridization patterns obtained from patient DNAs and control DNAs were indistinguishable. In one kindred, *Hgi*AI polymorphism inheritance results are consistent with the presence of a mutant C$\bar{1}$ inhibitor gene on a "0.7-kb allele".

Discussion

The primary structure of human C$\bar{1}$ inhibitor has been determined and will be helpful for studying how it functions to inhibit, and therefore regulate, key enzymes of the complement, coagulation, fibrinolytic, and kinin-generating pathways.

The protein portion of the circulating inhibitor constitutes only 51% of its total molecular mass and is a single polypeptide chain of 478 amino acid residues. The sites of attachment for six glucosamine-based and five galactosamine-based oligosaccharides have been determined (Figures 1a and 2). An additional nine threonine residues are also probably glycosylated. Seventeen of the probable twenty oligosaccharides are located in the N-terminal region of the polypeptide, and of these, ten are clustered in a 35-residue region where the sequence Glx-Pro-Thr-Thr, or variations of it, occurs 7 times. This tetrapeptide repeat is generated from tandem repetitions of a 12-base nucleotide sequence. The nucleotide repeat actually occurs 9 times (Figure 4); however, in two cases base substitutions in codon second positions generate peptides that do not conform to the Glx-Pro-Thr-Thr pattern. The Glx-Pro-Thr-Thr type repeat is a substrate for modification. Galactosamine-based oligosaccharides have been unequivocally identified on threonine residues in three repeats, and there is partial evidence for additional modification on five threonine residues in three other repeat units of this type. Additionally, threonines in the neighboring, related tetrapeptide sequences, Gln(86)-Leu-Pro-Thr and Asp(90)-Ser-Pro-Thr, are probably also glycosylated.[2]

Cysteine positions and disulfide bonding patterns have not been conserved between C$\bar{1}$ inhibitor and other members of the serpin family. C$\bar{1}$ inhibitor contains four cysteine residues

63

Glu	Pro	Thr	Thr	
GAA	CCC	ACC	ACA	
Gln	Pro	Thr	Thr	
CAA	CCC	ACC	ACA	
Glu	Pro	Thr	Thr	
GAG	CCC	ACC	ACC	
Gln	Pro	Thr	Ile	
CAA	CCC	ACC	ATC	
Gln	Pro	Thr		
CAA	CCC	ACC		
Gln	Pro	Thr	Thr	
CAA	CCA	ACT	ACC	
Gln	Leu	Pro	Thr	
CAG	CTC	CCA	ACA	
Asp	Ser	Pro	Thr	
GAT	TCT	CCT	ACC	
Gln	Pro	Thr	Thr	97
CAG	CCC	ACT	ACT	

FIGURE 4: Amino acid and nucleotide sequences between residues 63 and 97 of C$\bar{1}$ inhibitor, showing imperfect, tandem repetitions of a 12-base nucleotide sequence (one nucleotide repeat unit per line) and the associated Glx-Pro-Thr-Thr type peptides (boxed).

forming two disulfide bridges in a 1–4, 2–3 pattern (Figure 2). The positions of the cysteines and consequently the pattern of disulfide formation are clearly different from those of α1-antitrypsin and α1-antichymotrypsin, each of which has a single cysteine, and antithrombin III, which has six half-cystines in a 1–4, 2–3, 5–6 pattern (Petersen et al., 1979). The disulfide bridge patterns of ovalbumin, angiotensinogen, heparin cofactor II, and contrapsin have not been fully determined. Although the number and positions of cysteine residues have not been conserved in different serpins, the locations of disulfide bridges in C$\bar{1}$ inhibitor and antithrombin III are consistent with the concept of conserved tertiary structure in these inhibitors and α1-antitrypsin (see Homology and Tertiary Structure, under Results).

We identified regions on the surface of the homologous inhibitor, α1-antitrypsin, that are not conserved between members of the serpin family. These regions are indicated with shading and bold lines in Figure 3b. The P1 and P1′ residues (Met-358 and Ser-359) are located nearly 70 Å apart in the crystal structure but must have been adjacent to each other in the uncleaved, intact inhibitor. This would allow many of the nonconserved regions to form a continuous surface that includes the reactive site and varies in the details of its geometry from one serpin to another. Part of this surface, containing the P1 residue and its neighbors in the tertiary structure, could constitute the recognition site(s) for cognate target protease(s). Evidence from families with genetically variant C$\bar{1}$ inhibitor molecules implies that different target proteases [C$\overline{1s}$, plasma kallikrein, activated Hageman factor (XIIa), Hageman factor fragments, and plasmin] engage different sites on C$\bar{1}$ inhibitor (Donaldson et al., 1985). However, these sites probably overlap partially, with at least the P1 residue being common to all.

The C$\bar{1}$ inhibitor gene was localized to human chromosome 11, p11.2-q13, near the centromere. Assignment of the C$\bar{1}$ inhibitor gene to chromosome 11 indicates that it is not genetically linked to other evolutionarily related members of the human plasma serpin family that have been mapped; the antithrombin III locus is found at 1q23-1q25 (Bock et al., 1985b) while α1-antitrypsin (14q32.1) (Purello et al., 1985) and α1-antichymotrypsin (14q31-qter) (Rabin et al., 1985) are syntenic and may perhaps be closely linked. In this regard,

[2] Recent evidence indicates that Thr-50 is also glycosylated.

it is interesting to note that the relative degree of homology between α1-antitrypsin and α1-antichymotrypsin (39%) is much greater than that between either of them and C$\bar{1}$ inhibitor (27% and 27%) or antithrombin III (ATIII) (28% and 31%). [The degree of homology between pairs of serpins was calculated by using the FASTP algorithm (Lipman & Pearson, 1985).]

HANE patients have decreased levels of functional C$\bar{1}$ inhibitor and suffer from episodic attacks of debilitating gastrointestinal, subcutaneous, and/or pharyngeal edema. The disorder is transmitted in an autosomal dominant manner and is heterogeneous at the biochemical level (Donaldson & Evans, 1963; Rosen et al., 1971). Affected individuals in most pedigrees exhibit reductions in both their C$\bar{1}$ inhibitor functional activity and their antigen levels (type I deficiency). However, in 20–30% of HANE kindreds, functional activity is decreased in the presence of normal or elevated antigen levels (type II deficiency), and the associated dysfunctional C$\bar{1}$ inhibitor molecules from the different families have been demonstrated to be different from each other and from the normal inhibitor (Donaldson et al., 1985). No gross alterations of the C$\bar{1}$ inhibitor structural gene were detected in a preliminary study of genomic DNA from patients in one kindred with type I HANE and three kindreds with type II HANE, suggesting that the mutations responsible for the disorder in these four families are small deletions, insertions, or limited nucleotide substitution(s) in the C$\bar{1}$ inhibitor gene or that there are defects at other loci involved in the processing and modification of biologically active plasma C$\bar{1}$ inhibitor. The identification of a HgiAI DNA polymorphism in the C$\bar{1}$ inhibitor gene will permit linkage studies to distinguish these alternatives and facilitate isolation of mutant C$\bar{1}$ inhibitor genes from HANE patients, all of whom are heterozygous for the trait and carry a normal copy of the C$\bar{1}$ inhibitor gene as well. Identification of mutations in dysfunctional C$\bar{1}$ inhibitor genes will further understanding of C$\bar{1}$ inhibitor structure–function relationships.

ACKNOWLEDGMENTS

We thank B. Christensen, M. Frandsen, and L. Kristensen for technical assistance, Drs. S. L. C. Woo and T. Chandra for supplying the λgt11 cDNA library, Drs. L.-S. Huang and S. Pinsky for advice, and Professor E. T. Kaiser for his interest and encouragement of this project. One batch of the five used for protein sequencing was the kind gift of Dr. N. Heimburger, Behringwerke, Marburg/Lahn, FRG.

REFERENCES

Ames, B. R. (1966) *Methods Enzymol.* 8, 116.

Atlas of Protein Sequence and Structure (1985) National Biomedical Research Foundation, Washington, DC.

Birktoft, J. J., & Blow, D. M. (1972) *J. Mol. Biol.* 68, 187.

Bock, S. C., Wion, K. L., Vehar, G. A., & Lawn, R. M. (1982) *Nucleic Acids Res.* 10, 8113.

Bock, S. C., Harris, J. F., Schwartz, C. E., Ward, J. H., Hershgold, E. J., & Skolnick, M. H. (1985a) *Am. J. Hum. Genet.* 37, 32.

Bock, S. C., Harris, J. F., Balazs, I., & Trent, J. M. (1985b) *Cytogenet. Cell. Genet.* 39, 67.

Botstein, D., White, R. L., Skolnick, M. H., & Davis, R. W. (1980) *Am. J. Hum. Genet.* 32, 314.

Carrell, R. (1984) *Nature (London)* 312, 14.

Carrell, R. W., Jeppson, J.-O., Laurell, C.-B., Brennan, S. O., Owen, M. C., Vaughan, L., & Boswell, D. R. (1982) *Nature (London)* 298, 329.

Chandra, T., Stackhouse, R., Kidd, V. J., Robson, K. H. J., & Woo, S. L. C. (1983) *Biochemistry* 22, 5055.

Chapuis, R. M., Isliker, M., & Assimeh, S. N. (1977) *Immunochemistry* 14, 313.

Colten, H. R. (1972) *J. Clin. Invest.* 51, 725.

Davis, A. E., Whitehead, A. S., Harrison, R. A., Dauphinais, A., Bruns, G. A. P., Cicardi, M., & Rosen, F. S. (1986) *Proc. Natl. Acad. Sci. U.S.A.* 83, 3161.

Dixon, H. B. F., & Perham, R. N. (1968) *Biochem. J.* 129, 312.

Donaldson, V. H., & Evans, R. R. (1963) *Am. J. Med.* 35, 37.

Donaldson, V. H., Harrison, R. A., Rosen, F. S., Bing, D. H., Kindness, G., Canar, J., Wagner, C. J., & Awad, S. (1985) *J. Clin. Invest.* 75, 124.

Doolittle, R. F. (1983) *Science (Washington, D.C.)* 122, 417.

Doolittle, R. F. (1985) *Sci. Am.* 253, 88.

Edge, A. S. B., Faltynek, C. R., Hof, L., Reichert, L. E., & Weber, P. (1981) *Anal. Biochem.* 118, 131.

Forbes, C., Pensky, J., & Ratnoff, O. (1970) *J. Lab. Clin. Med.* 76, 809.

Gigli, I., Ruddy, S., & Austen, K. F. (1968) *J. Immunol.* 100, 1154.

Gigli, I., Mason, J., Colman, R., & Austen, K. F. (1970) *J. Immunol.* 104, 574.

Gray, W. (1967) *Methods Enzymol.* 11, 469.

Harpel, P. C., & Cooper, N. R. (1975) *J. Clin. Invest.* 55, 593.

Harrison, R. A. (1983) *Biochemistry* 22, 5001.

Haupt, H., Heimburger, N., Krantz, T., & Schwick, H. G. (1970) *Eur. J. Biochem.* 17, 254.

Hejgaard, J., Rasmussen, S. K., Brandt, A., & Svendsen, I. (1985) *FEBS Lett.* 180, 89.

Helfman, D. M., Feramisco, J. B., Fiddes, J. C., Thomas, G. P., & Hughes, S. H. (1983) *Proc. Natl. Acad. Sci. U.S.A.* 80, 31.

Hill, R. E., Shaw, P. H., Boyd, P. A., Baumann, H., & Hastie, N. D. (1984) *Nature (London)* 311, 175.

Hunt, L. T., & Dayhoff, M. O. (1980) *Biochem. Biophys. Res. Commun.* 95, 864.

Jackson, R. C., & Blobel, G. (1980) *Ann. N.Y. Acad. Sci.* 343, 391.

James, M. N. G., Delbaere, L. T. J., & Brayer, G. D. (1978) *Can. J. Biochem.* 56, 396.

Jörnvall, H., Fish, W. W., & Björk, I. (1979) *FEBS Lett.* 106, 358.

Kageyama, R., Ohkubo, H., & Nakanishi, S. (1984) *Biochemistry* 23, 3603.

Knowles, B. B., Howe, C. C., & Aden, D. P. (1980) *Science (Washington, D.C.)* 209, 497.

Kurachi, K., Chandra, T., Degen, S. J. F., White, T. T., Marchiorol, T. L., Woo, S. L. C., & Davie, E. W. (1981) *Proc. Natl. Acad. Sci. U.S.A.* 78, 6826.

Lepow, I. H., & Leon, M. A. (1962) *Immunology* 5, 222.

Levy, L. R., & Lepow, I. H. (1959) *Proc. Soc. Exp. Biol. Med.* 101, 608.

Lijnen, H. R., Wiman, B., & Collen, D. (1982) *Thromb. Haemostasis* 48, 311.

Lipman, D. J., & Pearson, W. R. (1985) *Science (Washington, D.C.)* 227, 1435.

Loebermann, H., Tokuoka, R., Deisenhofer, J., & Huber, R. (1984) *J. Mol. Biol.* 177, 531.

Marquart, M., Walter, J., Deisenhofer, J., Bode, W., & Huber, R. (1983) *Acta Crystallogr., Sect. B: Struct. Sci. B39*, 480.

McReynolds, L., O'Malley, B. W., Nisbet, A. D., Fothergill, J. E., Givol, D., Fields, S., Robertson, M., & Brownlee, G. G. (1978) *Nature (London)* 273, 723.

Nilsson, T., & Wiman, B. (1982) *Biochim. Biophys. Acta 705*, 271.

Nilsson, T., Sjöholm, I., & Wiman, B. (1983) *Biochem. J. 213*, 617.

Owen, M. C., Brennan, S. O., Lewis, J. H., & Carrell, R. W. (1983) *N. Engl. J. Med. 309*, 694.

Pensky, J., & Schwick, H. G. (1969) *Science (Washington, D.C.) 163*, 698.

Pensky, J., Levy, L. R., & Lepow, I. H. (1961) *J. Biol. Chem. 236*, 1674.

Petersen, T. E., Dudek-Wojciechowska, G., Sottrup-Jensen, L., & Magnusson, S. (1979) in *The Physiological Inhibitors of Coagulation and Fibrinolysis* (Collen, D., Wiman, B., & Verstraete, M., Eds.) pp 43–54, Elsevier/North-Holland Biomedical Press, Amsterdam.

Proudfoot, N. J., & Brownlee, G. G. (1976) *Nature (London) 263*, 211.

Purello, M., Alhadeff, B., Esposito, D., Whittington, E., Daniel, A., Buckton, K. E., & Siniscalco, M. (1985) *Cytogenet. Cell Genet. 40*, 725.

Rabin, M., Watson, M., Breg, W. R., Kidd, V., Woo, S. L. C., & Ruddle, F. H. (1985) *Cytogenet. Cell Genet. 40*, 728.

Ragg, H. (1986) *Nucleic Acids Res. 14*, 1073.

Ratnoff, O. D., & Lepow, I. H. (1957) *J. Exp. Med. 106*, 327.

Ratnoff, O. D., Pensky, J., Ogston, D., & Naff, G. B. (1969) *J. Exp. Med. 129*, 315.

Rosen, F. S., Alper, C. A., Pensky, J., Klemperer, M. R., & Donaldson, V. H. (1971) *J. Clin. Invest. 50*, 2143.

Salvesen, G. S., Catanese, J. J., Kress, L. F., & Travis, J. (1985) *J. Biol. Chem. 260*, 2432.

Sanger, F., Nicklen, S., & Coulson, A. R. (1977) *Proc. Natl. Acad. Sci. U.S.A. 74*, 5463.

Sawyer, L., Shotton, D. M., Campbell, J. W., Wendell, P. L., Muirhead, H., Watson, H. C., Diamond, R., & Ladner, R. C. (1978) *J. Mol. Biol. 118*, 137.

Schultze, H. E., Heide, K., & Haupt, H. (1962) *Naturwissenschaften 49*, 133.

Scott, C. F., Carrell, R. W., Glaser, C. B., Kueppers, F., Lewis, J. H., & Colman, R. W. (1986) *J. Clin. Invest. 77*, 631.

Shows, T. B. (1983) *Isozymes: Curr. Top. Biol. Med. Res. 10*, 523.

Shows, T. B., Brown, J. A., Haley, L. L., Beyers, M. G., Eddy, R. L., Cooper, E. S., & Goggin, A. P. (1978) *Cytogenet. Cell Genet. 21*, 99.

Shows, T. B., Sakaguchi, A. Y., & Naylor, S. L. (1982) *Adv. Hum. Genet. 12*, 341.

Shows, T., Eddy, R., Haley, L., Beyers, M., Henry, M., Fujita, T., Matsui, H., & Tanigushi, T. (1984) *Somatic Cell Mol. Genet. 10*, 315.

Sim, R. B., Reboul, A., Arlaud, G. J., Villiers, C. L., & Colomb, M. G. (1979) *FEBS Lett. 97*, 111.

Sim, R. B., Arlaud, G. J., & Colomb, M. G. (1980) *Biochim. Biophys. Acta 612*, 433.

Skorstengaard, K., Thøgersen, H. C., Vibe-Pedersen, K., Petersen, T. E., & Magnusson, S. (1982) *Eur. J. Biochem. 128*, 605.

Skorstengaard, K., Thøgersen, H. C., & Petersen, T. E. (1984) *Eur. J. Biochem. 140*, 235.

Spiro, R. G., & Bhoyroe, V. P. (1974) *J. Biol. Chem. 249*, 5704.

Weaver, C. A., Gordon, D. F., & Kemper, B. (1981) *Proc. Natl. Acad. Sci. U.S.A. 78*, 4073.

Young, R. A., & Davis, R. W. (1983) *Proc. Natl. Acad. Sci. U.S.A. 80*, 1194.

Human inhibitor of the first component of complement, C1: Characterization of cDNA clones and localization of the gene to chromosome 11

(protease inhibitors/serpins)

ALVIN E. DAVIS III*†, ALEXANDER S. WHITEHEAD‡, RICHARD A. HARRISON§, ANDRE DAUPHINAIS*, GAIL A. P. BRUNS¶, MARCO CICARDI*, AND FRED S. ROSEN*

Division of *Immunology, †Nephrology, ‡Cell Biology, and ¶Genetics, Childrens' Hospital, 300 Longwood Avenue, Boston, MA 02115; and §Mechanisms in Tumour Immunity Unit, Medical Research Council Centre, Hills Road, Cambridge, United Kingdom

Communicated by Ruth Sager, December 31, 1985

ABSTRACT C1 inhibitor is a heavily glycosylated plasma protein that regulates the activity of the first component of complement (C1) by inactivation of the serine protease subcomponents, C1r and C1s. C1 inhibitor cDNA clones have been isolated, and one of these (pC1INH1, 950 base pairs) has been partially sequenced. Sequence analysis demonstrates that the C1 inhibitor is a member of the serpin "superfamily" of protease inhibitors. In the region sequenced, C1 inhibitor has 22% identity with antithrombin III, 26% with α_1-antitrypsin and α_1-antichymotrypsin, and 18% with human angiotensinogen. C1 inhibitor has a larger amino-terminal extension than do the other plasma protease inhibitors. In addition, inspection of residues that are invariant among the other protease inhibitors shows that C1 inhibitor differs at 14 of 41 of these positions. Thus, it appears that C1 inhibitor diverged from the group relatively early in evolution, although probably after the divergence of angiotensinogen. Southern blot analysis of BamHI-digested DNA from normal individuals and from rodent–human somatic cell hybrid cell lines (that contain a limited but varied human chromosome complement) was used to localize the human C1 inhibitor gene to chromosome 11.

C1 inhibitor regulates the activity of the first component of complement (C1) by inhibition of the proteolytic activity of its subcomponents C1r and C1s. This prevents the activation of C4 and C2 by C1s, thereby providing an important control over classical pathway activation. In addition to C1r and C1s, C1 inhibitor also inhibits several other serine proteinases including plasmin, kallikrein, and coagulation factors XIa and XIIa (1–4). Although each of these other enzymes is inhibited by other protease inhibitors, C1r and C1s are inhibited only by C1 inhibitor, which functions in a manner similar to the other plasma protease inhibitors in that it forms an apparent covalent complex with C1r and C1s in an equimolar ratio (5–7). This results in the dissociation of macromolecular C1, with the release of C1r–C1s–(C1 inhibitor)$_2$ complexes (8–10).

C1 inhibitor is the most heavily glycosylated plasma protein, containing about 35% carbohydrate by weight (11, 12). Its carbohydrate composition suggests that it has a number of O-glycosidic-linked oligosaccharide units (12). It consists of a single polypeptide chain with an apparent M_r of 105,000 as determined by NaDodSO$_4$/PAGE (5, 11–14). The amino-terminal amino acid sequence (40 residues) has been reported, as has the sequence (12 residues) surrounding the reactive center (12, 15). Although the mechanism of protease inhibition by C1 inhibitor is analogous to that of other plasma

protease inhibitors, the available sequence data do not yet confirm a relationship.

Hereditary angioneurotic edema is a dominantly inherited disease caused by apparent heterozygous deficiency of C1 inhibitor (16–18). There are two forms of the disease, types I and II (19). Type I is characterized by diminished plasma levels of an apparently normal C1 inhibitor protein. In type II hereditary angioneurotic edema, a dysfunctional C1 inhibitor protein that is unable to inhibit C1 activity is present at levels varying from 30% to 400% of normal, as measured antigenically.

To determine the structural basis of C1 inhibitor function, to define its evolutionary relationship to other protease inhibitors, and to analyze the molecular genetic basis of hereditary angioneurotic edema, we have begun to examine the C1 inhibitor gene. In this report, we have characterized a C1 inhibitor cDNA clone that represents approximately half the coding sequence of the protein, and we have compared the sequence of this clone with the analogous regions of other protease inhibitors. In addition, we provide evidence that the human C1 inhibitor gene is on chromosome 11.

MATERIALS AND METHODS

Protein and Peptide Isolation. C1 inhibitor was isolated from normal human plasma as described (12). Digestion with CNBr was done by incubation of salt-free reduced and alkylated protein with CNBr (100-fold molar excess over total methionine) in 70% formic acid. Peptides were separated by initial gel filtration on Sepharose CL-6B (2.5 × 170 cm) equilibrated in 0.2 M Tris/5 mM EDTA/6 M guanidine·HCl, pH 8.0. The pool of smaller peptides from this column was fractionated by HPLC on an Aquapore RP300 column (Brownlee Labs, Santa Clara, CA) equilibrated in 0.1% CF$_3$COOH and developed with a linear acetonitrile gradient to 70%.

Amino Acid Sequence Analysis. Automated Edman degradations were performed with a Beckman 890C sequencer modified with a cold trap. A 0.1 M Quadrol program was used (20). Conversion was performed with methanolic HCl (1 part acetyl chloride and 7 parts methanol at 65°C for 10 min). Phenylthiohydantoin derivatives were identified by HPLC using a Zorbax ODS column (DuPont Instruments) equilibrated in 0.01 M sodium acetate, pH 5.5/20% acetonitrile and developed with an acetonitrile gradient (21). Repetitive yields in all sequencing runs ranged from 92% to 95%.

Synthetic Oligonucleotides. Six C1 inhibitor CNBr peptides were subjected to sequence analysis (Table 1). One of these (CB5) was the amino-terminal peptide (12), while another

Abbreviations: C1, first component of complement: bp, base pair(s); kb, kilobase(s).

Reprinted with permission from Alvin E. Davis III. *Proc Natl Acaol Sci U S A*. 1986;83:3161–3165.

Table 1. Amino-terminal sequences of C1 inhibitor CNBr peptides

CB1:	Leu-Phe-Val-Glu-Pro-Ile-Leu-Glu-Val-Xaa-Leu
CB2:	Ala-Phe-Ser-Pro-Phe-Ser-Ile-Ala-Ser-Leu-Leu-Xaa-Gln-Val-Leu-Leu-Gly-Ala-Gly-Asn-Ala-Glu-Ala-Xaa-Asn-Xaa-Glu
CB3:	Asn-Ser-Lys-Lys-Tyr-Pro-Val-Ala-His-Phe-Ile-Asp-Gln-Thr-Leu-Lys-Ala-Lys-Val-Gly-Gln-Leu-Gln-Leu-Ser-His-Xaa-Leu-Ser-Leu-Val-Ile-Leu-Val-Pro-Gln-Asn-Leu-Xaa-Xaa-Xaa-Leu-Glu
CB4:	Gln-His-Gln-Thr-Val-Leu-Glu-Leu-Thr-Glu-Thr-Gly-Val-Glu-Ala
CB5:	Asn-Pro-Xaa-Ala-Thr-Ser-Ser-Ser-Ser-Gln-Asp
CB6:	Glu-Lys-Leu-Glu-Met*-Ser-Lys-Phe-Gln-Pro-Thr-Leu-Leu-Thr-Leu-Pro-Xaa-Ile-Lys-Val-Thr-Thr-Ser-Gln-Asp

*Cleavage apparently did not occur at this methionine. It was detected at the appropriate yield during sequencing, and no peptide with a sequence beginning at residue 6 was found.

(CB1, apparent M_r 45,000 on NaDodSO$_4$/PAGE) had an amino-terminal sequence beginning at residue 32 of the intact protein (12). From the amino-terminal sequences of two of the other four peptides, two hexapeptide sequences (His-Phe-Ile-Asp-Gln-Thr from CB3 and Met-Gln-His-Gln-Thr-Val from CB4) were chosen to construct oligonucleotide mixtures for screening of the cDNA library. Each of these two mixtures contained 64 different 17-nucleotide-long oligonucleotides, comprising all sequences that could code for the respective hexapeptides. Oligonucleotides for screening and for use as nucleotide sequencing primers were synthesized either on a Biosearch Sam One automated

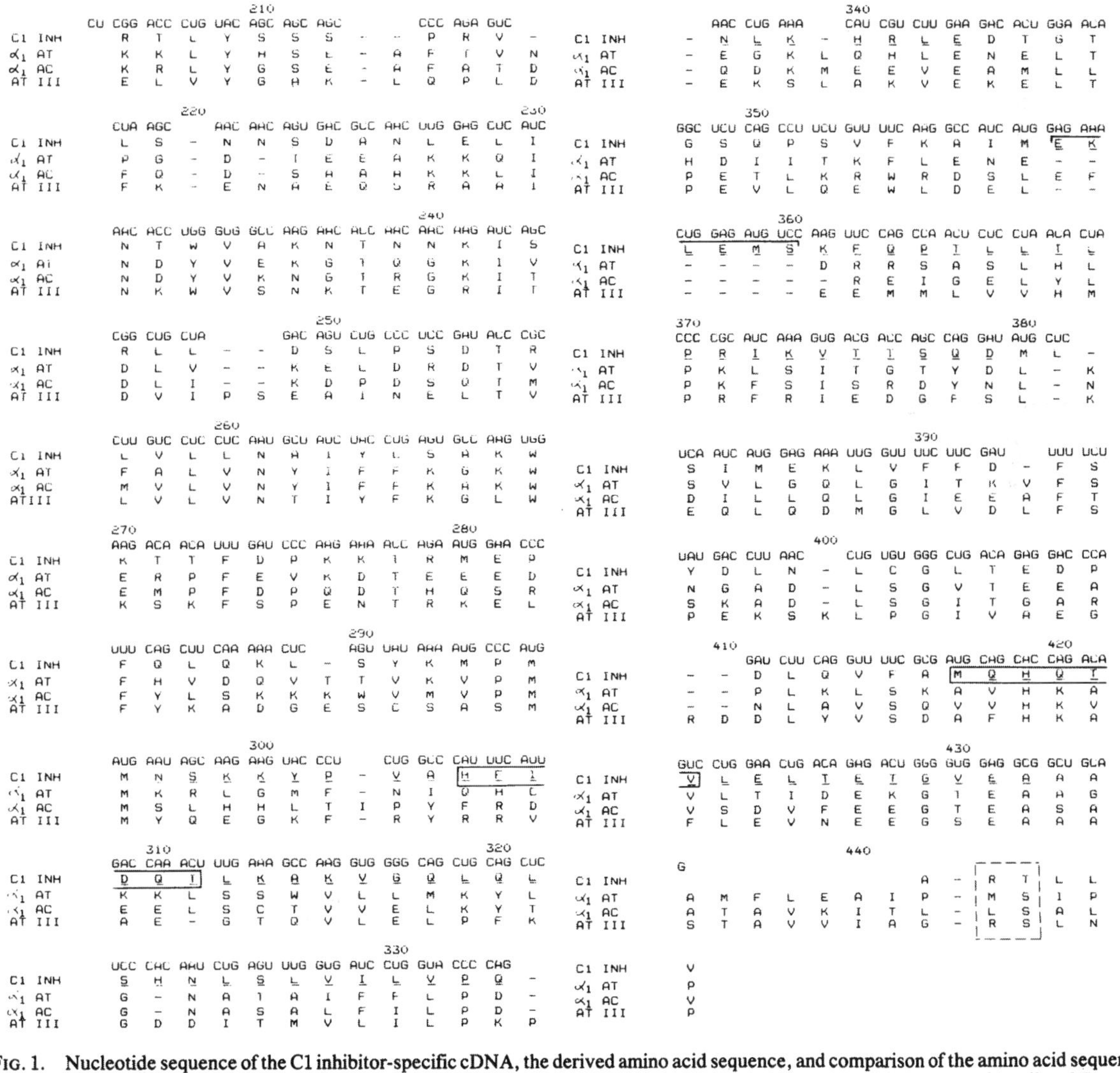

FIG. 1. Nucleotide sequence of the C1 inhibitor-specific cDNA, the derived amino acid sequence, and comparison of the amino acid sequence with those of other human plasma proteinase inhibitors. The numbering used refers to amino acid numbering and is from Carrell and Boswell (35). C1 INH, C1 inhibitor; α_1 AT, α_1-antitrypsin; α_1 AC, α_1-antichymotrypsin; AT III, antithrombin III. The standard single-letter amino acid code is used. The C1 inhibitor hexapeptide sequences used for construction of synthetic oligonucleotides are enclosed, and the amino acid residues determined also by protein sequence analysis are underlined. The insertion in C1 inhibitor relative to the other proteinase inhibitors is bracketed. The reactive centers are enclosed with a dashed line.

nucleotide synthesizer or on an Applied Biosystems 380B DNA synthesizer.

Screening for and Isolation of C1 Inhibitor cDNA Clones. An adult human liver cDNA library containing more than 200,000 recombinant clones (23) was plated on 82-mm-diameter nitrocellulose filters at high density and screened as described (24). The oligonucleotide mixtures were 5'-end-labeled with [γ-^{32}P]ATP and T4 polynucleotide kinase (Bethesda Research Laboratories). Hybridization was done at 40°C, and filters were washed in 0.9 M NaCl/90 mM sodium citrate/0.05% sodium pyrophosphate at 42, 46, and 50°C. After each wash, filters were dried and exposed overnight on Kodak XAR-5 film. Plasmids were isolated by the alkaline NaDodSO$_4$ method (25). The C1 inhibitor-specific cDNA inserts were excised with *Pst* I (New England Biolabs) and isolated by preparative agarose gel electrophoresis. The C1 inhibitor cDNA clone was sequenced by the dideoxy chain-termination method of Sanger (49) after subcloning in the phage vector M13 mp18.

Messenger RNA Isolation and RNA Blot Analysis. RNA was isolated from the human hepatoma cell line, Hep G2 (26) as described (27), was size-fractionated by agarose/formaldehyde gel electrophoresis (28), and was transferred to nitrocellulose filters. The 600-base-pair (bp) *Pst* I fragment of the C1 inhibitor cDNA clone (pC1INH1) was labeled by nick-translation (29) and used as a hybridization probe. Hybridization was in 10% dextran/50% formamide buffer at 42°C; final washing was at 65°C.

Chromosomal Localization. The somatic cell hybrids used have been described and characterized for human chromosome content by isozyme and cytogenetic techniques (30–32). They also have been analyzed with cloned DNA probes for 21 of the human autosomes and the X chromosome. DNA isolated (33) from human peripheral blood leukocytes, mouse RAG cells, hamster E36 cells, and somatic cell hybrids was digested with *Bam*HI and subjected to agarose gel electrophoresis, and Southern blots were done (34). These blots were hybridized with the 600-bp *Pst* I fragment of pC1INH1 radiolabeled by nick-translation (29). Filters were washed in 30 mM NaCl/3 mM sodium citrate at 65°C for 1 hr and exposed overnight with Kodak XAR-5 film.

RESULTS AND DISCUSSION

Isolation and Sequence Analysis of C1 Inhibitor cDNA. Approximately 40,000 recombinant colonies were screened of which 4 were positive with both oligonucleotide mixtures; of these 1 (pC1INH1) was further characterized. This clone consisted of ≈932 bp and contained an internal *Pst* I site that divides the insert into a 3' 332-bp fragment and a 5' 600-bp fragment. The 332-bp fragment has been fully sequenced, and 325 nucleotides of the 600-bp fragment have been determined. The nucleotide and derived amino acid sequences are shown in Fig. 1. The amino acid sequence contained three of the six CNBr peptides. Amino acid sequences derived also from protein sequence analysis are underlined. The nucleotide and known amino acid sequences agreed at all positions. The clone contained the sequences that matched the two synthetic oligonucleotide sequences. These hexapeptides are enclosed in Fig. 1. The molecular weight of the C1 inhibitor polypeptide chain is ≈64,000, as determined from cell-free synthesis studies (unpublished data). From this molecular weight and the amino acid composition reported by Harrison (12), C1 inhibitor consists of about 580 amino acids. The cDNA insert thus represents slightly more than half the coding sequence for C1 inhibitor (932 of an estimated 1740 nucleotides).

The amino acid sequence derived from the nucleotide sequence is aligned in Fig. 1 with the homologous portions of three other known human plasma protease inhibitors that are

members of the serpin "superfamily" (22, 36–40). As shown, by comparison, the 3' end of the clone terminates 27–30 nucleotides 5' to the reactive centers of the other inhibitors (enclosed by a dashed line). The C1 inhibitor reactive center sequence is from Salvesen *et al.* (15). Although it has been assumed that C1 inhibitor was a member of this group, the previous limited sequence data did not show homology (12, 15). As shown in Fig. 1, C1 inhibitor is related to these other protease inhibitors and to the other members of the superfamily, such as ovalbumin and angiotensinogen. In the region shown, C1 inhibitor as aligned in Fig. 1 has 22% identity with antithrombin III and 26% with α_1-antitrypsin and α_1-antichymotrypsin. It also has 18% identity with human angiotensinogen (not shown) (41). This degree of homology is similar to but slightly less than the degree of homology (29% to 44%) among the other antiproteases over the same region. It is, however, somewhat greater than the degree of homology between angiotensinogen and each of the protease inhibitors. There are several interesting and perhaps significant differences observed in comparing C1 inhibitor with the other serpins.

The alignment shown in Fig. 1 is essentially that of Carrell and Boswell (35), with alignments based on the secondary structure of α_1-antitrypsin (42) and insertion of gaps penalized in regions of defined secondary structure. The first difference that is apparent on inspection of Fig. 1, combined with previous knowledge of the C1 inhibitor molecule, is that the C1 inhibitor has a larger amino-terminal extension than do most of the other serpins. The other serpins have 45–55 amino acid residues between the end of the derived C1 inhibitor sequence shown in Fig. 1 and the carboxyl termini and ≈130–180 residues between their amino termini and the beginning of the sequences shown in Fig. 1. In addition to the CNBr peptides included in Fig. 1 (CB3, CB4, and CB6 in Table 1), C1 inhibitor contains two larger CNBr peptides (CB1 and CB2 in Table 1) (43). The sequence of CB1 overlaps with the reported amino-terminal sequence, beginning at residue 32 from the amino terminus (12). This data, together with the homology and the known variation in amino-terminal extensions among the other serpins, indicate that these larger peptides are both amino-terminal to the sequence shown in Fig. 1. If it is assumed that C1 inhibitor has about 50 amino acid residues carboxyl-terminal to the sequence in Fig. 1, then there must be slightly more than 300 amino acids amino-terminal to the sequence shown. Thus, C1 inhibitor has an amino-terminal extension that is more than 100 residues longer than those of the other serpins. The relationship of this extension to the function of C1 inhibitor remains to be defined. Virtually all of the carbohydrate side chains are in this portion of the molecule (12, 43). There are no potential sites for N-linked oligosaccharide in the sequence in Fig. 1.

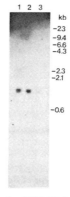

FIG. 2. RNA blot analysis of C1 inhibitor-specific mRNA. Lanes: 1, 15 μg of RNA; 2, 10 μg of RNA; 3, 5 μg of RNA.

Table 2. Chromosomal localization of the gene for C1 inhibitor

Cell line	C1 Inh. band	1	2	3	4	5	6	7	8	9	10	11	12	13	14	15	16	17	18	19	20	21	22	X
													Human chromosome											
G17 11	−	−	−	−	−	+	+	+	−	−	+	−	+	+	+	−	−	+	+	+	+	+	−	−
G17 5	−	±	−	−	+	−	+	−	+	−	+	−	−	+	+	+	−	−	−	+	−	−	+	−
G24 A4	±	±	R	−	−	+	+	+	−	+	−	±	+	+	+	+	−	−	−	+	−	+	−	−
G35 D3	−	−	R	−	+	−	−	+	+	+	+	−	−	−	±	−	+	+	−	+	+	+	+	−
G35 A4	−	+	−	+	+	−	+	−	+	+	−	−	−	+	−	+	−	−	+	+	+	−	+	+
G35 D5	−	+	+	+	−	−	+	+	−	−	+	−	+	+	+	+	+	+	+	+	−	+	−	−
G46 C2	−	−	−	−	−	−	−	−	−	−	+	−	+	−	+	−	−	−	−	−	−	+	+	+
G35 C4	−	−	−	−	−	−	+	+	−	R	−	−	+	−	+	−	−	−	±	+	+	−	+	−
G89 E5	−	−	−	−	−	−	−	−	−	−	−	−	−	−	−	−	−	−	−	−	−	−	−	+
G35 E3	+	−	−	−	−	+	+	−	+	−	−	+	+	+	+	−	+	−	+	+	+	+	+	−
G35 A5	+	R	R	+	+	−	+	+	−	+	+	+	−	+	+	+	+	−	+	+	+	+	+	−
G35 D2	+	+	−	−	−	+	+	−	−	±	−	+	+	−	−	+	+	−	±	+	+	−	+	−
G35 A2	+	−	−	+	+	−	+	−	−	−	+	−	−	+	−	−	−	−	+	+	+	+	+	±
G35 B5	+	−	−	−	−	−	R	+	−	−	−	+	R	+	−	−	−	+	−	+	−	−	−	−
G24 B5	+	+	−	−	+	+	−	−	+	−	+	+	+	+	−	+	−	−	+	+	−	+	+	+
G35 C1	+	±	−	R	+	+	R	+	−	−	+	+	R	−	+	+	+	−	+	+	−	−	+	−
G35 F5	+	±	−	+	+	+	−	+	−	−	+	−	+	+	−	+	+	+	+	+	±	+	+	+
G35 D4	+	+	+	+	−	+	+	−	−	+	+	+	+	+	+	−	−	+	+	−	+	+	+	+
Concordant		9	7	11	10	10	9	9	6	7	7	18	10	10	9	10	12	7	9	11	9	9	12	8
Discordant		6	8	5	7	7	6	8	11	8	10	0	5	7	7	7	5	10	6	6	7	8	5	8

The designations are: +, presence of the 6.0-kb C1 inhibitor *Bam*HI fragment; −, absence of the fragment; ±, weakly positive signal for the above fragment on Southern blot analysis. Similar designations are used for the presence or absence of human chromosomes in the hybrid lines. The designation "R" indicates a chromosome rearrangement as evidenced by cytogenetic techniques or disruption of a known syntenic group. The chromosome 19 column represents the 19q⁺ translocation chromosome present in the hybrids, and the X chromosome column represents the intact X and the Xq- translocation chromosome (31, 32). A single hybrid (not shown) hybridized very weakly with the 6.0-kb C1 inhibitor *Bam*HI fragment but failed to hybridize with two different chromosome 11-derived DNA probes. It is likely that this hybrid has retained only a fragment of chromosome 11 including the C1 inhibitor locus. "Concordant" indicates the sum of cell lines that contain the particular chromosome and are positive for the 6.0-kb C1 inhibitor-specific band or are negative for both. Discordant cell lines are those in which the chromosome in question is present and the 6.0-kb band is absent or in which the particular chromosome is absent and the 6.0-kb band is present. Inh., inhibitor.

Another difference between C1 inhibitor and the other serpins is apparent on examination of invariant residues observed when the sequences are aligned. There are 41 amino acid residues that are identical among the other three human plasma protease inhibitors. C1 inhibitor has a different amino acid at 14 of these positions. Similar analysis of each of the antiproteases in comparison with the other three shows appreciably less variation, with the exception of antithrombin III, which shows 11 differences among 37 positions that are identical in C1 inhibitor, α_1-antitrypsin, and α_1-antichymotrypsin. When this comparison is extended to the entire superfamily (the above inhibitors plus chicken ovalbumin, chicken gene *Y*, mouse contrapsin, mouse and baboon α_1-antitrypsin, and baboon and human angiotensinogen), C1 inhibitor differs at 3 of 11 positions that are invariant in the other serpins. The only other member that differs at any position that is invariant in the others is angiotensinogen. This is not surprising because it is obviously more distantly related to the other members of the group.

In addition to the above, C1 inhibitor shows two other variations. Between positions 350 and 360, it shows an insertion of four to six amino acid residues relative to the other serpins (bracket in Fig. 1). Also, proline-351, eight residues prior to this insertion, is within a region that in α_1-antitrypsin is in an α-helix. However, because of the insertion, the alignment through this segment (which shows a low degree of homology) may not be correct. This proline residue may in fact align with the prolines in antithrombin III and α_1-antichymotrypsin (position 348), which are just at the beginning of the α-helix (35).

RNA Blot Analysis. A C1 inhibitor mRNA of ≈1500 bp (compared with DNA markers) was identified in RNA isolated from a human hepatoma cell line (Hep G2) (Fig. 2) and from cultured human monocytes (not shown). A mRNA with a minimum size of 1740 bp would be expected from the size of the C1 inhibitor polypeptide. The C1 inhibitor mRNA, when compared with 18S and 28S RNA as markers, had a calculated length of 2100 bp. Thus, it is compatible with the expected size.

Chromosomal Localization of the Human C1 Inhibitor Gene.

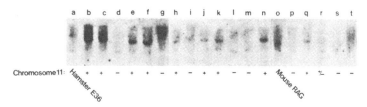

FIG. 3. Southern blot analysis of *Bam*HI-digested DNA from rodent–human somatic cell hybrids and rodent parent cell lines. The DNA samples in lanes: a, hamster parent cell line E36; b–l, hamster–human hybrids G35-B5, -C1, -C4, -A2, -D2, -D3, -D4, -D5, -E3, -F5, -A4; m, hamster–human hybrid G89-E5; n, hamster–human hybrid G35-A5; o, mouse parent cell line RAG; p–t, mouse–human hybrids G46-C2, G24-B5, G24-A4, G17-5, G17-11. The 6.0-kb band represents human C1 inhibitor. The presence or absence of chromosome 11 is shown below each track.

Somatic cell hybrids between human leukocytes and mouse RAG or hamster E36 cells were analyzed for the presence of the C1 inhibitor gene. These hybrids contain a limited but varied human chromosome complement, with a full rodent chromosome complement. Southern blot analysis of BamHI-digested DNA isolated from peripheral blood leukocytes from seven normal individuals revealed a fragment of ≈6.0 kilobases (kb). This band was not detected in the DNA from the mouse RAG cells or the hamster E36 cells. DNA isolated from the somatic cell hybrids was also digested with BamHI and subjected to Southern blot analysis. The presence or absence of the 6.0-kb C1 inhibitor-specific band correlated only with the presence or absence of chromosome 11 (Table 2, Fig. 3), thus allowing the assignment of the human C1 inhibitor gene to this chromosome. The gene for α_1-antitrypsin maps to chromosome 14 (44), and that for antithrombin III maps to chromosome 1 (45). Thus, although these proteinase inhibitors are ancestrally related, they do not constitute a linkage group on the same chromosome in man.

C1 inhibitor thus is a member of the serpin superfamily of serine protease inhibitors and related proteins. Based on comparison of the available sequences, C1 inhibitor very likely diverged from the group relatively early, although after the divergence of angiotensinogen. Interestingly, however, the structure of the genes for angiotensinogen and α_1-antitrypsin are remarkably similar in that each has four introns and the position of the introns is the same in the two genes (39, 46). The gene for ovalbumin, on the other hand, has seven introns that are arranged differently within the gene (47, 48). Preliminary Southern blot analysis of C1 inhibitor genomic clones indicate that the gene is at least 7–8 kb (unpublished data), but the gene structure is not yet known. Comparison of the structure of the gene for C1 inhibitor with the other genes may help to clarify the relationships among them.

Note Added in Proof. Since this manuscript was submitted, sequence analysis of other cDNA clones has shown that there are 42 additional amino acids between the end of the sequence shown in Fig. 1 and the carboxyl terminus of the protein. The sequence of the active center region agrees completely with that reported by Salvesen et al. (15), as shown in Fig. 1. In addition, these data indicate that the sequence at residues 427–431 (Glu-Thr-Gly-Val-Glu) is in the correct position and has a sequence compatible with that of the "hinge region" preceding the active center in serpins.

We thank Dr. Harvey R. Colten for providing the human liver cDNA library used in these studies. This work was supported by Public Health Service Grants AM 34604 and HD 18658 and by the March of Dimes Birth Defects Foundation Grant 1-775. A.S.W. is supported by a Helen Hay Whitney Foundation Fellowship (F488). This work was done during the tenure of an established investigatorship of the American Heart Association (A.E.D.) and with funds contributed in part by the American Heart Association, Massachusetts Affiliate, Inc.

1. Ratnoff, O. D., Pensky, J., Ogston, D. & Naff, G. B. (1969) *J. Exp. Med.* **129**, 315–331.
2. Forbes, C. D., Pensky, J. & Ratnoff, O. D. (1971) *J. Lab. Clin. Med.* **76**, 809–815.
3. Gigli, I., Mason, J. W., Colman, R. W. & Austen, K. F. (1970) *J. Immunol.* **104**, 574–581.
4. Schreiber, A. D., Kaplan, A. P. & Austen, K. F. (1973) *J. Clin. Invest.* **52**, 1394–1401.
5. Harpel, P. C. & Cooper, N. R. (1975) *J. Clin. Invest.* **55**, 593–604.
6. Sim, R. B., Reboul, A., Arlaud, G. J., Villiers, C. L. & Colomb, M. G. (1979) *FEBS Lett.* **97**, 111–115.
7. Sim, R. B., Arlaud, G. J. & Colomb, M. G. (1980) *Biochim. Biophys. Acta* **612**, 433–449.
8. Sim, R. B., Arlaud, G. J. & Colomb, M. G. (1979) *Biochem. J.* **179**, 449–457.
9. Ziccardi, R. J. & Cooper, N. R. (1979) *J. Immunol.* **123**, 788–792.
10. Laurell, A.-B., Martensson, U. & Sjoholm, A. G. (1976) *Acta Pathol. Microbiol. Scand.* **84**, 455–464.
11. Haupt, H., Heimburger, N., Kranz, T. & Schwick, G. (1970) *Eur. J. Biochem.* **17**, 254–261.
12. Harrison, R. A. (1983) *Biochemistry* **22**, 5001–5007.
13. Pensky, J., Levy, L. R. & Lepow, I. H. (1961) *J. Biol. Chem.* **236**, 1674–1679.
14. Reboul, A., Arlaud, G. J., Sim, R. B. & Colomb, M. G. (1977) *FEBS Lett.* **79**, 45–50.
15. Salvesen, G. S., Catanese, J. J., Kress, L. F. & Travis, J. (1985) *J. Biol. Chem.* **260**, 2432–2436.
16. Osler, W. (1888) *Am. J. Med. Sci.* **95**, 362–367.
17. Donaldson, V. H. & Evans, R. R. (1963) *Am. J. Med.* **35**, 37–44.
18. Landermann, N. S., Webster, M. E., Becker, E. L. & Ratcliffe, H. E. (1962) *J. Allergy* **33**, 330–341.
19. Rosen, F. S., Charache, P., Pensky, J. & Donaldson, V. (1965) *Science* **148**, 957–958.
20. Brauer, A. W., Margolies, M. N. & Haber, E. (1975) *Biochemistry* **14**, 3029–3035.
21. Zalut, C., Henzel, W. S. & Harris, H. W. (1980) *J. Biochem. Biophys. Methods* **3**, 11–30.
22. Petersen, T. E., Dudek-Wojciechowska, G., Sottrup-Jensen, L. & Magnussen, S. (1979) in *The Physiological Inhibitors of Coagulation and Fibrinolysis*, eds. Collen, D., Wiman, B. & Verstraete, M. (Elsevier–North Holland Biomedical Press, Amsterdam), pp. 43–54.
23. Woods, D. E., Markham, A. F., Ricker, A. T., Goldberger, G. & Colten, H. R. (1982) *Proc. Natl. Acad. Sci. USA* **79**, 5661–5665.
24. Grunstein, M. & Hogness, D. S. (1975) *Proc. Natl. Acad. Sci. USA* **72**, 3961–3965.
25. Birnboim, H. C. & Doly, J. (1979) *Nucleic Acids Res.* **7**, 1513–1523.
26. Knowles, B. B., Howe, C. C. & Aden, D. P. (1980) *Science* **209**, 497–499.
27. Chirgwin, J. M., Przybyla, A. E., MacDonald, R. J. & Rutter, W. J. (1979) *Biochemistry* **18**, 5294–5299.
28. Lehrach, H., Diamond, D., Wezney, J. M. & Boedtker, H. (1977) *Biochemistry* **16**, 4743–4751.
29. Jeffreys, A. J. & Flavell, R. A. (1977) *Cell* **12**, 429–439.
30. Latt, S. A., Willard, H. F. & Gerald, P. S. (1976) *Chromosoma (Berlin)* **57**, 135–153.
31. Brook, J. D., Shaw, D. J., Meredith, L., Bruns, G. A. P. & Harper, P. S. (1984) *Hum. Genet.* **68**, 282–285.
32. Bruns, G. A. P., Mintz, B. J., Leary, A. C., Regina, V. M. & Gerald, P. S. (1979) *Biochem. Genet.* **17**, 1031–1059.
33. Gross-Bellard, M., Oudet, P. & Chambon, P. (1977) *Eur. J. Biochem.* **36**, 32–38.
34. Southern, E. M. (1975) *J. Mol. Biol.* **98**, 503–517.
35. Carrell, R. W. & Boswell, D. R. (1986) in *Proteinase Inhibitors*, eds. Barrett, A. & Salvesen, G. (Elsevier–North Holland Biomedical Press, Amsterdam), in press.
36. Carrell, R. W., Jeppsson, J.-O., Laurell, C.-B., Brennan, S. O., Owen, M. C., Vaughan, L. & Boswell, D. R. (1982) *Nature (London)* **298**, 329–334.
37. Hunt, L. T. & Dayhoff, M. O. (1980) *Biochem. Biophys. Res. Commun.* **95**, 864–871.
38. Doolittle, R. F. (1983) *Science* **222**, 417–419.
39. Tanaka, T., Ohkubo, H. & Nakanishi, N. (1984) *J. Biol. Chem.* **259**, 8063–8065.
40. Chandra, J., Stackhouse, R., Kidd, V. J., Robson, K. J. H. & Woo, S. L. C. (1983) *Biochemistry* **22**, 5055–5061.
41. Kageyama, R., Ohkubo, H. & Nakanishi, S. (1984) *Biochemistry* **23**, 3603–3609.
42. Loebermann, H., Tokuoka, R., Deisenhofer, J. & Huber, R. (1984) *J. Mol. Biol.* **177**, 531–556.
43. Harrison, R. A. & Rosen, F. S. (1982) *Mol. Immunol.* **19**, 1374 (abstr.).
44. Cox, D. W., Markovic, V. D. & Teshima, I. E. (1982) *Nature (London)* **297**, 428–430.
45. Kao, F. T., Morse, H. G., Law, M. L., Lidsky, A., Chandra, T. & Woo, S. L. C. (1984) *Hum. Genet.* **67**, 34–36.
46. Kidd, V. J., Wallace, R. B., Itakura, K. & Woo, S. L. C. (1983) *Nature (London)* **304**, 230–234.
47. Gannon, F., O'Hare, K., Perrin, F., LePennec, J. P., Benoist, C., Cochet, M., Breathnach, R., Royal, A., Garapin, A., Cami, B. & Chambon, P. (1979) *Nature (London)* **278**, 428–434.
48. O'Malley, B. W., Roop, D. R., Lai, E. C., Nordstrom, J. L., Catterall, J. F., Swanneck, G. E., Colbert, D. A., Tsai, M. J., Dugaiczyk, A. & Woo, S. L. C. (1979) *Recent Prog. Horm. Res.* **35**, 1–46.
49. Sanger, F., Nicklen, S. & Coulsen, A. R. (1977) *Proc. Natl. Acad. Sci. USA* **74**, 5463–5467.

Long-term prophylaxis with C1-inhibitor (C1 INH) concentrate in patients with recurrent angioedema caused by hereditary and acquired C1-inhibitor deficiency

Konrad Bork, MD, and Günther Witzke, PhD
Mainz, Federal Republic of Germany

A case of hereditary angioedema (HAE) type I (inherited C1-inhibitor [C1 INH] deficiency) and a case of late-onset acquired C1 INH with angioedema is described. In both patients, long-term prophylaxis with C1 INH had become necessary because treatment with danazol and ε-aminocaproic acid was not effective or not tolerated. Consequently, both patients received a pasteurized concentrate of C1 INH continuously for a period of 1 year in a dosage that kept them free of symptoms. The patient with HAE was administered 500 units of C1 INH intravenously every 4 or 5 days, whereas the patient with acquired angioedema required 1000 units of C1 INH every 5 days. As a result of this long-term prophylaxis, both patients became free or nearly free from their episodes of cutaneous and internal edema. The low plasma levels of C1 INH, C4, and C2, rose. In the patient with acquired C1 INH deficiency, the swellings increasingly reappeared after 10 months, although the patient's antibody titer did not rise during treatment. No side effects were recorded during therapy. In particular, both patients remained HIV and hepatitis B antibody negative. (J ALLERGY CLIN IMMUNOL 1989;83:677-82.)

The plasma serpins are proteins that form a tight 1:1 complex with their target protease; the complex is later removed from the circulation and catabolized. C1-esterase inhibitors (C1 INH) that can inactivate kallikrein, plasmin, C1r, C1s, and the activated coagulation factors XII and XI (Fig. 1) belongs to this superfamily of proteins. HAE is associated with a deficiency of functionally active C1 INH in the blood plasma. This biochemical abnormality was demonstrated to be inherited in an autosomal dominant manner and to be heterogeneous at the biochemical level. Immunochemical studies have defined two major forms of C1 INH deficiency. The predominant form (HAE type I, common form) is characterized by reduced levels of C1 INH protein caused by a decreased synthetic rate of functional C1 INH.[1] Individuals af-

From the Department of Dermatology, Johannes Gutenberg University, Mainz, Federal Republic of Germany.
Presented in part at the Eleventh Congress of the International Society on Thrombosis and Haemostasis, Brussels, Belgium, July 5-10, 1987.
Received for publication Feb. 10, 1988.
Accepted for publication Aug. 27, 1988.
Reprint requests: Konrad Bork, MD, Department of Dermatology, Johannes Gutenberg University, Langenbeckstrasse 1, 6500 Mainz, Federal Republic of Germany.

Abbreviations used
C1 INH:	Inhibitor of first component of complement
HAE:	Hereditary angioedema
CH_{50}:	Total hemolytic complement
EACA:	ε-Aminocaproic acid

---

fected with the variant form of the disease (HAE type II) have normal or raised C1 INH protein concentrations but synthesize a functionally defective C1 INH species.[2-4] Thus, the low levels of functional C1 INH activity in HAE result from either deficient or defective C1 INH synthesis. Both types of HAE are further characterized by low or absent titers of C2 and C4, by low CH_{50}, by the presence of a positive family history, and the onset of symptoms in childhood or early adolescence. The pathogenesis of edema formation is not clearly understood. The reduced levels of functional C1 INH can lead to uncontrolled activation of the classic pathway of complement. This may elicit rise to the release of a C2 kinin[5, 6] and/or contact system activation with release of bradykinin[7-9] that have been assumed to cause the increased vascular permeability responsible for the clinical symptoms.

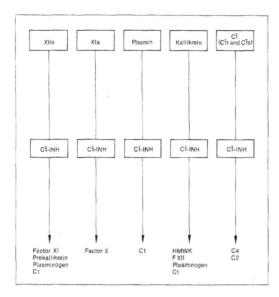

FIG. 1. Inhibition of the initial phases and activation of the coagulation, fibrinolytic, kinin, and complement systems by C$\overline{1}$ INH.

Characteristics of the rare acquired angioedema are low or absent levels of C1 INH, C1q, C1, C4, and C2, a low CH$_{50}$, the lack of heredity, and the onset of symptoms in middle age. In contrast to HAE, the synthesis of C1 INH is normal or slightly elevated. Increased activation of C1 is proposed to bring about accelerated catabolism of C1 INH in this type of acquired angioedema.[10, 11] In all cases, underlying diseases were reported, nearly all of which consisted of benign or malignant lymphoproliferative disorders or B cell abnormalities with autoantibody production.[12] The literature now contains articles of approximately 35 cases of this type. Recently, a new type of acquired C1 INH deficiency has been reported.[13-15] These cases differ from the other reported cases of acquired angioedema in the following respects: First, no associated diseases, especially no malignant or benign lymphoproliferative disorders or B cell abnormalities with anti-idiotypical antibodies, could be identified. Second, the levels of C1 INH protein were only slightly reduced (60% to 70% of normal; in the other forms of acquired angioedema, usually <30% of normal). Third, the purified C1 INH molecule had a molecular weight of only 96,000 daltons (normal C1 INH, 105,000 daltons). Fourth, the patients' sera contained large amounts of C1 INH antibodies.

In patients with HAE, acute swelling is only treated if it is likely to lead to life-threatening edema or it is already life threatening. For this reason, only those patients who develop edema in the region of the head, which may progress to glottis edema, or those patients who suffer from severe edema of the internal organs, require treatment. Peripheral cutaneous edemas of the extremities or of the trunk do not need to be treated. The therapy of choice in acute attacks consists of replacement therapy with commercially available C1-inhibitor concentrates (e.g., C1-inactivator P, Behringwerke AG, Marburg/Lahn, West Germany) or with fresh, frozen plasma.[16-19] In life-threatening cases, intubation and other intensive care measures may become necessary, depending on the symptoms and the location of the edema. Prophylaxis is necessary in patients who suffer from frequent and/or severe edema. The medication of choice is danazol (e.g., Winobanin, Winthrop GmbH, Norderstedt, West Germany), 50 to 600 mg daily. Danazol is a synthetic androgen. The mode of action is not known for certain. Stanazolol has also been tried successfully. Another possibility is the prophylactic regimen with antifibrinolytic agents, such as EACA or tranexamic acid. In this article, we describe two patients in whom long-term prophylaxis with C1 INH concentrates was necessary since it was impossible to resort to danazol or EACA.

MATERIAL AND METHODS

For complement investigation, plasma was separated and tested immediately. The C1 INH, C3, and C4 protein levels were measured antigenically by standard radioimmunodiffusion with Partigen M plates (Behringwerke AG). Serum levels of CH$_{50}$ were determined according to the method of Heinz et al.[20] Functionally active C1 and C2 were measured on a molecular basis according to the method of Rapp and Borsos.[21] C1 INH functional activity was estimated according to the method of Alsenz and Loos.[22] The presence of anti-C1 INH antibodies was established by the use of an ELISA with purified C1 INH, as described elsewhere.[15]

For replacement therapy, a concentrate of purified C1 INH (C1-inactivator P, Behringwerke AG,) was used. For this, C1-inactivator was adsorbed out of the plasma by means of an ion exchanger, eluted, and then stabilized and heat treated in aqueous solution at 60° C for 10 hours (pasteurization). The heat treatment was followed by further purifications by hydrophobic chromatography on phenyl-sepharose. The final product, C1-inactivator P, has a specific activity of 60 U/mg of protein.[23] One vial contains 500 units that corresponds to the C1 INH activity present in 500 ml of pooled plasma. Immunization tests in rabbits and guinea pigs yielded no evidence that the pasteurization process elicits rise to new antigenic structures.[24] For laboratory experiments, samples of the C1-inactivator solution were taken from a production batch before heat treatment. After adding sucrose and glycine as stabilizers, these samples were mixed with a defined amount of the particular virus to be tested, stirred well, and then incubated at 60° C. Samples were taken before and at various times during

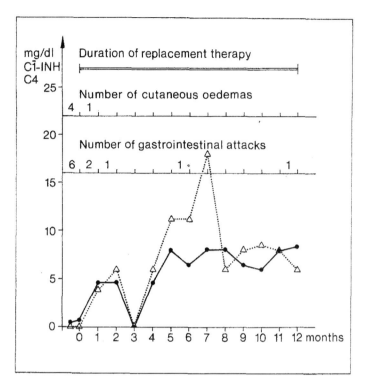

FIG. 2. Course of the disease and levels of C1 INH (●) and C4 (△) in patient No. 1 during replacement therapy (═) with 500 units of C1 INH concentrate every 4 or 5 days. Normal range of C1 INH, 15 to 35 mg/dl. Normal range of C4, 20 to 50 mg/dl.

pasteurization for titration of infectious virus. These experiments demonstrated that pasteurization at 60° C for 10 hours effectively inactivates HIV-1, Epstein Barr, cytomegalovirus, herpes simplex, poliovirus, and Rous sarcoma virus.[25, 26]

The treatment with C1 INH concentrate is highly expensive. In Europe, the cost of one vial is approximately $550.00.

RESULTS
Patient No. 1

Case history. A 47-year-old white man was first observed for assessment of HAE. Attacks began at the age of 9 years and occurred on an average every 3 to 4 weeks, sometimes even more often. The episodes were characterized by massive cutaneous swelling, often in the face, or by colicky abdominal pains lasting 2 to 6 days. Twelve attacks of life-threatening laryngeal edema required admission with oxygen therapy to the intensive care unit. The family history revealed similar edemas in his mother, who died from laryngeal edema when she was 52 years of age. All the patient's eight siblings died from laryngeal edema before they reached the age of 10 years. The diagnosis of HAE was made in 1974 and established by low or absent C1 INH and C4 serum levels. The patient was treated with danazol, of which a dose of 400 mg daily was necessary to control the symptoms. Lower doses were ineffective. This dose led to moderate symptomatic improvement with no further serious

attacks of angioedema. After 6 months of therapy, the patient refused further treatment with danazol because his weight had increased by >10 kg. Dietary control of the patient was not effective.

Several years later, therapy with EACA was started but had to be stopped after 3 months because of several episodes of thrombophlebitis and phlebothrombosis. On clinical examination, there was no evidence of associated disease. Laboratory investigations demonstrated essentially normal haematologic and biochemical parameters. Complement investigation demonstrated depressed C1 INH, C4, and CH_{50} levels. Clinical and laboratory findings led to the diagnosis of HAE type I.

Treatment. The patient suffered from depressive episodes and several times attempted suicide. Control of these episodes with various tricyclic and tetracyclic antidepressants was not successful. Therefore, and since danazol and EACA were not tolerated or refused, we resorted to replacement therapy with C1 INH during a prolonged period. The patient was treated with C1 INH concentrate intravenously during a period of 1 year. The dose was determined empirically. It corresponded to the lowest dose needed to achieve complete freedom from clinical symptoms. The patient required 500 units of C1 INH concentrate every fourth or fifth day. The clinical condition improved, and the attacks ceased almost completely, as can be observed in Fig. 2. No undesirable side effects caused by the replacement therapy were observed. The results of complement investigations

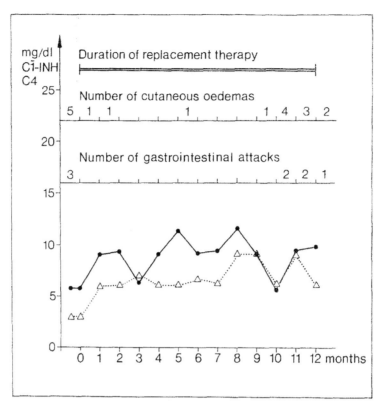

FIG. 3. Course of the disease and levels of C1 INH (●) and C4 (△) in patient No. 2 during replacement therapy (═) with 1000 units of C1 INH concentrate every 5 days. Normal range of C1 INH, 15 to 35 mg/dl. Normal range of C4, 20 to 50 mg/dl.

TABLE I. Laboratory investigations carried out in the patients before and during long-term replacement therapy with C̄1 INH concentrate

	Patient No. 1		Patient No. 2		
	Before treatment	After 6 months of therapy	Before treatment	After 6 months of therapy	Normal range
C̄1 INH protein (mg/dl)	1	6.4	5.6	8.0	15-35
C̄1 INH activity (%)	0	8	0	7	80-120
CH_{50} (U/ml)	0	0	0	0	13-26
C4 mg/dl	0	11.6	4	6.8	20-50
C2 (U/ml)	ND	ND	20	20	1,500-3,000
C̄1 (U/ml)	ND	ND	800	1000	100,000-300,000
C̄1 INH antibody titer	0	0	400	400	0

ND, Not determined.

before treatment and after 6 months of therapy are presented in Table I. During treatment, blood samples were obtained immediately before the next injection of C1 INH concentrate. There was no change in the other laboratory parameters examined, particularly the transaminase and virus-marker levels that were measured regularly.

Patient No. 2.

Case history. A 55-year-old man was first observed with a 5-year history of episodes of recurrent angioedema, mainly involving lips and hands, associated with attacks of severe cramp-like abdominal pain and nausea. The patient had had >100 attacks. Family history was negative; 12 relatives were investigated without any evidence of C1 INH deficiency. Treatment with danazol (600 mg per day) for 6 months and with EACA (6 gm per day) failed to reduce the number of attacks.

Clinical examination was basically normal. There was no evidence of lymphadenopathy or splenomegaly. Routine blood analysis was normal. No antinuclear antibodies, antitissue antibodies, rheumatoid factors, cryoglobulins, cold agglutinins, monomeric IgM, or antilymphocyte antibodies were found. Quantitative IgG, IgA, IgM, and IgE were normal. No B cell abnormalities could be detected. C1, C1 INH, C4, and C2 were reduced (Table I). Anti-C1 INH antibodies were found in this patient before therapy.[15] The diagnosis of acquired C1 INH deficiency with angioedema was made on the basis of family and personal history and confirmed by the complement findings. The patient's angioedema was classified as acquired angioedema with autoantibodies to C1 INH (AAE II), although the level of C1 INH was markedly reduced, more than usual in this form.

Treatment. Therapy with danazol and EACA did not relieve the symptoms sufficiently. A further trial with EACA at a larger dose was refused by the patient who is a professional trumpeter in a famous symphony orchestra. Therefore, we tried to reduce the cutaneous angioedema, especially the lip swelling, by long-term replacement prophylaxis with C1 INH concentrate. During an attack of angioedema with swelling of the lips, the patient initially received 500 units. When the edema became more severe within an hour, he was administered another injection of 500 units, after which the edema subsided. This patient needed 1000 units of C1 INH concentrate every fifth day, and the regimen has been carried out for a period of 1 year. Before treatment, the patient developed one to two skin swellings a week and one to two attacks of abdominal pain every month. In the first few months of replacement therapy, the number and duration of the attacks were markedly reduced (Fig. 3). After 10 months, the number and severity of the attacks slowly increased. Because there was no explanation for this, the treatment was stopped after 12 months. Another trial with EACA (10 gm daily) followed. During replacement therapy with the C1 INH concentrate, C1 INH and C4 serum levels were slightly increased (Fig. 3). The C1 INH antibody titer did not change during the entire treatment period. During treatment, blood samples were obtained immediately before the next injection of C1 INH concentrate. No undesirable side effects caused by replacement therapy were observed.

DISCUSSION

In patients with HAE, long-term prophylaxis with danazol, stanozolol, EACA, and tranexamic acid is usually effective, danazol being the medication of choice. Replacement therapy with C1 INH is normally used for the treatment of acute attacks; it is necessary in laryngeal edema and in life-threatening angioedema of the internal organs. Replacement therapy can be performed with a concentrate of purified C1 INH or with fresh, frozen plasma. C1 INH concentrate is more

appropriate and frequently used. It has been available in Europe for years. In cases of life-threatening edema, 500 to 1000 units are injected. Remission of edema begins within 2 or 3 hours of injection and is usually complete within 24 hours. In severe cases, repeated injections may be necessary. In addition, intensive care is needed. Complement investigations demonstrated an increased level of C1 INH, C2, C4, and CH_{50} after injection of C1 INH concentrate.[27] This study also demonstrated that high-molecular-weight kininogen levels rose after C1-INH concentrate infusion and paralleled the clinical course. The biologic half-life of C1 INH in healthy subjects is 64 ± 1.4 hours.[28] In cases of acute angioedema, consumption is increased. The clinical effect lasts for several days, depending on the plasma levels and dose. Both patients studied benefited from the long-term replacement therapy with C1 INH. The attacks were reduced in number and severity for a year (patient No. 1) and for 9 months (patient No. 2). The second patient responded to therapy, although therapy did not restore the initially low titers of C1 INH, CH_{50}, C4, or C2. The reason may be that circulating levels of C1 INH may not correspond to tissue levels. After 10 months, the patient became resistant to this form of therapy; the reason remains unclear. The resistance does not appear to be related to increased formation of antibodies to C1 INH. This patient displayed antibodies to C1 INH even before therapy, although he had never received C1 INH before, and the antibody titer did not rise during or after replacement therapy with C1 INH. The cause of the antibody formation still has to be clarified. No side effects of long-term prophylaxis with C1 INH were observed, and in particular, no clinical or serologic signs of hepatitis or antibodies to HIV were detectable before or after treatment. To sum up, longterm substitution with pasteurized C1 INH concentrates is safe and of clinical benefit to a group of patients selected in accordance with strict criteria. At least a temporary remission can be achieved.

REFERENCES

1. Donaldson VH, Evans RR. A biochemical abnormality in hereditary angioneurotic edema: absence of serum inhibitor of C1-esterase. Am J Med 1963;35:37-44.
2. Rosen FS, Charache P, Pensky J, Donaldson VH. Hereditary angioneurotic edema: two genetic variants. Science 1965;18:957-8.
3. Rosen FS, Alper CA, Pensky J, Klemperer MR, Donaldson VH. Genetically determined heterogeneity of the C1 esterase inhibitor in patients with hereditary angioneurotic edema. J Clin Invest 1971;50:2143-9.
4. Donaldson VH, Harrison RA, Rosen FS, Bing DH, Kindness G, Wagner CJ, Awad S. Variability in purified dysfunctional C1-inhibitor proteins from patients with hereditary angioneurotic edema: functional and analytical gel studies. J Clin Invest 1985;75:124-32.

5. Donaldson VH, Ratnoff OD, Da Silva WD, Rosen FS. Permeability-increasing activity in hereditary angioneurotic edema plasma. II. Mechanism of formation and partial characterization. J Clin Invest 1969;48:642-53.

6. Donaldson VH, Rosen FS, Bing DH. Role of the second component (C2) and plasmin in kinin release in hereditary angioneurotic edema (H.A.N.E.) plasma. Trans Assoc Am Physicians 1977;40:174-83.

7. Landerman NS, Webster ME, Becker EL, Ratcliffe HE. Hereditary angioneurotic edema. II. Deficiency of inhibitor for serum globulin permeability factor and/or plasma kallikrein. J ALLERGY 1962;33:330-41.

8. Curd JG, Yelvington M, Burridge N, Stimler NP, Gerard C, Prograis LJ Jr, Cochrane CG. Generation of bradykinin during incubation of hereditary angioedema plasma [Abstract]. Mol Immunol 1983;19:1365.

9. Fields T, Ghebrehiwet B, Kaplan AP. Kinin formation in hereditary angioedema plasma: evidence against kinin derivation from C2 and in support of "spontaneous" formation of bradykinin. J ALLERGY CLIN IMMUNOL 1983;72:54-60.

10. Melamed J, Alper CA, Cicardi M, Rosen FS. The metabolism of C1 inhibitor and C1q in patients with acquired C1-inhibitor deficiency. J ALLERGY CLIN IMMUNOL 1986;77:322-6.

11. Geha RS, Quinti I, Austen KF, Cicardi M, Sheffer A, Rosen FS. Acquired C1-inhibitor deficiency associated with antiidiotypic antibody to monoclonal immunoglobulins. N Engl J Med 1985;312:534-40.

12. Sheffer AL, Austen KF, Rosen FS, Fearon DT. Acquired deficiency of the inhibitor of the first component of complement: report of five additional cases with commentary on the syndrome. J ALLERGY CLIN IMMUNOL 1985;75:640-6.

13. Jackson J, Sim RB, Whelan A, Feighery C. An IgG autoantibody which inactivates C1 inhibitor. Nature 1986;323:722-4.

14. Bork K, Alsenz J, Böckers M, Noah E, Loos M. IgG-Antikörperbildung gegen C1-Inhibitor als Ursache lebensbedrohlicher Angioödeme. Dtsch Med Wochenschr 1987;112:503-6.

15. Alsenz J, Bork K, Loos M. Autoantibody-mediated acquired deficiency of C1 inhibitor. N Engl J Med 1987;316:1360-6.

16. Agostoni A, Bergamaschini L, Martignoni GC, Cicardi C, Marasini B. Treatment of acute attacks of hereditary angioedema with C1 INH concentrate. Ann Allergy 1980;44:299-301.

17. Bergamaschini L, Cicardi M, Tucci A, Gardinali M, Frangi D, Valle C, Agostoni A. C1 INH concentrate in the therapy of hereditary angioedema. Allergy 1983;38:81-4.

18. Bork K, Kreuz W, Witzke G. Hereditäres angioneurotisches Ödem. Dtsch Med Wochenschr 1984;35:1331-5.

19. Gadek JE, Hosea SW, Gelfand JA, Santaella M, Wickerhauser M, Triantaphyllopoulos DC, Frank MM. Replacement therapy in hereditary angioedema. N Engl J Med 1980;6:542-6.

20. Heinz HP, Hitschold T, Latsch M, Loos M. Vereinfachter Mikroassay zur Bestimmung der gesamthämolytischen Komplementaktivität, CH_{50}. Lab Med 1983;9:320-3.

21. Rapp H, Borsos T. Molecular basis of complement action. New York: Appleton-Century-Crofts, 1970:97.

22. Alsenz J, Loos M. Simplified methods for the purification, quantitation, and functional estimation of human complement C1 inhibitor (C1 INH) with a monoclonal anti-C1-INH antibody. J Immunol Methods 1987;96:107-14.

23. Fuhge P, Gratz P, Geiger H. Modern methods for the manufacturing of coagulation factor concentrates. Behring Inst Mitt 1986;79:164-76.

24. Ronneberger H. Need for additional safety assays for heattreated plasma protein factors. Trends Pharm Sci 1986;7:130-1.

25. Mauler R, Merkle W, Hilfenhaus J. Inactivation of HTLV-III/LAV, hepatitis B, and non-A/non-B viruses by pasteurization in human plasma protein preparations. Dev Biol Stand 1987;67:337-51.

26. Hilfenhaus J, Gregersen JP. Inactivation of AIDS-causing retroviruses by the manufacturing procedures for human plasma protein. Behring Inst Mitt 1988;82:82-93.

27. Kodama J, Uchida K, Yoshimura S, Katayama Y, Kushiro H, Yutani C, Funahashi S, Takamiya O, Matsumoto Y, Ando Y, Hashimoto T, Nagaki K, Katori M, Uchida Y, Ohishi S, Inai S. Studies of four Japanese families with hereditary angioneurotic edema: simultaneous activation of plasma protease systems and exogenous triggering stimuli. Blut 1984;49:405-18.

28. Brackertz D, Isler E, Kueppers F. Half-life of C1 INH in hereditary angioneurotic oedema (HAE). Clin Allergy 1975;1:89-94.

Hereditary and Acquired C1-Inhibitor Deficiency: Biological and Clinical Characteristics in 235 Patients

ANGELO AGOSTONI AND MARCO CICARDI

Introduction

The first complete clinical description of hereditary angioedema (HAE) was compiled by William Osler in 1888 (65). The mode of inheritance was identified in 1917 (23), and the disease was defined biochemically in 1963, when Donaldson and Evans (31) demonstrated that subjects with HAE lack the serum inhibitor of the first component of human complement (C1-INH). This discovery led to the rapid growth of knowledge about the disease, and shortly thereafter, to recognition of an acquired form of C1-INH deficiency (15), now called acquired angioedema (AAE). More recently, the pathogenetic mechanisms of symptoms (11, 16, 25, 28, 35–37, 72, 81) and phenotypic variants (45, 70) have been recognized. The development of rational therapeutic approaches (44, 48, 60, 67) has resulted in the wide availability of medications to prevent and treat the symptoms of the disease. Recently the defective gene has been identified and cloned (13, 26) and the molecular basis of HAE defined (22, 80). In parallel with advances in the understanding of HAE, the acquired form of the disorder, which was initially described in association with lymphoproliferative disease, has been recognized in an increasing number of patients (17, 19, 47, 50, 73, 74). Its pathogenetic aspects have been defined (46, 52, 62), and it has recently also been shown to exist in an autoantibody-mediated form (known as autoimmune AAE) (4, 42, 54).

As a result of these discoveries, HAE is now described as a disease due to mutations within the C1-INH gene, transmitted as an autosomal dominant trait, leading to plasma deficiency of C1-INH. There are two phenotypic variants of HAE: type I is characterized by low antigenic and functional plasma levels of a normal C1-INH protein. Type II is characterized by the presence of normal or elevated antigenic levels of a dysfunctional mutant protein together with reduced levels of the functional protein. C1-INH plasma deficiency allows autoactivation of the first component of complement (C1), with consumption of C4 and C2. Probably because of uncontrolled activation of the contact system (physiologically regulated by C1-INH), a kinin-like mediator or mediators are episodically released, resulting in edema of the subcutaneous or submucosal tissues. Increasing the synthesis of normal C1-INH by therapy with attenuated androgens prevents angioedema in patients, and administration of C1-INH plasma concentrate can reverse attacks. In AAE, C1-INH is catabolized more rapidly by an autoantibody or by an associated disease than in HAE. The clinical characteristics of AAE are similar to those of HAE, but effectiveness of treatment is impaired by the rate of C1-INH catabolism.

In this study, we review our clinical experience with 80 kindreds with HAE and with 9 patients with AAE. We relate our experience to the biological studies that have been performed on the same patients in cooperation with other groups.

Materials and Methods

All patients are Italian except for 1 patient from Spain. All were observed and tested at our clinic between 1973 and January 1992. Their present ages range from 7 to 89 years. Usually a single proband (and rarely more than 1 member in the family) was referred directly to us with symptoms of angioedema. After diagnosis, all available members of the family were examined, laboratory tests were performed, and genealogic trees constructed. Patients were seen thereafter for periodic follow-up, as well as at their own request or at the request of their family doctor. Data reported here include information from records kept for each patient.

Blood sampling

Blood samples, obtained by clean venipuncture, were collected into tubes containing 0.9% sodium citrate. The plasma was aliquoted and stored at −70°C until tests were performed.

Methods

C1-INH, C4 and C1q antigen were measured by radial immunodiffusion (RID) (Nor-Partigen or Low-Partigen, Behring, Marburg, Germany).

Functional C1-INH was measured by a chromogenic assay performed with a C1-inhibitor kit (Immuno, Vienna, Austria).

From the Clinica Medica III, Istituto di Medicina Interna, Università di Milano Italy

Address reprint request to: Angelo Agostoni, M.D., Istituto di Medicina Interna, Via Pace 9, 20122 Milan, Italy.

Diagnostic criteria

Diagnosis of HAE was based on a personal and/or family history of recurrent non-inflammatory subcutaneous edema, episodic abdominal pain, and laryngeal edema in patients with functional C1-INH below 40% of normal. Diagnosis of AAE was based on a personal history of the onset of symptoms of angioedema after the fourth decade of life, low functional C1-INH levels, and a negative family history. Patients without a positive family history, but with typical symptoms of angioedema that began in childhood, C1-INH deficiency, and normal C1q levels were included in the study as having new mutations of the C1-INH gene.

Results

Hereditary angioedema

During the 19 years of this study, 226 patients were diagnosed as having HAE and 9 were diagnosed with AAE. Thirty-two percent of the probands were not referred by physicians, seeking treatment on their own or on the advice of friends. All patients had typical symptoms of HAE, but the diagnosis had been established previously in only 10% of them. Nine subjects were lost to follow-up.

The demographic characteristics of patients, their age of onset of symptoms and age of diagnosis, the length of follow-up, frequency of symptoms, involvement of single sites, triggering factors, and laboratory values are reported in Tables 1 to 7. All clinical characteristics were identical in both sexes,

TABLE 1. Phenotypic distribution of 226 patients with hereditary angioedema

	Type I	Type II
No. patients	180	46
No. families	69	11
Possible new mutants	15	3
Male	86	21
Female	94	25
Age range (yrs)	7–89	12–78

TABLE 2. Age at symptom presentation and diagnosis in 226 patients with hereditary angioedema

Age Range (yrs)	Presentation (%)	Diagnosis (%)
0–10	50	13
11–20	35	19
21–30	11	21
>30	1	47

TABLE 3. Length of follow-up for 226 patients with hereditary angioedema

Follow-up (yrs)	% of Patients
<3	21
4–6	6
7–10	18
>10	55

TABLE 4. Frequency of symptoms per year in 226 patients with hereditary angioedema

No. Symptoms	% of Patients
No symptoms	5
<1	26
1–5	23
6–12	16
>12	30

TABLE 5. Presence of single symptoms in 226 patients with hereditary angioedema

Site Involved	% Patients
Subcutaneous	91
Abdominal	73
Laryngeal	48

TABLE 6. Triggering factors as recognized by patients

Factor	% Patients
Psychological stress	26
Minor trauma	53
Menstruation	15

TABLE 7. Mean laboratory values (±SD) at diagnosis in 226 patients with hereditary angioedema

Type of HAE	C1-INH Ag* (% NHPP)	C1-INH fn† (% NHPP)	C4 (% NHPP)
I	16.2 ± 10	15.0 ± 11	20.4 ± 16
II	112.5 ± 97	18 ± 12	23.8 ± 15
Normal range	63–137	69–119	67–130

Abbreviation: NHPP = normal human pooled plasma.
* Immunochemical measurement.
† Functional measurement.

as well as in different phenotypes and genetic variants.

Genetics: Informative genealogic trees for at least 3 generations were constructed for most kindreds. The relative rarity of HAE in the general population (estimated prevalence 1:50,000) suggests that it derived from a recent mutation. In accordance with this assumption, we found that symptoms were recorded from more than 2 generations in only 19 families. Eighteen patients (15 with type I and 3 with type II) had no affected relatives (Table 1). For 9 of them, both parents were available for laboratory tests and had normal C1-INH levels; however, no tests for paternity were ever performed. These data give a rough estimation that disease in up to 20% of affected kindreds may be caused by new mutations.

In 180 patients with type I HAE, belonging to 69 families, the plasma levels of functional and antigenic C1-INH were reduced to an almost identical extent. In these patients the mutation in the C1-INH structural gene led to impairment of the synthesis of a protein detectable in plasma. Restriction fragment length polymorphisms (RFLPs) were investigated in the genomic DNA from 28 of our type I families and were found in 3 of them (20 and Cicardi M, Frangi D: Unpublished data). However, another group of investigators using different restriction enzymes identified RFLPs in 20% of families with type I HAE (79).

In type II HAE, diagnosed in 46 subjects from 11 different families, antigenic plasma levels of C1-INH were variably higher than the functional ones (Table 7).

Treatment: Continuous prophylactic treatment was considered for patients with more than 1 attack per month. Tranexamic acid, an antifibrinolytic agent used in doses of 1.5–3 g/day, was widely employed until 1977 or 1978 and then replaced by attenuated androgens (danazol, stanozolol) (Table 8, Fig 1). Fifty-nine patients in our series were treated with danazol or stanozolol (both used with-

TABLE 8. Long-term prophylaxis in patients with hereditary angioedema

Drug	No. Patients	Mean Length (yrs ± SD)	Effectiveness* (% Patients)
Tranexamic acid	27	1.8 ± 0.8	28
Androgen derivatives	59	4.8 ± 3.4	97

* Reduction in frequency of attacks >80%.

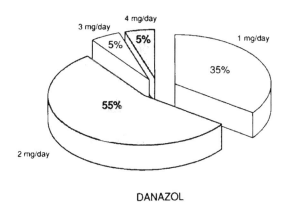

FIG. 1. Doses of stanozolol (41 patients) and of danazol (30 patients) required for prevention of attacks in patients receiving long-term treatment for hereditary angioedema.

out significant differences in outcome, with a preference for stanozolol because it is less expensive) and all but 2 patients reported complete disappearance of symptoms (18). However, because of toxicity, it is critical to administer minimal effective doses determined for each patient based on clinical criteria. With the doses shown in Figure 1, 1 patient had signs of liver cell necrosis which disappeared after treatment with the drug was stopped, 2 had polyglobulia, and the rest complained only of minor side effects (irregularities in menstruation, acne, slight virilization, or increase in body weight) (18). However we did not detect any sign of liver degeneration in our histologic study (1).

Laryngeal edema and severe bowel edema were treated with C1-INH plasma concentrate (Table 9). Before this plasma concentrate was available, attacks were treated with aprotinin (Trasylol, Bayer, Germany). Subcutaneous attacks were not usually treated.

Outcome: Twenty-one patients had needed tracheostomy or tracheal intubation for laryngeal edema 1 or more times before diagnosis. Genealogic information showed that 30% of relatives, who had characteristic symptoms of HAE, had died from laryngeal edema. Neither deaths nor intensive care unit admissions for laryngeal edema were recorded after the correct diagnosis had been made.

Associated diseases: Associated diseases were reported for a few patients (Table 10). We found only 1 case of rheumatoid arthritis, 1 of acute glomerulonephritis, and 1 of Sjögren syndrome. In addition, as a possible late complication of an autoimmune disorder, 3 patients had adult hypothyroidism, and 1 was on dialysis for end-stage chronic renal failure. No other diseases were encountered with any significant frequency among our patients. Four patients had neoplasia of different origins. None of the deaths recorded among our patients (cerebrovascular accidents, myocardial infarction, neoplasia, heroin overdose) appeared to be in any way related to the disease.

Acquired angioedema

All 9 patients with AAE had low C1-INH antigen and function and low C4. C1q levels were undetectable in 8 patients and normal in 1. Characteristics of these patients are reported in Table 11.

Discussion

Hereditary angioedema

Genetics: The sites of the mutations in the common form of HAE span the entire gene. Stoppa-Lyonnet and his colleagues (79, 80) defined muta-

TABLE 9. Treatment of attacks with C1-INH concentrate in patients with hereditary angioedema

Site of Edema	No. Patients	No. Infusions	Units of C1-INH*	Effectiveness
Subcutaneous	1	1	500	Ineffective
Abdominal	4	15	1000	60/120 min
Laryngeal	23	67	1000/1500	30/60 min

* 1 unit corresponds to the amount of C1-INH present in 1 ml of normal human plasma.

TABLE 10. Associated diseases observed in 226 patients with hereditary angioedema

Disease	No. Patients
Neoplasia	4
Hypothyroidism	3
End-stage chronic renal failure	1
Sjögren syndrome	1
Rheumatoid arthritis	1

TABLE 11. Characteristics of 9 patients with acquired angioedema

Patients	Sex	Present Age (yrs)	Age at Diagnosis (yrs)	Associated Diseases
1	M	64	57	None
2	M	54	52	None
3	F	63	41	Echinococcus granulosus
4	F	70	64	Breast cancer
5	M	70	55	M component
6	M	66	62	Chronic lymphocytic leukemia
7	M	72	70	None
8	M	71	69	None
9	M	55	54	None

genic regions in the C1-INH locus caused by clusters of intragenic Alu repeats, more frequently located in the 5' half. Deletion of exon VII at the 3' end of the gene, once again due to recombination between Alu repeats, was reported by Ariga et al (5). All these mutations within Alu clusters determine various degrees of rearrangement with deletions or duplications of a large part of the gene. However, point mutations have also been demonstrated to cause type I HAE (40).

The analysis of mRNA extracted from monocytes and skin fibroblasts demonstrated that cells from most patients with type I HAE have reduced levels of cytoplasmic C1-INH mRNA (22, 55). These data are therefore consistent with the fact that the mutations leading to type I HAE usually impair transcription of the C1-INH gene. However, the first exception was reported for a type I family with an abnormally short C1-INH mRNA (due to deletion of exon VII) together with normal mRNA transcribed from the wildtype allele (6, 22). We used Northern blots to analyze the total RNA extracted from the monocytes of 12 unrelated patients with type I HAE and identified 3 families with levels of C1-INH message markedly above those found in normal individuals (20). This observation has re-

cently been confirmed, with the demonstration in 2 of these families of a single base deletion or insertion resulting in abundant cytoplasmic levels of abnormal mRNA, probably due to a slower rate of catabolism (40). In 2 of the families studied by Stoppa-Lyonnet et al (79) (with deletion of exon IV), stable transcripts had also accumulated in monocyte cytoplasm. Therefore, it is apparently not uncommon for patients with type I HAE to have a mutation affecting the ability of mRNA to direct translation of a protein detectable in plasma. Whether translation, secretion, plasma stability, or antigenicity prevents the protein product of these transcripts from being detectable in plasma is still unclear.

The incidence of families with type II HAE in our series (14%) is similar to that reported by others (29, 69). Patients with type II HAE characteristically have a plasma protein that reacts with anti-C1-INH antibodies, but totally or partially (32, 34, 38) without C1-INH physiological functions. The heterogeneity of the dysfunctional proteins among type II families was pointed out long ago, some having different electrophoretic patterns and some existing in unusually high concentrations; these latter are complexed in plasma with albumin (69). By measuring the plasma levels of a cleavage product of C1-INH (iC1-INH), an indicator of its catabolism, we confirmed the existence of genetically determined differences in the catabolism of the dysfunctional proteins (24), as first demonstrated in in vivo turnover studies (68). In our study (24) we identified 1 group (2 families) with more than 20 times the amount of iC1-INH detected in normal human pooled plasma and with C1-INH antigen between 55 and 70% of the normal mean. In the second group (3 families) iC1-INH was normal and the amount of C1-INH antigen was above the normal mean of 100%. Subsequent studies demonstrated that the 2 families in the first group had the same dysfunctional C1-INH, which resulted from a single base substitution $(G \rightarrow A)$ at position $P10$, coding for the amino acid residue 436, and giving the structural change $Ala \rightarrow Thr$. As a member of the family of the serum protease inhibitors (SERPIN), C1-INH is first cleaved by the interaction with its target protease and then binds to the amino-terminal polypeptide residue. The result is the formation of a stable complex and the inhibition of the activity of the protease (78). The two amino acids, those immediately N-terminal and C-terminal to the split bond (reactive center, residues 444–445), are termed *P1* and *P1'*; adjacent residues are numbered progressively *P2*, *P3*, etc. and *P2'*, *P3'* etc. in either direction. In the case of the 2 families with elevated iC1-INH, the mutation, 10 residues apart from the reactive center, appears to allow interaction of the dysfunctional protein with the protease, but not the formation of a stable complex nor the generation of an inhibitory action. In summary, such a mutation would render C1-INH a true substrate for the protease, thus explaining the increased catabolism. Skriver et al (77) obtained experimental evidence of this assumption, demonstrating that a similar dysfunctional C1-INH (*Ala→Glu* substitution at position *P12*), expressed in cosmid cells, was cleaved by kallikrein, C1s and activated factor XII (C1-INH target proteases), but did not form complexes with them.

Another group of mutations, accounting for the majority of patients with type II HAE (8–10), are those affecting the reactive center of C1-INH (*Arg* 444). Several of these mutations have been identified so far (8, 10, 58, 66, 76, 77). The *P1* mutation *Arg→Cys* (76) results in the dysfunctional C1-INH, which was originally described as complexed in plasma with albumin (69). We detected such complexes in 2 of our families. In these 2 families, in which the mutation was not characterized, C1-INH antigen was 2 to 3 times normal levels and iC1-INH was normal. Therefore, it appears that the binding of albumin totally prevents protease-inhibitor interaction and reduces the catabolic rate of these dysfunctional proteins. In 1 additional type II kindred in our series, with a mutation in the reactive center (39a), iC1-INH levels were within the normal mean. In the range of mutations known to be responsible for type II HAE, only one so far described is distant from the reactive center (66). In this case, deletion of a *Lys* at residue 251 creates a new glycosylation site, accounting for the differences in electrophoretic mobility of this protein (69).

Clinical and pathogenetic aspects of attacks: As already pointed out by several investigators (29, 41), patients with HAE have local swellings at 3 main sites: subcutaneous tissues (face, hand, arms, legs, genitals, buttocks), abdominal organs (stomach, gut, bladder), and the upper airway (larynx). The subcutaneous attacks last for 2 to 5 days. A typical feature is the absence of inflammatory signs, although transient and mild urticarial eruptions and lymphangitic striae can occasionally precede the overt swelling. Perioral and periorbital involvements—typical presentations of allergic angioedema—are not characteristic of HAE.

Abdominal attacks are specific for HAE. They usually begin with continuous pain and vomiting, and rarely include watery diarrhea. It is well known that these abdominal attacks can mimic surgical emergencies. None of our patients ever registered hypovolemic shock from extravascular fluid loss, but this event has been reported (41). Because of misdiagnosis of HAE, 34% of our patients underwent appendectomy, exploratory laparotomy, or both during abdominal attacks. The usual findings at surgery were ascitic fluid or edematous bowel mucosa. No pathognomonic signs can distinguish abdominal attacks due to HAE from a true surgical emergency, but bowel sounds in the absence of abdominal tenderness and leukocytosis always suggest a need for conservative management. However, the main problem in dealing with abdominal attacks is most physicians' lack of experience with the disease; consequently, the diagnosis is often missed. No complications due to bowel edema have been reported and symptoms generally subside in 12 to 24 hours.

In contrast to the favorable prognosis for subcutaneous and abdominal edema, the laryngeal edema still remains a life-threatening event. More than 10% of our patients, before diagnosis of HAE, had needed to undergo resuscitation maneuvers (tracheostomy or intubation) at least once. We are also aware of at least 2 recent deaths from laryngeal edema in patients with undiagnosed HAE. The high incidence of death from this cause in the past has declined recently, even in the absence of a correct diagnosis, owing to the improvement of emergency care units. It is interesting to note that the pulmonary tree is never involved in attacks of HAE. One possible explanation is suggested by experimental data on the kinetics of disappearance of the polypeptide hormones, bradykinin and angiotensin I, in the pulmonary vascular system. It is now acknowledged that bradykinin and probably other kinins (see below) are inactivated and angiotensin I is activated by enzymes on or very close to the innermost surface of the cells lining the pulmonary vessels. The ability to inactivate kinin compounds and to activate angiotensin I through a simple enzyme system is not limited to the vascular bed of the lungs. However, no other vascular bed drains into the systemic arterial circulation (71). Thus, the absence of mediators in the systemic arterial circulation could also explain why the angioedema of patients with HAE remains strictly limited to the area in which the phenomenon is generated.

The most intriguing and mysterious problem in attacks of HAE remains the variation in their recurrence. Patients usually become symptomatic within the second decade of life and then demonstrate a wide range of variability in the frequency of episodes. Some patients can have swelling every week and some others may have only a few or no attacks. The course of the disease is not correlated with the age of presentation nor with its severity in childhood. Moreover, the frequency of attacks is not uniform within families, nor can any correlation be found between different genetic and clinical forms of the disease. Fifty-eight percent of our patients recognize one or more triggering factors as the cause for some of the attacks, but the large majority of attacks occur without any apparent reason.

In contrast to others (41), we did not find any reduction of symptoms during pregnancy. During pregnancy, symptoms may intensify or diminish. Women taking estrogens have low levels of plasma C1-INH (49) and patients with HAE taking this drug usually report an exacerbation of their swelling. Estrogens are therefore contraindicated in HAE; for contraceptive purposes, we suggest norgestrienone. An initial report indicating that this progestational drug could reduce attacks of HAE by increasing C1-INH plasma levels (82), has not been confirmed subsequently (57); we also found norgestrienone to have no effect on the symptoms of HAE.

The biochemical events underlying the generation of a local increase in vascular permeability have been widely investigated. C1-INH regulates the activation of complement, contact, and fibrinolytic systems (27, 64), but only the complement system is clearly activated between and during attacks of edema (36). It is a common notion that stimuli that activate the contact or fibrinolytic system, e.g., physical and psychological stress, frequently precede attacks. Moreover data from in vitro studies suggest that a vasoactive peptide identical to the one isolated from HAE plasma during attacks can be released by incubation of activated C1, C4, C2, and plasmin (37). It is therefore tempting to assume that episodic activation of the contact system, triggered by external factors, leads to plasmin generation and thus to the swelling. With this in mind, several investigators approached the problem of identifying the in vivo factors that reliably activate the systems regulated by C1-INH (25, 56, 72). Our contribution to this enigma was based on identification of contact system activation by electrophoretic measurement of the cleavage of high molecular weight kininogen (HK), and the demonstration of in vivo plasmin generation by measuring plasma levels of plasmin-antiplasmin complexes. We have demonstrated that HAE attacks are characterized by significant cleavage of HK and generation of plasmin, and that the 2 events are statistically correlated (Cugno M, Hack CE, Cicardi M: Unpublished data). The final target of such a mul-

tiple-system activation is the local release of a vasoactive mediator whose identity is controversial. It is widely accepted that such a mediator has kinin-like activity, but whether it is bradykinin itself or a split product derived from the activation of C2 is still under investigation (27). The contraindication to the use of angiotensin-converting enzyme inhibitors in patients deficient in C1-INH probably arises from the potentiation of kinin-like activity (3).

Associated diseases in patients with HAE: An increased incidence of autoimmune diseases was found in a systematic study of patients with HAE (14), and such diseases were occasionally encountered in several series (33, 53, 59). The consumption of the classical pathway complement components may, in fact, expose these patients to an increased risk of immune-complex disease, as in subjects with inherited deficiencies of C1, C2, and C4 (63).

Management of patients with HAE—long-term prophylaxis: Three distinct phases in the treatment of HAE are classically recognized: long-term and short-term prophylaxis, and treatment of acute attacks (41).

The demonstration that attenuated androgens cure the symptoms and correct the biochemical defect in HAE (48) opened the era of rational and effective treatment. However, it has always been clear that these drugs, which require a few days to become effective, are strictly limited to prophylactic use. A dose- and time-dependent toxicity of attenuated androgens analogous to those used in HAE (danazol and stanozolol) has been reported. Special attention has been given to their capacity to induce liver neoplasia (39, 83). Moreover, being hormonal derivatives, they retain some effects on developing tissues and the ovarian cycle. It is therefore clear that the prevention of attacks in HAE is now merely a problem of risk-benefit evaluation. First to be considered is the actual harm of HAE attacks to the patient's life. Frequent attacks may, in fact, impair normal working activity and in certain circumstances (inefficient medical assistance or inadequate patient compliance) may be life-threatening. Prepubertal age, female sex, pregnancy, and coexistent liver disease are additional risks for androgen treatment. For these reasons, each patient must be individually evaluated. It is our policy to consider as candidates for androgen derivative prophylaxis those patients who have more than 1 attack a month. The other drugs proposed for prophylaxis of HAE are the antifibrinolytic agents (ε-aminocaproic acid and tranexamic acid), which presumably act through inhibition of plasmin (60). We often used tranexamic acid before use of attenuated androgens were proposed and found it to have some beneficial effects in 70% of the cases (2). However, important reductions in attacks were achieved in only 28%. For this reason, the use of antifibrinolytic agents is now restricted to patients such as children, who have major contraindications to androgen treatment.

Management of patients with HAE—short-term prophylaxis: This therapeutic approach is used mainly for patients undergoing oral manipulations such as dental care, endoscopy, and endotracheal intubation, in whom local trauma might trigger laryngeal attacks. For this kind of prophylaxis, we administer attenuated androgens (600 mg/day danazol or 6 mg/day stanozolol) 6 days before and 3 days after the event. Such an approach has been successful in over 30 subjects undergoing dental manipulations; it failed in 1 who developed laryngeal edema despite prophylaxis (Agostoni A, Cicardi M: Unpublished data). Satisfactory results with similar schedules have recently been reported (7). C1-INH plasma concentrate can be effectively administered if it is anticipated that laryngeal edema will develop, because of its rapid action. However, although it does not appear to be primarily a prophylactic drug, this use may be indicated when there is no time for androgen prophylaxis and it is important to avoid edema.

Management of patients with HAE—treatment of acute attacks: The large majority of acute attacks of HAE are harmless to the patient's life, but result in disfiguration and severe abdominal pain. In these cases, we obtained satisfactory results with high doses of antifibrinolytic agents (tranexamic acid 1 g every 3 to 4 hours), given orally over a period of 12 to 15 hours. Their administration early in the attack is critical and no effect can be expected when the edema has already spread (Agostoni A, Cicardi M: Unpublished data). Drugs such as metoclopramide and antispasmodics, along with fluid replacement, may be helpful in the management of abdominal symptoms. Particularly severe abdominal attacks—those which are difficult to differentiate from a surgical emergency, or those causing intractable pain—may require C1-INH therapy.

The most serious complication of HAE remains edema of the larynx. Effective treatments used in the past were replacement therapy with fresh frozen plasma (FFP) (67) and infusion of the kallikrein inhibitor aprotinin (61). Use of FFP is now obsolete because, besides causing contamination of plasma, it contains not only the deficient protein, but also the substrates active in edema formation that impair its action. We have employed aprotinin for treatment of 15 episodes of laryngeal edema, with favorable clinical effects: dysphonia, dysphagia, and tirage, when present, disappeared 1 to 2 hours after the beginning of the infusion (61). Reports of deaths due to allergic reactions to this drug (67a), however,

render its use questionable. (One death occurred in one of our patients' relatives, who was diagnosed and treated elsewhere.)

We now consider C1-INH plasma concentrate the treatment of choice for laryngeal edema in patients with HAE (12, 44, 75). We have experience with a total of 83 such infusions (Table 8). Several C1-INH preparations have been approved in European countries, but are being tested in the United States. Our experience is based mainly on the C1-INH concentrate from Immuno (Vienna, Austria), the one approved in Italy. However we have also infused, for study purposes, the preparations from The Netherlands Red Cross and from Behring (Marburg, Germany) and did not find any marked difference among the 3 preparations. Administration of 1000/1500 units of the preparation from Immuno (1 unit corresponds to the amount of C1-INH contained in 1 ml of normal human plasma) has been consistently effective in reversing laryngeal and abdominal edema. No acute adverse reactions have been reported. The main problem with this preparation arose in 1983/84 when, probably due to a contaminated batch, 13 patients developed cases of acute non-A, non-B hepatitis. Since 1986, the preparation has been steam-treated, and since then, in 56 infusions, no infections have occurred.

Acquired Angioedema

This term is applied to a condition with symptoms identical to those of HAE, but with onset after the fourth decade of life and in the absence of a family history of these symptoms. Initially recognized in patients with lymphoproliferative disorders (15, 47, 73), AAE is now characterized as having at least 2 distinct forms. The first is caused by an associated disease (usually lymphoproliferative) (15, 17, 19, 46, 47, 50, 52, 62, 73, 74); the second results from the presence of autoantibodies to C1-INH (autoimmune AAE) (4, 42, 54).

The complement profile in AAE reproduces the C1-INH, C4, and C2 deficiencies of HAE, but the biochemical characteristic is the low level of C1 complex (64). The demonstration of rapid *in vivo* turnover of C1 and C1-INH (62) and some experimental proofs of C1 activation and C1-INH depletion by the underlying lymphoproliferative disease (46, 52, 73) led to the hypothesis that massive C1 activation is the cause of C1-INH deficiency through a consumption mechanism. Signs of the same massive C1 activation are also detected in autoimmune AAE. This finding is surprising, since one would expect that the autoantibody, depleting C1-INH function, reproduces the situation detected in HAE with normal C1. Therefore, in autoimmune

AAE there should also be a factor (the autoantibody-C1-INH complex itself or another unknown factor) that leads to massive C1 activation. The key role of such an activation is further suggested by several reports (17, 43, 52) and by our own experience that when the treatment of AAE patients leads to an increase or normalization of C1-INH, C1 complex and C4 invariably remain low.

We are now treating 9 patients with this disease. Since a sensitive method for detecting autoantibodies to C1-INH has been described (4), we have screened all 9 patients and found autoantibodies to C1-INH in all except the 1 with chronic lymphocytic leukemia (CLL). These autoantibodies belong to all 3 major immunoglobulin classes. It is interesting to note that 1 of the patients with autoantibodies has normal levels of C1q, and therefore low C1q levels cannot be considered a diagnostic criterion for AAE (Cicardi M, Agostoni A: Unpublished data). The limited number of such patients makes it impossible to determine the relative frequencies of the 2 forms of AAE. Our series shows a marked prevalence of the autoimmune form, but other investigators have had the opposite experience (Rosen FS: Personal communication).

The therapeutic approach to AAE requires, when possible, cure of the underlying disease. This may lead to suppression of the angioedema symptoms as well (17, 19, 52). Donaldson et al (30) recently reported reversing C1-INH deficiency in a patient with autoimmune AAE by suppressing autoantibody production with plasmapheresis and use of a cyclophosphamide (30). The treatment of angioedema symptoms *per se* in AAE is identical to the one used in HAE, but the responses in AAE are unpredictable (43, 47, 51, 52). In our experience, patients with autoantibodies benefit from prophylaxis with antifibrinolytic agents, while attenuated androgens are useless or even detrimental. On the other hand, our only patient with chronic lymphocytic leukemia had a strikingly favorable response to danazol. We used C1-INH concentrate replacement therapy for only 2 patients with autoimmune AAE and both of them required considerably higher doses of concentrate (3–4 times the dose in HAE) to obtain regression of symptoms.

In conclusion, acquired C1-INH deficiency appears to be a syndrome with polymorphic pathogenetic aspects, whose complete elucidation requires further investigation.

Summary

Two hundred and twenty-six patients with inherited C1 inhibitor (C1-INH) deficiency, also known as hereditary angioedema (HAE), have been studied. They belonged to 80 unrelated families, and in 11 of them C1-INH was functionally deficient but antigenically normal (type II HAE). Genetic analysis of type 1 families demonstrated restriction fragment length polymorphisms in 11% and abnormal mRNAs in 25%. In type II families, the site of the mutation appeared to determine the rate of catabolism of the dysfunctional C1-INH and its antigenic plasma levels. Clinical symptoms (subcutaneous and mucous swellings) generally first appeared within the second decade of life. The frequency of symptoms was highly variable from patient to patient, but a few patients remained asymptomatic throughout their lives. Prophylactic treatment with attenuated androgens was administered to 59 patients and was totally effective in 57, without significant side effects. Sixty-seven laryngeal and 15 abdominal attacks were treated with C1-INH plasma concentrate, yielding initial regression of symptoms in 30 to 90 minutes.

The acquired deficiency of C1-INH, also known as acquired angioedema, was diagnosed in 9 patients. Eight of them had an autoantibody against C1-INH; the only patient without the autoantibody had associated chronic lymphocytic leukemia. Prophylactic treatment with attenuated androgens was effective in this last patient, while those with the autoantibody against C1-INH benefited from prophylaxis with antifibrinolytic agents. Replacement therapy with C1-INH concentrate was necessary only for patients with autoantibodies and required doses 3 or 4 times higher than those used in HAE.

References

1. Agostoni A, Cicardi M, Martignoni GC, Bergamaschini L, Marasini B. Danazol and stanozolol in long-term prophylactic treatment of hereditary angioedema. J Allergy Clin Immunol 65: 75–79, 1980.
2. Agostoni A, Marasini B, Cicardi M, Martignoni GC, Uziel L, Pietrogrande M. Hepatic function and fibrinolysis in patients with hereditary angioedema undergoing long-term treatment with tranexamic acid. Allergy 33: 211–16, 1978.
3. Agostoni A, Cicardi M. Contraindications to the use of angiotensin converting enzyme inhibitors in patients deficient in C1 esterase inhibitor. Am J Med 90: 278, 1991.
4. Alsenz J, Bork K, Loos M. Autoantibody-mediated acquired deficiency of C1 inhibitor. N Engl J Med 316: 1360–66, 1987.
5. Ariga T, Carter PE, Davis AE III. Recombinations between *Alu* repeat sequences that result in partial deletion within the C1 inhibitor gene. Genomics 8: 607–13, 1990.
6. Ariga T, Igarashi T, Ramesh N, Parad R, Cicardi M, Davis III AE. Type I C1 inhibitor deficiency with a small messenger RNA resulting from deletion of one exon. J Clin Invest 83: 1888–93, 1989.
7. Atkinson JC, Frank MM. Oral manifestations and dental management of patients with hereditary angioedema. J Oral Pathol Med 20: 139–42, 1991.
8. Aulak KS, Cicardi M, Harrison RA. Identification of a new P-1 residue mutation (444 Arg→Ser) in a dysfunctional C1 inhibitor protein contained in a type II hereditary angioedema plasma. FEBS Letters 266: 13–16, 1990.
9. Aulak KS, Harrison RA. Rapid and sensitive technique for identification and analysis of "reactive-centre" mutants of C1 inhibitor protein contained in type II hereditary angioedema plasmas. Biochem J 271: 565–69, 1990.
10. Aulak KS, Pemberton PA, Rosen FS, Carrel RW, Lachmann PJ,

Harrison RA. Dysfunctional C1 inhibitor (At), isolated from type II hereditary angio-oedema plasma, contains a P1 "reactive centre" (Arg444 His) mutation. Biochem J 253: 615–18, 1988.

11. Austen KF, Sheffer AL. Detection of hereditary angioedema by demonstration of a profound reduction in the second component of human complement. N Engl J Med 272: 649–56, 1965.

12. Bergamaschini L, Cicardi M, Tucci A, Gardinali M, Frangi D, Valle C, Agostoni A. C1 inhibitor concentrate in the therapy of hereditary angioedema. Allergy 38: 81–84, 1983.

13. Bock SC, Skriver K, Nielsen E, Thogersen HC, Wiman B, Donaldson VH, Eddy RL, Marrinan J, Radziejewska E, Huber R, Shows TB, Magnusson S. Human C1 inhibitor primary structure, cDNA cloning, and chromosomal localization. Biochemistry 25: 4292–4301, 1986.

14. Brickman CM, Tsokos GC, Balow JE, Lawley TJ, Santaella M, Hammer CH, Frank MM. Immunoregulatory disorders associated with hereditary angioedema. II. Serologic and cellular abnormalities. J Allergy Clin Immunol 77: 758–67, 1986.

15. Caldwell JR, Ruddy S, Schur PH, Austen KF. Acquired C1 inhibitor deficiency in lymphosarcoma. Clin Immunol Immunopathol 1:39–52, 1972.

16. Carpenter CB, Ruddy S, Shehadeh IH, Muller-Eberhard HJ, Merril JP, Austen KF. Complement metabolism in man: Hypercatabolism of the fourth (C4) and third (C3) components in patients with renal allograft rejection and hereditary angioedema (HAE). J Clin Invest 48: 1495–1505, 1969.

17. Choen SH, Koethe SM, Kozin F, Rodey G, Arkins JA, Fink JN. Acquired angioedema associated with rectal carcinoma and its response to danazol therapy. J Allergy Clin Immunol 62: 217–21, 1978.

18. Cicardi M, Bergamaschini L, Cugno M, Hack E, Agostoni G, Agostoni A. Long-term treatment of hereditary angioedema with attenuated androgens: A survey of a 13 year experience. J Allergy Clin Immunol 87: 768–73, 1991.

19. Cicardi M, Frangi D, Bergamaschini L, Gardinali M, Sacchi G, Agostoni A. Acquired C1 inhibitor deficiency with angioedema symptoms in a patient infected with Echinococcus granulosus. Complement 2: 133–39, 1985.

20. Cicardi M, Igarashi T, Kim MS, Frangi D, Agostoni A, Rosen FS, Davis III AE. Genetic heterogeneity of hereditary angioneurotic edema (abstract). Clin Res 35: 606A, 1987.

21. Cicardi M, Igarashi T, Kim MS, Frangi D, Agostoni A, Davis III AE. Restriction fragment length polymorphism of the C1 inhibitor gene in hereditary angioneurotic edema. J Clin Invest 80: 1640–43, 1987.

22. Cicardi M, Igarashi T, Rosen FS, Davis AE III. Molecular basis for the deficiency of complement 1 inhibitor in type I hereditary angioneurotic edema. J Clin Invest 79: 698–702, 1987.

23. Crowder JR, Crowder TR. Five generations of angioneurotic edema. Arch Intern Med 20: 840–52, 1917.

24. Cugno M, Nuijens J, Hack E, Eerenberg A, Frangi D, Agostoni A, Cicardi M. Plasma levels of C1 inhibitor complexes and cleaved C1 inhibitor in patients with hereditary angioneurotic edema. J Clin Invest 85: 1215–20, 1990.

25. Curd JG, Prograis LJ Jr, Cochrane CG. Detection of active kallikrein in induced blister fluids of hereditary angioedema patients. J Exp Med 152: 742–47, 1980.

26. Davis AE III, Whitehead AS, Harrison RA, Duphinais A, Burns GAP, Cicardi M, Rosen FS. Human inhibitor of the first component of complement, C1: characterization of cDNA clones and localization of the gene to chromosome 11. Proc Natl Acad Sci USA 83: 3161–65, 1986.

27. Davis AE III. C1 inhibitor and hereditary angioneurotic edema. Ann Rev Immunol 6: 595–628, 1988.

28. Donaldson VH. Mechanisms of activation of C1 esterase in hereditary angioneurotic edema plasma in vitro. The role of Hageman factor. J Exp Med 127: 411–29, 1968.

29. Donaldson VH. C1 inhibitor in hereditary angioneurotic edema: Types I and II. Behring Inst Mitt 84: 151–60, 1989.

30. Donaldson VH, Bernstein DI, Wagner CJ, Mitchell BH, Scinto J, Bernstein IL. Angioneurotic edema with acquired C1-inhibitor deficiency and autoantibody to C1-inhibitor: Response to plasmapheresis and cytotoxic therapy. J Lab Clin Med 119: 397–406, 1992.

31. Donaldson VH, Evans RR. A biochemical abnormality in hereditary angioneurotic edema: absence of serum inhibitor of C1-esterase. Am J Med 31: 37–44, 1963.

32. Donaldson VH, Harrison RA, Rosen FS, Bing DH, Kindness G, Canar J, Wagner CJ, Awad S. Variability of purified dysfunctional C1 inhibitor proteins from patients with hereditary angioneurotic edema. J Clin Invest 75: 124–32, 1985.

33. Donaldson VH, Hess EV, Mc Adams AJ. Lupus erythematosus-like disease in three unrelated women with hereditary angioneurotic edema (letter). Ann Intern Med 86: 312, 1977.

34. Donaldson VH, Mitchell BH, Everson B, Ratnoff OD. Interactions of C1 inhibitor from normal persons and patients with type II hereditary angioneurotic edema with purified activated Hageman factor (Factor XIIa). Blood 75: 911–21, 1990.

35. Donaldson VH, Ratnoff OD, Dia da Silva W, Rosen FS. Permeability-increasing activity in hereditary angioneurotic edema plasma. J Clin Invest 48: 642–53, 1969.

36. Donaldson VH, Rosen FS. Action of complement in hereditary angioneurotic edema: The role of C1 esterase. J Clin Invest 43: 2204–13, 1964.

37. Donaldson VH, Rosen FS, Bing DH. Role of the second component of complement (C2) and plasmin in kinin release in hereditary angioneurotic edema (HANE) plasma. Trans Assoc Am Physicians 90: 174–83, 1977.

38. Donaldson VH, Wagner CJ, Tsuei B, Kindness G, Bing DH, Harrison RA. Interaction of plasma kallikrein and C1s with normal and dysfunctional C1-inhibitor proteins from patients with hereditary angioneurotic edema: analytical gel studies. Blood 69: 1096–1101, 1987.

39. Falk H, Thomas LB, Popper H, Ishak KG. Hepatic angiosarcoma associated with androgenic anabolic steroids. Lancet 2: 1120–22, 1979.

39a. Frangi D, Aulak KS, Cicardi M, Harrison RA, Davis AE III. A dysfunctional C1 inhibitor protein with a new reactive center mutation (ARG-444→Leu). FEBS Letters 301: 34–36, 1992.

40. Frangi D, Cicardi M, Sica A, Colotta F, Agostoni A, Davis III AE. Nonsense mutations affect C1 inhibitor messenger RNA levels in patients with type I hereditary angioneurotic edema. J Clin Invest 88: 755–59, 1991.

41. Frank MM, Gelfand JA, Atkinson JP. Hereditary angioedema: the clinical syndrome and its management. Ann Intern Med 84: 580–93, 1976.

42. Frank MM, Malbran A, Simms H, Melez K, Santaella M, Hammer C, Fries L. Acquired angioedema type II: A new autoimmune disease (abstract). Clin Res 35: 641A, 1987.

43. Frigas E. Angioedema with acquired deficiency of the C1 inhibitor: a constellation of syndromes. Mayo Clin Proc 64: 1269–75, 1989.

44. Gadek JE, Hosea SW, Gelfand JA, Santaella M, Wickerhauser M, Triantaphyllopoulos DC, Frank MM. Replacement therapy in hereditary angioedema: Successful treatment of acute episodes of angioedema with partly purified C1 inhibitor. N Engl J Med 302: 542–46, 1980.

45. Gadek JE, Hosea SW, Gelfand JA, Frank MM. Response of variant hereditary angioedema phenotypes to danazol therapy. Genetic implications. J Clin Invest 64: 280–86, 1979.

46. Geha RS, Quinti I, Austen KF, Cicardi M, Sheffer A, Rosen FS. Acquired C1 inhibitor deficiency associated with antiidiotypic antibody to monoclonal immunoglobulins. N Engl J Med 312: 534–40, 1985.

47. Gelfand JA, Boss GR, Conley CL, Reinhart R, Frank MM. Acquired C1 esterase inhibitor deficiency and angioedema: A review. Medicine 58: 321–28, 1979.

48. Gelfand JA, Sherins RJ, Alling DW, Frank MM. Treatment of hereditary angioedema with danazol. Reversal of clinical and biochemical abnormalities. N Engl J Med 295: 1444–48, 1976.

49. Gordon EM, Ratnoff OD, Saito H, Jones PK. Rapid fibrinolysis, augmented Hageman factor (factor XII) titers, and decreased C1 esterase inhibitor titers in women taking oral contraceptives. J Lab Clin Med 96: 762–69, 1980.

50. Hauptmann G, Lang JM, North ML, Oberling F, Mayer G, Lachmann PJ. Acquired C1 inhibitor deficiencies in lymphoproliferative diseases with serum immunoglobulin abnormalities. Blut 32:195–206, 1976.

51. Hauptmann G, Mayer S. Treatment of acquired C1 inhibitor deficiency with danazol. Ann Intern Med 87: 577–78, 1977.

52. Hauptmann G, Petitjean F, Lang JM, Oberling F. Acquired C1 inhibitor deficiency in a case of lymphosarcoma of the spleen. Reversal of complement abnormalities after splenectomy. Clin Exp Immunol 37: 523–31, 1979.

53. Hory B, Haultier JJ. Glomerulonephritis and hereditary angioedema: Report of 2 cases. Clin Nephrol 31: 259–63, 1989.

54. Jackson J, Sim RB, Whelan A, Feighery C. An IgG autoantibody which inactivates C1 inhibitor. Nature 323: 722–24, 1986.

55. Kramer J, Katz Y, Rosen FS, Davis AE III, Strunk RC. Synthesis of C1 inhibitor in fibroblast from patients with type I and type II hereditary angioneurotic edema. J Clin Invest 87: 1614–20, 1991.

56. Landermann NS, Webster ME, Becker EL, Ratcliffe HE. Hereditary angioneurotic edema. II. Deficiency of inhibitor for serum globulin permeability factor and/or plasma kallikrein. J Allergy 33: 330, 1962.

57. Laurent J, Jamin C, Lagrue G. Oedème angioneurotique héréditaire: La norgestriénone n'est pas active dans tous les cas. Presse Méd 16: 2132, 1987.

58. Levy NJ, Ramesh N, Cicardi M, Harrison RA, Davis AE III. Type II hereditary angioneurotic edema that may result from a single nucleotide change in the codon for alanine-436 in the C1 inhibitor gene. Proc Natl Acad Sci 87: 265–68, 1990.

59. Ley SJ, Williams RC. A family with hereditary angioedema and multiple immunologic disorders. Am J Med 82: 1046–51, 1987.

60. Lundh B, Laurell AB, Wetterqvist H, White T, Granerus G. A case of hereditary angioneurotic edema, successfully treated with epsilon aminocaproic acid. Studies on C'1 esterase inhibitor, C'1 activation, plasminogen level and histamine metabolism. Clin Exp Immunol 3: 733–45, 1968.

61. Marasini B, Cicardi M, Martignoni GC, Agostoni A. Treatment of hereditary angioedema. Klin Wschr 56: 819–23, 1978.

62. Melamed J, Alper CA, Cicardi M, Rosen FS. The metabolism of C1 inhibitor and C1q in patients with acquired C1 inhibitor deficiency. J Allergy Clin Immunol 77: 322–26, 1986.

63. Morgan BP, Walport MJ. Complement deficiencies and disease. Immunology Today 12: 301–6, 1991.

64. Oltvai ZN, Wong ECC, Atkinson JP, Tung KSK. C1 inhibitor deficiency: Molecular and immunologic basis of hereditary and acquired angioedema. Lab Invest 65: 381–88, 1991.

65. Osler W. Hereditary angioneurotic edema. Am J Med Sci 95: 362–67, 1888.

66. Parad RB, Kramer J, Strunk RC, Rosen FS, Davis AE III. Dysfunctional C1 inhibitor Ta: Deletion of *Lys*-251 results in acquisition of N-glycosylation site. Proc Natl Acad Sci USA 87: 6786–90, 1990.

67. Pickering RJ, Kelly JR, Good RA, Gewurz H. Replacement therapy in hereditary angioedema: successful treatment of two patients with fresh frozen plasma. Lancet 1: 326–30, 1969.

67a.Pzoud G, Chamberlain J. Anaphylactic reaction to aprotinin (letter). Lancet 2: 48, 1976.

68. Quastel M, Harrison RA, Cicardi M, Alper CA, Rosen FS. Behaviour in vivo of normal and dysfunctional C1 inhibitor in normal subjects and in patients with hereditary angioneurotic edema. J Clin Invest 71: 1041–46, 1983.

69. Rosen FS, Alper CA, Pensky J, Klemperer MR, Donaldson VH. Genetically determined heterogeneity of the C1 esterase inhibitor in patients with hereditary angioneurotic edema. J Clin Invest 50: 2143–49, 1971.

70. Rosen FS, Charache P, Pensky J, Donaldson VH. Hereditary angioneurotic edema: Two genetic variants. Science 148: 957–58, 1965.

71. Ryan US, Frokjaer-Jensen J. Pulmonary endothelium and processing of plasma solutes: Structure and function. In: Said SJ, ed. The Pulmonary Circulation and Acute Lung Injury. Mount Kisco, NY: Futura, pp 37–60, 1985.

72. Schapira M, Silver LD, Scott CF, Schmaier AH, Prograis LJ Jr, Curd JC, Colman RW. Prekallikrein activation and high-molecular-weight kininogen consumption in hereditary angioedema. N Engl J Med 308: 1050–53, 1983.

73. Schreiber AD, Zweiman B, Atkins P, Goldwein F, Pietra G, Atkinson B, Abdou NI. Acquired angioedema with lymphoproliferative disorder: Association of C1 inhibitor deficiency with cellular abnormality. Blood 48: 567–80, 1976.

74. Sheffer AL, Austen KF, Rosen FS, Fearon DT. Acquired deficiency of the inhibitor of the first component of complement: Report of five additional cases and commentary on the syndrome. J Allergy Clin Immunol 75: 640–46, 1985.

75. Sim TC, Grant JA. Hereditary angioedema: Its diagnostic and management perspectives. Am J Med 88: 656–64, 1990.

76. Skriver K, Radziejewska E, Silbermann J, Donaldson VH, Bock SC. CpG mutations in the reactive site of human C1 inhibitor. J Biol Chem 264: 3066–71, 1989.

77. Skriver K, Wikoff WR, Patston PA, Tausk F, Schapira M, Kaplan AP, Bock SC. Substrate properties of C1 inhibitor Ma (Alanine 434 glutamic acid). J Biol Chem 266: 9216–21, 1991.

78. Stein PE, Leslie AGW, Finch JT, Turnell WG, McLaughlin PJ, Carrel RW. Crystal structure of ovalbumin as a model for reactive centre of serpins. Nature 347: 99–102, 1990.

79. Stoppa-Lyonnet D, Carter PE, Meo T, Tosi M. Clusters of intragenic Alu repeats predispose the human C1 inhibitor locus to deleterious rearrangements. Proc Natl Acad Sci 87: 1551–55, 1990.

80. Stoppa-Lyonnet D, Tosi M, Laurent J, Sobel A, Lagrue G, Meo T. Altered C1 inhibitor genes in type I hereditary angioedema. N Engl J Med 317: 1–6, 1987.

81. Strang CJ, Cholin S, Davis AE, Schneeberger EE, Donaldson VH, Rosen FS. Angioedema induced by a peptide derived from complement component C2. J Exp Med 168: 1685–88, 1988.

82. Wautier JL, Caen JP. Norgestriénone, une thérapeutique possible dans l'oedème angioneurotique héréditaire (letter). Presse Méd 15: 2023, 1986.

83. Westaby D, Ogle SJ, Paradinas FJ, Randell JB, Murray-Lyon JM. Liver damage from long-term methyltestosterone. Lancet 2: 261–63, 1977.

TREATMENT OF HEREDITARY ANGIOEDEMA WITH A VAPOR-HEATED C1 INHIBITOR CONCENTRATE

A. Thomas Waytes, M.D., Ph.D., Fred S. Rosen, M.D., and Michael M. Frank, M.D.

Abstract *Background.* Hereditary angioedema results from a congenital deficiency of functional C1 inhibitor and is characterized by episodic bouts of edema, which may be life-threatening when they involve the larynx. We evaluated the effectiveness of a C1 inhibitor concentrate in the prevention and treatment of attacks of hereditary angioedema. The concentrate was vapor-heated to inactivate hepatitis and human immunodeficiency viruses.

Methods. We conducted two double-blind, placebo-controlled studies. The first was a crossover study consisting of two 17-day trials in which prophylactic infusions of either C1 inhibitor (25 plasma units per kilogram of body weight) or placebo were given intravenously every third day to six patients with hereditary angioedema. The second study was conducted in patients with acute attacks of hereditary angioedema and assessed the length of time to a clinical response after infusions of either 25 plasma units of C1 inhibitor per kilogram (55 in-

fusions in 11 patients) or placebo (49 infusions in 11 patients).

Results. The infusions of C1 inhibitor concentrate resulted in close to normal functional levels of C1 inhibitor and C4. As compared with placebo, prophylactic infusions of C1 inhibitor resulted in significantly lower daily symptom scores for the severity of edema of the extremities ($P<0.01$), larynx ($P<0.05$), abdomen ($P<0.05$), and genitourinary tract ($P<0.05$). Likewise, during the treatment study the time from the start of an infusion to the beginning of improvement in symptoms was shorter for the C1 inhibitor infusions than the placebo infusions (55 vs. 563 minutes, $P<0.001$). There was no evidence of toxicity.

Conclusions. Infusions of a vapor-heated C1 inhibitor concentrate are a safe and effective means of both preventing attacks of hereditary angioedema and treating acute attacks. (N Engl J Med 1996;334:1630-4.)

©1996, Massachusetts Medical Society.

HEREDITARY angioedema, first reported by Quincke in 1882[1] and described by Osler in 1888,[2] is characterized by episodic bouts of well-circumscribed, nonpitting subepithelial edema that primarily involve the extremities, larynx, face, and abdomen.[3,4] The condition is inherited as an autosomal dominant trait and characterized by functional levels of C1 inhibitor activity in the blood that are approximately 30 percent of normal values.[5] About 15 percent of patients, however, have normal levels of antigenic C1 inhibitor, but most of it is nonfunctional.[6] As a result of the failure of C1 inhibitor to block the enzymatic activity of C1, levels of the early-acting complement components C4 and C2 are low.[7,8] The role of C1 inhibitor in the pathogenesis of hereditary angioedema has been reviewed in detail.[9]

Attacks of hereditary angioedema generally last one to four days. Swelling of the extremities is typically painless and resolves without harm. Abdominal attacks from edema in the submucosa and serosa of the bowel wall are often associated with nausea, vomiting, and pain severe enough to necessitate the use of narcotic medications. Edema of the upper airway may result in asphyxiation; before modern prophylactic therapy approximately 25 percent of patients died of this complication.[10]

Prophylactic administration of either androgens[11-13] or antifibrinolytic agents[14,15] has proved useful in reducing the frequency or severity of attacks. Some patients,

however, are resistant to or cannot tolerate these drugs, and their use in children and pregnant women is fraught with difficulty. The availability of purified C1 inhibitor from human plasma led to several investigations of the usefulness of these concentrates in treating hereditary angioedema.[16-18] Unfortunately, their use was associated with a significant risk of transmission of the human immunodeficiency virus (HIV) and hepatitis. A lyophilized C1 inhibitor concentrate, which is vapor-heated to 60°C for 10 hours under pressure, conditions that effectively inactivate HIV and hepatitis B and C viruses,[19] was subsequently developed and was found to be useful in the treatment of hereditary angioedema.[20]

The symptoms of hereditary angioedema have a strong psychological component, as is evidenced by the fact that up to 30 to 40 percent of attacks are precipitated by emotional stress.[4] Therefore, blinded, controlled studies are critical in the evaluation of the effectiveness of any treatment for this disease. We performed two randomized, placebo-controlled, double-blind studies. One was a crossover study in which the efficacy and safety of multiple prophylactic infusions of C1 inhibitor concentrate and placebo were evaluated in six patients with hereditary angioedema whose symptoms could not be controlled with standard therapy. In the other study, 22 patients with acute attacks of hereditary angioedema were treated with C1 inhibitor concentrate or placebo.

METHODS

Patients

To be eligible for the study patients had to have an established diagnosis of hereditary angioedema, with functional C1 inhibitor levels of less than 30 percent of normal before the study and a history of more than five attacks of hereditary angioedema in the previous year. Participation in the prophylaxis study also required the lack of an ad-

From the Laboratory of Clinical Investigation, National Institute of Allergy and Infectious Diseases, National Institutes of Health, Bethesda, Md. (A.T.W., M.M.F.); and the Center for Blood Research, Division of Immunology, Children's Hospital, and the Department of Pediatrics, Harvard Medical School — both in Boston (F.S.R.). Address reprint requests to Dr. Rosen at the Center for Blood Research, 800 Huntington Ave., Boston, MA 02115.

Supported by grants from the National Institutes of Health (GCRC RR-02172) and the Food and Drug Administration (FD-R-000659-03).

equate response to conventional treatment with androgens or antifibrinolytic agents or the occurrence of adverse reactions.

C1 Inhibitor Concentrate

The C1 inhibitor preparation used (Immuno, Vienna, Austria) is a freeze-dried, sterile, human plasma fraction containing the inhibitor of the first component of complement in a concentrated and purified form. The moistened product was subjected to vapor heating at a mean temperature of 60°C (range, 55.5°C to 60.5°C) and a pressure of 190±20 millibars for 10 hours to inactivate blood-borne viruses. Each vial, when reconstituted with 10 ml of sterile water, contained approximately 55 plasma units per milliliter, with 1 plasma unit being equivalent to the functional activity of C1 inhibitor in 1 ml of fresh average human plasma. The lyophilized material was reconstituted immediately before the infusion and was administered at a dose of 25 plasma units per kilogram of body weight. Placebo (5 percent human albumin), which was identical in appearance to the C1 inhibitor concentrate, was administered in the same volume, at the same rate, and according to the same schedule.

Study Designs

In the prophylaxis study, which was approved by the National Institute of Allergy and Infectious Diseases (NIAID) Clinical Research Subpanel, the director of the National Institutes of Health Clinical Center, and the Food and Drug Administration (FDA), each patient was admitted to the clinical center for two 17-day periods that were separated by at least 3 weeks. Six patients were randomly assigned to receive five intravenous infusions of either C1 inhibitor or placebo during the first admission and the alternate preparation during the second. Plasma and serum were collected for measurements of complement before and 2, 24, and 72 hours after each infusion. Functional measurements of C1 inhibitor were performed with a microtiter adaptation of the Immunochrom C1 inhibitor diagnostic kit.[21] Levels of C4 activity in plasma (sodium citrate) were determined with a hemolytic assay.[22] The results are expressed as a hemolytic titer, with the mean normal level being 168,000 units per milliliter (range, 98,000 to 308,000).

Each time a patient reported a new or increasingly severe attack of hereditary angioedema or requested medications for hereditary angioedema (including narcotics), an NIAID medical-staff fellow, who had no knowledge of the patient's therapy, would evaluate the symptoms; document the date, time, and location of the attack; and objectively score the severity of the attack from 0 for no relevant symptoms to 3 or 4 for symptoms of greatest severity. The following symptoms were evaluated: abdominal edema (score, 0 to 3), edema of the extremities (0 to 3), laryngeal edema (0 to 4), and genitourinary edema (0 to 3). The highest scores recorded for each system during a given six-hour period were used for comparative purposes, with the daily symptom score for each system representing the average of the four consecutive six-hour periods. This provided a combined measurement of the severity, as well as the frequency and persistence, of symptoms of hereditary angioedema. The episodic nature of this disease, with swelling episodes typically being separated by symptom-free periods lasting days or weeks, is such that a typical patient can be expected to have one or two mild-to-moderate attacks per month. This would result in mean daily symptom scores of about 0.1 to 0.2. Daily symptom scores were compared with a repeated-measures Kruskal–Wallis analysis of variance.[23] In cases in which there was no variance (i.e., no symptoms in one treatment group), two-way contingency tables were analyzed and the mid P values were determined.[24]

In the treatment study, which was approved by the Children's Hospital and Brigham and Women's Hospital institutional review boards and the FDA, patients were required to report for an infusion within five hours after the beginning of an attack of hereditary angioedema. The time from the start of the infusion to the beginning of symptom abatement was used as a measure of clinical efficacy. Open-label C1 inhibitor was available for use as rescue therapy if the physician felt that the symptoms were life threatening. Only one patient was treated immediately with C1 inhibitor because of life-threatening laryngeal edema; this patient did not qualify for statistical evaluation. In other instances open-label C1 inhibitor was administered if there was no

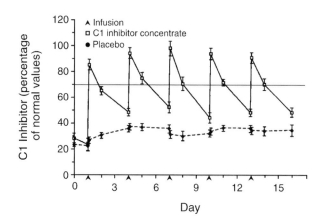

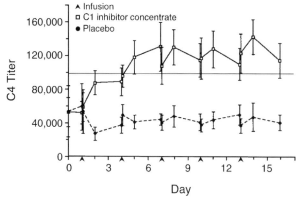

Figure 1. Mean Functional C1 Inhibitor Levels and C4 Levels in Patients with Hereditary Angioedema after Infusions of C1 Inhibitor Concentrate or Placebo.

Each point represents the mean plasma level of six recipients. The bars show the range. The lower limits of normal are represented by the solid horizontal lines.

abatement of symptoms after 240 minutes; patients with these attacks remained eligible for statistical evaluation. Significance testing was performed with repeated-measures analysis of variance to compare the mean response time between treatment groups.[25] Pre-infusion and post-infusion levels of functional C1 inhibitor were determined as described above.[21]

RESULTS

Prophylaxis Study

Of the six patients enrolled in the prophylaxis study, four continued to take androgens (8 mg of stanozolol per day or 400 to 800 mg of danazol per day) throughout the study, which had been prescribed at the maximal tolerated dose, but with suboptimal results. The remaining two patients had been receiving no daily medications for hereditary angioedema, because previous treatments had not been effective. All six patients had previously received antifibrinolytic agents, which either were ineffective or caused serious adverse effects.

The mean functional C1 inhibitor and C4 levels in the six patients are shown in Figure 1. Infusions of C1 inhibitor concentrate, but not placebo, resulted in a dramatic increase in plasma levels of C1 inhibitor and C4. C1 inhibitor levels fell to approximately the lower limit of normal by 24 hours, but were still above base line by 72 hours.

Levels of C4 at base line were not significantly different from those measured two hours after the first infusions of either C1 inhibitor concentrate or placebo. Beyond that time, however, the levels of functional C4 after the C1 inhibitor infusions were markedly higher than those after placebo. Unlike C1 inhibitor levels, which increased immediately, C4 levels tended to increase more slowly, not reaching the normal range until 24 hours after the first infusion. Although C4 levels declined between infusions, they did not have the marked "sawtooth" pattern of C1 inhibitor levels.

As shown in Table 1, the mean daily scores for edema of the extremities, larynx, abdomen, and genitourinary tract revealed that there was significantly less disease activity — over 60 percent less — during treatment with C1 inhibitor concentrate than during placebo infusions. Abdominal discomfort was by far the most common side effect and was also the most difficult to evaluate objectively, since some patients were suspected of feigning symptoms in order to receive narcotic medications. Not one patient receiving the C1 inhibitor concentrate had objective evidence of either laryngeal or genitourinary edema, whereas four of the six patients receiving placebo had disease-related edema of one or both of these systems.

Treatment Study

Eleven patients randomly assigned to receive C1 inhibitor concentrate were treated for a total of 55 attacks. An identical number of patients were given placebo for a total of 49 attacks. The number (and percentage) of attacks in each treatment group that began to improve within 30 minutes after the start of the infusion is shown in Table 2. Sixty-nine percent of the attacks treated with C1 inhibitor responded within this period, as compared with 2 percent of the placebo-treated attacks. Two hundred forty minutes after the start of infusion, 95 percent of the attacks treated with C1 inhibitor had begun to improve, as compared with 12 percent of those treated with placebo. Laryngeal, abdominal, and facial attacks are the most likely to become severe or life-threatening and thus represent situations in which effective therapy is most critical. All at-

Table 1. Daily Symptom Scores in Six Patients with Hereditary Angioedema Who Were Receiving C1 Inhibitor Concentrate or Placebo.*

LOCATION OF EDEMA	INHIBITOR C1	PLACEBO	P VALUE
	mean (±SE) daily score		
Extremities	0.022±0.011	0.125±0.037	<0.01†
Larynx	0.000±0.000	0.036±0.022	<0.05‡
Abdomen	0.169±0.041	0.308±0.057	<0.05†
Genitourinary tract	0.000±0.000	0.031±0.123	<0.05‡
Total	0.191±0.044	0.500±0.089	<0.001†

*Ninety measurements were made during each treatment period.
†By analysis of variance.
‡Mid P values determined with two-way contingency tables.[24]

Table 2. Length of Time to the Response to C1 Inhibitor Concentrate or Placebo.

LOCATION OF EDEMA	RESPONSE IN ≤30 MINUTES		RESPONSE IN <240 MINUTES	
	C1 INHIBITOR	PLACEBO	C1 INHIBITOR	PLACEBO
	no. of responses/no. of attacks (% responding)			
Abdomen	25/35 (71)	0/34	35/35 (100)	2/34 (6)
Larynx	3/4 (75)	0/4	4/4 (100)	1/4 (25)
Face	7/7 (100)	0/8	7/7 (100)	1/8 (12)
Extremities	9/16 (56)	1/16 (6)	13/16 (81)	3/16 (19)
First 3 locations*	33/44 (75)	0/40	44/44 (100)	4/40 (10)
All locations*	38/55 (69)	1/49 (2)	52/55 (95)	6/49 (12)

*For single attacks involving more than one location, the location with the earliest response was used for statistical analysis.

tacks involving these three areas improved within 240 minutes after C1 inhibitor treatment, 75 percent of them within 30 minutes. In contrast, only 10 percent responded within 240 minutes after the administration of placebo, and none within 30 minutes (Table 2).

As shown in Table 3, the mean interval between the start of the infusion and the beginning of an effect for all attacks treated with C1 inhibitor was 55 minutes, as compared with 563 minutes for those treated with placebo (P<0.001). Only four episodes of laryngeal edema were treated in each group. Although the mean time to relief of laryngeal edema after the administration of C1 inhibitor (35 minutes) appeared to be much shorter than that observed after placebo (512 minutes), the difference was not statistically significant because of the small sample. At 240 minutes, 21 of the attacks not responding to the initial infusion were treated with open-label C1 inhibitor. All were subsequently determined to have been treated with placebo initially, and all responded to the C1 inhibitor. Excluding these attacks from the analysis increased the mean response time of placebo-treated attacks to 799 minutes (Table 3). Seven additional attacks (all treated with placebo) were of such severity that open-label C1 inhibitor was given before 240 minutes, and thus, they did not qualify for evaluation.

Functional C1 inhibitor levels were measured during 34 attacks subsequently determined to have been treated with C1 inhibitor concentrate. The mean level rose from 11.0 percent of normal before the infusion to 69.4 percent of normal after the infusion. The mean level of C1 inhibitor achieved after the treatment of abdominal, laryngeal, and facial attacks with the concentrate was 66.0 percent of normal, with no differences in either pre-infusion or post-infusion levels between attacks that responded within 30 minutes and those that did not. The C1 inhibitor levels in 49 attacks that were subsequently determined to have been treated with placebo remained at approximately 10 percent of normal before and after the infusion.

DISCUSSION

We assessed the efficacy of a vapor-heated C1 inhibitor preparation in a double-blind, placebo-controlled setting in patients with hereditary angioedema. Levels

Table 3. Interval between the Start of the Infusion and the Beginning of an Effect.*

LOCATION OF EDEMA	C1 INHIBITOR (ALL ATTACKS)			PLACEBO (ALL ATTACKS)				PLACEBO (ALL ATTACKS BUT THOSE INVOLVING RESCUE THERAPY)†			
	NO. OF PATIENTS	NO. OF ATTACKS	MINUTES TO RESPONSE	NO. OF PATIENTS	NO. OF ATTACKS	MINUTES TO RESPONSE	P VALUE‡	NO. OF PATIENTS	NO. OF ATTACKS	MINUTES TO RESPONSE	P VALUE‡
Abdomen	9	35	29 ± 4	11	34	556 ± 92	<0.001	9	13	1055 ± 166	<0.001
Larynx	3	4	35 ± 23	4	4	512 ± 161	NS	4	4	512 ± 161	NS
Face	5	7	14 ± 5	4	8	694 ± 163	0.005	4	7	757 ± 174	0.005
Extremities	7	16	120 ± 53	5	16	691 ± 136	0.023	5	14	754 ± 148	0.020
First 3 locations§	10	44	28 ± 4	11	40	547 ± 81	0.001	11	19	878 ± 135	<0.001
All locations§	11	55	55 ± 16	11	49	563 ± 72	<0.001	11	28	799 ± 105	<0.001

*Plus–minus values are means ±SE.

†In 21 instances patients who had no response after four hours were given C1 inhibitor concentrate as rescue therapy.

‡For the comparison of mean response times between treatment groups by repeated-measures analysis of variance. NS denotes not significant.

§For single attacks involving more than one location, the location with the earliest response was used for statistical analysis.

of C1 inhibitor increased dramatically after the initial infusions of concentrate, to a mean of 85 percent of normal values, confirming that the activity of the infused protein, as assessed by an in vitro assay, remained intact after vapor heating. These increases compare favorably with those in other studies, in which the mean post-infusion levels were 70 percent of normal (range, 54 to 110 percent).[17,18,20] Direct comparisons of these studies cannot be made, however, because of differences in the amount of C1 inhibitor infused. Twenty-four hours after the infusion, the mean levels of C1 inhibitor were approximately 70 percent of normal, which is the lower limit of normal values, and fell to about 48 percent of normal — a value still significantly above the base-line level — by 72 hours.

Plasma C4 is extremely sensitive to the protective effects of C1 inhibitor, and levels are often very low in patients with hereditary angioedema, especially during attacks. After the administration of C1 inhibitor concentrate, the functional levels of C4 rose well into the normal range. In contrast to the sharp rise and fall seen with C1 inhibitor, levels of C4 increased more slowly, as reported elsewhere.[18]

Some of the patients in the study were suspected of feigning symptoms in an effort to be given narcotics, a factor that sometimes made clinical assessments difficult. Nevertheless, objective determinations of symptoms during each phase of the study demonstrated the effectiveness of the C1 inhibitor concentrate, even in patients who had no response to any other therapy. This underscores the critical importance of double-blind studies in attempting to evaluate the clinical response of patients with hereditary angioedema.

On the basis of the clinical benefit seen in these patients, there may be a role for short-term or long-term prophylactic use of C1 inhibitor concentrates in some children and pregnant women with particularly severe hereditary angioedema. The availability of a C1 inhibitor concentrate to reverse the pain of abdominal attacks quickly may, in fact, be an important adjunct in reducing the narcotic dependence of some patients with hereditary angioedema. Of much greater importance, however, is the use of this concentrate as a safe and effective treatment for acute attacks of hereditary angio-

edema, particularly those involving the larynx and abdomen. In the treatment study, the submucosal swelling in these two areas responded better to infusions of C1 inhibitor concentrates than did subcutaneous edema of the extremities, as has been noted previously.[17] A clinical response was noted within 30 minutes after most infusions of C1 inhibitor, as compared with many hours after the infusions of placebo.

All patients with hereditary angioedema are at increased risk for attacks of laryngeal edema during and after procedures involving manipulation of the oral cavity and upper airway. Of particular concern are dental surgery, including tooth extractions, and surgical procedures requiring general anesthesia and intubation. It would be reasonable to consider the use of C1 inhibitor concentrate for short-term prophylaxis in these circumstances. The mean plasma levels of C1 inhibitor protein more than tripled, from 26 percent to 85 percent of normal levels, after the initial prophylactic infusions of the C1 inhibitor concentrate. This response compares favorably with the 1.5-fold increase seen after a series of seven prophylactic infusions of fresh-frozen plasma, which prevented complications of hereditary angioedema resulting from dental procedures.[26]

Eighty-five blinded and 21 compassionate infusions of C1 inhibitor, delivering a total of more than 200,000 plasma units, were administered over the course of this study. All were tolerated well, with no evidence of serious immediate or short-term adverse effects. The patients were monitored for up to four years for HIV and hepatitis B and C seroconversion. All remained seronegative. Serum from all patients in the prophylaxis study and 13 patients in the treatment study was screened for evidence of autoantibodies to C1 inhibitor that could have resulted from exposure to the concentrates. All samples were negative.

This study demonstrates the safety and efficacy of this viral-inactivated C1 inhibitor concentrate in the treatment and prophylaxis of hereditary angioedema.

We are indebted to the nurses and clinical-immunology fellows of the NIAID and Children's Hospital, Boston, for their important contributions to this study, and to Ms. Debra Mozill, Ms. Rinda Mary Payne, Ms. Mary Huber, Ms. Gilda Linton, Dr. Albert Sheffer, Dr. Steven Banks, and Dr. Alexa Beiser for their help.

REFERENCES

1. Quincke H. Über akutes umschriebenes Hautödem. Monatsh Prakt Dermatol 1882;1:129-31.
2. Osler W. Hereditary angioneurotic oedema. Am J Med Sci 1888;95:362-7.
3. Donaldson VH, Rosen FS. Hereditary angioneurotic edema: a clinical survey. Pediatrics 1966;37:1017-27.
4. Frank MM, Gelfand JA, Atkinson JP. Hereditary angioedema: the clinical syndrome and its management. Ann Intern Med 1976;84:580-93.
5. Donaldson VH, Evans RR. A biochemical abnormality in hereditary angioneurotic edema: absence of serum inhibitor of $C'1$-esterase. Am J Med 1963;35:37-44.
6. Rosen FS, Alper CA, Pensky J, Klemperer MR, Donaldson VH. Genetically determined heterogeneity of the C1 esterase inhibitor in patients with hereditary angioneurotic edema. J Clin Invest 1971;50:2143-9.
7. Donaldson VH, Rosen FS. Action of complement in hereditary angioneurotic edema: the role of $C'1$-esterase. J Clin Invest 1964;43:2204-13.
8. Austen KF, Sheffer AL. Detection of hereditary angioneurotic edema by demonstration of a reduction in the second component of human complement. N Engl J Med 1965;272:649-56.
9. Davis AE III. C1 inhibitor and hereditary angioneurotic edema. Annu Rev Immunol 1988;6:595-628.
10. Landerman NS. Hereditary angioneurotic edema. I. Case reports and review of the literature. J Allergy 1962;33:316-29.
11. Spaulding WB. Methyltestosterone therapy for hereditary episodic edema (hereditary angioneurotic edema). Ann Intern Med 1960;53:739-45.
12. Gelfand JA, Sherins RJ, Alling DW, Frank MM. Treatment of hereditary angioedema with danazol: reversal of clinical and biochemical abnormalities. N Engl J Med 1976;295:1444-8.
13. Sheffer AL, Fearon DT, Austen KF. Hereditary angioedema: a decade of management with stanozolol. J Allergy Clin Immunol 1987;80:855-60. [Erratum, J Allergy Clin Immunol 1988;81:1208.]
14. Frank MM, Sergent JS, Kane M, Alling DW. Epsilon aminocaproic acid therapy of hereditary angioneurotic edema: a double-blind study. N Engl J Med 1972;286:808-12.
15. Sheffer AL, Austen KF, Rosen FS. Tranexamic acid therapy in hereditary angioneurotic edema. N Engl J Med 1972;287:452-4.
16. Brackertz D, Kueppers F. Possible therapy in hereditary angioneurotic edema (HAE). Klin Wochenschr 1973;51:620-2.
17. Agostoni A, Bergamaschini L, Martignoni GC, Cicardi M, Marasini B. Treatment of acute attacks of hereditary angioedema with C1-inhibitor concentrate. Ann Allergy 1980;44:299-301.
18. Gadek JE, Hosea SW, Gelfand JA, et al. Replacement therapy in hereditary angioedema: successful treatment of acute episodes of angioedema with partly purified C1 inhibitor. N Engl J Med 1980;302:542-6.
19. Mannucci PM, Schimpf K, Abe T, et al. Low risk of viral infection after administration of vapor-heated factor VIII concentrate. Transfusion 1992;32:134-8.
20. Agostoni A. Inherited C1 inhibitor deficiency. Complement Inflammation 1989;6:112-8.
21. Kleindel M, Lang H, Philapitsch A, Wöber G. A rapid method for determination of C1-esterase inhibitor activity using a new chromogenic substrate. Thromb Haemost 1983;50:244. abstract.
22. Gaither TA, Alling DW, Frank MM. A new one-step method for the functional assay of the fourth component (C4) of human and guinea pig complement. J Immunol 1974;113:574-83.
23. Shirley EAC. Applications of ranking methods to multiple comparison procedures and factorial experiments. Appl Stat 1987;36:205-13.
24. Agresti A. Categorical data analysis. New York: John Wiley, 1990.
25. Winer BJ. Statistical principles in experimental design. 2nd ed. New York: McGraw-Hill, 1971.
26. Jaffe CJ, Atkinson JP, Gelfand JA, Frank MM. Hereditary angioedema: the use of fresh frozen plasma for prophylaxis in patients undergoing oral surgery. J Allergy Clin Immunol 1975;55:386-93.

Degradation of C1-Inhibitor by Plasmin: Implications for the Control of Inflammatory Processes

Eleanor M. Wallace,[1] Stephen J. Perkins,[2] Robert B. Sim,[3] Anthony C. Willis,[3] Con Feighery,[1] and John Jackson[1,4]

[1]Department of Immunology, St. James' Hospital, Dublin 8, Ireland
[2]Department of Biochemistry and Molecular Biology, Royal Free Hospital School of Medicine, London, U.K.   [3]MRC Immunochemistry Unit, Department of Biochemistry, University of Oxford, Oxford, U.K.   [4]The Dublin Institute of Technology, Dublin, Ireland

ABSTRACT

Background: A correct balance between protease and inhibitor activity is critical in the maintenance of homoeostasis; excessive activation of enzyme pathways is frequently associated with inflammatory disorders. Plasmin is an enzyme ubiquitously activated in inflammatory disorders, and C1-inhibitor (C1-Inh) is a pivotal inhibitor of protease activity, which is particularly important in the regulation of enzyme cascades generated in plasma. The nature of the interaction between plasmin and C1-Inh is poorly understood.

Materials and Methods: C1-Inh was immunoadsorbed from the plasma of normal individuals ($n = 21$), from that of patients with systemic lupus erythematosus ($n = 18$) or adult respiratory distress syndrome ($n = 9$), and from the plasma and synovial fluid of patients with rheumatoid arthritis ($n = 18$). As plasmin is a putative enzyme responsible for C1-Inh degradation, the interaction between plasmin and C1-Inh was examined using SDS-PAGE. In addition, peptides cleaved from C1-Inh by plasmin were isolated and sequenced and the precise cleavage sites determined from the known primary sequence of C1-Inh. Homology models of C1-Inh were then constructed.

Results: Increased levels of cleaved and inactivated C1-Inh were found in each of the inflammatory disorders examined. Through SDS-PAGE analysis it was shown that plasmin rapidly degraded C1-Inh in vitro. The pattern of C1-Inh cleavage seen in vivo in patients with inflammatory disorders and that produced in vitro following incubation with plasmin were very similar. Homology models of C1-Inh indicate that the majority of the plasmin cleavage sites are adjacent to the reactive site of the inhibitor.

Conclusions: This study suggests that local C1-Inh degradation by plasmin may be a central and critical event in the loss of protease inhibition during inflammation. These findings have important implications for our understanding of pathogenic mechanisms in inflammation and for the development of more effectively targeted therapeutic regimes. These findings may also explain the efficacy of anti-plasmin agents in the treatment of C1-Inh deficiency states, as they may diminish plasmin-mediated C1-Inh degradation.

INTRODUCTION

Inflammation occurs as a result of the host's response to tissue injury and is a consequence of a complex series of interactions involving cellular and chemical mediators. The characteristic

movement of fluid and white cells from blood into the extravascular tissues is the host's attempt to contain and eliminate damaged tissues, foreign particles, and microorganisms. The ultimate aim of this process is to limit damage and initiate tissue repair. If the effort to restore homeostasis is unsuccessful, inflammation may become harmful and lead to extensive tissue destruction and injury (1). This is well illustrated in many common inflammatory disorders, such as

Address correspondence and reprint requests to: John Jackson, Dept. of Immunology, Central Pathology, St. James Hospital, Dublin 8, Ireland. Tel: 01 4537941 Ext. 2921; Fax: 01 4545609.

inflammatory bowel disease, rheumatoid arthritis (RA) and psoriasis and in other less common disorders such as systemic lupus erythematosus (SLE) and adult respiratory distress syndrome (ARDS) (1). An important prerequisite for a successful inflammatory response and a return to homeostasis is the effective control of damaging enzymes generated during inflammation (1). To this end, plasma protease inhibitors represent 10% of total plasma protein, controlling proteolytic events critical in the inflammatory response, such as those occuring during kinin, coagulation, fibrinolysis, and complement activation, as well as controlling the enzymes released from activated leucocytes (2,3). Serine protease inhibitors (serpins) are an important family of inhibitors that play an essential role in the regulation of serine proteases generated during inflammatory processes (4). Their central role is underlined by deficiency states such as hereditary angioedema (C1-Inh deficiency) (5); emphysema (α-1-proteinase inhibitor deficiency) (6); recurrent hemorrage (α-2-anti-plasmin deficiency) (7); and thrombosis (antithrombin III deficiency) (8). Furthermore, serpins behave as acute phase proteins and their synthesis is increased in response to tissue damage (9).

C1-inhibitor (C1-Inh) is a member of the serpin family that has a pivotal role in the control of proteases involved in the early phase of the inflammatory response. These proteases include proteins of the complement (C1r and C1s), kinin (plasma kallikrein), coagulation (factors XIa, XIIa and XIIf), and fibrinolytic (plasmin) pathways (5,10).

Deficiency of C1-Inh leads to defective regulation of the inflammatory pathways and recurrent bouts of tissue swelling, or angioedema. These episodes of angioedema are thought to occur when C1-Inh is depleted to a critical level. Interestingly, C1-Inh deficiency may be effectively treated with anti-plasmin agents, which suggests that plasmin activation is central to the pathogenesis of this disorder (10). Plasmin, an enzyme activated during many inflammatory processes, is important in controlling fibrin deposition in tissue, which is a very early response to tissue injury (11). Furthermore, fibrin deposition and plasmin activation are hallmarks of many common inflammatory disorders. C1-Inh is thought to inhibit plasmin according to the general mechanism of serpin action; however, little is known about the C1-Inh/plasmin interaction (2,3,10). Early studies investigating the nature of the C1-Inh/plasmin encounter observed that it is different from the serpin mechanism of protease inhibition (12–14).

In this study, we examined C1-Inh consumption and degradation in plasma from patients with a variety of inflammatory disorders as well as in plasma and synovial fluid from patients with active rheumatoid arthritis, and found increased levels of degraded, low molecular weight forms of C1-Inh. As plasmin is a putative enzyme involved in C1-Inh degradation, the interaction between C1-Inh and plasmin was examined in detail in vitro. Our results show that C1-Inh is rapidly cleaved by plasmin at several sites in the molecule, resulting in inactivated C1-Inh. Furthermore, degraded forms of C1-Inh, which were similar to those generated in vitro, were found in the plasma of patients with inflammatory disorders.

Local depletion of C1-Inh by plasmin could contribute significantly to the pathogenesis of inflammatory conditions by altering the protease inhibitor balance. In addition, our results also provide an explanation for the efficacy of anti-plasmin agents in the treatment of C1-Inh deficiency states. Finally, it is also suggested that proteolytic degradation of other serpins could be an important pathogenic mechanism in other inflammatory processes.

MATERIALS AND METHODS

Examination of C1-Inh Consumption and Degradation

Blood from the following individuals was collected in siliconized vacutainer tubes to which EDTA (10 mM) and polybrene (0.05%, w/v) had been added to prevent in vitro activation of the complement and the contact system: 21 normal controls, 24 individuals with SLE, 18 patients with RA, and 9 patients with ARDS. Paired synovial fluids from the same RA patients were collected in an identical manner. Plasma and synovial fluid supernatant were obtained by centrifugation and were immediately aliquoted and stored at −70°C. All processing was performed in plastic tubes. The plasma was thawed immediately before analysis. C1-Inh was immunoadsorbed from plasma for analysis according to a previously published method (15). The various forms of immunopurified C1-Inh were separated by SDS-PAGE (nonreduced) and visualized by Western blotting. Native, cleaved, and complexed forms of C1-Inh were scanned and quantified by densitometry.

SDS-PAGE

SDS–PAGE (7.5% acrylamide) was performed according to the general method of Laemmli (16). The samples were added to an equal volume of sample buffer (0.125 M Tris, 8 M urea, 4% w/v SDS, 20% v/v glycerol, pH 6.8). Protein bands were visualized using 0.1% (w/v) Coomassie brilliant blue-R250 (CBB) in 40% methanol (v/v) and 7% acetic acid (v/v). The molecular mass of visible bands was determined by the electrophoresis of protein standards of known molecular mass (29 kDa–205 kDa: SDS-6H, Sigma).

Purification of C1-Inhibitor

C1-Inh was prepared from 200 ml of fresh frozen plasma using a modification of previously published procedures (17,18). All procedures were performed at 4°C. Fractions were monitored for the presence of C1-Inh by rocket electrophoresis with a polyclonal rabbit anti-human C1-Inh antibody (Dako). Fresh frozen plasma was made 0.01 M with EDTA and benzamidine (Sigma) and was made 1 mM with phenylmethylsulfonyl fluoride (PMSF; Sigma). A stock solution of polybrene in EDTA (12.5 ml) was then added to produce final polybrene and EDTA concentrations of 1.2 mg/ml and 20 mM, respectively. The plasma was adjusted to pH 7.0 and chilled to 4°C. Solid polyethylene glycol 4000 was added all at once, resulting in a final concentration of 5% (w/v), and stirred for 1 hr. The precipitate was removed by centrifugation for 30 min at 10,000 × g. The supernatant was mixed with PMSF to make a 1 mM final concentration and applied to a lysine-Sepharose column (2.6 × 9.5 cm) (Pharmacia) to remove plasminogen (19). All of the unadsorbed protein was pooled, mixed with PMSF to make a 1 mM solution, equilibrated with 20 mM sodium phosphate, 50 mM NaCl, 5 mM EDTA, pH 7.0, and applied to a column of Q-Sepharose (20 × 2.6 cm) (Pharmacia) that was equilibrated with the same buffer. C1-Inh was eluted using a linear gradient (500 ml) made from starting buffer and the same buffer made 300 mM with NaCl. Fractions containing C1-Inh were pooled, made 1 mM with PMSF dialyzed against 20 mM Tris-HCl, 100 mM NaCl, pH 8.0, and applied to a column of Concanavalin A (Con-A)-Sepharose (8 × 5 cm) (Pharmacia) that was equilibrated in the same buffer. Elution was achieved with starting buffer made 0.5% (w/v) with α-methylmannoside

(Sigma). The final pool of C1-Inh was dialyzed against 20 mM Tris-HCl, 100 mM NaCl, pH 8.0, and stored at −70°C. The concentration of C1-Inh in the final preparation (0.16 mg/ml) was determined at 280 nm, assuming $E^1\%$ (280 nm) of 3.6 and a molecular mass of 105 kDa (18). The discrepancy between the calculated molecular weight of C1-Inh determined from sequence data and that from SDS-PAGE analysis probably reflects the heavily glycosylated nature of C1-Inh; this is further discussed by Perkins et al. (20). In addition, there is a further disparity between the apparent molecular weight of C1-Inh determined by SDS-PAGE, depending on the presence (105 kDa) or absence (115 kDa) of reducing agents.

Purification of Activated C1s

Activated C1s was isolated from fresh serum and stored at −70°C (21).

Functional Activity of C1-Inh Purified from Plasma

The functional activity of C1-Inh was assessed by examining its ability to form stable complexes with the protease C1s. Equimolar amounts of C1-Inh (0.16 mg/ml) and activated C1s were incubated together at 37°C in 0.02 M sodium phosphate, 100 mM NaCl, pH 7.2 (PBS). At the end of 15- and 30-min incubation periods, identical aliquots (approximately 10 μg total protein) were incubated with nonreducing sample buffer and boiled for 4 min. These samples were analyzed by 7.5% SDS-PAGE and stained with CBB.

Purification of Plasminogen

Plasminogen was isolated from outdated plasma by lysine-Sepharose affinity chromatography and stored at −70°C (19). Just before use, plasminogen was activated by incubating it with streptokinase (Sigma) at 37°C for 120 min, using a molar ratio of 200:1 plasminogen to streptokinase. The plasminogen was fully activated by streptokinase as visualized by 7.5% SDS-PAGE of reduced and nonreduced samples (results not shown).

Interaction of C1-Inh with Plasmin and C1s in Vitro

Equimolar quantities of C1-Inh (0.16 mg/ml) were incubated separately with plasmin (0.35

mg/ml) or C1s (0.06 mg/ml) at 37°C in PBS. At the end of 15- and 30-min incubation periods, identical aliquots of inhibitor and protease were incubated with nonreducing sample buffer, separated by 7.5% SDS-PAGE, and visualized with CBB.

Time Course of the C1-Inh/Plasmin Interaction: SDS-PAGE Analysis

C1-Inh inactivates its target proteases through the formation of equimolar stoichiometric complexes between inhibitor and protease. Therefore, equimolar quantities of C1-Inh (0.16 mg/ml) and plasmin (0.35 mg/ml) were incubated under physiological conditions at 37°C in PBS. At varying time intervals (10 sec, 5, 15, 45, and 120 min), identical aliquots, calculated to contain approximately 10 μg of inhibitor and protease, were added to an equal volume of sample buffer and boiled for 4 min. The following controls were included: C1-Inh in PBS, and plasmin in PBS. These samples were then subjected to 7.5% SDS-PAGE under nonreducing conditions and stained with CBB.

Isolation of Peptides Generated from C1-Inh by Plasmin Using HPLC

C1-Inh (0.16 mg/ml), plasmin (0.35 mg/ml), and C1-Inh/plasmin (molar ratio 8:1 inhibitor to enzyme) were incubated in PBS, pH 7.2, at 37°C for 60 min. At the end of this incubation period, each preparation was acidified with HCl to pH 4.5 to prevent further proteolysis.

The peptides generated from the C1-Inh/plasmin interaction were purified on a Vydac C4 column (150 × 2 mm) equilibrated in 0.1% v/v trifluoroacetic acid, 2% v/v acetonitrile. Peptides were eluted with a linear gradient of 2–50% v/v acetonitrile applied over 50 min and then a further linear gradient of 50–90% acetonitrile over 18 min. The samples were run on a Severn Analytical HPLC system consisting of a gradient controller utilizing Flowmaster software, two model SA6410B high-pressure pumps, and a model SA6504 detector fitted with a microbore flowcell. All detection was performed at E215 and data were collected using Waters' Expert Ease software from Millipore (Watford, U. K.).

N-terminal Sequencing of C1-Inh Peptides

The HPLC profiles for C1-Inh, plasmin, and each of the C1-Inh/plasmin mixtures were compared,

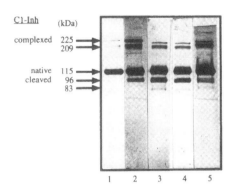

FIG. 1. C1-Inh consumption in plasma of a normal individual and of patients with the inflammatory conditions SLE, ARDS, and RA and in the synovial fluid of a patient with RA

C1-Inh consumption and degradation was visualized by immunoblotting for C1-Inh which revealed native (115 kDa), cleaved (96 and 83 kDa), and complexed C1-Inh (225 and 209 kDa): normal plasma (lane 1); SLE plasma (lane 2); ARDS plasma (lane 3); RA plasma (lane 4); RA synovial fluid (lane 5). Native, cleaved, and complexed C1-Inh were scanned and quantified by densitometry. Lanes 2–5 represent samples with relatively large amounts of cleaved or complexed C1-Inh.

and protein peaks not found in C1-Inh or plasmin alone were selected for N-terminal sequencing.

All samples were run on an Applied Biosystems (ABI) 470A protein sequencer with on-line PTH analyzer. The samples were applied to a glass fiber disc pretreated with polybrene to limit sample wash-out and were run using the standard 03CPTH program from Applied Biosystems.

C1-Inhibitor Modeling

Protein structures were visualized through the INSIGHT 11 95.0 program (Biosym/MSI, San Diego, CA) on Silicon Graphics INDY workstations. The rigid body fragment assembly method used in HOMOLOGY was used to construct an atomic model for the C1-Inh serpin fold based on the uncleaved structure seen in ovalbumin (Brookhaven code 1ova: molecule A) and the reactive-site cleaved structure of α_1-antitrypsin (7api), together with the multiple-sequence alignment based on three known serpin crystal structures (22). After the definition of a protein core of 326 residues in ovalbumin, the remaining 39 residues in loop regions were constructed from a database of Brookhaven database fragments, and all of the side chains were replaced with those in C1-Inh. Energy refinements using

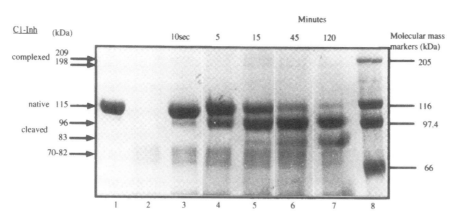

FIG. 2. Time course of the interaction of C1-Inh with plasmin

C1-Inh and plasmin were incubated together at 37°C in PBS and aliquots containing 10 μg were removed at time intervals from 10 sec to 120 min and analyzed by 7.5% SDS-PAGE under nonreducing conditions and stained with Coomassie brilliant blue: C1-Inh (lane 1); plasmin (lane 2); C1-Inh incubated with plasmin for 10 sec, 5, 15, 45, and 120 min (lanes 3 to 7); molecular mass markers (lane 8).

DISCOVER were performed at the loop-splice junctions, then on the loop regions, and finally, the mutated core residues. The refinements improved the connectivity of the model and reduced the proportion of bad contacts or stereochemistry, as confirmed by the use of PROCHECK (23). Solvent accessibitility calculations were performed by the method of Lee and Richards (24).

Statistical Analysis

Analysis of variance (ANOVA) was used to test for differences in the levels of C1-Inh consumption between normal and patient groups. Using the estimate of pooled variance from the ANOVA, the following unpaired t-tests were performed: normal plasma and SLE plasma; normal plasma and ARDS plasma; normal plasma and RA plasma; and normal plasma and RA synovial fluid. A p-value of ≤ 0.05 indicated a significant difference.

RESULTS

C1-Inh Consumption and Degradation in Normal, SLE, RA, and ARDS Plasma

C1-Inh was found in three forms in the plasma of normal individuals: native C1-Inh (115 kDa), cleaved C1-Inh (96 kDa), and a high molecular weight form that probably represents C1-Inh complexed with proteases (209–225 kDa). These species of C1-Inh were distinguished on the basis of their apparent molecular weight (nonreduced) in SDS-PAGE. In the plasma of patients

with SLE [mean (percentage of total C1-Inh circulating in cleaved and/or complexed form) = 24.6%, $p < 0.001$], ARDS (mean = 34.1%, $p < 0.001$), and RA (mean = 26.5%, $p < 0.001$), and in the synovial fluid of patients with RA (mean = 25.5%, $p < 0.001$), there was an increase in the proportion of C1-Inh circulating in the cleaved and/or complexed forms in comparison with normal plasma (mean = 12.7%). Furthermore, an additional lower molecular weight form of C1-Inh was also observed migrating at 83 kDa in the majority of plasma samples from patients with ARDS and in the synovial fluid of patients with RA. Analysis of a representative plasma sample from a normal individual, a patient with lupus, or ARDS, and of plasma and synovial fluid from a patient with RA is illustrated in Fig. 1.

To assess the role of plasmin in this C1-Inh degradation, C1-Inh was incubated with plasmin in vitro and the reaction products were monitored by SDS-PAGE.

Interaction of C1-Inh with Plasmin or C1s

The incubation of C1-Inh with plasmin (10 sec–120 min) resulted in a reduction in the amount of native C1-Inh at 115 kDa and the appearance of new major bands at 96 kDa and 83 kDa. C1-Inh complexed with plasmin was only observed in trace amounts, at 209 kDa and 198 kDa (Fig. 2). (This interaction is compared with that of C1-Inh and C1s in Fig. 3.) In contrast to its interaction with plasmin, the interaction of C1-Inh with C1s results in the appearance of a high molecular weight complex at 225 kDa (C1-Inh complexed with C1s). The interaction of C1-Inh

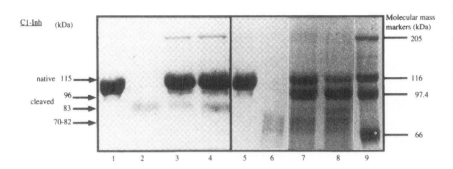

FIG. 3.   Interaction of C1-Inh with plasmin and C1s

C1-Inh was incubated separately with plasmin or C1s at 37°C in PBS for 15 and 30 min. Analyses of these interactions were carried out by SDS-PAGE (7.5%) under nonreducing conditions: C1-Inh (lanes 1 and 5); C1s (lane 2); plasmin (lane 6); C1-Inh incubated with C1s (lanes 3 and 4), or plasmin (lanes 7 and 8) for 15 and 30 min; molecular mass markers (lane 9).

with C1r also results in the generation of complexed inhibitor and protease (results not shown).

HPLC Analysis of C1-Inh/Plasmin Interaction: Profiles

Figure 4 illustrates the reverse-phase HPLC profiles of C1-Inh, plasmin, and C1-Inh/plasmin (molar ratio 8:1 inhibitor to enzyme) that were incubated together at 37°C for 60 min. Initially, C1-Inh and plasmin were incubated in equimolar amounts resulting in extensive digestion of C1-Inh. The reaction was therefore limited by incubating C1-Inh in an inhibitor/plasmin ratio of 8:1. Peptide peaks not present in either plasmin or C1-Inh alone were selected for amino acid sequence analyses (Fig. 4).

N-terminal Sequence Analysis of Peptides Generated from C1-Inh by Plasmin

The amino acid sequences obtained from the selected HPLC protein peaks are detailed in Table 1.

The sites at which C1-Inh is cleaved to produce these peptides are indicated in Fig. 5. Numbering is according to Bock et al. (25) i.e., from the N-terminus of the mature protein. Glycosylated amino acids are indicated by black dots.

Modeling Studies

Homology modeling of the serpin fold in C1-Inh was based on the sequence alignment with the structure of uncleaved ovalbumin (22). The conversion of ovalbumin to C1-Inh involved the

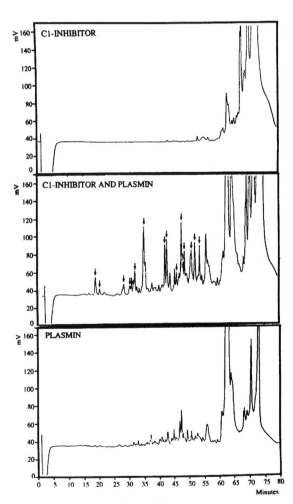

FIG. 4.   HPLC profiles of the C1-Inh/plasmin interaction products

C1-Inh, C1-Inh and plasmin (8:1), and plasmin incubated at 37°C for 60 min were analyzed by reverse phase HPLC as described in Materials and Methods. Peptide peaks not present in C1-Inh or plasmin alone were selected for sequencing and are indicated by arrows.

TABLE 1. Peptides Generated from C1-Inh by Plasmin

Peptide no.	Peptide sequence	C1-Inh cleavage sites (amino acids)	Location in C1-Inh model
N-terminal	NP-ATSSSSQDPESL		
1	GVTSVSQI	Residue 194-195 (KG)	α-helix D
2	KTRMEPFHFK	Residue 284-285 (KK)	Loop
3	TRMEPFHFK	Residue 285-286 (KT)	Loop
4	MEPFHFK	Residue 287-288 (RM)	Loop
5	NSVIKV	Residue 294-295 (KN)	Loop
6	KYPVAHFIDQ	Residue 306-307 (KK)	β-sheet C (strand 3)
7	AKVGQLQLS	Residue 319-320 (KA)	β-sheet B (strand 2)
8	VGQLQLSHNL	Residue 321-322 (KV)	β-sheet B (strand 2)
9	HRLEDMEQAL	Residue 342-343 (KH)	Loop
10	AIMEKLEMSK	Residue 359-360 (KA)	α-helix H

Cleavage sites that generate these peptides are indicated. Numbering is according to Bock et al. (25), i.e., from the N-terminus of the circulating protein. Glycosylated amino acids are indicated by a hyphen.

deletion of two (10-residue and 11-residue) surface regions in ovalbumin together with four minor 1- and 2-residue deletions. Peptide main-chain breaks were annealed by energy refinements. Evidence that the model is satisfactory was provided by the surface locations of loop deletions, three carbohydrate sites at Asn216, Asn231, and Asn330, and the Cys residues Cys183 and Cys406 that form interdomain disulphide bridges with the N-terminus of C1-Inh. The model shows that 37 lysine and arginine residues are evenly distributed in the serpin fold of C1-Inh (Fig. 6A). Of the 10 plasmin cleavage sites in Table 1, 9 correspond to residues located at the end of the structure close to the reactive site loop in the uncleaved serpin fold (Fig. 6A). Lys194 is the tenth cleavage site and is located in the central region of the serpin fold next to the 11-residue deletion site. All 10 lysine and arginine residues were solvent accessible to varying degrees and all are sufficiently exposed for proteolysis by plasmin.

DISCUSSION

The damaging potential of inflammatory processes is dictated largely by the equilibrium between proteases and their inhibitors. The serpins are a family of inhibitors that regulate proteolytic

```
                                     1
      masrltlltl   lllllagdra ss   npnatsss   sqdpeslqdr   gegkvattvi
 29   skmlfvepil   evsslpttns   ttnsatkita   nttdepttqp   ttepttqpti
 79   qptqpttqlp   tdsptqpttg   sfCpgpvtlC   sdleshstea   vlgdalvdfs
129   lklyhafsam   kkvetnmafs   pfsiaslltq   vllgagentk   tnlesilsyp
179   kdftCvhqal   kgfttkgvts   vsgifhspdl   airdtfvnas   rtlvsssprv
229   lsnnsdanle   lintwvaknt   nnkisrllds   lpsdtrlvll   naivlsakwk
279   ttfdpkktrm   epfhfknsvi   kvpmmnskkv   pvahfidqtl   kakvgqlqls
329   hnlslvilvp   qnlkhrledm   egalspsvfk   aimeklemsk   fqptlltlpr
379   ikvttsqdml   simekleffd   fsydlnlCgl   tedpdlqvsa   mqhqtvlelt
429   etgveaaaas   aisvaRTllv   fevqqpflfv   lwdqqhkfpv   fmgrvydpra
```

FIG. 5. C1-Inh cleavage sites after incubation with plasmin

Plasmin cleavage sites are indicated by arrows. Single and double underlining represent the different peptides generated from sequence data on cleavage products. Reactive site residues are in uppercase and indicated by (*), glycosylation sites by (●), and cys 1 linked to cys 4, cys 2 to cys 3 are represented by uppercase bold letters.

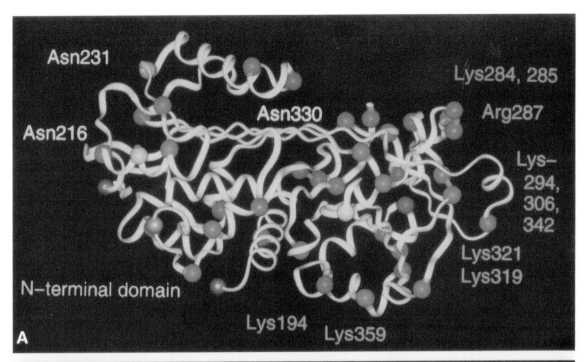

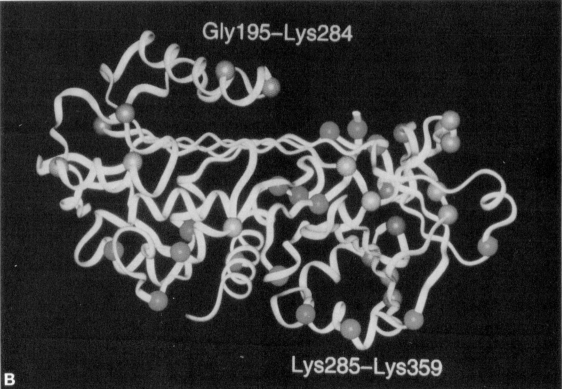

FIG. 6. Models of C1-Inh cleavage sites

(A) The homology-modeled serpin fold is denoted as a ribbon on which all 37 α-carbon atoms of Lys and Arg residues appear as blue and green spheres. The structure is viewed in the same orientation as Fig. 2 of Perkins (16). On the right, the 10 green spheres correspond to the proteolysis sites listed in Table 1, as identified by residue labeling. On the left, three orange spheres indicate the α-carbon atoms of Glu 117, Cys 182, and Cys 406 which define the location of the major glycosylated N-terminal extension of C1-Inh relative to the serpin fold (16). The location of three yellow spheres indicates the positions of glycosylation sites at Asn 216, Asn 231, and Asn 330. (B) The peptide released by cleavage between Gly 195 and Lys284 is marked in yellow while that between Lys 285 and Lys 359 is marked in purple. The structure is viewed at the same orientation as in A above. In (A) and (B), the reactive site loop in a helical conformation is located at the far right of the model as shown.

activity generated by the homeostatic pathways of coagulation, fibrinolysis, complement, and kinin pathways or by proteases released from tissues during inflammatory processes (4). Activation of these pathways is a hallmark of many inflammatory disorders and contributes significantly to tissue damage in these situations. For example, the persistent inflammation and tissue damage observed in the joint in rheumatoid arthritis is partly mediated by the accumulation of the products of complement and coagulation activation (26). For these reasons an important goal of the acute phase response is to limit proteolysis by increasing the availability of serpins (9). Local serpin depletion could therefore have dramatic effects on the control of many physiological processes.

As C1-Inh is a pivotal inhibitor controlling several inflammatory pathways, a polyclonal antibody capture assay was established to examine C1-Inh consumption in vivo by measuring the relative amounts of native, cleaved, and complexed inhibitor circulating in plasma (15). C1-Inh consumption was examined in the plasma from 21 normal individuals, 24 individuals with SLE, 9 individuals with ARDS, and the paired plasma and synovial fluid of 18 patients with RA. It was found that C1-Inh circulates in three forms in normal plasma: native, cleaved, and complexed inhibitor migrating at 115, 96, and 209–225 kDa, respectively (Fig. 1). However, C1-Inh consumption and degradation was increased in all of the inflammatory disorders examined in comparison to normal plasma (Fig. 1). This increase in C1-Inh consumption was evident in the increased amount of cleaved and/or complexed inhibitor present. The pattern of cleavage found in patients with ARDS, for example, indicates considerable degradation of C1-Inh in vivo. This increased consumption of C1-Inh is probably a result of the increase in proteolytic activity associated with each of the inflammatory conditions.

C1-Inh and plasmin were purified and incubated together and it is notable that the successful isolation of undegraded C1-Inh requires the early removal of plasminogen (17,18). SDS-PAGE analysis of the C1-Inh/plasmin interaction revealed a decrease in the amount of 115-kDa C1-Inh, new C1-Inh derivatives at 96 and 83 kDa, and barely detectable amounts of high molecular mass complexes at 209 kDa and 198 kDa (Fig. 2). Thus the main species generated when normal C1-Inh interacts with plasmin migrated

at 96 and 83 kDa. This is similar to the degraded forms of C1-Inh circulating in the plasmas of patients with inflammatory disorders (Fig. 1).

It has been previously shown that plasmin generates two derivatives of C1-Inh migrating at approximately 96 kDa, only one of which retained functional activity (12,14). The 83-kDa species has also been shown to be functionally inactive as it does not bind to activated C1s (14). Therefore, the major derivatives from the interaction between plasmin and C1-Inh are inactivated C1-Inh molecules. Further investigations of this interaction were aimed at identifying the precise cleavage events occurring. The strategy employed to identify cleavage sites was to isolate the peptides generated from C1-Inh by plasmin, perform amino acid sequence analysis of the isolated peptides, and in this way locate the precise cleavage sites on the C1-Inh molecule. The peptides generated from C1-Inh were successfully isolated by reverse phase chromatography (HPLC) (Fig. 4, Table 1). Plasmin cleaves C1-Inh in a very specific manner at 1 arginine residue and 9 lysine residues (Fig. 5). Even under limiting conditions, plasmin generates many peptides from C1-Inh. All of the cleavage sites are at either lysine or arginine residues, although there is a strong preference for lysine. This is in keeping with the known amino acid target preference of plasmin. However, it is striking that the reactive site (Arg 444-Thr 445) (27,28) located by other studies with C1-Inh/C1s or C1-Inh/plasma kallikrein, was not cleaved by plasmin under these conditions. This further reinforces the observations from the SDS-PAGE analysis (Fig. 4) that a minimal amount of plasmin is engaged and captured by C1-Inh at its reactive site.

Spectroscopy indicates that large parts of the native serpin fold exist in a stressed state, and that cleavage of the reactive site loop relieves this general stress (29). It is of interest that most plasmin cleavage sites occur close to the reactive site loop in the native protein (Fig. 6A). Such cleavages would be expected to affect the integrity of the serpin fold by disruption of the β sheets B and C and the loops connecting these (Table 1), thereby releasing stress in the native inhibitor. The central β sheet A is not directly affected by plasmin. The C1-Inh model offers an explanation of the sequential effects of C1-Inh cleavage on its physiological activity. If the first two cleavages occur at sites 1 and 2 (Table 1), this releases a peptide Gly195-Lys284 which encompasses one-half of β sheet A (Fig. 6B, yellow), generating a 96-kDa cleavage product. If this peptide remained in place on C1-Inh, β sheet A would continue to act as the receptor of the reactive site loop after its cleavage and the activity of C1-Inh could be maintained. This may account for the finding of a functional 96-kDa cleavage product. If cleavages occur between sites 2 and 10 (Table 1), the integrity of β sheets B and C will be disrupted (Fig. 6B, purple), and this will have more severe effects on the physiological activity of C1-Inh. This cleavage will ultimately lead to the generation of a C1-Inh cleavage product of 83 kDa.

The C1-Inh model also offers an explanation for the location of the plasmin cleavage sites. All the cleavage sites are distant from the heavily glycosylated N-terminal domain of C1-Inh (Fig. 6A). The position of the N-terminal domain is defined by covalent links to the serpin fold at His 141, Cys182, and Cys406, and is positioned at the end of the serpin fold away from the plasmin cleavage sites (20). The plasmin cleavage sites are distant from all three glycosylation sites at Asn216 and Asn231 at the end of the fold furthest from the reactive site, and also from Asn330 in the central region of the fold. The resulting steric hindrance offered by these four groups would direct plasmin activity toward the reactive site loop region at the other end of the serpin fold as depicted in Fig. 6.

The results of the studies on patients' plasma show that degradation of C1-Inh is a feature of several inflammatory situations. Although there are apparently large amounts of native C1-Inh circulating in each of the disorders examined, local degradation of C1-Inh could lead to a loss of functional C1-Inh activity at the site of inflammation. It is also confirmed that degradation of C1-Inh can readily be accomplished in vitro by plasmin, an enzyme activated during many inflammatory disorders. In addition, the pattern of C1-Inh degradation in vivo is very similar to that occuring with plasmin in vitro. Furthermore, the isolation of uncleaved C1-Inh (115 kDa) from plasma requires the early removal of plasmin, and the pattern of C1-Inh cleavage (96 and 83 kDa) produced by plasmin has not been reported following incubation with other proteases. Although C1-Inh is not thought to be an important inhibitor of plasmin in vivo, it can readily be inactivated by plasmin.

Other studies have suggested that additional enzymes such as neutrophil elastase may also be responsible for the degradation of C1-Inh (30–

32). These results raise intriguing possibilities with regard to the failure of the control of proteolysis occurring in inflammatory disorders. The results also suggest that specific treatment strategies aimed at either increasing serpin activity or diminishing protease action may offer an effective alternative therapeutic approach. In support of this, studies of endotoxin-induced ARDS have shown that C1-Inh infusion prevented the development of ARDS in animal models (33,34). Furthermore, purified preparations of protease inhibitors have proved to be effective therapy for some of the manifestations of fulminant sepsis in human trials (35).

It has also been known for some time that the anti-plasmin agent epsilon-aminocaproic acid and its analogue tranexamic acid are effective in preventing attacks of edema in C1-Inh-deficient patients (10). Although these agents are potent inhibitors of plasmin and the fibrinolytic pathway, the precise mechanism by which they attenuate attacks of angioedema is unknown (10). However, activation of the fibrinolytic, complement, and contact phase of blood coagulation has been documented during attacks of edema in C1-Inh-deficient patients and it has been suggested that anti-plasmin agents exert their effect by directly inhibiting plasmin (36–38). It has also been shown that a critical level of C1-Inh is necessary to prevent attacks of angioedema (39). As our results indicate that plasmin cleaves C1-Inh very effectively, it is probable that in situations of C1-Inh deficiency, activation of plasmin may locally degrade C1-Inh and diminish the quantity of functional C1-Inh available, thus predisposing to attacks edema. Therefore, anti-plasmin agents may be effective by blocking degradation of C1-Inh by plasmin.

In summary, it has been shown that high levels of inactivated C1-Inh, a pivotal inhibitor of the contact phase of inflammation, circulate in patients with a variety of inflammatory disorders. It has also been shown that plasmin rapidly degrades C1-Inh in vitro in a way very similar to that observed in inflammatory disease. We postulate that serpin degradation by proteases may be an important event furthering tissue damage in many common disorders. These findings provide an explanation for the efficacy of anti-plasmin agents in C1-Inh deficiency disorders and they also have important implications for the design of therapeutic regimes in inflammatory diseases.

ACKNOWLEDGMENTS

S. J. P. thanks the Wellcome Trust and the Royal Society for financial support.

REFERENCES

1. Rubin E, Farber JL (eds). (1988) *Pathology.* J. B. Lippincott, Philadelphia, pp. 34–1393.
2. Bode W, Huber R. (1992) Natural protein proteinase inhibitors and their interaction with proteinases. *Eur. J. Biochem.* **204:** 433–451.
3. Travis J, Salvesen G. (1983) Human plasma proteinase inhibitors. *Annu. Rev. Biochem.* **52:** 655–709.
4. Carrell RW, Boswell DR. (1986) Serpins: The superfamily of plasma protease inhibitors. In: Barrett AJ, Salvesen G (eds). *Proteinase Inhibitors. Research Monographs in Cell and Tissue Physiology, Vol. 12.* Elsevier, Amsterdam, pp. 403–420.
5. Davis III, AE. (1988) C1-Inhibitor and hereditary angioneurotic edema. *Annu. Rev. Immunol.* **6:** 595–628.
6. Heidtmann H, Travis J. (1986) Human α-1-proteinase inhibitor. In: Barrett AJ, Salvesen G (eds). *Proteinase Inhibitors. Research Monographs in Cell and Tissue Physiology Vol. 12.* Elsevier, Amsterdam, pp. 441–455.
7. Miura O, Hirosawa S, Kato A, Aoki N. (1989) Molecular basis for congenital deficiency of α-2-plasmin inhibitor. *J. Clin. Invest.* **83:** 1598–1604.
8. Beresford CH, Owen MC. (1990) Antithrombin III. *Int. J. Biochem.* **22:** 121–128.
9. Sellar GC, Whitehead AS. (1993) The acute phase response and major acute phase proteins in early host defense. *J. Biomed. Sci.* **4:** 1–9.
10. Kerr MA, Yeung-Laiwah AAC. (1986) C1-inhibitor deficiency and angio-oedema. In: Whaley K (ed). *Complement in Health and Disease.* MTP Press, Lancaster, U.K., pp. 53–78.
11. Gaffney PJ. (1993) Fibrinolysis. In: Bloom AL, Thomas DP (eds). *Haemostasis and Thrombosis.* Churchill Livingstone, Edinburgh, pp. 223–244.
12. Harpel PC, Cooper NR. (1975) Studies on human plasma C1 inactivator-enzyme interactions. *J. Clin. Invest.* **55:** 593–604.
13. Donaldson VH, Harrison RA, Rosen FS, Bing DH, Kindness G, Canar J, Wagner CJ, Awad S. (1985) Variability in purified dysfunctional C1-inhibitor proteins from patients with hereditary angioneurotic edema. *J. Clin. Invest.* **75:** 124–132.
14. Jackson J, Sim RB, Whaley K, Feighery C. (1989) Autoantibody facilitated cleavage of C1-Inhibitor in autoimmune angioedema. *J. Clin. Invest.* **83:** 698–707.
15. Wallace EM, Feighery C, Jackson J. (1996) A solid phase antibody capture assay for the measurement of C1-inhibitor consumption *in vivo. Scand. J. Clin. Lab. Invest.* **56:** 1–9.
16. Laemmli UK. (1970) Cleavage of structural proteins during the assembly of the head bacteriophage T4. *Nature* **227:** 680–683.
17. Sim RB, Reboul A. (1981) Preparation and properties of human C1-inhibitor. *Methods Enzymol.* **80:** 43–54.
18. Harrison RA. (1983) Human C1-inhibitor: Improved isolation and preliminary structural characterisation. *Biochemistry* **22:** 5001–5007.
19. Deutsch DG, Mertz ET. (1970) Plasminogen: Purification from human plasma by affinity chromatography. *Science* **170:** 1095–1096.
20. Perkins SJ, Smith FS, Amatayakul S, Ashford D, Rademacher TW, Dwek RA, Lachmann PJ, Harrison RA. (1990) The two domain structure of the native and reaction centre cleaved forms of C1-inhibitor of human complement by neutron scattering. *J. Mol. Biol.* **214:** 751–763.
21. Arlaud GJ, Sim RB, Duplaa AM, Colomb MG. (1979) Differential elution of C1q, C1r and C1s from human C1 bound to immune aggregates. Use in the rapid purification of C1 subcomponents. *Mol. Immunol.* **16:** 445–450.
22. Perkins SJ. (1993) Three-dimensional structure and molecular modeling of C1-inhibitor. *Behring Inst. Mitteil.* **93:** 63–68.
23. Laskowski RA, McArthur MW, Moss DS, Thornton JM. (1993) PROCHECK—A program to check the stereochemical quality of protein structures. *J. Appl. Crystall.* **26:** 283–291.
24. Lee B, Richards FM. (1971) The interpretation of protein structures: Estimation of static accessibility. *J. Mol. Biol.* **55:** 379–400.
25. Bock SC, Skriver K, Nielson E, Thogersen H-C, Wiman B, Donaldson VH, Eddy RL, Marrinan J, Radziejewska E, Huber R, Shows TB, Magnusson S. (1986) Human C1-inhibitor: Primary structure, cDNA cloning, and chromosomal localisation. *Biochemistry* **25:** 4292–4301.

26. Harris E. (1993) Etiology and pathogenesis of rheumatoid arthritis. In: Kelly H, Harris E, Ruddy S, Sledge C (eds). *Textbook of Rheumatology*. W. B. Saunders, London, pp. 883–873.

27. Salvesen GS, Catanese JJ, Kress LF, Travis J. (1985) Primary structure of the reactive site of human C1-inhibitor. *J. Biol. Chem.* **260**: 2432–2436.

28. Patson PA, Gettins P, Beecham J, Schapira M. (1991) Mechanism of serpin action: That C1 inhibitor functions as a suicide substrate. *Biochemistry* **30**: 8876–8882.

29. Perkins SJ, Smith KF, Nealis AS, Haris PI, Chapman D, Bauer CJ, Harrison RA. (1992) Secondary structure changes stabilise the reactive-centre cleaved form of SERPINs: A study by ^{1}H-NMR and Fourier transform infra-red spectroscopy. *J. Mol. Biol.* **228**: 1235–1254.

30. Brower MS, Harpel PC. (1982) Proteolytic cleavage and inactivation of α_2-plasmin inhibitor and C1 inactivator by human polymorphonuclear leukocyte elastase. *J. Biol. Chem.* **257**: 9849–9854.

31. Knauper V, Triebel S, Reinke H, Tschesche H. (1991) Inactivation of human plasma C1-inhibitor by human PMN leucocyte matrix metalloproteinases. *FEBS Lett.* **290**: 99–102.

32. Schoenberger OL, Sprows JF, Schechter NM, Cooperman BS, Rubin H. (1989) Limited proteolysis of C1-inhibitor by chymotrypsin-like proteinases. *FEBS Lett.* **259**: 165–167.

33. Guerrero R, Velasco F, Rodriguez M, Lopez A, Rojas R, Alvarez MA, Villabis R, Rubio V, Torres A, del Castillo D. (1993) Endotoxin-induced pulmonary dysfunction is prevented by C1-esterase inhibitor. *J. Clin. Invest.* **91**: 2754–2760.

34. Dickneite G, Seiffge D. (1996) Efficacy of C1-inhibitor on capillary leakage and septic shock in the rat. In: Faist E, Baue AE, Schildberg FW (eds). *Immune Consequences of Trauma, Shock and Sepsis. Mechanistic and Therapeutic Approaches*. Pabst Science Publications, Berlin, pp. 44–50.

35. Kitchens C. (1995) Disseminated intravascular coagulation. *Curr. Opin. Haematol.* **2**: 402–406.

36. Cugno M, Nuijens J, Hack E, Eerenberg A, Frangi D, Agostoni A, Cicardi M. (1990) Plasma levels of C1 inhibitor complexes and cleaved C1 inhibitor in patients with hereditary angioneurotic edema. *J. Clin. Invest.* **85**: 1215–1220.

37. Cugno M, Hack CE, deBoer JP, Eerenberg JM, Agostoni A, Cicardi M. (1993) Generation of plasmin during acute attacks of hereditary angioedema. *J. Lab. Clin. Med.* **121**: 38–43.

38. Cugno M, Cicardi M, Agostoni A. (1994) Activation of the contact system and fibrinolysis in autoimmune acquired angioedema: A rationale for prophylactic use of tranexamic acid. *J. Allergy Clin. Immunol.* **93**: 870–876.

39. Madalinski K, Sabbouh K, Chorazykiewicz M, Gregorek H. (1991) C1-inhibitor defect as an example of deficiency disease. *Immunol. Invest.* **20**: 133–141.

Communicated R. Bucala. Accepted April 17, 1997.

Institute of Internal Medicine, University of Milan and IRCCS Ospedale Maggiore, Milan, Italy

Pathogenetic and Clinical Aspects of C1 Inhibitor Deficiency

MARCO CICARDI, LUIGI BERGAMASCHINI, MASSIMO CUGNO, ANDREA BERETTA, LORENZA C. ZINGALE, MONICA COLOMBO, and ANGELO AGOSTONI

Abstract

People deficient in C1-INH present recurrent angioedema localized to subcutaneous or mucous tissues. The defect can be caused by impaired synthesis, due to a genetic defect (hereditary angioedema), or by increased catabolism (acquired angioedema). In our experience the majority of patients with acquired angioedema (16 of 18) have autoantibodies to C1-INH in their serum. These autoantibodies bind to C1-INH with different and generally low affinity. The vaso-permeability mediator responsible for attacks is still undefined: bradykinin (derived from cleavage of high molecular weight kininogen) and a kinin-like peptide (derived from the second component of complement) still remain the two primary candidates. We examined the systems controlled by C1-INH (complement, contact system, fibrinolysis and coagulation) and found that all of them are activated during angioedema attacks. Activation of the coagulation leads to generation of thrombin whose vasoactive effect can thus influence edema formation. Treatment of severe angioedema attacks is satisfactorily performed with C1-INH plasma concentrate although patients with an acquired defect frequently need very high doses. Attenuated androgens effectively prevent attacks in hereditary angioedema, but their safety, on the very long-term, needs to be further assessed. Acquired angioedema generally fail to respond to these drugs, but can be treated prophylactically with antifibrinolytic agents.

Introduction

Impaired synthesis, due to genetic defects, or increased consumption can result in low plasma levels of C1 inhibitor (C1-INH). People deficient in C1-INH present recurrent subcutaneous or mucous swellings (1). However, despite the fact that it is rare to find this condition without symptoms, an extreme variability in their frequency and severity is the rule. Physicians experienced in C1-INH deficiency know that such a variability is not related to its ethiology. In fact, the phenotypic expression of the disease can be very different in relatives sharing the same mutation as cause of hereditary angioedema (HAE), while symptoms in patients with acquired and inherited forms can easily be identical.

During the last decade there have been major advances on the knowledge of the molecular basis of the genetic defect (2–5). Identification and characterization of autoantibodies against C1-INH shed some light also on the mechanisms leading to the acquired deficiency (acquired angioedema, AAE) (6–7). Nevertheless, the mediator of the attacks is still uncertain as well as the mechanism leading to its release.

This paper is focused on ethiopathogenetic and clinical problems of HAE and AAE.

Patients and methods

The studies were based on 342 patients with HAE, belonging to 120 different kindred (Table 1), and on 18 patients with AAE followed at our Institute.

Antigenic levels of C1-INH, C1q, C4, and C3 were measured by radial immunodiffusion using NorPartigen or LowPartigen plates (Behringwerke). Functional levels of C1-INH were measured by commercial chromogenic assay (Immuno Vienna). All measurements were performed in citrated plasma and expressed as percentage of normal human pooled plasma (NHPP).

Plasma levels of Factor XIIa (FXIIa) (Shield Diagnostic Ltd., Dundee, UK), and Prothrombin fragment 1 + 2 (Enzygnost F1 + 2, Behringwerke Ag Marburg, Germany) were measured by ELISA techniques and factor VIIa by a protrombin-time-based assay (8) .

Cleaved HK and cleaved C1-INH were evaluated with sodium dodecyl sulfate-polyacrylamide gel electrophoresis (SDS-PAGE) and immunoblotting in EDTA/polybrene plasma samples (9).

Autoantibodies to C1-INH in serum were detected by ELISA. All values were expressed by arbitrary units (AU). The serum of one patient, a 1:1000 dilution of which gave 50% of maximal binding, was used as an internal standard. This serum was arbitrarily set at 1000 AU (9).

Results and discussion

Table 1. Hereditary angioedema.

Patients	342	(120 families)
Type 1	273	(101 families)
Type 2	69	(19 families)
Age	5–88	
Age of onset of symptoms	0–35	
Patients on long-term attenuated androgens	82	

Anti-C1-INH autoantibodies in AAE

Onset of symptoms within the second decade of life in HAE or after the fourth in AAE, remain the only noticeable clinical difference between the two forms which instead present some biochemical diversity. Hyperactivation of the classical complement pathway is a distinguishing characteristic and probably a pathogenic mechanism of acquired C1-INH deficiency. When this form was first described, the frequent association with lymphoproliferative diseases and some evidence that the neoplastic tissues could massively activate C1 suggested that

C1-INH defect was a consequence of the activation of the classical complement pathway (10). It was later demonstrated that in plasma of patients with AAE there were antiidiotypic antibodies recognizing the idiotypes of the monoclonal immunoglobulins (11). Since these idiotype-antiidiotype immunecomplexes were able to fix C1q it was hypothesized that it could be the mechanism by which linfoproliferating clones consumed C1-INH. Shorty thereafter autoantibodies impairing C1-INH function were demonstrated in plasma of one AAE patient (6). In the following years more and more cases of autoimmune acquired C1-INH defect were described and it was proposed the existence of two separate forms of AAE: one associated with linfoproliferative diseases and the other with autoantibodies (12–15).

At present we are following 18 patients with AAE; autoantibodies against C1-INH are detectable in 16 of them (Table 2). Many of these patients have paraproteins in their serum as sign of B cell proliferation. In this case-list we could not confirm the existence of two different forms of AAE. In fact we found that several anti-C1-INH autoantibodies detected in our patients were themselves the M-component and therefore represented the product of the proliferating B cell clones (9).

As reported by others, we confirmed that hypercatabolism of C1 complex, detected as C1q depletion, is a feature of autoimmune AAE: only 2 of our patient had normal C1q in remission (Table 2). Nevertheless the mechanism leading to C1 consumption in autoimmune AAE is unclear. Autoantibodies *per se* should in fact impair C1-INH function creating a situation identical to that found in the genetic defect where C1q is invariably normal in remission. Experimental evidence suggests that in presence of autoantibodies C1-INH still can interact with its target proteases being cleaved, but can not form stable comple-

Table 2. Clinical date in 16 patients with autoimmune acquired angioedema.

Patient	Angioedema presentation	Associated disease	Autoantibody Ig class	Autoantibody title (AU)
GS	1977	Waldenstrom	IgM	1000
GB	1989	Waldenstrom	IgG	200
ES	1989	M component	IgA	9000
JB	1985	Breast cancer	IgA	1000
GF	1968	Echinococcus	IgG	3000
EM	1984	None	IgG	2700
TO	1990	M component	IgM	1000
GAP	1991	None	IgG	1000
CP	1989	None	IgM	1700
AM	1988	None	IgG	2700
IS	1987	None	IgA	2700
GC	1993	M component	IgG	70
EP	1996	M component	IgA	4500
MB	1994	M component	IgG	1200
UC	1995	M component	IgM	3800
AP	1995	None	IgM	1000

xes: as a consequence C1-INH circulates in its cleaved form of 96 kDa in plasma of patients with autoimmune AAE. Thus, autoantibodies convert C1-INH from an inhibitor to a substrate. It is conceivable that these events, involving the interaction between the immune complex C1-INH autoantibody and C1, could at some extent be relevant to the hypercatabolism of C1: nevertheless such a hypothesis has never been assessed.

Epitope mapping of autoantibodies to C1-INH suggest that they are different from each other (16–18). To analyze the heterogeneity of the autoantibodies in our patients we measured their affinity characteristics using an ELISA based method (19). Autoantibodies were purified on an affinity column from serum of 6 AAE patients. A constant amount of each purified autoantibody (1 μg) was incubated for 1 h at 37 °C with serial amounts of pure C1-INH. After incubation the free autoantibody was measured on the regular ELISA. With these experiments we found that 50% saturation of 2 autoantibodies (GAP and GS) was achieved by relatively limited amounts of C1-INH (10 μg and 70 μg respectively), while amounts ten times higher were required for the remaining 4 (GF, JB, ES, EM) (Fig. 1).

Quantification of specific anti C1-INH immunoglobulins in original serum, performed using each purified autoantibody as reference, showed that the autoantibody concentrations were different and the correlation factor between the measurements in milligrams and in units varied from patient to patient (Table 3). Such a variability could be explained by the demonstration that the affinity characteristics of the 6 autoantibodies were extremely different: the mole/mole excess of C1-INH, necessary for the saturation of a constant (in mg) amount of autoantibody, ranged from 28-fold of GAP to 770-fold of EM (Table 3). These results suggest that the autoantibodies bind C1-INH in the fluid phase with different, and generally very low, affinities.

Pathogenesis of attacks

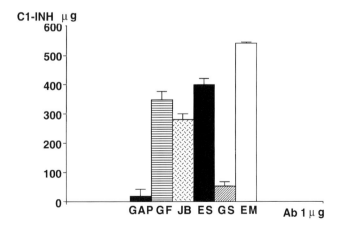

Figure 1. Saturation of the free autoantibody from the 6 AAE patients by C1-INH. A constant amount (1 μg) of purified autoantibody was incubated with serial amounts of purified C1-INH and added to microtiter plates for the determination of the free autoantibody. The amount of C1-INH giving 50% reduction in free autoantibody was reported. All experiments were performed in triplicate, results were expressed as mean of the 3 experiments ±S.D.

Table 3. Levels of autoantibodies expressed in arbitrary units/ml (AU/ml) and in mg/ml in serum and in affinity purified preparations from 6 patients with Acquired C1-INH Deficiency. The last column refers to the molar ratio between C1-inhibitor (C1-INH) and affinity purified autoantibodies (Ab) to obtain the saturation.

Patient	Serum		Affinity purified		C1-INH/Ab
	(AU/ml)	(mg/ml)	(AU/ml)	(mg/ml)	(molar ratio)
GAP	1000	3.5	10	0.03	28
GF	3000	0.9	1500	0.4	500
EM	270	0.67	1500	0.4	770
JB	1000	1.5	10	0.015	400
ES	9000	11.2	130	0.15	570
GS	1020	1.4	55	0.075	75

The vasopermeability mediator responsible for attacks in C1-INH-deficient patients is still undefined. Histamine was ruled out long time ago with the demonstration that specific anti-H1 receptor antagonists had no effect on angioedema symptoms. There has been instead increasing evidence that such a mediator belonged to the kinin family. Peptides with kinin-like activity were isolated from plasma of patients with C1-INH deficiency and two primary candidates still remain: bradykinin (BK) (derived from cleavage of high molecular weight kininogen, HK) and a kinin-like peptide derived from the second component of complement (C2) (20–23). Effectiveness of specific antagonists of such peptides in controlling angioedema, would definitively demonstrate their pathogenetic relevance. Unfortunately, despite the fact that potent BK receptor antagonists have been recently used experimentally in humans, no such drugs have yet been available for trials in C1-INH deficiency. To provide indirect proof that BK participates to the pathogenesis of angioedema in C1-INH-deficient patients, we evaluated the systems leading to its release. This vasoactive peptide comes from the cleavage of HK by kallikrein during contact system activation (24). Plasmin, the main component of the fibrinolytic system, can also cleave HK, increasing its susceptibility to kallikrein action, but does not *per se* release BK (15). C1-INH is the main inhibitor of kallikrein and *in vitro* it inhibits also plasmin. We studied plasma from 23 patients with HAE, 18 during remission and 5 during attacks and found that in attacks HK was cleaved and complexes formed by plasmin with its inhibitor a2-antiplasmin (PAP complexes) were markedly increased. Since PAP complexes reflect the amount of plasmin that has been generated, these data prove that in plasma of HAE patients during attacks there are the conditions for the release of BK (26).

When these parameters were used to evaluate 8 patients with an acquired deficiency of C1-INH, we found that already during remission their cleaved HK and PAP complexes were higher than in normal subjects (27). Nevertheless angioedema attacks again resulted in a further increase of these parameters. Since the method that we used to detect HK cleavage does not distinguish the cleavage due kallikrein (which releases BK) from the cleavage due to plasmin (which does not release BK), it is possible that in AAE patients in remission we are detecting plasmin-mediated HK cleavage. If this is the case AAE patients present a continuous generation of plasmin that facilitate, but does not *per se* release BK. Such an hyperfibrinolytic state could be the target for the activity of antifibrinolytic agents as Tranexamic acid that have been proved to be highly effective in patients with AAE. Although its *in vivo* relevance remains uncertain, activation of the contact system can trigger hemostasis and generate thrombin, the final enzyme of the coagulation cascade (28). On the other side there has been experimental evidence that thrombin can increase vascular permeability (29). Considering the marked activation of contact system that we detected in C1-INH-deficient patients during attacks, we investigated the possibility that in this condition there could be also

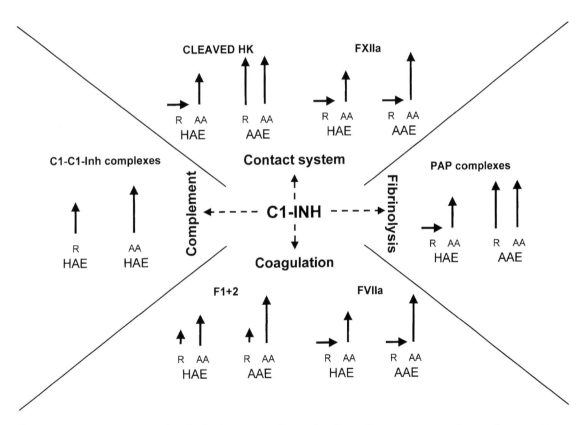

Figure 2. C1-INH controls (dashed arrows) the activation of components of complement (C1s, C1r), contact system (FXII and Kallikrein), coagulation (FXI) and fibrinolysis (Plasmin). Patients with hereditary (HAE) and acquired (AAE) C1-INH deficiency during remission (R) and during acute attacks (AA) present several abnormalities in these systems (as indicated by the solid arrows): 1) Activation of C1 detected by the increase of complexes formed by C1s and C1-inhibitor (C1-C1-Inh complexes). 2) Activation of contact system detected by the increase in cleaved high molecular weight kininogen (HK) and activated factor XII (FXIIa). 3) Generation of plasmin detected by the increase of complexes formed by plasmin and its inhibitor α_2-antiplasmin (PAP complexes). 4) Thrombin generation detected by the increase in prothrombin fragment F1 + 2 and activation of the tissue factor pathway of coagulation detected by the increase in activated factor VII (FVIIa).

generation of thrombin which could thus contribute to edema formation. We have studied 19 patients with HAE during remission, 5 HAE patients during acute attacks, and 6 patients with AAE in remission and during 7 attacks (8). Generation of thrombin was measured as plasma levels of F1 + 2; the initiator of tissue factor and contact coagulation pathways were investigated by measuring plasma levels of FVIIa and FXIIa. Our data, reported in Figure 2, indicate that in C1-INH-deficient patients there is increased generation of thrombin during attacks, with signs of activation of both the contact and tissue factor coagulation pathways. These findings demonstrate that there is a significant activation of the coagulation pathway during angioedema attacks. The relevance of such an activation for edema formation and for risk of thrombosis remain to be assessed. Thrombotic problems in HAE patients have not been reported and in our case list we only record the case of one women, who suffered from an acute thromboembolic obstruction of the right brachial artery during an episode of angioedema and 3 heavy-smoker men with chronic obliterans arteriopathy. These few cases prevent from any conclusion, but careful surveillance remains important.

In conclusion, as summarized in Figure 2, all the 4 protease systems controlled by C1-INH are at various extent activated during angioedema attacks. Since these systems, upon cleavage of their components, release different vasoactive peptides it is likely that more than one mediator could intervene in causing swelling in C1-INH-deficient patients.

Treatment of C1-INH deficiency

Acute attacks can easily become serious emergency problems not only in the well known lifethreatening condition of laryngeal edema, but also in those abdominal attacks mimicking surgical emergencies. Before diagnosis is established, HAE patients frequently undergo unnecessary appendicectomy or explorative laparotomy. But the opposite can also be a serious problem: in one of our HAE patients a true peritonitis was misdiagnosed as angioedema attack and surgery was postponed which lead to serious complications. As tool to differentiate surgical emergencies from angioedema and in laryngeal edema, C1-INH plasma concentrate is the treatment of choice. In countries where it is not available fresh frozen plasma remains the only alternative.

In our experience with HAE patients, 1,000 to 2,000 U. of C1-INH concentrate are effective to stop laryngeal or abdominal attacks within 30–60 minutes. On the other hand problems can arise in patients with autoantibodies. These patients present a wide variability in the response to treatment which is probably due to the affinity characteristics of the autoantibodies which cause different rate of consumption of C1-INH (Fig. 3). In one single patient we had to increase the dose of C1-INH concentrate up to 9,000 U. in order to revert a laryngeal attack. Immediate reactions to C1-INH concentrate are rare. One of our HAE patients, with pollen sensitivity, reacted twice (cutaneous rush, dyspnea and hypotension, reverted by antihistamine and steroids) to C1-INH concentrate. It is interesting to notice that both reactions occurred during pollen season; outside from this season the patient tolerated the infusion of C1-INH without side effects. Risk of trans-

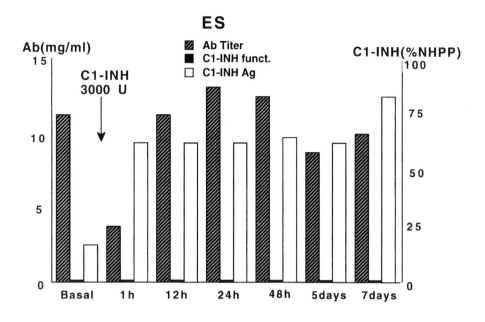

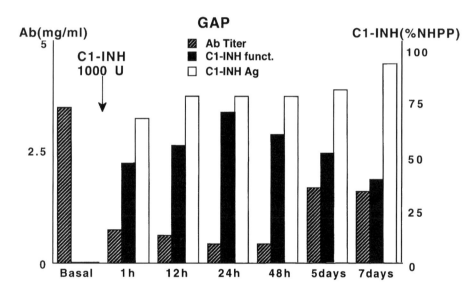

Figure 3. Changes in plasma levels of anti-C1-INH autoantibodies, C1-INH function and C1-INH antigen at different sampling times after the infusion of C1-INH concentrate in patients GAP and ES. In GAP there was a stable increase of C1-INH function and antigen and decrease of autoantibody titer following 1,000 Units of C1-INH concentrate. In ES, 3,000 Units of C1-INH concentrate, rose C1-INH antigen without changes in functional levels and decreased the autoantibody titer only at the first sampling time.

mission of blood-borne infections remain the main concern on the use of an emo-derivative as C1-INH concentrate. Blood donors' selection and virus inactivating procedures drastically reduced this risk. The rate of transmission of hepatitis C virus (HCV) dropped from 51% with non-virus-inactivated concentrates to 4% with virus inactivated preparations (30). No cases of human immunodeficiency virus infection were ever reported, probably due to the relatively low frequency of infusion (less than once a year) in these patients (31). Recently we found that another blood-borne flavovirus, hepatitis G virus, fortunately only rarely associated with liver disease, was transmitted by both unmodified and virus inactivated concentrates (32). This finding highlights that unknown viruses can always be transmitted and recall the need to limit concentrate infusions to severe attacks with potentially serious complications. The other critical task in treating patients with C1-INH deficiency is the optimal use of attenuated androgens. Their effectiveness in long term prophylaxis is well established (33), but questions remain on the risk/benefit balance of a lifelong treatment. HAE patients are the only ones maintained for such a long term on these drugs. Several our patients have been on these drugs since 1976. Twenty year is certainly an acceptable length of time to asses safety, but although long-term follow-up tend to exclude serious side-effect, the overall number of patients remain too small to draw definitive conclusions. We compared 70 HAE patients, treated and not treated with attenuated androgens and found that in the treated group there was a larger number (25%) of patients with arterial hypertension compared to the not treated group (3%) (34). It is evident that the large prevalence of hypertension in the general population minimize the significance of the finding. Nevertheless these data claim for the need of continuous surveillance of patients under long term treatment.

As for treatment of acute attacks it is worth to mention the differences that are encountered when dealing with patients with autoimmune C1-INH deficiency. The different rate of hypercatabolism of C1-INH that characterized these patients influenced also the response to androgen derivatives. These drugs increase C1-INH plasma levels, probably stimulating its synthesis, and their effectiveness depends on the balance between synthesis and catabolism. Turnover studies demonstrate that the normal synthetic rate of C1-INH is around 0.4 mg/Kg/h. It is therefore obvious that in a patient like E.S. who can clear from circulation 3000 U. (600 mg) of C1-INH concentrate in a few minutes (Fig. 3), the increase in C1-INH synthesis which can be obtained by the administration of an attenuated androgen will never be able to overcome such a huge catabolism. In these patients we obtained satisfactory results using the antifibrinolytic agent Tranexamic acid (15). To prevent thrombotic complications in patients at risk, frequently encountered in AAE which affects the elderly, it is our policy to associate low doses of oral anticoagulant.

Acknowledgements

This paper has been supported by Telethon Project n. EC469.

References

1. DONALDSON, V. H., and R. R. EVANS. 1963. A biochemical abnormality in hereditary angioneurotic edema: absence of serum inhibitor of C1 esterase. Am. J. Med. **31**: 37–44.
2. BÖCK, S. C., K. SKRIVER, E. NIELSEN, H. C. THOGERSEN, B. WIMAN, V. H. DONALDSON, R.

L. Eddy, J. Marrinan, E. Radziejewska, R. Huber, T. B. Shows, and S. Magnusson. 1986. Human C1 inhibitor primary structure, cDNA cloning, and chromosomal localization. Biochemistry 25: 4292–4301.

3. Davis, A. E. III, K. Aulak, R. B. Parad, et al. 1992. C1 inhibitor hinge region mutations produce dysfunction by different mechanisms. Nature Genetics 1: 354–358.

4. Verpy, E., E. Couture-Tosi, E. Eldering, M. Lopez-Trascasa, P. Späth, and T. Meo. 1995. Crucial residues in the carboxy-terminal end of C1 inhibitor revealed by pathogenic mutants impaired in secretion and function. J. Clin. Invest. 95: 350–359.

5. Eldering, E., E. Verpy, D. Roem, T. Meo, and M. Tosi. 1995. COOH-terminal substitutions in the serpin C1 inhibitor that cause loop overinsertion and subsequent multimerization. J. Biol. Chem. 270: 2579–2587.

6. Jackson, J., R. B. Sim, A. Whelan, et al. 1986. An IgG autoantibody which inactivates C1-inhibitor. Nature 323: 722–724.

7. Alsenz, J., K. Bork, and M. Loos. 1987. Autoantibody-mediated acquired deficiency of C1 inhibitor. N. Engl. J. Med. 316: 1360–1366.

8. Cugno, M., M. Cicardi, B. Bottasso, R. Coppola, R. Paonessa, P. M. Mannucci, and A. Agostoni. 1997. Activation of the coagulation cascade in C1-inhibitor deficiencies. Blood 89: 3213–3218.

9. Cicardi, M., A. Beretta, M. Colombo, D. Gioffrè, M. Cugno, and A. Agostoni. 1996. Relevance of lymphoproliferative disorders and of anti-C1 inhibitor autoantibodies in acquired angioedema. Clin. Exp. Immunol. 106: 475–480.

10. Schreiber, A. D., B. Zweiman, P. Atkins, F. Goldwein, G., B. Atkinson, and N. I. Abdou. 1976. Acquired angioedema with lymphoproliferative disorder: Association of C1-inhibitor deficiency with cellular abnormality. Blood 48: 567–580.

11. Geha, R. A., I. Quinti, K. F. Austen, et al. 1985. Acquired C1-inhibitor deficiency associated with antiidiotypic antibody to monoclonal immunoglobulins. N. Engl. J. Med. 312: 534–540.

12. Malbran, A., C. H. Hammer, M. M. Frank, and L. F. Fries. 1988. Acquired angioedema: Observations on the mechanism of action of autoantibodies directed against C1 esterase inhibitor. J. Allergy Clin. Immunol. 81: 1199–1204.

13. Späth, P. J., B. Wüthrich, L. Matter, N. Loos, and J. Alsenz. 1989. Acquired angioedema and anti-C1-inhibitor autoantibody. Arch. Intern. Med. 149: 1213–1214.

14. Alsenz, J., J. D. Lambris, K. Bork, and M. Loos. 1989. Acquired C1 inhibitor (C1 INH) deficiency type II. J. Clin. Invest. 83: 1794–1799.

15. Cicardi, M., G. Bisiani, M. Cugno, P. Späth, and A. Agostoni. 1993. Autoimmune C1 inhibitor deficiency: report of eight patients. Am. J. Med. 95: 169–175.

16. Mandle, R., C. Baron, E. Roux, R. Sundel, J. Gelfand, K. Aulak, A. E. III Davis, F. S. Rosen, and D. H. Bing. 1994. Acquired C1 inhibitor deficiency as a result of an autoantibody to the reactive center region of C1 inhibitor. J. Immunol. 152: 4680–4685.

17. Donaldson, V. H., C. J. Wagner, and A. E. III Davis. 1996. An autoantibody to C1 inhibitor recognizes the reactive center of the inhibitor. J. Lab. Clin. Med. 127: 229–232.

18. He, S., S. Tsang, J. North, N. Colan, R. J. Sim, and K. Whaley. 1996. Epitope mapping of C1 inhibitor autoantibodies from patients with acquired C1 inhibitor deficiency. J. Immunol. 156: 288–294.

19. Friguet, B., A. F. Chaffotte, L. Djavadi-Ohaniance, and M. E. Goldberg. 1985. Measurement of the true affinity constant in solution of antigen-antibody complexes by enzyme-linked immunosorbent assay. J. Immunol. Methods. 77: 305–319.

20. Fields, T., B. Ghebrehiwet, and A. P. Kaplan. 1983. Kinin formation in hereditary angioedema plasma: evidence against kinin derivation from C2 and in support of «spontaneous» formation of bradykinin. J. Allergy Clin. Immunol. 72: 54.

21. Schapira, M., L. D. Silver, C. F. Scott, et al. 1983. Prekallikrein activation and high molecular weight kininogen consumption in hereditary angioedema. N. Engl. J. Med. 308: 1050–1053.

22. Strang, C. J., S. Cholin, A. E. III Davis, E. E. Schneeberger, V. H. Donaldson, and F.

S. ROSEN. 1988. Angioedema induced by a peptide derived from complement component C2. J. Exp. Med. **168**: 1685–1688.

23. DAVIS, A. E. III. 1988. C1 inhibitor and hereditary angioneurotic edema. Ann. Rev. Immunol. **6**: 595–628.
24. DE LA CADENA, R. A., Y. T. WACHTFOGEL, and R. W. COLMAN. 1994. Contact activation pathway: inflammation and coagulation, in COLMAN, R. W., HIRSH, J., MARDER, W. J., SALZMAN, E. W. (eds.): Hemostasis and thrombosis: principles and clinical practice. Philadelphia, PA, J. B. Lippincott Company, 219–240.
25. KLENIEWSKY, J., D. T. BLANKENSHIP, A. D. CARDIN, and V. DONALDSON. 1992. Mechanism of enhanced kinin release from high molecular weight kininogen by plasma kallikrein after its exposure to plasmin. J. Lab. Clin. Med. **120**: 129–139.
26. CUGNO, M., C. E. HACK, J. P. DE BOER, A. J. M. EERENBERG, A. AGOSTONI, and M. CICARDI. 1993. Generation of plasmin during acute attacks of hereditary angioedema. J. Lab. Clin. Med. **121**: 38–43.
27. CUGNO, M., M. CICARDI, and A. AGOSTONI. 1994. Activation of the contact system and fibrinolysis in autoimmune acquired angioedema: a rationale for prophylactic use of Tranexamic acid. J. Allergy Clin. Immunol. **93**: 870–876.
28. RAPAPORT, S. I., and L. V. M. RAO. 1995. The tissue factor pathway: how it has become «prima ballerina». Thromb. Haemost. **74**: 7.
29. DE MICHELE, M. A. A., D. G. MOON, J. W. II FENTON, and F. N. MINNEAR. 1990. Thrombin's enzymatic activity increases permeability of endothelial cell monolayers. J. Appl. Physiol. **69**: 1599.
30. AGOSTONI, A., and M. CICARDI. 1992. Hereditary and acquired C1-inhibitor deficiency: biological and clinical characteristics in 235 patients. Medicine **71**: 206–215.
31. CICARDI, M., P. M. MANNUCCI, R. CASTELLI, M. G. RUMI, and A. AGOSTONI. 1995. Reduction in transmission of hepatitis C after the introduction of heat treatment step in the production of C1-inhibitor concentrate. Transfusion **35**: 209–212.
32. DE FILIPPI, F., R. CASTELLI, M. CICARDI, et al. 1998. Transmission of hepatitis G virus in patients with angioedema treated with steam-inactivated plasma concentrates of C1-inhibitor. Transfusion **38**: 307–311.
33. GELFAND, J. A., R. J. SHERINS, D. W. ALLING, and M. M. FRANK. 1976. Treatment of hereditary angioedema with Danazol. Reversal of clinical and biochemical abnormalities. N. Engl. J. Med. **293**: 1444–1448.
34. CICARDI, M., R. CASTELLI, L. C. ZINGALE, and A. AGOSTONI. 1997. Side effect of long-term prophylaxis with attenuated androgens in hereditary angioedema: Comparison of treated and untreated patients. J. Allergy Clin. Immunol. **99**: 194–196.

MARCO CICARDI, MD, Dipartimento di Medicina Interna, Via Pace 15, 20122 Milano-Italy

The American Journal of Medicine (2006) 119, 267-274

ELSEVIER

THE AMERICAN
JOURNAL *of*
MEDICINE ®

CLINICAL RESEARCH STUDY

Hereditary Angioedema: New Findings Concerning Symptoms, Affected Organs, and Course

Konrad Bork, MD,[a] Gabriele Meng, MD,[a] Petra Staubach, MD,[a] Jochen Hardt, MD[b]

[a]*Department of Dermatology, and* [b]*Department of Psychosomatic Medicine and Psychotherapy, Johannes Gutenberg University, Mainz, Germany.*

ABSTRACT

PURPOSE: Hereditary angioedema (HAE) due to C1 inhibitor deficiency is clinically characterized by relapsing skin swellings, abdominal pain attacks, and life-threatening upper airway obstruction. Our aim was to examine a temporal and spatial pattern of the edema episodes by evaluating the long-term course of hereditary angioedema in order to establish a specific swelling pattern.

SUBJECTS AND METHODS: Data were generated from 221 patients with C1 inhibitor deficiency by asking them about symptoms they experienced during their edema episodes. Documentation was accomplished through the use of standardized questionnaires.

RESULTS: A total of 131 110 edema episodes were observed. Clinical symptoms started at a mean age of 11.2 (SD 7.7) years. During the following cumulative 5736 years, only 370 (6.5%) symptom-free years occurred. Skin swellings, including extremity, facial, genital, and trunk swellings, and abdominal attacks occurred in 97.4% of all edema episodes of the disease. The other episodes were laryngeal edema (0.9%); edema of the soft palate (0.6%); tongue swellings (0.3%); headache episodes (0.7%); episodes affecting urinary bladder (0.3%), chest (0.2%), muscles (0.4%), joints (0.1%), kidneys (0.1%), and esophagus (0.05%), and were partly combined with other edema episodes. The per-patient analysis and the per-episode analysis revealed markedly discrepant results. On average, women had a more severe course of the disease than men. Patients with early onset of clinical symptoms were affected more severely than those with late onset.

CONCLUSION: The described swelling pattern is specific for HAE and allows a tentative diagnosis based on clinical symptoms and the course of the disease. © 2006 Elsevier Inc. All rights reserved.

KEYWORDS: Angioedema; Hereditary angioedema; C1 inhibitor deficiency

Hereditary angioedema (HAE) was first described clinically by Quincke[1] and Osler.[2] Classic HAE types I and II (Mendelian Inheritance in Man #106100) are associated with functional deficiency of C1-INH in plasma due to mutations of the C1 inhibitor gene.[3-5] The defective C1-INH gene produces either no C1-INH (type I HAE) or a dysfunctional C1-INH (type II HAE). A third type of HAE was described a few years ago; this type is not associated with a C1-INH deficiency, and its related genetic defect is still not known.[6]

HAE due to C1-INH deficiency is clinically characterized by unpredictably occurring episodes of edema at various body sites followed by disease-free intervals of variable duration. Since the first descriptions of the disease, it has been well known that the skin, the gastrointestinal tract, and the upper airways may be affected; various reports have confirmed these results.[7-12] However, some basic features of the disease have not been investigated until now, namely, how frequently various organs and body sites are affected during the long-term course of the disease. Such an investigation examining frequency of HAE episodes at various skin regions and at frequently, as well as rarely, affected organs could reveal a pattern of edema that may be specific for HAE due to C1-INH deficiency. If such a pattern exists, valuable information for diagnosing HAE could be derived. The aims of the present article are to examine temporal

Requests for reprints should be addressed to Konrad Bork, MD, Universitaets-Hautklinik, Langenbeckstr. 1, 55131 Mainz, Germany.
E-mail address: bork@hautklinik.klinik.uni-mainz.de

patterns, spatial patterns, and associations among both types of patterns and additional parameters.

METHODS

Study Design

Our analysis was based on retrospective clinical case reports. We chose this design in order to obtain information not only about frequent complaints but also about swelling episodes at rare edema sites. Data were generated by asking patients about symptoms they experienced during episodes of HAE. Criteria evaluated were the frequency of episodes and their body sites at various ages of the patients. Documentation was accomplished through the use of standardized questionnaires and scores.

Patients

A total of 221 patients with C1-INH deficiency were surveyed in the angioedema outpatient service at the Department of Dermatology, University of Mainz, Germany. Diagnosis of HAE was made on the basis of patient history, clinical examination, and laboratory results, including deficiency of functional C1-INH and C4 in plasma. Patients came from 108 unrelated kindreds. Twelve of the 221 individuals with inherited C1-INH deficiency had no clinical signs of HAE. Seven of these 12 patients were children or adolescents below the age of 15 years; the others were 21, 37, 39, 41, and 61 years old. The 12 individuals belonged to 12 families in which other family members had symptomatic HAE.

The following data describe the 209 patients who presented with clinical symptoms of the disease. Types of HAE, age, sex, and laboratory results are summarized in Table 1. All patients had recurrent episodes of self-limiting edemas of the skin, intestinal tract, larynx, or other organs. Some patients experienced only a limited number of episodes, (ie, had 3 or fewer years with clinical symptoms [12 children, 2 adults]). This group of patients was excluded from the third part of the analysis (ie, examining disease severity and associations among different aspects of HAE) because they may not have had enough experience to report about the episodes. However, they were included in parts 1 and 2 of the analysis because we did not want to exclude patients at the beginning of the disease. In addition, in the third part we did not consider time periods when patients received long-term prophylaxis. Up to the end of 2004, the lifetimes of the here-described patients added up to 8443 years. The total number of years with clinical symptoms (between the first and last episode) was 5736. The sum of symptom-free years, including the time before onset, was 2707 years.

Data Collection and Presentation

When the patients were seen for the first time, they were asked about the affected organs in all episodes they had experienced until that time. Then, for each individual organ, they were asked about the onset of the first episode and the frequency of edema episodes per year. The visit included a physical examination and laboratory confirmation of the diagnosis of HAE. Later, the patients were seen every 4 to 6 months during the first year and yearly thereafter. At each contact, frequency of episodes and affected body sites of the symptoms were assessed. In the follow-up examinations, the number of bouts of angioedema was determined by questioning the patients and by analyzing a swelling calendar that the patients filled out at home noting time, duration, and severity of their angioedema episodes and the organs involved. Angioedema episodes were counted separately for abdominal attacks, laryngeal edema, uvular edema, tongue swellings, and episodes at the other rarely affected organs. Many skin swellings started at the hand and were limited to this region. Others started at the hand and extended during the following day or days to the

---

CLINICAL SIGNIFICANCE

- Hereditary angioedema due to a genetic deficiency of C1-esterase inhibitor shows a specific temporal and spatial pattern of edema episodes.

- The disease may not only affect the skin, gastrointestinal tract, and larynx, but also various other organs.

- On average, women have a more severe course of the disease than men.

- Patients with early onset of clinical symptoms are affected more severely than those with late onset.

Table 1 Clinical Symptoms and Laboratory Results Regarding 209 Patients From 108 Families with Hereditary Angioedema Due to C1-INH Deficiency

HAE Type I	
Patients	196
Families	102
Patients without affected family members	20
HAE Type II	
Patients	13
Families	6
Patients without affected family members	1
Age (years)	40.4 ± 17.8
Sex (M/F)	82/127
C1-INH protein (g/L)	0.049 ± 0.03
HAE Type I	
C1-INH protein (g/L)	0.29 ± 0.16
HAE Type II	
C1-INH activity (%)	16.9 ± 9.6
C4 (g/L)	0.09 ± 0.047

HAE = hereditary angioedema.
Normal range for C1-INH protein, 0.15 to 0.35 g/L.
Normal range for C1-INH activity, 70% to 130%.
Normal range for C4, 0.20 to 0.50 g/L.

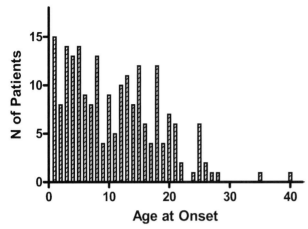

Figure 1 Age at onset of the clinical symptoms in 209 patients with hereditary angioedema due to C1 inhibitor deficiency.

longer than 12 months. The remaining 51 patients had an average of 7.4 symptom-free years ranging from 1 to 34 years. Thirty-six of those 51 patients did not receive any prophylactic treatment during that time period, ie, their symptom-free years were part of the natural course of their disease. The other 15 of 51 patients were asymptomatic because the patients received long-term prophylactic treatment and responded very well to it; the average symptom-free duration was 10 years. Among the 209 patients, 34 were aged 60 years old or older (mean: 68 years, range 60 to 87 years). Thirty of these patients had experienced clinical symptoms as of the time of data collection (end of 2004). In the four other patients, the symptoms had ended 3, 7, 16, and 18 years previously.

whole arm; a similar pattern occurred for the lower extremities. Swellings at another extremity that followed directly after an initial extremity swelling (usually within a few hours or one day), as well as simultaneous swellings at one or more other extremities, were not counted as separate swellings. Data were presented on a per-patient and a per-episode basis. This procedure was followed because the per-episode basis is closer to the clinical view than the per-patient basis; however, the procedure does not provide independent data because some patients present with many episodes and others with only a few. No significance tests were performed on the per-episode basis.

Laboratory Methods

Protein levels of C1-INH antigen, C4, and C1q were assayed by radial immunodiffusion, and C1-INH activity was determined using the chromogenic substrate C_2H_5CO-Lys(ϵ-Cbo)-Gly-Arg-pNA (Immunochrom C1-INH, Technoclone, Vienna, Austria).

RESULTS

Temporal Pattern: Symptom-Free Periods and Years with Clinical Symptoms

Symptom-free periods lasting longer than 12 months include the years from birth to the first clinical sign of the disease and symptom-free years during the phase of clinical symptoms (due to either the natural course of the disease or prophylactic treatment). In most patients, clinical symptoms started in childhood or adolescence (Figure 1); the mean age at onset of the disease was 11.2 years (SD ±7.7, range 1 to 40 years). Onset of clinical symptoms occurred in the first decade of life in 107 patients, in the second decade in 79 patients, and later in 23 patients. In 15 of 209 patients, clinical symptoms started within the first year of life. From the onset of the first clinical symptoms until the time of data collection, the majority of patients (158 of 209) had recurrent swelling episodes without symptom-free intervals

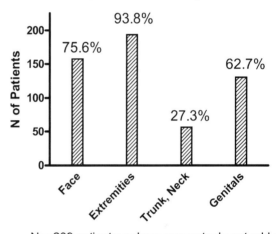

N = 209 patients; column percents do not add up to 100% due to patients having multiple sites affected

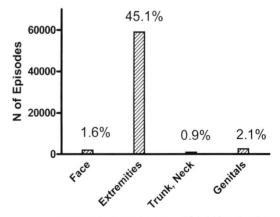

percentage based on n = 131,110 episodes; column percents do not add up to 100% due to edema episodes in other organs

Figure 2 Location of skin swellings.

A: per-Patient Analysis

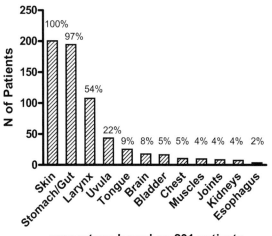

percentage based on 201 patients
with skin swellings

B: per-Episode Analysis

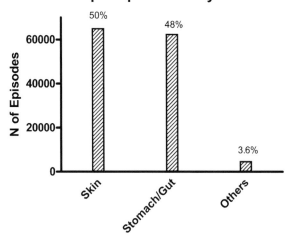

percentage based on n = 131,110 episodes;
others comprise the columns Larynx to
Esophagus from A

Figure 3 Frequency of skin swellings, abdominal pain episodes, and edema episodes in other organs.

Spatial Pattern: Swellings in Various Organs and Body Sites

During the symptomatic period a total of 131 110 edema episodes occurred. The distributions of skin swellings are shown in Figure 2 on a per-patient and a per-episode basis. The respective distributions of sites affected by the edema episodes are shown in Figure 3. The great majority of the edema episodes were skin swellings and abdominal attacks (Figure 3B). The frequency of episodes in the rarely affected organs (column 3 of Figure 3B) is shown in Figure 4.

Skin Swellings

On a per-patient basis, recurrent skin swellings occurred in 201 of 209 patients; the 8 patients without skin swellings were children and adolescents aged 5 to 16. The total number of skin swellings observed was 65 102.

Swellings of the extremities. Of all 201 patients with skin swellings, 196 (97.5%) reported swelling of the extremities (hands and arms, feet, legs and thighs). Among the total number of 65 102 skin swellings, 59 095 (90.8%) affected the extremities; 34 884 (59.0%) of these swellings occurred at the upper extremities. Three patients reported blister formation in severe skin swellings. In 2 patients, blisters occurred in the crook of the elbow; in one patient, at the instep 1 day after onset of the skin swelling.

Facial swellings and their association with upper airway obstruction. On a per-patient basis, 158 of 201 (78.6%) of the patients with skin swellings had facial swellings, yielding a total of 2134 facial swellings. The per-episode view leads to a different result in this case: Only 2134 (3.3%), from the total of 65 102, skin swellings affected the face. Patients with facial swellings exclusively, ie, without any skin swellings at other body sites, were rare (5 patients, number of facial swellings: 14, 2, 1, 1, 1). In 50 of 158 patients (31.6%), 608 of 2134 episodes of facial edema (28.5%) extended to laryngeal edema at least 1 time.

Genital swellings and skin swellings in other regions. In the per-patient view, 131 of 201 (65.2%) of the patients with skin swellings had genital swellings lasting about 3 days. The per-episode view provides a result similar to that for facial swellings: among the total of 65 102 skin swellings, only 2741 (4.2%) affected the genitals. A figure of 57 of 201 patients (28.4%) had skin swellings of the trunk. Among the total of 65 102 skin swellings, 1132 (1.7%) affected the trunk.

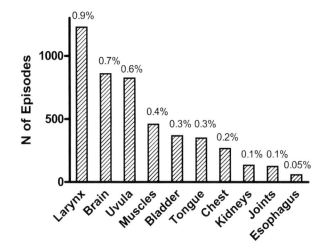

percentage based on n = 131,110 episodes

Figure 4 Edema episodes at rare edema sites.

Abdominal Attacks

A large portion of patients—195 of 209 (93.3%)—had recurrent abdominal attacks. The 14 other patients consisted of 10 adults (22 to 65 years old) and 4 children (2 to 15 years old). All 14 patients had other family members with skin and abdominal involvement of the disease. The total number of abdominal attacks was 62 503.

Laryngeal Edema

Laryngeal edema was assumed when there were voice changes (deeper voice, hoarseness, aphonia) associated with dyspnea and fear of asphyxiation. Most patients also had a feeling of a lump, tightness of the throat, and dysphagia. Such episodes occurred in 108 of 209 patients (51.7%). The total number of laryngeal edemas was 1229—ie, only 0.9% of all 131 110 edema episodes. Isolated laryngeal edema, ie, laryngeal edema without a simultaneous edema of the soft palate or the tongue, occurred in 91 of 108 patients (84.3%) and 793 of 1229 episodes (64.5%). An edema of the uvula or the whole soft palate was associated with 207 of 1229 episodes of laryngeal edema in 28 patients. In 252 of 1229 episodes among 18 patients, there was a simultaneous tongue swelling.

Uvular Edema, Edema of the Soft Palate

A total of 44 of 209 patients (21.1%) had 826 of 131 110 episodes (0.6%) of edema of the uvula or the total soft palate including the uvula. In 28 patients with 207 of 826 episodes, there was an associated laryngeal edema. Sixteen patients had 586 edema episodes of the uvula/soft palate that occurred alone and were not associated with voice changes of a simultaneous laryngeal edema—ie, 586 of 826 (70.9%) occurred in isolation. In 1 patient the uvula was so enormously swollen that it was hanging outside of her mouth.

Tongue Swellings

Tongue swellings occurred in 26 of 209 patients. The total number of tongue swellings was 351. In 18 patients, 252 tongue swellings were associated with an obstruction of the upper airways (eg, dyspnea, voice changes). In 10 patients, 99 of 351 (28.2%) tongue swellings occurred in isolation, without laryngeal edema. Two patients had both kinds of tongue swellings (ie, with and without laryngeal edema) and, therefore, belong to both groups.

Headache Episodes

Eighteen patients (8 males and 10 females) reported about 862 episodes of severe headache. The headache episodes were not associated with edema episodes at other sites or organs. The severe headaches lasted for 4 hours to 4 days, in most patients for 1 to 2 days. The headache was accompanied by various other signs, including feeling of pressure in the head (18 patients), feeling of pressure in the eyes (18 patients), visual disturbances (6 patients) such as: blurred vision, double vision, difficulty in focusing, and narrowed visual field; also, giddiness (1 patient), disorders of balance (1 patient), ataxia (1 patient), impaired orientation (1 pa-

tient), vomiting (2 patients), and decrease in physical and mental powers (1 patient). No patient reported photophobia, sensitivity to noise, osmophobia, or an excessive urinary discharge following a headache episode. No female observed an association with menstruation. All patients reported that analgesics were not effective. Five patients received C1-INH concentrate because of 134 headache episodes (2 patients received 500 U because of 110 episodes, and 3 patients received 1000 U because of 24 episodes). The C1-INH concentrate was effective in all treated episodes. In most episodes relief occurred after 30 minutes, and in all treated episodes after 5 to 60 minutes.

Involvement of the Urinary Bladder and Urethra

Seventeen of the 209 patients reported an involvement of their bladder or their urethra. The 370 episodes lasted from 1 to 3 days and were not associated with abdominal attacks. In 6 patients and 136 episodes, skin swellings preceded the symptoms for 1 or 2 days or occurred simultaneously. All patients had strangury, urinary stammering, retention of urine in the bladder, or anuria. Pain at micturition was reported by 15 of 17 patients. Additional symptoms were painful spasms or stabbing pain of the bladder (7 patients). In one patient a cystoscopy revealed a marked edema of the mucosa of the bladder. One patient was a medical laboratory technician and made a urinalysis of the mid-stream urine in 19 of her 60 episodes; there were no pathologic findings. In 2 other patients urinalysis was also normal. Four patients received C1-INH concentrate for 60 episodes. Relief and resolution of the complaints occurred within 1 hour after the injection in all episodes.

Involvement of the Muscles

Ten patients reported a total of 461 episodes of muscle involvement lasting 2 to 3 days; all cases were characterized by a circumscribed induration of muscles. At the time of the palpable and painful muscle swellings, there were no skin swellings or attacks in other organs. The muscles of the dorsal region were affected the most (9 patients); the muscles at the back of the neck (2 patients), the shoulder (2 patients), the forearm (1 patient), and the pectoral muscles (1 patient) rarely were affected. Two patients received C1-INH concentrate for treatment of 3 episodes and reported a marked effect 1 hour after the injection.

Involvement of the Shoulder and Hip Joints

Four patients reported 55 unilateral pain episodes in the shoulder joint lasting 1 to 2 days. Fifty-one of the 55 episodes were associated with a skin swelling of the shoulder. One patient received 500 U C1-INH concentrate because of 2 pain episodes in the shoulder joint. Relief started after 1 hour, and the complaints disappeared 3 hours after the injections. Five patients reported 71 unilateral painful episodes of the hip joint lasting for 1 to 2 days. Pain increased when the patients were walking and, thus, led to limping. In 24 episodes, a skin swelling of the thigh or buttock on the same side preceded or accompanied the joint complaints.

Chest Episodes with Breathing Difficulties and Feelings of Tightness and Pain

Eleven patients reported 268 retrosternal chest episodes with feelings of tightness and pressure in the chest and severe pain. Breathing was painful and, therefore, impaired and was associated with dyspnea. Breathing deeply was impossible because of stabbing pain. There was no associated edema at any other organ. One patient reported that he had the feeling that food could not pass through his esophagus at that time. There was no trigger for these episodes. The duration was 1 to 2 days. In 2 patients, during such episodes, radiographs of the chest and electrocardiograms were performed but revealed no pathologic findings. Electrocardiograms performed during the symptom-free intervals among all 11 patients were normal. No patients had signs of heart failure or coronary insufficiency. A total of 251 of 268 episodes occurred in patients between their 20th and 50th years of life. Two patients received 500 U C1-INH concentrate during 35 and 20 of these episodes, respectively; those patients reported relief 30 and 60 minutes after the injections, respectively. Four patients started long-term prophylaxis with danazol because of their frequent skin swellings and abdominal attacks; after the commencement of that regimen, 3 of the 4 had no further chest episodes with feelings of tightness, pain, and breathing difficulties, and 1 patient had mild and less frequent episodes.

Involvement of the Kidneys

Eight patients reported 136 episodes of renal pain. Three patients had renal colics, and the others had severe permanent pain. The episodes usually lasted 1 to 2 days, ranging 14 hours to 4 days. Four patients underwent diagnostic procedures: No renal calculi or inflammatory changes were found. Four patients received 500 or 1000 U C1-INH concentrate for 67 of these episodes; relief occurred after 20 to 30 minutes in 3 patients and in 1 patient after 1 to 2 hours.

Esophageal Involvement

Four patients had 60 episodes that they ascribed to an involvement of the esophagus. One patient had 50 such episodes. The episodes presented with pain in the region of the esophagus. During swallowing the pain moved through the whole esophagus along with the swallowed food. Pain was severe, "as if the esophagus was sore and too narrow" or "as if there were knives crosswise in the esophagus." Because of the pain, eating was impaired and for several hours was impossible. The episodes lasted 1 or 2 days. In 2 patients, 41 episodes were associated with abdominal attacks; in 4 patients, 19 episodes occurred without such attacks. One episode was associated with chest pain. Two patients received C1-INH concentrate for 5 episodes and reported that relief occurred 1 and 2 hours after the injec-

tion, respectively; the episodes lasted a shorter time (8 and 10 hours, respectively, vs 24 hours).

CROSS MODAL PATTERN: DISEASE SEVERITY RELATED TO SEX, AGE AT ONSET, AND VARIATIONS AMONG DIFFERENT MEMBERS OF A FAMILY

Women Versus Men

To test for sex differences, we contrasted the group of patients having many episodes (>12 per year) with the group having fewer episodes. In the per-patient view, 46 of 117 women (39.3 %) and 44 of 78 men (56.4%) had 12 episodes or fewer per year. In 71 of 117 women (60.7%) and 34 of 78 men (43.6%), more than 12 episodes occurred per year. The difference is significant at $\chi^2_{(1)} = 5.50$, $P<.020$. The mean number of episodes per year was also higher in women (24.0) than in men (20.1).

Early Versus Late Onset of Clinical Symptoms

In about one third of the patients (64 of 209), clinical symptoms started at age 5 or earlier. These patients had a total of 50 913 episodes during 1621 symptomatic years, or 31.4 ± 22.3 episodes per year on average. In another third (68 of 209 patients), clinical symptoms started at age 15 or later. These patients had a total of 24 117 episodes during 1355 symptomatic years, or a mean of 17.8 ± 21.1 episodes per year. A t test revealed that the early-onset group had significantly more episodes per year than the late-onset group ($t_{130} = 3.60$, $P <.001$).

Variations of Severity of Clinical Symptoms in Affected Members of the Same Family

For this dimension, we evaluated the information concerning 55 families with 155 HAE patients. Subjects who had no second family member affected or had less than 1 year of symptoms were not regarded. Among all the patients, severity was classified according to 4 steps: mild (1 to 6 episodes per year), moderate (5 to 12 episodes per year), severe (more than 12 episodes per year), or very severe (more than 24 episodes per year). The maximal differences among different members of a family were determined; the differences varied between 0 and 3 steps. As shown in Table 2, in 12 of 55 families the severity of the 2 affected family members' symptoms was equal; within all other families, the severity of symptoms varied among the family members, sometimes considerably.

DISCUSSION

In this retrospective study, we analyzed a relatively large number of patients with HAE due to C1-INH deficiency and their edema episodes. For most HAE patients the time pattern resembled the following: after a symptom-free period, the onset of clinical symptoms occurred in childhood or adolescence. Only a small proportion of patients had

Table 2 Variability of Disease Severity of the Affected Members in 55 Families

Discrepancy of Disease Severity*	Number of Family Members Affected					
	2	3	4	5	6	> 6
None	12†	-	-	-	-	-
Max 1 step	11	5	-	1	-	-
Max 2 step	4	7	1	1	1	1‡
Max 3 step	4	5	1	-	-	1§

*For the definition of disease severity, see the text.
†7 families mild episodes only; 5 families severe episodes only.
‡8 members affected.
§10 members affected.

symptom-free periods due to the natural course of their disease, either with preceding and subsequent clinical symptoms or after the last clinical symptoms. Therefore, we can conclude that after onset of the clinical symptoms, the disease persists for a lifetime in the vast majority of patients.

Concerning the spatial pattern, our results demonstrate that most HAE patients suffer from recurrent skin swelling, recurrent abdominal pain episodes, and from rarely occurring laryngeal edema. This pattern of organ involvement, which reflects the 3 cardinal symptoms of HAE, is well known. In 1992 Agostoni and Cicardi observed skin involvement in 91% of 226 patients, abdominal pain episodes in 73%, and laryngeal edema in 48%.[11] These findings, however, provide insight only into the affected organs per patient, but no information about the frequency of single episodes in the different organs. Our results based on the per-episode view demonstrate that nearly all episodes consisted of skin swellings and abdominal attacks (96.5%). Laryngeal edema was rare (0.9%), although it showed a prevalence of 51.7% in the per-patient view.

Skin swellings are one of the cardinal symptoms of HAE. According to our results, we can presume that all adult patients with HAE have skin swellings; any exceptions would be very rare. Skin swellings at the extremities are a notable symptom; upper extremities are involved more often than lower. In some cases the edema may be so severe that blisters occur (tension blisters). Our data show that facial swelling is a relatively rare event. However, the associated risk of an upper airway obstruction is rather high. The skin swelling pattern specific for HAE due to C1-INH deficiency is the following: there usually are extremity swellings in which facial, genital, and, more rarely, trunk and neck swellings are intermingled from time to time. Very few patients do not fit this pattern, namely, patients in whom the first symptoms are facial swellings and who did not experience many skin swellings at all. This should not be regarded as a separate pattern because it is possible that it reflects patients at the beginning of their disease.

Abdominal attacks occurred in most of our patients; only 10 adult patients had skin swellings but never an abdominal attack. Symptoms different from skin swellings and abdom-

inal attacks are rare in HAE. Laryngeal edema is potentially life threatening, and many cases of asphyxiation have been reported.[13,14] In our patient series, laryngeal edema occurred alone or was accompanied by swelling of the soft palate, including the uvula and the tongue. In a recent analysis of a smaller patient group (61 patients with 1 or more laryngeal edemas), we showed that the frequency of laryngeal edema compared with other swellings was 1:125.[15] Our results demonstrate that edema of the uvula or the total soft palate is a distinct clinical symptom of HAE. It frequently occurs in isolation, ie, without an accompanying laryngeal edema and without a tongue edema. One patient with a recurrent isolated edema of the soft palate has been described, in whom this type of edema acted as a 1-way valve leading to severe dyspnea and fear of asphyxiation.[16] Isolated tongue swelling is a very rare symptom of HAE. This result differs from ACE-I-induced angioedema, in which tongue swellings are considerably more frequent.[17,18]

The 862 headache episodes reported by 18 patients seemed to be similar to migraine episodes. However, some clinical features typical for migraine were lacking in these episodes. The prompt response of patients to treatment with C1-INH concentrate in the 134 treated episodes provides a further argument that these headache episodes are symptoms of HAE. Isolated edema episodes of the urinary bladder and urethra seem to be a rare but clear symptom of HAE. This finding is supported by the clinical symptoms and patients' prompt response to C1-INH concentrate when treated. Up to now, one patient with an involvement of the bladder has been reported.[19] Nielsen et al mentioned urinary infections during or after attacks.[20] Involvement of the muscles as well as shoulder and hip joints were not mentioned as symptoms of HAE until now. Although also rare, chest episodes are very significant for the affected patients. The relapsing occurrence of chest episodes in young patients and the patients' rapid responses to treatment with C1-INH concentrate identify these complaints as symptoms of HAE. The pathogenesis of the chest episodes is not clear. Renal and esophageal involvements have also not been mentioned until the present time.

Women seem to be affected more severely by HAE than men; we can only speculate about the reasons for that finding. Exposure to estrogen via oral contraceptives and hormone replacement therapy promotes the clinical symptoms of HAE.[21] Periods of pregnancy and lactation are associated with an increased number of edema episodes, at least in some women. Menstruation and ovulation may trigger skin swelling and episodes of abdominal pain. Patients with an early onset of the clinical symptoms have a more severe course of the disease compared with patients with a late onset. As of now there is no adequate explanation for this phenomenon. The C1-INH deficiency itself obviously is not the reason, because there are a few patients with a C1-INH deficiency who have no clinical symptoms. The kind of mutation of the C1-INH gene, likewise, is not responsible. According to our results, in most families there is a high variability in disease severity among the affected family members. Factors that contribute to swellings or protective factors that could explain the difference between patients with frequent episodes and patients with rare episodes have not yet been identified.

The present investigation has several limitations. It is partly a retrospective study; data regarding swelling frequency and swelling sites depend on patients' recall. We are aware that information about swellings that occurred a long time ago may not be precise; such imprecision is especially likely concerning information about swellings in frequent swelling sites, namely, swellings of the extremities and abdominal episodes. Information about rare swelling sites such as laryngeal edema or genital swelling is more precise, because the swellings usually are very significant for the patient and his or her relatives. A detailed comparison of retrospective and prospective data in HAE was performed by Bork et al and showed no major discrepancies.[22] Despite these limitations, the study yields observations about a relatively large sample and spans a long time period.

CONCLUSIONS

The typical time pattern of HAE shows an onset of clinical symptoms in the first or second decade of life. The following years are characterized by recurrent attacks with only a minority of patients having symptom-free years in between. Through this study, a swelling pattern consisting of frequent and rare swelling sites and the corresponding episode frequencies has been established. This pattern is specific for HAE and allows a tentative diagnosis based on clinical symptoms. Our analysis also revealed that a number of organs including chest, muscles, joints, kidneys, and esophagus may be involved in HAE.

References

1. Quincke HI. Über akutes umschriebenes Hautödem. *Monatsh Prakt Dermatol*. 1882;1:129-131.
2. Osler W. Hereditary angioneurotic edema. *Am J Med Sci*. 1888;95: 362-367.
3. Donaldson VH, Evans RR. A biochemical abnormality in hereditary angioneurotic edema: absence of serum inhibitor of C1-esterase. *Am J Med*. 1963;31:37-44.
4. Tosi M. Molecular genetics of C1 inhibitor. *Immunobiology*. 1998; 199:358-365.
5. Drouet C, Blanch A, Roche O, et al. HAE: Mutation analysis of the C1INH gene. *J Allergy Clin Immunol*. 2004;114:S66-S74.
6. Bork K, Barnstedt S-E, Koch P, Traupe H. Hereditary angioedema with normal C1-inhibitor activity in women. *Lancet*. 2000;356:213-217.
7. Landerman NS. Hereditary angioneurotic edema. *J Allergy Clin Immunol*. 1962;33:316-329.
8. Frank MM, Gelfand JA, Atkinson JP. Hereditary angioedema: the clinical syndrome and its management. *Ann Intern Med*. 1976;84:580-593.
9. Atkinson JP. Diagnosis and management of hereditary angioedema (HAE). *Ann Allergy*. 1979;42:348-352.
10. Cicardi M, Bergamaschini L, Marasini B, et al. Hereditary angioedema: an appraisal of 104 cases. *Am J Med Sci*. 1982;284:2-9.
11. Agostoni A, Cicardi M. Hereditary and acquired C1-inhibitor deficiency: biological and clinical characteristics in 235 patients. *Medicine (Baltimore)*. 1992;71:206-215.
12. Cicardi M, Zingale L. Clinical manifestation of HAE. *J Allergy Clin Immunol*. 2004;114:S55-S58.
13. Bork K, Siedlecki K, Bosch S, Schopf RE, Kreuz W. Asphyxiation by laryngeal edema in patients with hereditary angioedema. *Mayo Clin Proc*. 2000;75:349-354.
14. Bork K, Barnstedt S-E. Laryngeal edema and death from asphyxiation after tooth extraction in four patients with hereditary angioedema. *J Am Dent Assoc*. 2003;134:1088-1093.
15. Bork K, Hardt J, Schicketanz KH, Ressel N. Clinical studies of sudden upper airway obstruction in patients with hereditary angioedema due to C1 esterase inhibitor deficiency. *Arch Intern Med*. 2003;163:1229-1235.
16. Bork K, Koch P. Episodes of severe dyspnea due to snoring-induced recurrent edema of the soft palate in hereditary angioedema. *J Am Acad Dermatol*. 2001;45:968-969.
17. Sabroe RA, Kobza Black A. Angiotensin-converting enzyme (ACE) inhibitors and angio-oedema. *Br J Dermatol*. 1997;136:153-158.
18. Cicardi M, Zingale LC, Bergamaschini L, Agostoni A. Angioedema associated with angiotensin-converting enzyme inhibitor use. *Arch Intern Med*. 2004;164:910-913.
19. Van Dellen RG, Myers RP. Bladder involvement in hereditary angioedema. *Mayo Clin Proc*. 1980;55:277-278
20. Nielsen EW, Gran JT, Straume B, et al. Hereditary angio-edema: new clinical observations and autoimmune screening, complement and kallikrein-kinin analyses. *J Intern Med*. 1996;239:119-130.
21. Bork K, Fischer B, Dewald G. Recurrent episodes of skin angioedema and severe attacks of abdominal pain induced by oral contraceptives or hormone replacement therapy. *Am J Med*. 2003;114: 294-298.
22. Bork K, Meng G, Staubach P, Hardt J. Treatment with C1 inhibitor concentrate in abdominal pain attacks of patients with hereditary angioedema. *Transfusion*. 2005;45:1774-1784.

ELSEVIER
SAUNDERS

Immunol Allergy Clin N Am
26 (2006) 633–651

IMMUNOLOGY
AND ALLERGY
CLINICS
OF NORTH AMERICA

Mechanism of Angioedema in First Complement Component Inhibitor Deficiency

Alvin E. Davis III, MD

CBR Institute for Biomedical Research, Harvard Medical School,
800 Huntington Avenue, Boston, MA 02115, USA

Characterization of the pathophysiology of hereditary angioedema (HAE) began in 1962 with the observation by Landerman and colleagues [1] that plasma of patients who had hereditary angioedema was deficient in plasma kallikrein inhibitory capacity and the subsequent demonstration by Donaldson and Evans [2] that the deficient protein was first complement component (C1) inhibitor. The role of C1 inhibitor in regulation of complement system activation had been described shortly after the first description of the isolation and characterization of the first complement component; it was characterized as a heat labile factor in plasma that inhibited the esterolytic activity of C1 [3]. C1 was shown to consist of three separate proteins, C1q, C1r, and C1s, the last two of which are zymogen serine proteases that are converted to their proteolytically active forms following binding of C1q to an immune complex. Subsequent studies demonstrated that C1 inhibitor inactivates both C1r and C1s [4,5].

The role of C1 inhibitor in regulation of the contact system, by means of inactivation of both plasma kallikrein and factor XIIa, was elucidated during the 1970s and 1980s [6–14]. C1 inhibitor also is capable of inactivating a number of other proteases, including plasmin and tissue plasminogen activator (tPA) [15–19]. The evidence clearly indicates that C1 inhibitor is not a major regulator of plasmin, which, in vivo, is inhibited primarily by α_2 antiplasmin [20,21]. Some data, however, suggest that C1 inhibitor may participate in tPA inactivation [16]. Cugno and colleagues [22,23] have demonstrated activation of both the coagulation cascade and the fibrinolytic

Many of the studies described here were supported by USPHS grants HD22082, HD33727, and AI057366.

E-mail address: aldavis@cbrinstitute.org

pathway during attacks of HAE. Therefore, C1 inhibitor may be involved in regulation of these pathways in vivo or, alternatively, activation of these pathways by exogenous factors may trigger attacks of angioedema.

One might have expected that the demonstration of the specific deficiency responsible for HAE and characterization of the proteases inactivated by C1 inhibitor would lead rapidly to characterization of the mechanism of generation of angioedema symptoms. However, largely because C1 inhibitor is the primary regulator of activation of both the classic pathway of complement and the contact system of kinin generation, the mechanism remained unclear until recently. At this point, the accumulated information clearly indicates that the primary, and most likely the sole, mediator of symptoms is bradykinin generated by means of activation of the contact system. However, the specific biochemical events leading to the initiation of an angioedema attack remain ill defined.

Function of first complement component inhibitor

C1 inhibitor is a member of the serpins, a family of proteins consisting mostly, but not solely, of serine protease inhibitors. All members of the serpin family share similar sequences and three-dimensional structures and consist of seven to nine α helices and three β sheets. The most distinctive features of the native serpin structure are a five-stranded β sheet (sheet A) that makes up the prominent planar surface of the molecule and a peptide loop (the reactive center loop) consisting of approximately 17 amino acid residues that is exposed at one pole of the molecule. The reactive center loop is located near the carboxyl terminus of the protein. The native serpin structure is rather unstable and is sensitive to denaturing conditions. Cleavage by a nontarget protease within the reactive center loop results in a dramatic molecular rearrangement, with insertion of this loop into β sheet A as its fourth strand, converting sheet A to a six-stranded sheet. The cleaved inhibitor is a much more stable structure that may be demonstrated by enhanced resistance to thermal or chemical denaturation [24–26]. This rearrangement is indicated by the expression of neoepitopes on the cleaved molecule [27–29].

Serpins inactivate proteases after recognition by the protease of a substrate-like sequence located within the reactive center loop. The protease attacks the peptide bond carboxyl terminal to the P1 residue, which, in the case of C1 inhibitor, is an arginine. The inhibitor is cleaved at this site. However, rather than subsequent release of the protease, a covalent bond is formed between the reactive center amino acid residue of the serpin and the active site serine of the protease [30]. Subsequently, the reactive center loop inserts into β sheet A, as with cleavage by nontarget proteases. This insertion moves the protease to the opposite pole of the molecule. The result is a stable cleaved serpin structure covalently linked to a destabilized protease in which its catalytic triad is interrupted. Both the protease and the inhibitor are thereby inactivated, an aspect that led to the designation of serpins as suicide substrates [31]. The structural and functional data all indicate that the mechanism of inactivation of proteases by C1 inhibitor is the same as the mechanism with other serpins [31,32].

The most significant difference between C1 inhibitor and other serpins is in the size and characteristics of its nonserpin amino terminal domain. This domain in C1 inhibitor is quite large (approximately 100 residues) and is heavily glycosylated with three N-linked and at least seven O-linked carbohydrates [33]. Some portions of the sequence of this domain are mucin-like. Based on functional studies using a recombinant C1 inhibitor molecule with the amino terminal 100 residues deleted, this domain plays no role in protease inhibitor function [34]. Recent studies have indicated that the amino terminal domain is required, however, for a direct interaction with gram-negative bacteria and endotoxins [35,36]. This interaction may play a role in C1 inhibitor–mediated protection from sepsis and septic shock.

C1 inhibitor is the only protease inhibitor that inactivates C1r and C1s [4,5] and is, therefore, the primary regulator of classic pathway activation (Fig. 1). It also plays a role in regulation of the lectin pathway, which is activated by interaction of mannan-binding lectin or ficolins with surface structures of a variety of micro-organisms [37–39]. C1 inhibitor inactivates MASP2, a C1s-like protease that is associated with mannan binding lectin and ficolins and is activated following binding. However, in vivo, MASP2 also most likely is inactivated by α_2 macroglobulin [40]. The relative importance of each is not yet clear. Another complement regulatory function of C1 inhibitor has been described, in which C1 inhibitor was shown to bind to C3b, which resulted in inhibition of factor B binding, similar to the mechanism of action of factor H [41]. This function was independent of protease inhibitor activity. Although the resulting alternative pathway inhibition was shown to take place at physiologic concentrations in vitro, the importance of this activity in vivo remains unclear.

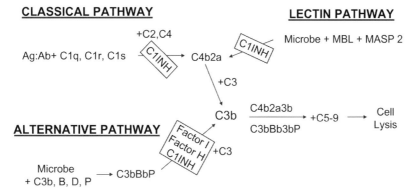

Fig. 1. Complement system activation. The components enclosed within rectangles are inhibitors of activation. Ag:Ab, antigen-antibody complexes; B, factor B; C1INH, C1 inhibitor; D, factor D; MASP 2, Mannan-binding lectin associated protease 2; MBL, mannan-binding lectin; P, properdin.

C1 inhibitor is the primary inhibitor of both plasma kallikrein and coagulation factor XIIa, although these proteases can also be inactivated by α_2 macroglobulin [6,9,12–14]. It is therefore the major regulator of contact system–mediated bradykinin generation. By virtue of its inactivaton of both factor XIIa and factor XIa, C1 inhibitor also inhibits activation of the intrinsic coagulation pathway. The contact system is activated by a variety of exogenous negatively charged surfaces, such as glass, kaolin, elagic acid, dextran sulfate, and possibly endotoxin lipopolysaccharide [42–47]. Factor XII binds to these surfaces; this binding induces its autoactivation to proteolytically active factor XIIa, which activates both plasma prekallikrein and additional factor XII (Fig. 2). Activated kallikrein then cleaves two peptide bonds in high molecular weight kininogen to release bradykinin. A biologically relevant negatively charged substance responsible for activation in vivo has not been described. Activation in vivo most likely takes place primarily on the surface of endothelial cells [48–53].

At least two pathways that lead to activation of kallikrein in the absence of factor XII have been described. One of these is reported to be mediated by an interaction between the kallikrein–high molecular weight kininogen complex and heat shock protein 90 [50,54,55], whereas the other depends on activation of prekallikrein by prolylcarboxypeptidase (see Fig. 2) [56–59]. Some data suggest that the prolylcarboxypeptidase-mediated activation mechanism is quite efficient and may be the primary mechanism of contact system activation in vivo [56,59]. By contrast, other data suggest that both this and heat shock protein 90–mediated activation are quite slow, but that they are greatly accelerated in the presence of factor XII [50,54,55]. Although the details of contact system activation remain to be resolved, it is

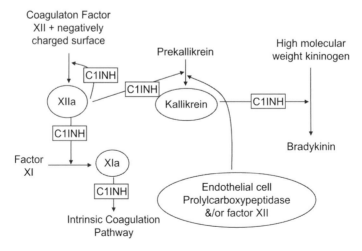

Fig. 2. Contact system activation. The diagram indicates the two pathways of contact system activation, one by means of exogenous negatively charged surfaces and the other taking place on the surface of endothelial cells. Activation of prekallikrein on endothelial cells is proposed to be mediated by prolylcarboxypeptidase or by factor XII. C1INH, C1 inhibitor.

clear that the primary mechanism of regulation of activation of the contact system is inhibition of kallikrein (and factor XIIa) by C1 inhibitor.

Mutations resulting in first complement component inhibitor deficiency

Individuals who have HAE are heterozygous for mutations that result either in lack of expression of C1 inhibitor protein or in the synthesis of a nonfunctional protein from one allele together with expression of normal protein from the other allele. Clinically, these two types are referred to as type 1 and type 2, respectively, based on whether a dysfunctional protein is detectable in the patient's plasma. However, this division is not precisely accurate. A number of mutations result in a dysfunctional protein that is either degraded intracellularly, secreted inefficiently, or cleared rapidly from the circulation. Strictly speaking, these should be referred to as type 2, but, because they are either absent or present in very small quantities in the blood, they are usually classified as type 1. In clinical practice, a patient is classified as type 2 based on the finding of a normal (or elevated) C1 inhibitor level determined immunochemically, together with a decreased functional level of C1 inhibitor. Using these criteria, approximately 80% to 85% of patients are classified as type 1.

Mutations resulting in deficiency may be of virtually any type, including deletions (and duplications) that range in size from a few base pairs to multiple exons and a variety of single base substitutions. Large deletions and single base changes at the reactive center are somewhat overrepresented in comparison with the other types of mutations. All of the large mutations appear to be a consequence of recombination involving the multiple Alu repetitive elements that are present within the introns of the gene. The reactive center mutations most likely are a result of the cytosine-guanine (CG) dinucleotide within the codon for the reactive center arginine (CGC). The CG dinucleotide is susceptible to mutation due to deamidation of methylated cytosine, which results in conversion to a thymine. This process may occur in the CG dinucleotide in the coding strand or in the complementary strand. With C1 inhibitor, this results in substitution of the reactive center arginine with either cysteine or histidine. These make up the largest single group of mutations within the C1 inhibitor gene. However, it should be noted that some other mechanism may also be at play here, because several serine and leucine substitutions at the reactive center have been described, which cannot result from the deamidation mechanism.

Whether a patient is type 1 or type 2 is of no known clinical importance. No differences exist between the two in clinical presentation, severity, or clinical course. Furthermore, with two possible exceptions, the specific mutation does not appear to have any clinical effect. These potential exceptions are one family with a large deletion, in which the abnormal transcript appears to inhibit transcription of the normal gene, and another family with a small duplication, which appears to result in inhibition of translation of the normal C1 inhibitor transcript [60,61]. It is not known whether these mechanisms apply in other families with different mutations.

Pathophysiologic interpretation of clinical characteristics

Patients who have HAE develop recurrent acute episodes of localized edema that may involve the skin, the mucosa of the gastrointestinal tract, the pharynx, or the larynx. Therefore, patients who have C1 inhibitor deficiency have an intermittent defect in the regulation of vascular permeability. This increased vascular permeability results from a sudden local loss of endothelial barrier function within the postcapillary venule. Signs or symptoms of inflammation are absent, as are any signs of an allergic component. Although early reports suggested that urinary histamine levels were elevated during attacks of angioedema, antihistamines are ineffective, and a study of a number of patients who had HAE (both symptomatic and asymptomatic) demonstrated that urinary histamine levels are not elevated [62]. The angioedema in HAE does not respond to treatment with epinephrine.

Serpins are suicide substrates, which may be one important factor in the initiation of attacks of angioedema. Activation of any protease inhibited by C1 inhibitor, whether a complement, contact, or fibrinolytic system protease, will result in inactivation and consumption of the inhibitor. If the rate of consumption exceeds the rate of ongoing synthesis, the C1 inhibitor plasma level will decrease. C1 inhibitor levels in patients who have HAE average approximately 30% of normal during symptom-free periods. Significant reduction below this level is associated with the development of symptoms. Therefore, any event that triggers activation of any of the three proteolytic pathways would increase C1 inhibitor consumption and suppress the plasma level and could result in an episode of angioedema. Clearly, trauma and inflammation, which are known initiators of attacks of angioedema, can result in activation of each pathway. However, not all episodes of angioedema are associated with an obvious precipitating factor. In addition, consumption of C1 inhibitor could be amplified if activation of one system directly resulted in activation of either or both of the other two systems (Fig. 3). Activated factor XII and plasmin may activate C1, and factor XIIa or kallikrein may generate plasmin from plasminogen, but the biologic significance of these findings has not been clearly demonstrated [63–69].

Another possibility with some clinical support is that plasmin generation might activate the contact system, with resulting bradykinin generation, and might thus result in the development of angioedema. Angioedema sometimes develops during therapy with recombinant tissue plasminogen activator [70,71]. Experimental evidence suggests that this angioedema is mediated by bradykinin released by the plasmin that is generated by the infused tissue plasminogen activator [71,72]. It is possible that, in a patient who has HAE, activation of the fibrinolytic pathway during trauma or inflammation might generate sufficient plasmin for a similar phenomenon to occur.

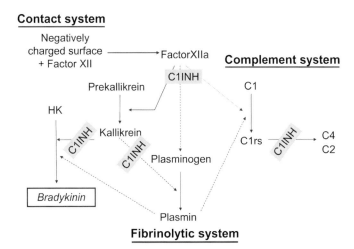

Fig. 3. Proposed interactions among the complement, contact, and fibrinolytic systems. Arrows with solid lines indicate reactions of known biologic relevance. Arrows with dotted lines indicate reactions demonstrated to take place in vitro, but that are of uncertain in vivo importance. C1INH, C1 inhibitor; HK, high molecular weight kininogen.

This hypothesis is consistent with the clinical observation that plasmin inhibitors are frequently effective in HAE.

The mediation of angioedema

Complement system activation

In HAE, the low plasma levels of C1 inhibitor result in apparent spontaneous activation of both the complement and contact systems. Although this is most obvious during an overt attack of angioedema, it is highly likely that activation occurs to some degree during symptom-free periods. C2 and C4 levels, which are virtually always low during an attack, may also be low when the patient is asymptomatic [73–75]. Another indication of activation is the observation that the catabolic rate of C1 inhibitor in symptom-free HAE patients is elevated in comparison with that of normal individuals [76]. This aspect also probably accounts for the finding that plasma levels of C1 inhibitor are much less than 50% of normal, which would be expected in a heterozygous deficiency state [77]. During periods of angioedema, circulating activated C1 [73,78] and complexes of C1 inhibitor with both C1r and C1s may be detected [79], in addition to decreased plasma levels of C2 and C4, which may be so low as to be undetectable.

During the 1970s and 1980s, a number of studies were published that suggested that the mediator of angioedema was a product of complement system activation. On a clinical basis, a complement-derived mediator appeared most likely to many investigators because angioedema is nonpainful, whereas subcutaneous injection of bradykinin, which also produces edema, is quite painful. Donaldson and colleagues [80] showed that plasma taken from

HAE patients during symptom-free periods, following incubation at 37°C, generated a factor that contracted smooth muscle and had vascular permeability–enhancing activity when it was injected intradermally into guinea pig skin. The data suggested that this kinin-like activity was derived from complement activation; furthermore, both C2 and C4 appeared to be required for its generation [80–82]. Specifically, the factor appeared to differ from bradykinin in size, electrophoretic mobility, isoelectric point, and susceptibility to trypsin, and its generation was inhibited by antibodies to C2 and C4.

Various other data also appeared to support the hypothesis that the mediator was complement derived. Intradermal injection, in guinea pigs and humans, of proteolytically active C1s resulted in local swelling without pain or itching (ie, it was similar to angioedema) [83–85]. Furthermore, C2-deficient people did not respond to intradermal injection of C1s, whereas a C3-deficient patient did respond [84,86]. C2-deficient guinea pigs also were unresponsive, but the response was restored following intravenous infusion of C2 [87]. Therefore, to induce a vascular permeability response by means of complement activation, C2 was required. However, these studies did not identify the source of the mediator. In addition, there were no clearcut direct data to indicate that the mediator resulting from complement system activation was the same as the mediator responsible for angioedema in HAE.

Several studies suggested that the complement-derived factor might result from plasmin cleavage of C2 during complement activation. First, mixtures of C1s, C2, and plasmin, in the presence or absence of C4, generated vascular permeability–enhancing and smooth muscle–contracting activity [88,89]. This event appeared to coincide with the release of a group of small peptides from the carboxyl terminus of C2b [88]. In addition, several synthetic peptides matching the carboxyl terminal sequence of C2b possessed vascular permeability and smooth muscle–contracting activity [88]. The most active of these was 25 amino acids long. However, although this synthetic peptide clearly enhanced vascular permeability, its specific activity was low in comparison with bradykinin. Another study was unable to demonstrate any cleavage of C2 or C2b with plasmin, and no kinin-like activity resulted from such incubation mixtures [90].

Contact system activation

During the same period, evidence for contact system activation in HAE was also accumulating. Among the first of these findings was the demonstration that large amounts of active kallikrein were present in induced blister fluid from patients who had HAE. This finding suggested a lower threshold for contact system activation in comparison with normal individuals [91]. In addition, during attacks, patients who had HAE had decreased levels of prekallikrein and of high molecular weight kininogen [92]. At least two early studies suggested that bradykinin was generated during attacks of angioedema [93,94]. One of these reported, unfortunately only in abstract form, that bradykinin was directly detectable in plasma from HAE patients following in vitro incubation [93]. In 1986, Berrettini and colleagues [95] demonstrated that high molecular weight kininogen was circulating in a cleaved form in a patient who had HAE. Subsequently, this group and a number of others have confirmed this finding in additional patients [96–99].

Therefore, by the end of the 1980s, it was clear that both the complement and contact systems were activated during episodes of angioedema. However, the precise mediator in HAE had not been unequivocally identified. Many investigators believed that the mediator was bradykinin, whereas others believed that a "C2 kinin" was responsible. In 1994, Shoemaker and colleagues [100] sought to begin to clarify this issue by repeating, as closely as possible, the protocol followed previously by Donaldson and colleagues [80]. For these experiments, in addition to HAE plasma, "artificial HAE plasma" was prepared by immunoabsorption with anti–C1 inhibitor antibody. This technique made possible the use of a variety of deficient plasmas, which then also were made deficient in C1 inhibitor. Vascular permeability–enhancing activity could be generated both from HAE remission plasma and from normal plasma depleted of C1 inhibitor. More importantly, the activity was also readily generated from C1 inhibitor–depleted C2-deficient plasma, but not from plasma deficient in prekallikrein, factor XII, or high molecular weight kininogen. Furthermore, the active factor was isolated and shown by amino acid sequence analysis to be bradykinin [100]. Subsequently, Nussberger and colleagues [101] demonstrated that bradykinin levels were elevated in the plasmas of patients who had HAE during episodes of angioedema. Although these data do not demonstrate a cause and effect relationship between bradykinin and angioedema, they strongly suggest that bradykinin is involved. The data also do not rule out the possibility that more than one mediator is involved.

A dysfunctional first complement component inhibitor
with diminished inhibition of complement proteases
but normal inhibition of contact system proteases

In 1994, Wisnieski and colleagues [102] described a kindred with extremely low C4 levels as a result of an apparent dysfunctional C1 inhibitor molecule that was defective in its capacity to inhibit C1. This defect presumably resulted in excessive C4 consumption. The propositus from this family presented with systemic lupus erythematosus. Subsequent studies demonstrated that every family member with a low C4 level expressed a C1 inhibitor molecule that was defective in its ability to inhibit both C1r and C1s but retained a perfectly normal ability to inactivate plasma kallikrein and coagulation factor XII [103–105]. This mutant C1 inhibitor retained only approximately 10% of its ability to inhibit proteolytically active C1r and C1s. This dysfunction was due to a mutation that resulted in substitution of the alanine residue immediately amino terminal to the reactive center arginine (the P2 position, Ala443) with a valine [103]. Most importantly, neither the single patient who has systemic lupus nor any of the seven other family members who express this dysfunctional protein has ever had angioedema. These individuals clearly had ongoing complement system activation, as indicated by their depressed plasma C4 levels. Therefore, complement system activation alone does not result in the generation of any peptide that induces angioedema. This family provides strong indirect evidence that the mediator in HAE is bradykinin.

The first complement component inhibitor–deficient mouse

Analysis of C1 inhibitor knockout mice has provided additional support for the hypothesis that bradykinin is the mediator of angioedema in HAE [106]. A database of genes randomly targeted with a retroviral-mediated gene trapping technique developed by Lexicon Genetics (The Woodlands, Texas) was screened. The C1 inhibitor gene was targeted in two embryonic stem cell lines, one of which was used to develop the deficient mice. Both the C1 inhibitor heterozygous deficient (C1INH$^{+/-}$) and homozyous deficient (C1INH$^{-/-}$) mice were normal in appearance, grew and developed normally, and reproduced normally. Litter size was normal in both C1INH$^{+/-}$ and C1INH$^{-/-}$ matings, which suggests that there was no increase in embryonic or fetal death. Neither C1 inhibitor mRNA nor protein was detected in C1INH$^{-/-}$ mice. Similar to observations in patients who have HAE, C1 inhibitor plasma levels in C1INH$^{+/-}$ mice were less than 50% of normal. C4 protein levels and functional complement levels were variably decreased in most C1 inhibitor–deficient mice, although probably not to such an extent as in humans who have HAE. Therefore, the mice appear to have unregulated complement activation, although possibly not to such an extent as do patients who have HAE.

Another indication that the consequences of C1-inhibitor deficiency in the mouse are less dramatic than in the human is provided by the observation that none of the mice have ever developed angioedema involving the skin. A total of only eight deficient mice have had spontaneous episodes of gastrointestinal edema with obstruction; one of these mice also had laryngeal edema. None of the wild-type littermate mice were affected, nor were any other mice in the colony. However, the episodes have not recurred in other deficient mice. Unfortunately, the trigger for these episodes is unknown, and attempts to reproduce such episodes have not been successful. Although these events did appear to be angioedema, it is not possible definitively to ascribe them to C1 inhibitor deficiency, both because they have not been reproduced and because no biochemical data exist from the time of the attacks.

Although C1 inhibitor–deficient mice do not have any clinically apparent abnormalities, when a marker for plasma protein extravasation (Evans Blue dye) was used, the mice were shown to have increased vascular permeability in comparison with wild-type littermate controls ($C1INH^{+/+}$). $C1INH^{-/-}$, $C1INH^{+/-}$, and $C1INH^{+/+}$ mice were injected intravenously with Evans blue dye, which readily binds to serum albumin. Within minutes, the skin of the feet and the skin around the nose and eyes of both the heterozygous and homozygous deficient mice became quite blue, whereas that of the wild-type mice became only slightly blue (Fig. 4) [106]. The vascular permeability was increased to a greater extent than in the wild-type mice by the topical application of mustard oil, which enhances local inflammation. The degree of vascular permeability was quantitated spectrophotometrically by extraction of the dye from the feet of the mice. The dye extravasation both in the $C1INH^{+/-}$ and in the $C1INH^{-/-}$ mice was approximately 1.5 times greater than that in the wild-type mice (Table 1). Enhancement with mustard oil increased the difference to 3- to 3.5-fold greater in the deficient mice. Treatment of the deficient mice with intravenous C1 inhibitor (100 μg) before injection with Evans blue dye completely reversed the increased vascular permeability. The amount of vascular leak in the treated deficient mice was indistinguishable from that of their wild-type littermates. This finding strongly indicates that the increase in vascular permeability in the knockout mice was solely a result of the deficiency of C1 inhibitor and not of some unexpected associated defect.

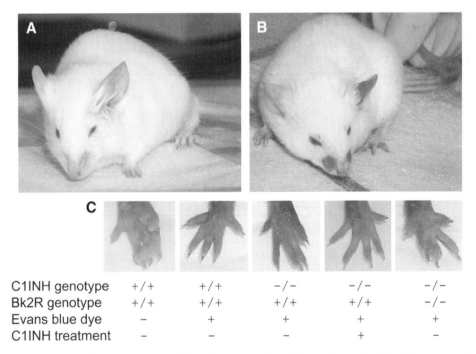

C1INH genotype	+/+	+/+	-/-	-/-	-/-
Bk2R genotype	+/+	+/+	+/+	+/+	-/-
Evans blue dye	-	+	+	+	+
C1INH treatment	-	-	-	+	-

Fig. 4. Analysis of vascular permeability. Extravasation of Evans blue dye 15 to 30 minutes after injection. (*A*) Wild-type mouse; (*B*) C1 inhibitor–deficient mouse; (*C*) rear footpads of mice of the indicated genotypes with or without C1 inhibitor treatment. Bk2R, bradykinin 2 receptor; C1INH, C1 inhibitor.

Table 1
Vascular permeability in C1-inhibitor-deficient mice

C1INH genotype	Bk2R genotype	No. of mice	C1INH treatment	Fold change in dye extravasation vs. WT[a]
+/−	+/+	5	None	1.5*
−/−	+/+	5	None	1.6*
−/−	−/−	5	None	1.0
+/−	+/+	4	C1INH	1.1
−/−	+/+	4	C1INH	1.0
−/−	+/+	22	DX-88	1.0
−/−	+/+	25	Icatibant	0.9
−/−	+/+	11	P2 A→V	1.0

Abbreviations: Bk2R, bradykinin 2 receptor; C1INH, C1 inhibitor; P2 A→V, P2 alanine to valine; WT, wild type.

[a] The dye extravasation was quantitated spectrophotometrically at 600 nm. The mean values of each group are expressed as the fold increase compared with an untreated wild-type control group.

* $P < .002$ compared with wild-type controls.

Data from Han ED, MacFarlane RC, Mulligan AN, et al. Increased vascular permeability in C1 inhibitor deficient mice is mediated by the bradykinin type 2 receptor. J Clin Invest 2002:109:1057–63; and Han Lee E, Pappalardo E, Scafidi J, et al. Approaches toward reversal of increased vascular permeability in C1 inhibitor deficient mice. Immuno Letters 2003;89:155–60.

To test the hypothesis that the increased vascular permeability was mediated by bradykinin, C1INH$^{-/-}$ mice were crossed with bradykinin 2 receptor (Bk2R) knockout mice. The resulting C1INH$^{+/-}$, Bk2R$^{+/-}$ mice then were mated, which resulted in all the expected genotypes in the predicted proportions. The C1INH$^{+/-}$, Bk2R$^{+/-}$ and the C1INH$^{-/-}$, Bk2R$^{-/-}$ mice all appeared normal. Furthermore, they were indistinguishable from the wild-type mice in their vascular permeability response (see Table 1). Therefore, the Bk2R is required to mediate the increased vascular permeability response. Bradykinin is the only known ligand for the Bk2R. These data strongly indicate that bradykinin is the mediator of the increased vascular permeability in the mice.

To confirm and strengthen these observations, mice also were treated with two agents that inhibit contact system activation but have little or no effect on complement system activation, and with another that is a Bk2R antagonist. The first agent, DX-88 (Dyax Corp., Cambridge, Massachusetts), is an engineered Kunitz domain protease inhibitor prepared using phage display. It is a potent and highly specific inhibitor of plasma kallikrein. The second kallikrein inhibitor used was the recombinant mutated C1 inhibitor in which the P2 Ala had been substituted with a Val [103–105], diminishing its inhibition of C1r and C1s but having no effect on its ability to inhibit plasma kallikrein. The bradykinin receptor antagonist used was Icatibant (Jerini AG, Berlin, Germany), a decapeptide antagonist with a structure similar to that of bradykinin. Each of these agents completely reversed the increased vascular permeability (see Table 1).

Because the bradykinin receptor antagonist and both inhibitors of contact system activation prevent the increased vascular permeability, it appears unlikely that any mediator other than bradykinin is involved.

Although the C1 inhibitor–deficient mice have an obvious defect in vascular permeability, they appear to have compensated quite well for this defect. Furthermore, it is surprising that the phenotype in these mice appears identical in the $C1INH^{+/-}$ and $C1INH^{-/-}$ mice. No human with complete deficiency of C1 inhibitor has been described, which suggests that complete deficiency might be lethal. The explanation for the relative mildness of the phenotype in the mice in comparison with humans who have angioedema is unknown, as is that for the lack of difference between the heterozygous and homozygous deficient mice. A likely potential explanation for both findings is that, in the mouse, other inhibitors play a larger role in regulation of C1 inhibitor target proteases than is the case in the human. For example, although in both the mouse and the human, C1 inhibitor appears to be the only inhibitor of activated C1r and C1s, in the human it is not the only inhibitor of factor XIIa and plasma kallikrein. Depending on the methods used, in human plasma C1 inhibitor provides from 42% to 84% of the kallikrein inhibitory capacity and as much as 90% of the inhibitory capacity toward activated factor XII [9,12–14,107]. The remainder of the plasma inhibitory activity toward both kallikrein and factor XIIa is provided by α_2 macroglobulin. It is possible that α_2 macroglobulin, or perhaps other inhibitors, provides a higher proportion of the inhibition of murine contact system proteases. This hypothesis remains uninvestigated.

Another potential explanation for the lack of difference between $C1INH^{+/-}$ and $C1INH^{-/-}$ mice is that, below a critical C1 inhibitor level, activation of the complement and contact systems is maximal, and a further decrease in the C1 inhibitor level has no additional effect. However, at least for the complement system, this is unlikely to be the case, because the C4 and hemolytic complement levels, although lower than in wild-type mice, are only moderately reduced. It also appears unlikely, therefore, that maximal activation of the contact system would occur. Another possibility is that the kallikrein substrate, high molecular weight kininogen, is depleted in both the $C1INH^{+/-}$ and $C1INH^{-/-}$ mice. The resolution of these questions awaits the development of appropriate reagents for these measurements.

The contributions of new therapeutic approaches toward definition of the pathophysiology of angioedema

Clinical trials using DX88 and Icatibant, the two new therapeutic agents described earlier, have provided further evidence supporting the hypothesis that angioedema in HAE is mediated by bradykinin. In the case of DX-88, two Phase II clinical trials have been completed, a third Phase II trial is nearly complete, and a Phase III trial is ongoing [108]. Icatibant has been used in one completed Phase II clinical trial, and two Phase III trials are currently ongoing [109]. From the available data, both agents appear to be quite effective, in that they decrease the time to beginning of symptom relief. Furthermore, at appropriate doses, they both appear to be effective in nearly all patients. The available results from these trials, therefore, confirm the conclusions from the experiments in the C1 inhibitor knockout mice and indicate clearly that the primary mediator of attacks of angioedema in humans is bradykinin.

References

[1] Landerman NS, Webster ME, Becker EL, et al. Hereditary angioneurotic edema. II. Deficiency of inhibitor for serum globulin permeability factor and/or plasma kallikrein. J Allergy 1962;33:330–41.

[2] Donaldson VH, Evans RR. A biochemical abnormality in hereditary angioneurotic edema. Am J Med 1963;35:37–44.

[3] Ratnoff O, Lepow I. Some properties of an esterase derived from preparations of the first component of complement. J Exp Med 1957;106:327–43.

[4] Sim RB, Reboul A, Arlaud GJ, et al. Interaction of 125I-labelled complement components C1r and C1s with protease inhibitors in plasma. FEBS Lett 1979;97:111–5.

[5] Ziccardi RJ. Activation of the early components of the classical complement pathway under physiological conditions. J Immunol 1981;126:1768–73.

[6] de Agostini A, Lijnen HR, Pixley RA, et al. Inactivation of factor-XII active fragment in normal plasma: predominant role of C1-inhibitor. J Clin Invest 1984;93:1542–9.

[7] Gallimore MJ, Amundsen E, Larsbraaten M, et al. Studies on plasma inhibitors of plasma kallikrein using chromogenic peptide substrate assays. Thromb Res 1979;16:695–703.

[8] Gigli I, Mason JW, Colman RW, et al. Interaction of plasma kallikrein with the C1 inhibitor. J Immunol 1970;104:574–81.

[9] Harpel PC, Lewin MF, Kaplan AP. Distribution of plasma kallikrein between C1 inactivator and a2-macroglobulin in plasma utilizing a new assay for a2-macroglobulin-kallikrein complexes. J Biol Chem 1985;260:4257–63.

[10] Lewin MF, Kaplan AP, Harpel PC. Studies of C1 inactivator–plasma kallikrein complexes in purified systems and in plasma. Quantitation by an enzyme-linked differential antibody immunosorbent assay. J Biol Chem 1983;258:6415–21.

[11] McConnell DJ. Inhibitors of kallikrein in human plasma. J Clin Invest 1972;51:1611–23.

[12] Pixley RA, Schapira M, Colman RW. The regulation of human factor XIIa by plasma proteinase inhibitors. J Biol Chem 1985;260:1723–9.

[13] Schapira M, Scott CF, Colman RW. Contribution of plasma protease inhibitors to the inactivation of kallikrein in plasma. J Clin Invest 1982;69:462–8.

[14] van der Graaf F, Koedam JA, Bouma BN. Inactivation of kallikrein in human plasma. J Clin Invest 1983;71:149–58.

[15] Harpel PC, Cooper NR. Studies on human plasma C1-inactivator-enzyme interactions. I. Mechanisms of interaction with C1s, plasmin and trypsin. J Clin Invest 1975;55:593–604.

[16] Huisman LG, van Griensven JM, Kluft C. On the role of C1-inhibitor as inhibitor of tissue-type plasminogen activator in human plasma. Thromb Haemost 1995;73:466–71.

[17] Ranby M, Bergstorf N, Nilsson T. Enzymatic properties of one and two chain forms of tissue plasminogen activator. Thromb Res 1982;27:175–84.

[18] Ratnoff O, Pensky J, Ogston D, et al. The inhibition of plasmin, plasma kallikrein, plasma permeability factor, and the C1'r subcomponent of complement by serum C1' esterase inhibitor. J Exp Med 1969;129:315–31.

[19] Sulikowski T, Patston PA. The inhibition of TNK-t-PA by C1-inhibitor. Blood Coagul Fibrinolysis 2001;12:75–7.

[20] Aoki N, Moroi M, Matsuda M, et al. The behavior of alpha2-plasmin inhibitor in fibrinolytic states. J Clin Invest 1977;60:361–9.

[21] Harpel PC. Alpha2-plasmin inhibitor and alpha2-macroglobulin-plasmin complexes in plasma. Quantitation by an enzyme-linked differential antibody immunosorbent assay. J Clin Invest 1981;68:46–55.

[22] Cugno M, Cicardi M, Bottasso B, et al. Activation of the coagulation cascade in C1-inhibitor deficiencies. Blood 1997;89:3213–8.

[23] Cugno M, Hack CE, Boer JPD, et al. Generation of plasmin during acute attacks of hereditary angioedema. J Lab Clin Med 1993;121:38–43.

[24] Mast AE, Enghild JJ, Pizzo SV, et al. Analysis of the plasma elimination kinetics and conformational stabilities of native, proteinase-complexed, and reactive site cleaved serpins: comparison of alpha 1–proteinase inhibitor, alpha 1–antichymotrypsin, antithrombin III, alpha 2–antiplasmin, angiotensinogen, and ovalbumin. Biochemistry 1991;30:1723–30.

[25] Bruch M, Weiss V, Engel J. Plasma serine proteinase inhibitors (serpins) exhibit major conformational changes and a large increase in conformational stability upon cleavage at their reactive sites. J Biol Chem 1988;263:16626–30.

[26] Batra PP, Sasa K, Ueki T, et al. Circular dichroic study of conformational changes in ovalbumin induced by modification of sulhydryl groups and disulfide reduction. J Protein Chem 1989;8:609–17.

[27] de Agostini A, Patston PA, Marottoli V, et al. A common neoepitope is created when the reactive center of C1-inhibitor is cleaved by plasma kallikrein, activated factor XII fragment, C1 esterase, or neutrophil elastase. J Clin Invest 1988;82:700–5.

[28] Nuijens JH, Huijbregts CCM, Eerenberg-Belmer AJM, et al. Quantification of plasma factor XIIa–C1-inhibitor and kallikrein–C1-inhibitor complexes in sepsis. Blood 1988;72:1841–8.

[29] Nuijens JH, Eerenberg-Belmer AJM, Huijbregts CCM, et al. Proteolytic inactivation of plasma C1 inhibitor in sepsis. J Clin Invest 1989;84:443–50.

[30] Huntington JA, Read RJ, Carrell RW. Structure of a serpin-protease complex shows inhibition by deformation. Nature 2000;407:923–6.

[31] Patston PA, Gettins P, Beechem J, et al. Mechanism of serpin action: evidence that C1 inhibitor functions as a suicide substrate. Biochemistry 1991;30:8876–82.

[32] Bos IGA, Hack CE, Abrahams JP. Structural and functional aspects of C1-inhibitor. Immunobiology 2002;205:518–33.

[33] Bock SC, Skriver K, Nielsen E, et al. Human C1 inhibitor: primary structure, cDNA cloning, and chromosomal localization. Biochemistry 1986;25:4292–301.

[34] Coutinho M, Aulak KS, Davis AE III. Functional analysis of the serpin domain of C1 inhibitor. J Immunol 1994;153:3648–54.

[35] Liu D, Gu X, Scafidi J, Davis AE III. N-linked glycosylation is required for C1 inhibitor–mediated protection from endotoxin shock in mice. Infect Immun 2004;72(4):1946–55.

[36] Liu D, Cramer CC, Scafidi J, Davis AE III. N-linked glycosylation at Asn3 and the positively charged residues within the amino terminal domain of C1 inhibitor are required for its interaction with Salmonella typhimurium lipopolysaccharide and lipid A. Infect Immun 2005;73:4478–87.

[37] Matsushita M, Endo Y, Fujita T. Cutting edge: complement-activating complex of ficolin and mannose-binding lectin-associated serine protease. J Immunol 2000;164:2281–4.

[38] Matsushita M, Thiel S, Jensenius JC, et al. Proteolytic activities of two types of mannose-binding lectin associated serine protease. J Immunol 2000;165:2637–42.

[39] Matsushita M, Endo Y, Hamasaki N, et al. Activation of the lectin complement pathway by ficolins. Int Immunopharmacol 2001;1:359–63.

[40] Ambrus G, Gal P, Kojima M, et al. Natural substrates and inhibitors of mannan-binding lectin-associated serine protease–1 and –2: a study on recombinant catalytic fragments. J Immunol 2003;170:1374–82.

[41] Jiang H, Wagner E, Zhang H, et al. Complement 1 inhibitor is a regulator of the alternative complement pathway. J Exp Med 2001;194:1609–16.

[42] Colman RW, Schmaier AH. Contact system: a vascular biology modulator with anticoagulant, profibrinolytic, antiadhesive, and proinflammatory attributes. Blood 1997;90:3819–43.

[43] Cochrane CG, Revak SD, Wuepper KD. Activation of Hageman factor in solid and fluid phases: a critical role of kallikrein. J Exp Med 1973;138:1564–83.

[44] Griffin JH. The role of surface in the surface-dependent activation of Hageman factor (blood coagulation factor XII). Proc Natl Acad Sci U S A 1978;75:1998–2002.

[45] Kaplan AP, Joseph K, Shibayama Y, et al. The intrinsic coagulation/kinin-forming cascade: assembly in plasma and cell surfaces in inflammation. Adv Immunol 1997;66:225–72.

[46] Kirby E, McDevitt PJ. The binding of bovine factor XII to kaolin. Blood 1983;61:652–9.

[47] Revak SD, Cochrane CG, Griffin JH. The binding and cleavage characteristics of human Hageman factor during contact activation: a comparison of normal plasma with plasma deficient in factor XI, prekallikrein or high molecular weight kininogen. J Clin Invest 1977;59:1167–75.

[48] Mahdi F, Shariat-Madar Z, Todd RF III, et al. Expression and co-localization of cytokeratin 1 and urokinase plasminogen activator receptor on endothelial cells. Blood 2001;97:2342–50.

[49] Joseph K, Ghebrehiwet B, Peerschke EIB, et al. Identification of the zinc-dependent endothelial cell binding protein for high molecular weight kininogen and factor XII: identity with the receptor that binds to the globular "heads" of C1q (gC1q-R). Proc Natl Acad Sci U S A 1996;93:8552–7.

[50] Joseph K, Kaplan AP. Formation of bradykinin: a major contributor to the innate inflammatory response. Adv Immunol 2005;86:159–208.

[51] Herwald H, Dedio J, Kellner R, et al. Isolation and characterization of the kininogen-binding protein p33 from endothelial cells. J Biol Chem 1996;271:13040–7.

[52] Colman RW, Pixley RA, Najamunnisa S, et al. Binding of high molecular weight kininogen to human endothelial cells is mediated via a site within domains 2 and 3 of the urokinase receptor. J Clin Invest 1997;100:1481–7.

[53] Hasan AAK, Zisman T, Schmaier AH. Identification of cytokeratin 1 as a binding protein and presentation receptor for kininogens on endothelial cells. Proc Natl Acad Sci U S A 1998;95:3615–20.

[54] Joseph K, Tholanikunnel BG, Kaplan AP. Activation of the bradykinin-forming cascade on endothelial cells: a role for heat shock protein 90. Int Immunopharmacol 2002;2:1851–9.

[55] Joseph K, Tholanikunnel BG, Kaplan AP. Heat shock protein 90 catalyzes activation of the prekallikrein-kininogen complex in the absence of factor XII. Proc Natl Acad Sci U S A 2002;99:896–900.

[56] Shariat-Madar Z, Mahdi F, Schmaier AH. Identification and characterization of prolylcarboxypeptidase as an endothelial cell prekallikrein activator. J Biol Chem 2002;277:17962–9.

[57] Shariat-Madar Z, Mahdi F, Schmaier AH. Assembly and activation of the plasma kallikrein/kinin system: a new interpretation. Int Immunopharmacol 2002;2:1841–9.

[58] Schmaier AH. The plasma kallikrein-kinin system counterbalances the renin-angiotensin system. J Clin Invest 2002;109:1007–9.

[59] Schmaier AH. The physiologic basis of assembly and activation of the plasma kallikrein/kinin system. Thromb Haemost 2004;91:1–3.

[60] Kramer J, Rosen F, Colten H, et al. Transinhibition of C1 inhibitor synthesis in type I hereditary angioneurotic edema. J Clin Invest 1993;91:1258–62.

[61] Ernst SC, Circolo A, Davis AE III, et al. Impaired production of both normal and mutant C1 inhibitor proteins in type I hereditary angioedema with a duplication in exon 8. J Immunol 1996;157:405–10.

[62] Brickman CM, Frank MM, Kaliner M. Urine-histamine levels in patients with hereditary angioedema (HAE). J Allergy Clin Immunol 1988;82:402–6.

[63] Colman RW. Activation of plasminogen by human plasma kallikrein. Biochem Biophys Res Commun 1969;35:273–9.

[64] Goldsmith GH, Saito H, Ratnoff OD. The activation of plasminogen by Hageman factor (factor XII) and Hageman factor fragments. J Clin Invest 1978;62:54–60.

[65] Revak SD, Cochrane CG, Bouma BN, et al. Surface and fluid-phase activities of two forms of activated Hageman factor produced during contact activation of plasma. J Exp Med 1978;147:719–29.

[66] Kaplan AP, Austen KF. A pre-albumin activator of prekallikrein. J Immunol 1970;105:802–11.

[67] Ghebrehiwet B, Silverberg M, Kaplan AP. Activation of the classical pathway of complement by Hageman factor fragment. J Exp Med 1981;153:655–76.

[68] Donaldson DD. Mechanisms of activation of C1 esterase in hereditary angioneurotic edema plasma in vitro. The role of Hageman factor, a clot-promoting agent. J Exp Med 1968;127:411–29.

[69] Heinz HP, Loos M. Activation of the first component of complement, C1: comparison of the effect of sixteen different enzymes on C1. Immunobiology 1983;165:175–85.

[70] Francis CW, Brenner B, Leddy JP, et al. Angioedema during therapy with recombinant tissue plasminogen activator. Br J Haematol 1991;77:562–3.

[71] Hoffmeister HM, Szabo S, Kastner C, et al. Thrombolytic therapy in acute myocardial infarction: comparison of procoagulant effects of streptokinase and alteplase regimens with focus on the kallikrein system and plasmin. Circulation 1998;98:2527–33.

[72] Molinaro G, Gervais N, Adam A. Biochemical basis of angioedema associated with recombinant tissue plasminogen activator treatment: an in vitro experimental approach. Stroke 2002;33:1712–6.

[73] Donaldson VH, Rosen FS. Action of complement in hereditary angioneurotic edema: the role of C'1 esterase. J Clin Invest 1964;43:2204–13.

[74] Carpenter CB, Ruddy S, Shehadeh IH, et al. Complement metabolism in man: hypercatabolism of the fourth (C4) and third (C3) components in patients with renal allograft rejection and hereditary angioedema (HAE). J Clin Invest 1969;48:1495–505.

[75] Austen KF, Sheffer AL. Detection of hereditary angioneurotic edema by demonstration of a profound reduction in the second component of human complement. N Engl J Med 1965;272:649–56.

[76] Quastel M, Harrison R, Cicardi M, et al. Behavior in vivo of normal and dysfunctional C1 inhibitor in normal subjects and patients with hereditary angioneurotic edema. J Clin Invest 1983;71:1041–6.

[77] Lachmann P, Rosen F. The catabolism of C1-inhibitor and the pathogenesis of hereditary angioedema. Acta Pathol Microbiol Immunol Scand 1984;284:35–9.

[78] Laurell AB, Lindegren J, Malmros I, et al. Enzymatic and immunochemical estimation of C1 esterase inhibitor in sera from patients with hereditary angioedema. Scand J Clin Lab Invest 1969;24:221–5.

[79] Laurell AB, Martensson U, Sjoholm AG. C1 subcomponent complexes in normal and pathological sera studied by crossed immunoelectrophoresis. Acta Pathol Microbiol Scand 1976;84:455–64.

[80] Donaldson VH, Ratnoff OD, Silva WDD, et al. Permeability-increasing activity in hereditary angioneurotic edema plasma. J Clin Invest 1969;48:642–53.

[81] Donaldson VH, Merler E, Rosen FS, et al. A polypeptide kinin in hereditary angioneurotic edema plasma: role of complement in its formation. J Lab Clin Med 1970;76:986.

[82] Donaldson VH. Kinin formation in hereditary angioneurotic edema (HANE) plasma. Int Arch Allergy Appl Immunol 1973;45:206–9.

[83] Davies GE, Lowe JS. A permeability factor released from guinea pig serum by antigen-antibody precipitates. Brit J Exp Pathol 1960;41:335–44.

[84] Klemperer MR, Donaldson VH, Rosen FS. Effect of C1 esterase on vascular permeability in man: studies in normal and complement-deficient individuals and in patients with hereditary angioneurotic edema. J Clin Invest 1968;47:604–11.

[85] Ratnoff OD, Lepow IH. Complement as a mediator of inflammation. Enhancement of vascular permeability by purified C'1 esterase. J Exp Med 1963;118:681–98.

[86] Davis AE III, Davis JS IV, Rabson AR, et al. Homozygous C3 deficiency: detection of C3 by radioimmunoassay. Clin Immunol Immunopathol 1977;8:543–50.

[87] Strang CJ, Auerbach KS, Rosen FS. C1s-induced vascular permeability in C2-deficient guinea pigs. J Immunol 1986;137:631–5.

[88] Strang C, Cholin S, Spragg J, et al. Angioedema induced by a peptide derived from complement component C2. J Exp Med 1988;168:1685–98.

[89] Donaldson V, Rosen F, Bing D. Role of the second component of complement (C2) and plasmin in kinin release in hereditary angioneurotic edema (H.A.N.E.). Trans Assoc Am Physicians 1977;90:174–83.

[90] Smith M, Kerr M. Cleavage of the second component of complement by plasma proteases: implications in hereditary C1-inhibitor deficiency. Immunology 1985;56:561–70.

[91] Curd JG, Prograis LJ Jr, Cochrane CG. Detection of active kallikrein in induced blister fluids of hereditary angioedema patients. J Exp Med 1980;152:742–7.

[92] Schapira M, Silver LD, Scott CF, et al. Prekallikrein activation and high-molecular-weight kininogen consumption in hereditary angioedema. N Engl J Med 1983;308:1050–3.

[93] Curd JG, Yelvington M, Burridge N, et al. Generation of bradykinin during incubation of hereditary angioedema plasma [abstract]. Mol Immunol 1982;19:1365.

[94] Fields T, Ghebrewihet B, Kaplan A. Kinin formation in hereditary angioedema plasma: evidence against kinin derivation from C2 and in support of spontaneous formation of bradykinin. J Allergy Clin Immunol 1983;72:54–60.

[95] Berrettini M, Lammle B, White T, et al. Detection of in vitro and in vivo cleavage of high molecular weight kininogen in human plasma by immunoblotting with monoclonal antibodies. Blood 1986;68:455–62.

[96] Lammle B, Zuraw BL, Heeb MJ, et al. Detection and quantitation of cleaved and uncleaved high molecular weight kininogen in plasma by ligand blotting with radiolabeled plasma prekallikrein or factor XI. Thromb Haemost 1988;59:151–61.

[97] Nielsen EW, Johansen HT, Hogasen K, et al. Activation of the complement, coagulation, fibrinolytic and kallikrein-kinin systems during attacks of hereditary angioedema. Scand J Immunol 1996;44:185–92.

[98] Cugno M, Cicardi M, Coppola R, et al. Activation of factor XII and cleavage of high molecular weight kininogen during acute attacks in hereditary and acquired C1-inhibitor deficiencies. Immunopharmacology 1996;33:361–4.

[99] Buhler R, Hovinga JK, Aebi-Huber I, et al. Improved detection of proteolytically cleaved high molecular weight kininogen by immunoblotting using an antiserum against its reduced 47 kDa light chain. Blood Coagul Fibrinolysis 1995;6:223–32.

[100] Shoemaker LR, Schurman SJ, Donaldson VH, et al. Hereditary angioneurotic edema: characterization of plasma kinin and vascular permeability–enhancing activities. Clin Exp Immunol 1994;95:22–8.

[101] Nussberger J, Cugno M, Amstutz C, et al. Plasma bradykinin in angio-oedema. Lancet 1998;351:1693–7.

[102] Wisnieski JJ, Knauss TC, Yike I, et al. Unique C1 inhibitor dysfunction in a kindred without angioedema. I. A mutant C1 inhibitor that inhibits C1s but not C1r. J Immunol 1994; 152:3199–209.

[103] Zahedi R, Bissler JJ, Davis AE III, et al. Unique C1 inhibitor dysfunction in a kindred without angioedema. II. Identification of an Ala443-Val substitution and functional analysis of the recombinant mutant protein. J Clin Invest 1995;95:1299–305.

[104] Zahedi R, Wisnieski J, Davis AE III. Role of the P2 residue of complement 1 inhibitor (Ala443) in determination of target protease specificity. J Immunol 1997;159:983–8.

[105] Zahedi R, MacFarlane RC, Wisnieski JJ, Davis AE III. C1 inhibitor: analysis of the role of amino acid residues within the reactive center loop in target protease recognition. J Immunol 2001;167:1500–6.

[106] Han ED, MacFarlane RC, Mulligan AN, et al. Increased vascular permeability in C1 inhibitor–deficient mice is mediated by the bradykinin type 2 receptor. J Clin Invest 2002;109: 1057–63.

[107] Agostini AD, Lijnen HR, Pixley RA, et al. Inactivation of factor XII active fragment in normal plasma. Predominant role of C1-inhibitor. J Clin Invest 1984;73:1542–9.

[108] Dyax Corporation; 2004. Available at: www.dyax.com. Accessed July 6, 2006.

[109] Jerini. Available at: www.jerini.com. Accessed July 6, 2006.

Self-administration of C1-inhibitor concentrate in patients with hereditary or acquired angioedema caused by C1-inhibitor deficiency

Marcel Levi, MD,[a] Goda Choi, MD,[a] Charles Picavet, MA,[b] and C. Erik Hack, MD[c]*

Amsterdam, The Netherlands

Background: Administration of C1-inhibitor concentrate is effective for prophylaxis and treatment of severe angioedema attacks caused by C1-inhibitor deficiency. The concentrate should be administered intravenously and hence needs to be administered by health care professionals, which might cause considerable delay in treatment and inconvenience for patients. Objective: The aim of this study was to investigate the feasibility, efficacy, and safety of on-demand and prophylactic self-administration of C1-inhibitor concentrate in patients with frequent attacks of angioedema.
Methods: Patients with hereditary or acquired C1-inhibitor deficiency who had very frequent angioedema attacks were trained to self-administer C1-inhibitor concentrate. The study consisted of 31 patients using on-demand treatment and 12 patients using prophylaxis with C1-inhibitor concentrate. Mean follow-up was 3.5 years.
Results: All patients were capable of self-administering the concentrate, with technical failure rates of self-injection being less than 2%. Times between the onset of the attack and the initiation of relief or complete resolution of symptoms in the on-demand group were significantly shortened (2.2 hours and 7.9 hours, respectively) compared with the situation before the start of self-administration. In the prophylaxis group self-administration of C1-inhibitor concentrate decreased the angioedema attack rate from 4.0 to 0.3 attacks per month.
Conclusion: Intravenous self-administration of C1-inhibitor concentrate is a feasible and safe option and results in more rapid and more effective treatment or prevention of severe angioedema attacks in patients with C1-inhibitor deficiency.
Clinical implications: Self-administration of C1-inhibitor concentrate could be a valuable and convenient treatment modality to prevent or treat angioedema attacks in patients with C1-inhibitor deficiency. (J Allergy Clin Immunol 2006;117:904-8.)

From [a]the Department of Internal Medicine, Academic Medical Center, University of Amsterdam; [b]The Netherlands Patient Association of Hereditary Angio-edema and Quincke's Edema; and [c]the Landsteiner Laboratory, Academic Medical Center, University of Amsterdam, and the Department of Clinical Chemistry, Free University Medical Center, Amsterdam.

*Dr Hack is currently affiliated with Crucell Holland BV, Leiden, The Netherlands.

Disclosure of potential conflict of interest: The authors have declared they have no conflict of interest.

Received for publication November 26, 2005; revised January 1, 2006; accepted for publication January 4, 2006.

Available online February 14, 2006.

Reprint requests: Marcel Levi, MD, Department of Medicine (F-4), Academic Medical Center, University of Amsterdam, Meibergdreef 9, 1105AZ Amsterdam, The Netherlands. E-mail: m.m.levi@amc.uva.nl.

0091-6749/$32.00

© 2006 American Academy of Allergy, Asthma and Immunology

doi:10.1016/j.jaci.2006.01.002

Key words: C1-inhibitor deficiency, C1-inhibitor concentrate, hereditary angioedema, acquired angioedema

Deficiency of C1-inhibitor leads to recurrent angioedema attacks and can be an incapacitating disorder that might even result in life-threatening situations.[1-4] The deficiency might be due to an inherited (autosomal dominant) or spontaneously occurring genetic defect. It also might be caused by an acquired condition, such as the formation of autoantibodies toward C1-inhibitor or the formation of anti-idiotype antibodies in patients with lymphoproliferative disease, leading to consumption of C1-inhibitor. The angioedema attacks might occur at various sites of the body (often the extremities), but in particular, angioedema attacks in the orofacial region and upper airways (leading to airway obstruction and the risk of asphyxia) and in the abdomen (leading to severe symptoms of pain and vomiting, mimicking an acute abdomen) require immediate medical attention. Angioedema attacks might be prevented by administration of androgenic steroids, such as danazol.[5] However, this agent is sometimes not well tolerated by women, apart from its adverse effects on blood lipids and the risk of liver tumors on long-term use.[6-8] Alternatively, administration of lysine analogues, such as ε aminocaproic acid or tranexamic acid, is in some, although not all, patients effective as a preventive strategy or in case of an (imminent) angioedema attack.[9,10] The most rational form of treatment, however, is administration of C1-inhibitor. Purified concentrates of C1-inhibitor derived from human plasma have been available for many years, are licensed in Europe and under study in the United States, and have shown to be effective in the treatment of severe angioedema attacks in patients with hereditary and acquired C1-inhibitor deficiency.[11-14] A limitation of this treatment is that it can only be administered by means of intravenous injection, which might result in dependency on emergency departments or general practitioners and hence in a considerable physician delay and inconvenience for the patient. Therefore the ability that patients could self-administer the C1-inhibitor concentrate might hypothetically result in earlier and therefore more effective treatment and increased patient independence and treatment satisfaction. The feasibility, efficacy, and safety of self-administration of C1-inhibitor concentrate has not been reported in the literature thus far. We here report our experience with the preventive or therapeutic self-administration of C1-inhibitor concentrate in patients with hereditary or acquired C1-inhibitor deficiency and frequently occurring severe attacks of angioedema.

Basic and clinical immunology

METHODS

Patients

The diagnosis of hereditary angioedema was based on the clinical presentation, with recurrent attacks of angioedema and a low functional level of C1-inhibitor (<0.5 U/mL, chromogenic assay; Dade Behring, Marburg Germany) and C4 (<100 mg/L, nephelometric assay; Sanquin, Amsterdam, the Netherlands) in plasma. A family history of C1-inhibitor deficiency was an additional (but optional) criterion to establish a diagnosis of hereditary angioedema. In addition, in the majority of patients, genetic analysis was performed, revealing a mutation in the C1-inhibitor gene. Acquired angioedema was diagnosed when the onset of the angioedema attacks occurred at an age of more than 25 years, when there were low levels of C1q (<80 IU/mL, nephelometric assay, Sanquin) in combination with the low levels of C1-inhibitor and C4 (as above), (optionally) when the presence of anti-C1-esterase inhibitor antibodies (by means of ELISA)[15] could be demonstrated, or (optionally) when a diagnosis of a lymphoproliferative disorder was made.

In this study 2 types of patients were included: (1) patients who, despite preventive medication regularly (>1 per 3 weeks), presented with severe angioedema attacks (see definition of severe attacks below) and therefore frequently required administration of C1-inhibitor concentrate (on-demand treatment) for an observation period of more than 2 years, and (2) patients who, despite preventive medication or without preventive medication because of intolerance, had very frequent attacks of angioedema (>1 per 10 days) and who were therefore eligible for prophylactic administration of C1-inhibitor concentrate (prophylactic treatment) for an observation period of longer than 1 year.

The study was approved by the institutional review board, and patients provided informed consent on inclusion in the study.

Treatment

Regular preventive treatment in patients with C1-inhibitor deficiency consisted of danazol (100-400 mg daily) alone or in combination with tranexamic acid (2-3 g/d) in case of (imminent) angioedema attacks. When danazol was not tolerated, tranexamic acid was administered as prophylactic treatment on a daily basis. If, despite this treatment, a severe angioedema attack occurred, patients were treated with intravenous administration of 1000 U of plasma-derived C1-inhibitor concentrate (Cetor; Sanquin, Amsterdam, The Netherlands). C1-inhibitor is a highly purified product that is prepared from screened volunteer donor plasma from which the cryoprecipitate and prothrombin complex factors are removed. C1-inhibitor is obtained from the plasma through ion exchange chromatography and subsequent polyethylene glycol precipitation of the eluate. The C1-esterase inhibitor concentrate obtained is pasteurized in solution (10 hours at 60°C). The elimination half-life of this C1-inhibitor concentrate in patients with hereditary angioedema was shown to be 48 hours after a single intravenous administration of 1000 U in previous studies. These studies indicated that with a dose of 1000 U, patients would have an increase in plasma levels of greater than 0.3 U/mL for at least 4 days, which is thought to be sufficient to treat or prevent angioedema attacks. On the basis of this elimination half-life, patients eligible for prophylactic C1-inhibitor were assigned to a regimen of administration of C1-inhibitor concentrate every 5 to 7 days.

Self-administration of C1-inhibitor was done after extensive education of patients. This included additional background information on the disease and its treatment, the indications for administration of C1-inhibitor concentrate, and the requirement of proper documentation of symptoms and administration of the agent. Although the administration of C1-inhibitor has never been reported to cause allergic responses thus far, patients were nevertheless instructed how to handle such a reaction in case it might occur. Furthermore, patients were educated on how to prepare the lyophilized medication with sterile water for injection (total volume of 10 mL after reconstitution) and how to properly work with syringes and needles. Subsequently, patients were taught how to perform a self-venipuncture with a butterfly needle (mostly in an antecubital vein). Education on self-treatment consisted of 2 or 3 individual sessions of 1 hour each performed by a physician or a nurse specialized in intravenous self-administration of medical agents.

Outcome

A severe attack of angioedema was defined as an attack of angioedema in the orofacial region or in the upper airway or a serious abdominal attack (severe abdominal pain with nausea and vomiting). Other attacks, such as swelling of the extremities or angioedema in the genitourinary region, were recorded as less severe angioedema attacks.

Patients receiving on-demand treatment were asked to record the time from the onset of a severe angioedema attack to the time they received the intravenous injection of C1-inhibitor concentrate (attack-to-treatment time). Also, the time to improvement of symptoms, as well as the time to complete resolution of symptoms, was recorded.[13] As a control, patients reported on their regular attack-to-treatment time and time to improvement and resolution of symptoms at the 5 previous occasions of severe angioedema before they started with self-administration of the C1-inhibitor concentrate. This information was requested at the beginning of self-administration and again at the end of the follow-up period to minimize recall bias. In addition, 10 patients with angioedema caused by C1-inhibitor deficiency who were not participating in the self-administration program served as additional control subjects.

The mean follow-up of patients in the on-demand group was 3.8 years (range, 0.9-5.1 years), and the mean follow-up in the prophylaxis group was 3.5 years (range, 1.6-4.3 years).

Statistical analysis

Data are presented as means ± SD. Statistical analysis was performed by means of Kaplan-Meier survival analysis with a log-rank test and the Mann-Whitney U test. A P value of less than .05 was considered statistically significant.

RESULTS

Study population

The on-demand group consisted of 31 patients, 28 with hereditary C1-inhibitor deficiency and 3 with acquired C1-inhibitor deficiency. The prophylaxis group included 10 patients with hereditary C1-inhibitor deficiency and 2 patients with acquired C1-inhibitor deficiency (total of 12 patients). Five of the 12 patients in the prophylaxis group had very frequent (>1 per 10 days) angioedema attacks despite full treatment with danazol and tranexamic acid and were therefore considered for C1-inhibitor concentrate prophylaxis. The other 7 patients did not receive danazol because of intolerable virilization effects in women (n = 5), severe dyslipidemia in a patient with a history of cardiovascular disease (n = 1), and nonspecific side effects (n = 1). In these patients prophylaxis was started because all of them had very frequent (>1 per 10 days) angioedema attacks. Clinical characteristics of patients in both groups are given in Table I.

TABLE I. Characteristics of patients on on-demand treatment and prophylaxis with C1-inhibitor concentrate

	On-demand treatment	Prophylaxis
Total	31	12
Hereditary C1-inhibitor deficiency	28	10
Acquired C1-inhibitor deficiency	3	2
Age, y (±SD)	43 ± 8	38 ± 12
M/F ratio	14/17	4/8
Years from diagnosis (±SD)	24 ± 4	22 ± 7
Frequency of severe attacks (±SD)*	1 per 16.6 (± 4.1) days	1 per 7.9 (± 2.0) days
Site of attacks		
Orofacial	15%	18%
Laryngeal	2%	1%
Abdominal	31%	37%
Genitourinary	8%	10%
Extremities	44%	34%
Medication		
Danazol	94%	58%
Tranexamic acid	16%	50%

*During an observation period of at least 1 year.

Feasibility of self-administration of C1-inhibitor concentrate

All patients in both groups completed the education and instruction program without problems. All patients were capable of performing the self-venipuncture and self-injection of C1-inhibitor. They all kept adequate records, including the date of self-administration of C1-inhibitor concentrate, the reason for the injection, the lot number of the concentrate used, and any adverse effects. During the follow-up period, in the on-demand group a mean number of 21.4 ± 5.3 injections were self-administered per patient, with a reported mean technical failure rate of 1.8% (range, 0% to 5.7%) per patient. In the prophylaxis group the mean number of injections per patient during the follow-up period was 185.3 ± 28.4, with a reported mean technical failure rate of 0.8% (range, 0% to 3.1%) per patient.

Efficacy of self-administration of C1-inhibitor concentrate in the on-demand and prophylaxis groups

The time between the onset of a severe attack and the self-administration of C1-inhibitor (attack-to-treatment time) was 1.4 ± 1.0 hours compared with 3.4 ± 2.1 hours before the start of the self-administration when patients relied on medical professionals for administration (P = .01). As shown in Fig 1, the time to improvement of symptoms and complete resolution of symptoms after the onset of a severe angioedema attack was proportionally shorter after self-administration compared with during the historical control period. Fig 2 shows the mean time to initiation of relief and complete resolution of symptoms for patients with hereditary and acquired C1-inhibitor deficiency, respectively. Interestingly, the time to complete resolution

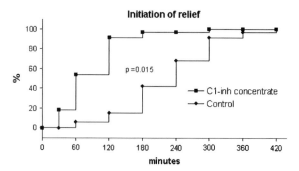

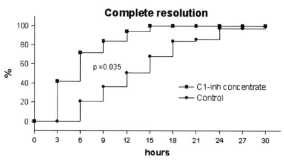

FIG 1. Effect of self-administration of C1-inhibitor *(C1-inh)* concentrate on the initiation of relief and the complete resolution of symptoms after the onset of the angioedema attack. *Controls* refers to historical control subjects before the start of self-administration of C1-inhibitor concentrate.

of angioedema from the start of an attack was markedly more reduced (5.9 ± 2.2 hours in self-treated patients compared with 13.8 ± 2.9 hours in patients after conventional treatment) than could be explained by the earlier administration of C1-inhibitor concentrate. There were no significant differences between patients with hereditary C1-inhibitor deficiency and patients with acquired C1-inhibitor deficiency regarding clinical responses to C1-inhibitor. Data from the historical control period were virtually identical with data from the 10 control patients who did not participate in the self-administration program (mean time to initiation of relief in historical control subjects of 171 minutes vs 185 minutes in control subjects and mean time to complete resolution in historical control subjects of 13.8 hours vs 14.3 hours in control subjects). In the prophylaxis group the number of angioedema attacks was dramatically reduced after the start of prophylaxis, both in patients with hereditary C1-inhibitor deficiency and in patients with acquired C1-inhibitor deficiency (Fig 3). The mean interval between 2 prophylactic injections was 6.8 ± 1.0 days. Seven (58%) of 12 patients were completely free of angioedema attacks after the start of prophylaxis, whereas 5 patients had occasional angioedema attacks despite prophylaxis but not more frequently than once per 6 months (3 patients [25%]) or once per 3 months (2 patients [17%]). Mean peak plasma levels of C1-inhibitor after the intravenous administration of 1000 U of C1-inhibitor concentrate were 1.1 ± 0.2 U/mL. At 48 hours after the administration, plasma levels were 0.7 ± 0.2 U/mL, and at 5 days after the administration, C1-inhibitor levels were 0.3 ± 0.1 U/mL. In case of a severe angioedema attack

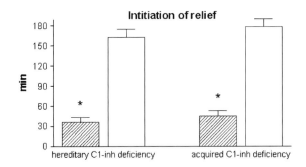

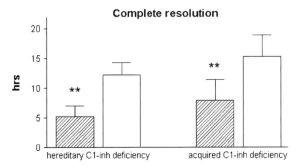

FIG 2. Mean time to initiation of relief and complete resolution of symptoms in patients with hereditary and acquired deficiency of C1-inhibitor *(C1-inh)* after the onset of the angioedema attack when patients self-administer C1-inhibitor concentrate *(striped bars)* compared with the situation before they started self-management *(open bars)*. Mean values and SDs are given. *$P < .01$, **$P < .05$.

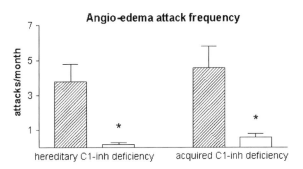

FIG 3. Frequency of angioedema attacks per month after initiation of prophylaxis with C1-inhibitor *(C1-inh)* concentrate *(striped bars)* compared with the situation before the start of prophylaxis in patients *(open bars)* with hereditary and acquired C1-inhibitor deficiency. Mean values and SDs are given. *$P < .001$.

during the prophylaxis period, patients used additional C1-inhibitor concentrate, which was successful in all instances. There was no need to seek medical attention for any of these episodes during the follow-up period. Patients with acquired C1-inhibitor deficiency had similar results as patients with hereditary deficiency, and in this series there were no indications that patients with acquired C1-inhibitor deficiency required more frequent injections or higher doses over time (although the number of patients with acquired angioedema was small).

Safety

No serious adverse events occurred with self-administration of C1-inhibitor during the follow-up period. Recorded adverse events included skin irritation at the site of injection (2.1% of injections), minor hematomas at the puncture site (1.6% of injections), dizziness at the time of injection (0.3% of injections), mild pain in the extremities after the injection (0.3% of injections), and a subfebrile increase in temperature (0.1% of injections). All adverse events were self-limiting and did not result in the need to seek medical assistance.

DISCUSSION

Hereditary or acquired C1-inhibitor deficiency results in angioedema attacks with important clinical consequences, depending on their localization and severity.[1] Apart from the morbidity caused by these attacks and the risk that a life-threatening situation will occur, patients suffer from the unpredictable nature of the disease and the dependence of medical facilities when they need intravenous treatment with C1-inhibitor. This might lead to unnecessary delays before appropriate treatment is instituted. Here we show that after a short education and training program, on-demand self-administration of C1-inhibitor concentrate is a feasible option in patients who have frequent, serious angioedema attacks. Patients are shown to be capable of self-administering the intravenous medication without technical problems or medical complications. The observation that patients are capable of self-administration of intravenous medication is reminiscent of the experience in other conditions, such as intravenous self-administration of clotting factor concentrates in patients with hemophilia.[16]

In patients with on-demand treatment, self-administration resulted in a decreased time between the onset of the attack and the administration of C1-inhibitor concentrate. Consequently, the time between the onset of the attack and the initial relief of symptoms was proportionally decreased. Unexpectedly, however, the time to complete disappearance of symptoms was much more reduced than could be expected on the basis of the earlier treatment of the patients, suggesting that early C1-inhibitor treatment during an angioedema attack more efficiently shortens the duration and reduces the severity of the attack.

Self-administration of C1-inhibitor concentrate also facilitates the use of this treatment as prophylaxis in patients with very frequent angioedema attacks despite full treatment with first-line drugs to prevent angioedema attacks (eg, the administration of danazol and tranexamic acid) or in patients who do not tolerate full first-line prophylaxis. These patients self-administered C1-inhibitor concentrate about once every week, resulting in a virtual elimination of angioedema attacks. In view of the half-life of C1-inhibitor of about 48 hours, the observation that approximately once-weekly prophylactic administration appears to be effective in almost completely preventing angioedema attacks in these patients confirms the notion that for prevention of attacks, subphysiologic levels of C1-inhibitor (as low as 40% of normal levels) are

Basic and clinical immunology

sufficient. The virtual lack of any angioedema attacks with the dosing schedule of once per 5 to 7 days might indicate that larger dosing intervals, with consequently less consumption of C1-inhibitor concentrate, might be possible, although this remains to be studied.

We did not formally assess sequential quality-of-life issues in our cohorts of patients. However, from previous studies, it is clear that the unpredictability of the disease and the dependence on physicians and others to receive timely and adequate treatment is a serious concern for patients with C1-inhibitor deficiency.[17] In addition, social issues, such as absence from work or school, might become seriously distressing as well. We speculate that self-administration of C1-inhibitor concentrate might be helpful in diminishing these worries and issues that might affect the quality of life in patients with C1-inhibitor deficiency.

Obviously, there are also some limitations associated with the use of C1-inhibitor concentrate in general and potential hazards of self-administration by patients. C1-inhibitor concentrate is a plasma-derived product and therefore carries the risk of transmission of blood-borne infections.[18] Although proper microorganism-reducing steps, such as careful donor selection and screening, heat treatment and, more recently, nanofiltration of the product, in addition to other measures, at present minimize the risk of transmission of infectious agents, the use of blood-derived products should in general be restricted as much as possible. This requirement was part of our education for patients, who, as a rule, actually did not need much encouragement to use as little as possible of this blood product. Our initial theoretic fear that self-administration of C1-inhibitor could result in overconsumption of the concentrate (eg, being used also for less severe but still annoying attacks) was not justified in our study. From the documentation of the patients receiving self-administration (discussed every 3-6 months during their visit at the outpatient clinic), it was clear that patients strictly adhered to the predefined indications for use of C1-inhibitor concentrate.

In conclusion, intravenous self-administration of C1-inhibitor concentrate is a feasible option for patients who frequently need this treatment and results in more rapid and potentially therefore more effective treatment of severe angioedema attacks in patients with C1-inhibitor deficiency. In addition, self-administration might facilitate prophylactic treatment schemes in patients with very frequent angioedema attacks if other options are insufficiently effective.

REFERENCES

1. Agostoni A, Cicardi M. Hereditary and acquired C1-inhibitor deficiency: biological and clinical characteristics in 235 patients. Medicine 1992;71: 206-15.
2. Cicardi M, Bergamaschini L, Cugno M, Beretta A, Zingale LC, Colombo M, et al. Pathogenetic and clinical aspects of C1 inhibitor deficiency. Immunobiology 1998;199:366-76.
3. Davis AE III. The pathophysiology of hereditary angioedema. Clin Immunol 2005;114:3-9.
4. Kaplan AP. C1 inhibitor deficiency: hereditary and acquired forms. J Investig Allergol Clin Immunol 2001;11:211-9.
5. Gelfand JA, Sherins RJ, Alling DW, Frank MM. Treatment of hereditary angioedema with danazol. Reversal of clinical and biochemical abnormalities. N Engl J Med 1976;295:1444-8.
6. Agostoni A, Aygoren-Pursun E, Binkley KE, Blanch A, Bork K, Bouillet L, et al. Hereditary and acquired angioedema: problems and progress: proceedings of the third C1 esterase inhibitor deficiency workshop and beyond. J Allergy Clin Immunol 2004;114(suppl):S51-131.
7. Bork K, Schneiders V. Danazol-induced hepatocellular adenoma in patients with hereditary angio-oedema. J Hepatol 2002;36:707-9.
8. Szeplaki G, Varga L, Valentin S, Kleiber M, Karadi I, Romics L, et al. Adverse effects of danazol prophylaxis on the lipid profiles of patients with hereditary angioedema. J Allergy Clin Immunol 2005; 115:864-9.
9. Frank MM, Sergent JS, Kane MA, Alling DW. Epsilon aminocaproic acid therapy of hereditary angioneurotic edema. A double-blind study. N Engl J Med 1972;286:808-12.
10. Cugno M, Cicardi M, Agostoni A. Activation of the contact system and fibrinolysis in autoimmune acquired angioedema: a rationale for prophylactic use of tranexamic acid. J Allergy Clin Immunol 1994;93: 870-6.
11. Gadek JE, Hosea SW, Gelfand JA, Santaella M, Wickerhauser M, Triantaphyllopoulos DC, et al. Replacement therapy in hereditary angioedema: successful treatment of acute episodes of angioedema with partly purified C1 inhibitor. N Engl J Med 1980;302:542-6.
12. Waytes AT, Rosen FS, Frank MM. Treatment of hereditary angioedema with a vapor-heated C1 inhibitor concentrate. N Engl J Med 1996;334: 1630-4.
13. Bork K, Barnstedt SE. Treatment of 193 episodes of laryngeal edema with C1 inhibitor concentrate in patients with hereditary angioedema. Arch Intern Med 2001;161:714-8.
14. Kunschak M, Engl W, Maritsch F, Rosen FS, Eder G, Zerlauth G, et al. A randomized, controlled trial to study the efficacy and safety of C1 inhibitor concentrate in treating hereditary angioedema. Transfusion 1998; 38:540-9.
15. Hack CE. C1-inhibitor: antigenic and functional analysis. Methods Mol Biol 2000;150:159-72.
16. Teitel JM, Bauer KA, Lau HK, Rosenberg RD. Studies of the prothrombin activation pathway utilizing radioimmunoassays for the F2/ F1 + 2 fragment and thrombin-antithrombin complex. Blood 1982; 59:1086-97.
17. Farkas H, Harmat G, Fust G, Varga L, Visy B. Clinical management of hereditary angio-oedema in children. Pediatr Allergy Immunol 2002;13: 153-61.
18. Cicardi M, Mannucci PM, Castelli R, Rumi MG, Agostoni A. Reduction in transmission of hepatitis C after the introduction of a heat-treatment step in the production of C1-inhibitor concentrate. Transfusion 1995; 35:209-12.

Best Practice & Research Clinical Haematology
Vol. 19, No. 1, pp. 205–242, 2006
doi:10.1016/j.beha.2005.04.001
available online at http://www.sciencedirect.com

ELSEVIER

14

Pathogen inactivation techniques [☆]

J.P.R. Pelletier MD

Lieutenant Colonel USAF, MC, FS

S. Transue MD

Transfusion Medicine Fellow

E.L. Snyder* MD

Transfusion Medicine Fellow

Department of Transfusion Medicine, Yale University School of Medicine, Yale-New Haven Hospital, New Haven, CT 06510-3202, USA

The desire to rid the blood supply of pathogens of all types has led to the development of many technologies aimed at the same goal—eradication of the pathogen(s) without harming the blood cells or generating toxic chemical agents. This is a very ambitious goal, and one that has yet to be achieved. One approach is to shun the 'one size fits all' concept and to target pathogen-reduction agents at the Individual component types. This permits the development of technologies that might be compatible with, for example, plasma products but that would be cytocidal and thus incompatible with platelet concentrates or red blood cell units. The technologies to be discussed include solvent detergent and methylene blue treatments—designed to inactivate plasma components and derivatives; psoralens (S-59—amotosalen) designed to pathogen-reduce units of platelets; and two products aimed at red blood cells, S-303 (a Frale—frangible anchor-linker effector compound) and Inactine (a binary ethyleneimine). A final pathogen-reduction material that might actually allow one material to inactivate all three blood components—riboflavin (vitamin B2)—is also under development.

The sites of action of the amotosalen (S-59), the S-303 Frale, Inactine, and riboflavin are all localized in the nucleic acid part of the pathogen. Solvent detergent materials act by dissolving the plasma envelope, thus compromising the integrity of the pathogen membrane and rendering it non-infectious. By disrupting the pathogen's ability to replicate or survive, its infectivity is removed. The degree to which bacteria and viruses are affected by a particular pathogen-reducing technology relates to its Gram-positive or Gram-negative status, to the sporulation characteristics for bacteria, and the presence of lipid or protein envelopes for viruses.

Concerns related to photoproducts and other breakdown products of these technologies remain, and the toxicology of pathogen-reduction treatments is a major ongoing area of investigation.

[☆] The views expressed in this article are those of the author and do not reflect the official policy or position of the United States Air Force, Department of Defense, or the US Government.

* Corresponding author. Tel.: +1 203 688 2441; Fax: +1 203 688 2748.
  E-mail address: edward.snyder@yale.edu (E.L. Snyder).

Clearly, regulatory agencies have a major role to play in the evaluation of these new technologies. This chapter will cover the several types of pathogen-reduction systems, mechanisms of action, the inactivation efficacy for specific types of pathogens, toxicology of the various systems and the published research and clinical trial data supporting their potential usefulness. Due to the nature of the field, pathogen reduction is a work in progress and this review should be considered as a snapshot in time rather than a clear picture of what the future will bring.

Key words: amotosalen; binary ethyleneimine; Frale; INTERCEPT blood system; methylene blue; pathogen reduction; PEN110; psoralen; riboflavin; S-303; S-59; solvent detergent; transfusion-associated graft versus host disease; transfusion-transmitted disease; Triton X-100; Uniplas®; vitamin B2.

The problem of blood-borne disease transmission has been a concern since the earliest days of transfusion. Bacterial contamination was the impetus for the development of the closed system collection method by Walter and Murphy in 1952; and eventually led to established storage practices. In 1943, Paul Beeson described post-transfusion hepatitis; this was later recognized as being due to transmission of viral hepatitis A, B (HAV, HBV), and later non-A non-B (hepatitis C; HCV). In 1944, Cohn and co-workers pasteurized 25% albumin to remove viral hepatitis. As early as 1963, the connection between paid donors and disease transmission became evident and, 10 years later, National Blood Policy promulgated that blood donors be derived from a pool of voluntary donors.

Despite the risk of hepatitis, the number of transfusions per year continued to rise. The recognition of human immunodeficiency virus (HIV) as transmissible by transfusion in the 1980s resulted in a plateau of the number of transfusions per year, and this persisted through the mid-1990s.

The specter of acquired immunodeficiency syndrome (AIDS) induced widespread fear and led to many changes. Some of these changes included more judicious blood use, the use of autologous units when possible, a more rigorous donor interviewing process, improved arm preparation techniques, removal of the first aliquot (first aliquot diversion), improved serologic and nucleic acid testing of blood components, and—in some countries—the use of pathogen-reduction or eradication techniques.[1,2] Even though the blood supply in industrialized countries is now considered to be very safe, concerns regarding transmission of existing, as well as emerging, transfusion-related pathogens still exist. A number of less threatening, although still troublesome, pathogens are also known to be transmissible by blood but are currently not tested, mainly because of prevalence and—sometimes—cost.[3] These include pathogens *Babesia*, *Erlichia*, parvovirus, cytomegalovirus (CMV), and enteroviruses.[4] Some of these pathogens do not cause disease, or cause disease only in immune-compromised patients. The recent identification and outbreaks of severe acute respiratory syndrome (SARS) and West Nile Virus (WNV) have reinforced this fear and the need to develop new ways of removing or inactivating blood-borne pathogens.

Currently, the risks for viral infection from transfusion is now reported to be[3,5–16]:

- 1:2 135 000 for HIV 1 and HIV 2
- 1:138 700 to 233 000 for HBV
- 1:1 935 000 for HCV
- 1:2 500 000 for human T lymphotropic virus 1 (HTLV 1) and HTLV 2 (after serologic and molecular testing are performed)
- 1:1 000 000 HAV

- 1:300 to 1:10 000 for parvovirus B19
- 1:50 for hepatitis G virus (single-strand RNA-enveloped virus)
- 1:250 for CMV in unfiltered blood
- Prior to nucleic acid testing (NAT), the risk for WNV was 1:833; this risk is expected to decrease with NAT testing.

Other viruses known to be transmitted by transfusion, but with less or unknown clinical significance include: transfusion-transmitted virus (TTV) (a non-enveloped single-strand DNA virus) and SEN-V (a non-enveloped single-strand DNA virus involved in 83% of non-A—E hepatitis). Wide prevalence of these viruses has been demonstrated in donor populations.[17] The risk for bacterial infection is 1:30 000 red blood cell (RBC) units or 1:1500–3000 for random-donor whole blood or apheresis platelet units. Two technologies are Food and Drug Administration (FDA) approved for bacterial screening of platelet units, although not all bacterial contamination is thought to be eliminated by such screening. Seroprevalence of the parasite *Trypanosoma cruzi* is estimated at 1:7500–33 000, and *Babesia microti* is estimated at levels at 1:100. Transmission levels vary depending on the donor population. Risks for leishmaniasis and toxoplasma are unknown.[17] Although the overall risk is low, significant risk of transfusion-transmitted infection remains. Emerging pathogens and as yet unknown future pathogens for which no screening tests exist might contaminate blood components. However, a new tier of protection—pathogen-reduction (PR) technology—is being developed to further decrease risks.[4] Thus, the development of pathogen-reduction and inactivation technologies have been avidly pursued over the last 10–15 years.[4]

IDEAL QUALITIES OF PATHOGEN-REDUCTION AGENTS

Pathogen reduction (PR) or pathogen inactivation (PI) is the use of a process that inactivates or removes a virus, bacteria, fungus, or protozoan pathogen from the product. Some criteria for these methods have been delineated by the FDA. The methods used should remove or inactivate pathogens, including emerging pathogens, without damaging the function or longevity of the blood product. In addition, any chemicals used and the resulting complexes must be demonstrated as non-toxic and non-immunogenic. Any risks of the altered products must be less than the risk of acquiring disease from unaltered products. An ideal PR agent does not currently exist.[2,18]

Pathogen-reduction chemicals have multiple sites of actions. Cross-linking of lipids in cellular membranes and organelles are one type. PR techniques interacting with proteins can cause cellular signal transduction mistakes, respiratory pathway deficiencies, or structural abnormalities. Chemical binding to nucleic acids or intercalating nucleic acid chains can lead to errors in transcription, translation, or replication.[2]

SHORTCOMINGS OF PATHOGEN-REDUCTION TECHNOLOGIES

The PR process or technique could cause damage to the components, resulting in a decreased in vivo lifespan of red cells or platelets or a decrease in coagulation proteins in fresh frozen plasma (FFP). Toxicities remain a concern. Even after passing through phase III trials, toxicity might not be revealed until large-scale exposure is seen.[2] Accordingly, phase IV post-marketing studies will be required when PR technology is FDA licensed.

METHODS OF EVALUATION

Evaluations of PR methods need to be performed early in product and process development. Models for in vitro testing of viruses, bacteria, and parasites also need to develop in a timely fashion. Ideally, at least a 6–10 $\log_{10}$ reduction in pathogen load is suggested to be an acceptable level of efficacy for the methodology. Peak viral load in the window period, however can be as high as 10^8–10^{14} units per milliliter. These high viral loads might prevent reduction of pathogen load to a level that does not transmit infection.[2]

Phase III trials demonstrating clinical efficiency can be clinically difficult. Many factors decrease phase III trial assessment feasibility: First, too large a study population might be necessary to see a statistical or clinical difference. Since the initiation of NAT assays, even larger cohorts are required to find additional benefits of PR above those achieved with testing alone because the risks of contamination with the current methods of testing are so small. Second, PR techniques are not applied to all blood products (i.e. cryoprecipitate) given to patients. Third, and epidemiologically, multiple transmission routes/vectors are present by which patients acquire infections making it difficult to prove the infection came from blood; therefore, reliance on phase IV or surveillance of use is required to evaluate for subtle risks and marginal benefits.[2]

Elimination of compounds that clearly damage labile blood components is necessary when evaluating PR procedures. Gross hemolysis ($> 1\%$), platelet dysfunction, and a $> 30\%$ reduction in coagulation factor activity are problems to be avoided. Subtle damage is more difficult to assess. Radiolabeling cells for autologous transfusions and monitoring survival or recovery can be used to evaluate clinical efficacy. Clinically, bleeding time is inadequate to assess platelet function, and delivery of oxygen to tissues is inadequate to assess red cell function after treatments with this technique.[2] The FDA currently favors a clinical assessment of bleeding using the WHO criteria.

The challenge of PR technologies is to continue or increase benefit as threat levels decrease. As techniques in donor selection, collection processes, screening test methodologies, and detection limits are improved, additional benefit from the use of PR techniques decreases. The risks to the recipients decrease as pathogen reduction increases, with development of less toxic and more efficient techniques. More benefit is apparent when new transfusion-transmissible pathogens emerge (SARS, Ebola virus). As PR technologies are developed, however, the likelihood of replacing pathogen-screening tests is not expected nor anticipated. Rather, such technologies should complement existing protocols.[2]

Numerous methods have been cultivated and are in various stages of development and use. Solvent detergent pathogen reduction of plasma is the most widely studied methodology and is currently in use across Europe. Other methods include photosensitizing chemicals that interact with pathogen DNA and/or RNA and cross-link following exposure to UVA or visible light, thus inactivating the nucleic acids. Alkylating agents and ethyleneimines are PR technologies that also cross-link nucleic acids but do not require light for activation.[19] An interesting side benefit of these technologies is that white cells are also inactivated, thus potentially eliminating the risk of transfusion-associated graft-versus-host disease (TA-GVHD). This chapter will discuss the more recent developments and address those technologies either in use or likely to be used in the near future.

THE SOLVENT DETERGENT PROCESS

Mechanism of action

Solvent detergent (SD) treatment disrupts the membranes of enveloped virus, bacteria, and eukaryotes. Infectivity is lost via this action. Many combinations of tri-(n-butyl)-phosphate (TNBP) or ethyl ether (organic solvents) with Tween 80, sodium cholate, and Triton X-100 (non-ionic detergents) have been used in the past. The SD combination most often used now is TNBP with Triton X-100. Because the chemical reaction is non-selective, the agents must be removed before the final product is transfused.[20,21]

Molecular biology

The molecular structure of TNBP is shown in Figure 1. This compound acts as an organic solvent and removes lipids during SD processing by extracting and sequestering them into a separate micellar (colloidal) phase.[22]

The molecular structure of polyoxyethelene-p-t-octylphenol (Triton X-100) is shown in Figure 2. This non-ionic detergent disrupts lipid bilayers for easier extraction and stabilizes TNBP.[22]

History

SD viral inactivation technologies were first licensed for treatment of clotting factor concentrates in 1985.[23,24] Before 1984, a combination of ethyl ether (20%) and Tween 80 (1%) were found effective in inactivating HBV and NANBHV in factor VIII and IX concentrates with minimal loss in activity.[25] In 1986, TNBP and 0.2% sodium cholate were shown to be effective at inactivating HBV, NANBHV, and HIV.

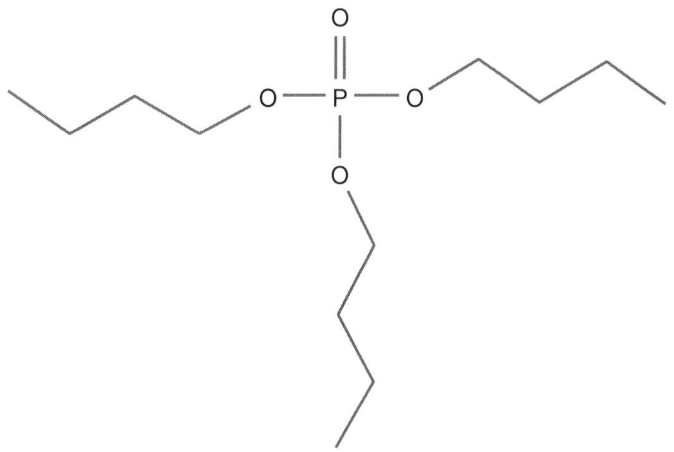

Figure 1. Molecular structure of tri-(n-butyl)-phosphate (TNBP). From Delipidation treatments for large scale protein purification process (from ref. 22).

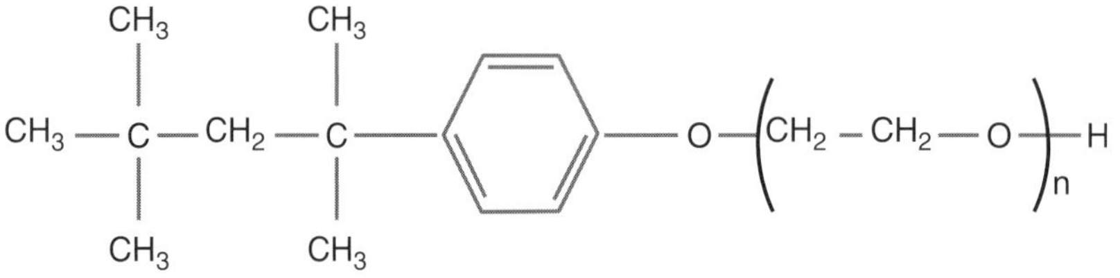

Figure 2. Partial molecular structure of Triton X-100 (from ref. 22).

SD technology was first developed in 1987–1988. Use of SD treatment was shown to effect a $6 \log_{10}$ viral load reduction in spiked samples. The SD-treated plasma coagulation factor profile was similar to untreated FFP. Removal of additives occurred at a 99.97% efficiency. During the period from 1991 to 1995, approximately 2×10^6 units of solvent detergent fresh frozen plasma (SD-FFP) were transfused without significant adverse sequelae. SD-FFP has been used in Germany, Switzerland, Austria, Belgium, France, the Netherlands, and Norway since the early 1990s. Initial tests from 1990 to 1992 used TNBP (1% organic solvent) and Triton X-100 (1% non-ionic detergent) to treat blood products. These additives were incubated with plasma for 4 hours at 30 °C. The pathogen reduction achieved was a $> 6 \log_{10}$ reduction of HBV, $> 5 \log_{10}$ reduction of HCV, and $> 6 \log_{10}$ reduction of HIV. In France, 1% TNBP and 1% octoxynol 9 were evaluated as PR agents and were found to have similar coagulation factor activities compared to untreated FFP. In some countries in Europe, SD-FFP completely replaced conventional FFP. No systemic mutagenic or reproductive abnormalities have been noted.[24,25]

The uses of SD-treated products from 1985 to 1997 have been wide and varied. Product use of this technology includes commercial factor VIII concentrates, factor IX concentrates, prothrombin complex, commercial factor VII, fibrinogen, protein C, factor XI, antithrombin III, fibrin glue, IM-Ig, IV-Ig, anti-D IgG, HBV-Ig, CMV-Ig, RSV-Ig, anti-tetanus, monoclonal antibody used in the treatment of malignancies, prothrombin complex, and plasma.[24] 'Double virus elimination' procedures have been developed to decrease the risk of transmission of HAV. These procedures involve the use of monoclonal antibody affinity, chromatography, nano-filtration, heat, or ultraviolet light in combination with solvent detergent.[24,25]

SD procedures, however, were discovered to be ineffective against non-enveloped viruses. In the US, development costs of SD plasma were never fully recovered because only 15% of the hospital market was using the product at peak usage. The reported occurrence of thrombosis and/or hemorrhage with use of SD-FFP in liver transplant patients markedly decreased usage in the US.[26] Cost, risks, and administrative problems caused further declines in use of SD-FFP in the US. Fewer risks were noted in Europe, and use there continues. Indeed, SD technologies are the most widely used virucidal methods in the world. Before 1998, 35×10^6 doses of SD-treated products had been given. Even though SD plasma continues to be a licensed product in the US, the last lot was made in 2001 and is available only in Europe.[24–28] Extensive studies for neonates, infants, and pregnant women are yet to be reported.

Treatment of labile blood products using SD technology

Many steps are required for the manufacture of SD-FFP. Up to approximately 300–1250 L (380–5000 donors) are processed simultaneously; the technique is not designed for single donor processing. The FFP is quick-thawed and passed through a 1-μm filter. This filtration, and an additional one, serves to remove cells, cell fragments, and membrane-associated viruses, assuring aggregate-free solutions. The plasma is then treated with 1% TNBP and 1% Triton X-100/polysorbate 80/octaxynol for 4 hours at 30 °C. A castor-oil extraction and phase separation are performed to remove TNBP, this is followed by a clear filtration. The Triton X-100 is removed by hydrophobic interaction chromatography. An additional sterile filtration at 0.2 μm is performed. The treated FFP is aseptically filled into 200 mL aliquots bags, sealed, fast frozen to ≤ -60 °C, and stored at -30 °C. After quality control, the batch is released for transfusion. No impairment of viral inactivation is seen with protein concentrations to 90 mg/mL or lipid levels of 1064 mg/dL for triglycerides and 243 mg/dL cholesterol.[23,29,30]

Plasma protein derivatives

In preparation of plasma-derived products, two additional steps are performed. The first is prior to SD treatment, when a Cohn–Oncley fractionation procedure is utilized on the recovered plasma batch. Fractionation is not effective by itself as an adequate pathogen-reduction technique. Transmission of viral infections occurred after batched products were infused post-processing. Recipients of IV-Ig products in the 1990s had frequent incidences of infections following infusions. A minimal degree of protection is given by fractionation, although a decrease in viral particle titers does occur by about 2 $\log_{10}$. However, a second step with a pH 4 treatment at 21 °C is required before the final filtration. This step decreases aggregation and inactivates both enveloped and non-enveloped viruses by 2 $\log_{10}$.[28,31–33]

Residual additives

Post-residual concentrations of TNBP and Triton X-100 present in the final product of several commercial manufacturers are as follows:

- TNBP was undetectable in 73% of 130 batches; 27% of batches contained 0.5–1.7 μg/mL TNBP
- Triton X-100 was undetectable in 91% of 130 batches; 9% of batches contained 1.0–1.6 μg/mL of the Octapharma product Octaplas®.

A study with the Vitex product VIPLAS-SD® revealed less than 2 ppm TNBP quantities, with one lot of 34 containing 2.1 ppm. Triton X-100 residual was ≤ 1 ppm with, two lots of 34 containing 1–2 ppm.[24,29]

Efficacy of pathogen reduction

For the initial licensure of VIPLAS-SD®, viral inactivation rates were reported as vesicular stomatitis virus (VSV) $>5.7 \log_{10}$, Sindbis (SIN) virus $\geq 5.8 \log_{10}$, HIV $\geq 6.0 \log_{10}$, bovine viral diarrheal virus (BVDV) $>6.0 \log_{10}$, HBV $\geq 6.0 \log_{10}$, and HCV $>5.0 \log_{10}$ reduction in active viruses. Non-enveloped viruses are less easily inactivated and show much lower log reductions. HAV had only a $\cong 1.22 \log_{10}$ reduction in viral particles, leading to an outbreak in the 1990s with a factor VIII product. Seroconversions have also been noted to parvovirus B19 (PVB19).[29,34,35]

A benefit of the broad-spectrum activity of SD treatment is that enveloped pathogens not picked up on routine screening assays will be inactivated by this technique. Examples of these include HIV type O and variants of HBV.[24,29]

Antibodies to non-enveloped viruses in the final products might protect recipients from these pathogens. Protection from acquiring HAV infection can occur as the result of the presence of antibody in the final SD product. Concentrations of anti-HAV antibodies in pooled SD-FFP are 30 times the prophylactic dose. These concentrations of antibody should protect recipients from HAV infection. SD-FFP has antibody concentrations of anti-PVB19 that are seen in IV-Ig used to treat chronic infections. These antibody concentrations should similarly protect recipients from acquiring parvovirus B19. Thus anti-HAV titers of 0.8 IU/mL and PVB19 titers of 8 IU/mL are thought to provide protection against their respective organisms. Screening with NAT is another way to decrease transfusion transmission because copy numbers as low as 10 copies/mL of pathogens can be detected.[24,29]

Purity of product

The potency goal of PR-treated plasma as stated by the FDA is to have 70% activity of coagulation factors and 1.7 mg/mL of fibrinogen. SD-FFP meets this goal. In 34 lots tested, coagulation activity ranged from 0.83 to 1.08 U/mL for factors V, VII, X, XI, and XII (83–103%) with 2.67 mg/mL of fibrinogen.[34]

Effects of SD technology on blood proteins

Even though SD-FFP has activity >0.7 U/mL of most clotting factors, approximately 15–20% is lost for individual factors compared with untreated FFP. Some feel that this loss requires an increased number of transfusions of SD-FFP to achieve the same clinical efficacy as standard FFP. This could increase the risk of non-infectious secondary to increased transfusion requirements.[27,36]

Protein S is decreased by 35–50% in SD-FFP, plasmin inhibitors are decreased by 76%, and alpha2-antiplasmin is decreased by 50%. These decreases in anticoagulation factors can lead to increased clotting risks in patients deficient in these factors.[29,37] Alpha2-antitrypsin is absent in SD-FFP. The clinical significance of the lack of this enzyme on acutely ill patients is unknown. Other therapies are available for patients with congenital deficiencies of this enzyme.[27,36]

In the year 2000, in the US, six patients undergoing orthotopic liver transplants for various underlying causes of end-stage liver disease died of thrombotic or hemorrhagic events. It is not known if this occurrence was causative or coincidental. Shortly after this episode, the use of SD-FFP (PLAS+SD) fell into disfavor in the US. The last lots were made in 2001. Studies in the UK in 1999 showed equal efficacy of SD-FFP and FFP. In Germany (2001), open-heart surgeries using SD-FFP and FFP were compared and demonstrated equivalent improvements as relates to hemostasis and fibrinolysis.[16,26,28,38–40]

Effects on viral pathogens

Vaccinia has been shown to be relatively resistant to SD treatment.[20] Even though this is an enveloped virus, intracellular non-envelope forms exist and are infectious. The active intracellular particles can potentially lead to infection. This study implies that normally enveloped viruses might still be infectious and resistant to SD treatment while in an intracellular environment.[20]

SD techniques do not inactivate non-enveloped viruses. Each year between 1991 and 1998, outbreaks of HAV have occurred worldwide with factors VIII and IX concentrates.[25,38,41] PVB19 is more difficult to evaluate secondary to increased incidence in the general population. Antibodies in pools of processed plasma might protect recipients from transmission. Nanofiltration can be used to remove non-enveloped viruses but a reduction in factor VII and in von Willebrand factor (vWF) is also seen. If higher titers of antibodies to these viruses are present in the final blood product, passive immunity might be acquired. SD technology cannot be used on cellular products because the plasma membranes will disintegrate.[25,31,39,41]

Toxicity associated with SD technology

When compounds interact with nucleic acids, mutagenicity becomes a concern. If present, mutagenic compounds can lead to genotoxicity, carcinogenicity, or toxicity to the reproductive system. Compounds interacting with membrane lipids or protein can adversely affect cellular function. If such reactions are occurring, the processing must ensure the compounds are not present in the final product administered to the patient.[2]

The risk associated with SD treatment also includes the toxicity of the chemical additives per se. When evaluating the toxicity of Triton X-100, the lethal dose at which 50% of animals are killed (LD_{50}) was used. Triton X-100 in animal studies has an LD_{50} of 1.2–1.8 g/kg via the oral route and LD_{50} of 108–150 mg/kg for the intraperitoneal or intravenous route. The lowest toxicity was found to be 33.7 mg/kg in mice and 15.7 mg/kg in rats, with a LD_{50} of 605–660 mg/kg in mice and 610–615 mg/kg in rats. No mutagenicity potential, embryo toxic, or teratogenic potential was demonstrated. A TTP patient could theoretically receive 63 L of PLAS/SD or Triton X-100 of 2.7 mg/kg. This is well below the toxicity levels. Because the chemical reaction is non-selective, the agents must be removed before the final product is transfused.[20,21] With present processing techniques, there often is no detectable TNBP or Triton X-100 in the final blood product.[34,42,43]

Benefits

Many of the benefits of SD treatment lie in the fact that in addition to pathogen reduction the process is unlikely to degrade the plasma proteins. Coagulation factor loss is not clinically significant; a loss of 5–20% activity is seen in multiple studies. Thirty percent activity is required to maintain normal hemostasis. Enveloped viruses are inactivated by this process. No transmission of such viruses was seen after the transfusion of 17 000 000 units between 1980 and 1993. In a 1995 study in the US, 3% of patients had hives, abdominal pain, nausea, vomiting, chills, headache, wheezing, fever, and hypertension, with an average recovery of 90% of clotting factors in this study population.[25,27,28]

Present research

Future studies are necessary to evaluate safety for use of these products in neonates, infants, and pregnant women. A study to evaluate the statistical/clinical relevance in the decrease of infection transmission risk would require hundreds of thousands in a cohort group. To be undertaken, this would require a multicenter trial over several years.[2] SD-FFP is still FDA licensed. However, at this time, SD-FFP is not used in the US.[25,44]

Costs

Producing and evaluating SD-FFP involves filtering, tracking, extracting, and monitoring residual pathogen or chemical agents. The additional steps and additives increase the cost of production to three to four times that of untreated FFP. Previous cost-effective analyses have suggested that SD-FFP costs go up to US$9 743 000 per quality of life year (QALY) gained. Some have argued that, taking into account the decreased incidence of transfusion-related acute lung injury (TRALI) with SD-FFP, the cost would be decreased to US$40 855–139 465 per QALY saved. The incidence of TRALI with SD-FFP is negligent given the dilutional affect of pooled plasma.[45] In other aspects of medicine, an accepted procedure typically costs less than $30 000 per QALY gained, i.e. cholesterol reduction ($13 300) or coronary artery bypass ($26 117). In other aspects of transfusion medicine, however, high-cost safety measures have been adopted to reduce the risk of transfusion-transmitted diseases. Costs for these programs range from $235,000 to $2.3 million per QALY. Such procedures include autologous donations, as well as p24 antigen assay for HIV. The costs should, therefore, not be the only determining factor considered in rejecting or accepting SD technology.[23,30,39,45–47]

Uniplas®

Another product currently available is Uniplas®, a solvent detergent-treated universal plasma. Anti-A and anti-B iso-agglutinin antibodies have been removed from this product. Immune complexes of anti-A and anti-B antibodies with soluble A and B antigens are hydrophobic and removed by SD treatment. Total protein and coagulation factors in Uniplas® are similar to SD-FFP. In a published study, no patients seroconverted to HIV, HTLV, HBC, CMV, HAV, or parvovirus B19 seropositivity.[48] Two studies showed equivalent efficacy of Uniplas® with Octiplas® in open-heart surgeries[48,49], although Uniplas® has the additional benefit of being compatible with all blood groups. Further studies are recommended to determine if Uniplas® is otherwise equivalent to standard SD.[48,49]

Phenothiazinium dyes: methylene blue

Methylene blue (MB) was first synthesized by Caro in 1876; in 1883 Bernsthen synthesized the parent ring system. Currently, this compound has been administered orally as an antiseptic, disinfectant, and an antidote for nitrate poisoning. MB has been used in the treatment of methemoglobinemia, in locating surgical sites, and for validation of properly following medication prescriptions. Long-term use in humans has not been associated with adverse effects in treating methemoglobin toxicities. In 1891, MB was instrumental in the cure of malaria in two patients. In 1928, it was demonstrated that MB could inactivate HSV vaccinia when exposed to light. Nucleic acids were found to be the target of MB in 1956, and oxygen was found to be necessary to this reaction in photodynamic activity reaction. Since 1962, MB has been known to photochemically degrade DNA.[50–54] The use of MB for viral inactivation of plasma was first described in 1991.[23]

Ideally, a photochemical dye first needs to penetrate membranes (whether pathogen or plasma membrane) to inactivate intra- as well as extracellular pathogens. Second, by adhering to predominately or exclusively nucleic acid compounds, there should be little damage to red blood cells. Third, since hemoglobin absorbs light at wavelengths of less than 600 nm, the ideal photocompound should absorb light at other wavelengths. Last, the unbound dye should not cause excessive damage to RBC. The compound needs to be active only in the presence of light and to be inactive while blood components are in storage.[55]

Phenothiazine dyes are more favorable because unwanted cell damage can be limited by ensuring that no light exposure occurs after the initial treatment is complete. By contrast, for SD techniques the reaction ceases only when the PR compounds are removed. In the last 100 years, both bacterial and tropical diseases (i.e. malaria) have been treated with MB. In the past 50 years, as specific antibiotics to these pathogens were developed, use of MB has decreased. A renaissance of interest in pathogen reduction has developed as *Plasmodium falciparum* has demonstrated an increasing incidence of chloroquine resistance, drug-resistant bacteria (e.g. MRSA, VRE, multi-drug resistant tuberculosis) have become more common, and opportunistic organisms in HIV patients are more widespread.[50,55]

Mechanism of action

MB binds DNA in two ways, depending on the ionic strength and concentration of Mg^{2+}: MB can bind the outside of the DNA helix or intercalate between the rungs in the helix. Its precise mode of action is guanine-specific cleavage. In solutions lacking an oxygen environment, a direct electron transfer is probably responsible for strand breakage via direct cleavage of phosphodiester bonds; in an oxygen-rich solution, reactive oxygen species (iO_2, OH, superoxides) are generated. MB has a peak absorption at 620–670 nm. Exposure to light of this wavelength produces a type I (redox) reaction or a type II (photodynamic, photo-oxidative) interaction. MB also binds to viral core proteins and has been shown to cause damage to bacteria (*Proteus mirabilis*) and RBC membrane proteins. Bacteria and hemoglobin can reduce MB and convert it to a leukomethylene form, which is neither a photosensitive nor an intercalater (maximum absorbance 340 nm). MB technology has been shown to inactivate enveloped and some non-enveloped viruses. However, given its hydrophobic nature at concentrations of 5 mM, this compound cannot penetrate plasma membranes and/or inactivate intracellular viruses.[26,39,51–54,56–59]

Molecular biology

The formal chemical name for MB is[3,7] bis(dimethylamino)-phenothiazine-5-ium chloride; it is classed as a thiazine dye.[60,61] The structural formula for MB is shown in Figure 3.[50,53,62] The leukobase inactive form is shown in Figure 4.[53] MB is not very lipophilic. The polarity/charge makes the compound more hydrophilic. For this reason, MB does not easily penetrate membranes.[53]

A study of MB binding to organic compounds showed it attaching preferentially to DNA and negatively-charged lipids. Albumin and electrically neutral lipids had < 3% binding with DNA, and negatively-charged lipids had 65 and 20% binding, respectively.

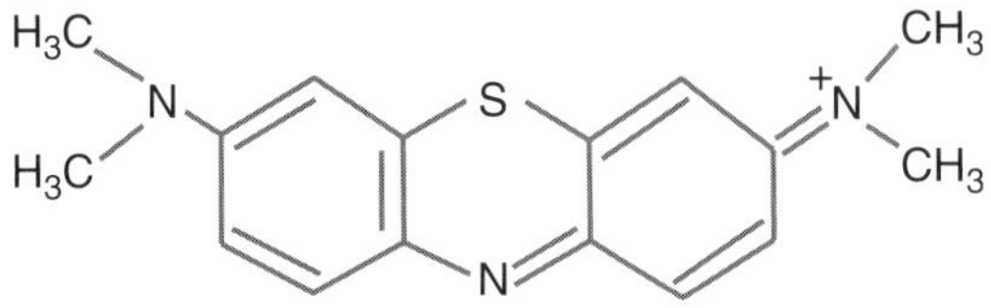

Figure 3. Molecular structure methylene blue (MB) (from refs 53, 56, 66).

Poly-guanine in the same solution accounted for the remaining 15% binding in that particular study.[63]

Present use in transfusion

After initial research in 1955 at Walter Reed Medical Center, MB-treated plasma became routine for use in 1992. A few countries in Europe still use this decontamination method. Between 1991 and 2000, 2 million units were transfused with no untoward events. MB has been used both as a marker in surgery and to reduce methemoglobin. As much as 50 mg t.i.d., for ifosfamide-induced encephalopathy, and 2 mg/kg, in septic shock, has been given to patients. Although MB has been used in much higher concentrations, the Paul Ehrlich Institute has refused to license MB-treated plasma because of toxicity concerns.[64] Adverse reactions associated with MB include a burning sensation in the mouth, nausea, vomiting, diarrhea, and gastritis. Large doses can cause abdominal and chest pain, headache, profuse sweating, mental confusion, painful urination, and methemoglobinemia (see the Material Safety Data Sheets, refs. 60,61). In life-threatening clinical situations, however, these adverse events do not outweigh the life-saving benefit of MB. Two different proprietary methods for processing FFP with MB—Pathinact MB® (Baxter) and Macotronic® (Macopharma)— are currently used in Europe.[50,53–55,57,65]

Procedure

In general, the MB treatment of plasma utilizes a 1 μm concentration of MB followed by exposure to red light (600–700 nm) with a fluence rate of 10 mW/cm^2 for 600 s. Freezing and thawing of the unit can liberate intracellular organisms. One study processed three units at a time by passing the contents of each unit through a 0.65-μm membrane filtration system.[55] After filtration, a dry tab of MB (80 μg) was placed in the line; the MB dissolved during filtration. Approximately, 180 J/cm^2 in less than 20 minutes was applied with 590 nm peak λ of light. The concentration of 1 μm MB in the unit was computer controlled.[55] Other procedures process MB with 5 μm concentration and a fluence of 11.3 J/cm^2. The product is then stored at $-30\,°C$.

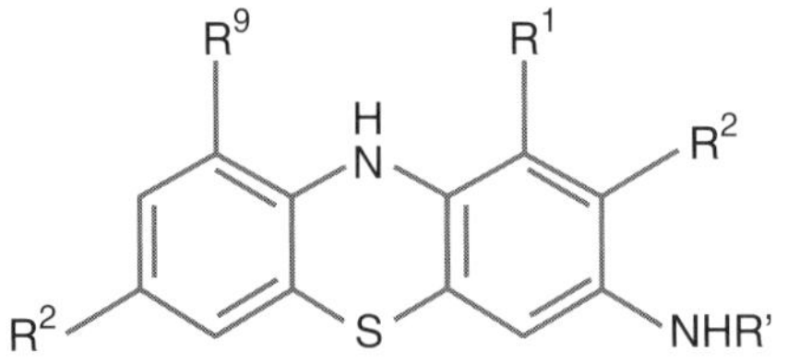

Figure 4. Generic molecular structure of the leukobase form of phenothiazinium dyes (from ref. 56).

When needed, each unit is then thawed and transfused in the same manner as untreated FFP.[66,67]

Efficacy

The efficacy of MB reduction is increased in the presence of oxygen. This process has demonstrated an ability to inactivate enveloped viruses with DNA and RNA genomes (HIV 6.32 $\log_{10}$, VSV 6 $\log_{10}$). Some non-enveloped viruses with large capsid pores are inactivated (i.e. WNV 5.7 $\log_{10}$ reduction). However, non-encapsulated viruses with tightly interdigitated capsid proteins (e.g. encephalomyocarditis virus) are not inactivated. Little bacterial inactivation is observed under virucidal phototherapeutic conditions. MB is more effective against Gram-positive than Gram-negative organisms; *Candida albicans* and *Trypanosoma brucei* are also inactivated.

MB has difficulty in penetrating plasma membranes and, as such, intracellular organisms are not inactivated. The viability of red cells when MB is used with an RBC product is decreased. After 42 days of storage in MB, 0.8% of the red blood cells lyse. In addition, MB-treated RBC membranes show dramatically increased ion leakage. MB binds to IgG and albumin (serum proteins); this might further alter RBC membranes by attaching to these membrane proteins. Despite concern over adverse events, MB has a long history of use with minimal toxicity.[11,25,52,53,56]

Problems

Secondary to binding to proteins, 10–30% of coagulation factors and 20–24% of fibrinogen are inactivated after MB treatment of plasma. This loss of activity is thought to be secondary to the oxidation of histidine residues and other amino acids. MB also binds to the alpha subunits of fibrinogen resulting in lower platelet-receptor binding results.[11,25,53–55,57,65,66,68,69]

MB does not inactivate intracellular pathogens or white blood cells. MB treatment of blood products cannot reduce the incidence TA-GVHD. In RBCs, up to one-half of the MB added is bound to membrane proteins or located within the RBCs. The compound within the RBCs is reduced to the leukobase form and can neither intercalate nor photosensitize. Binding of MB to RBC surface proteins also increases ion permeability of the membrane. MB also inactivates glutathione reductase and decreases red blood cells ability to handle oxidation toxicity. These effects decrease the life expectancy of red cells.[11,55,66]

Toxicity in animal studies reveals the LD_{50} oral route as being 1180 mg/kg and the intraperitoneal dose 180 mg/kg for rats. In mice studies, the oral LD_{50} was shown to be 3500 mg/kg; this indicates a low toxicity for this compound. MB is not reported to be carcinogenic, however, its toxocologic properties have not been fully investigated. At the concentrations used in clinical practice, toxicity appears to be minimal. This may relate to the final concentration in the bag at the micromolar level and not on the molar level. More research on the toxological properties of MB is needed.[53,60,61]

AMOTOSALEN

Compounds known as photosensitizers were first used in around 1550bc in ancient Egypt and India to treat depigmented lesions. The chemicals were obtained from parsley, parsnip, and St John's wort, applied to the skin and exposed to sunlight, which caused skin damage, re-epithelialization, and re-pigmentation of the skin. In 1897, Oscar Raab observed that paramecia placed in acrydine dye died on exposure to light but were unaffected if no light exposure occurred. Subsequently, these compounds were identified as furocoumarins, a group that includes psoralens. In the modern era, furocoumarins have been applied to biologic systems to treat various skin tumors and conditions, and to deactivate microorganisms, as well as being employed as a research tool to increase our knowledge of nucleic acids.[70]

Amotosalen is a synthetic psoralen specifically engineered to inactivate pathogens in blood products. Psoralens are naturally occurring heterocyclic compounds and are common in numerous plants, such as those mentioned above. With the addition of amine side chains, the compound becomes water soluble, which increases it's affinity for nucleic acids. Specific characteristics necessary for the psoralens to be useful in inactivating microorganisms in blood products include: the chemical purity, activation only upon light exposure, preferentially retained in the target organism(s), and rapidly excretion or elimation with minimal toxicity. In addition, the chemical has to have a high quantum yield for the photochemical event.[71,72]

Of the hundreds of psoralens evaluated, amotosalen was chosen because of its excellent activity against pathogens and minimal impact on the blood products, and because it essentially fulfilled the above criteria.

Mechanism of action

Amotosalen, also known as S-59, can be used to inactivate pathogens in plasma and platelets on exposure to UVA light at wavelengths of 320–400 nm. It cannot be used in red cell concentrates because hemoglobin absorbs the UVA light. Amotosalen works via a three-step chemical reaction: The chemical initially intercalates between strands of DNA or RNA. On exposure to UVA light, the molecule binds the olefinic moieties of

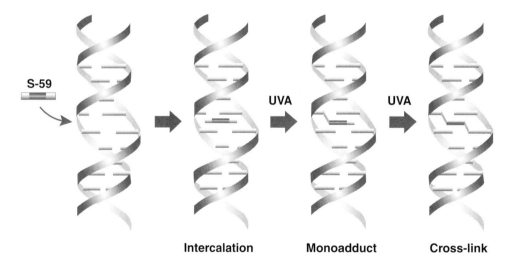

Figure 5. Mechanism of action of pathogen inactivation (PI). Amotosalen (S-59) is a synthetic psoralen that inhibits nucleic acid replication through UVA-light-mediated covalent addition to nucleic acids. Left: the molecule penetrates cells, viruses, bacteria, or other pathogens and seeks out DNA or RNA. 2nd left: amotosalen intercalates between the base pairs. 2nd right: once illuminated by UVA light, amotosalen forms monoadducts between pyrimidine bases. Right: another photon of light enables the molecule to form cross-links (diadducts) between DNA or RNA strands (from ref. 73).

Table I. Reported inactivation of pathogens in platelet concentrates after photochemical treatment with amotosalen with UVA light.

	Pathogen log-reduction in organisms
Non-enveloped viruses	
Bluetongue virus	6.1–6.4
Parvovirus B19[a]	4.0–4.9
Enveloped viruses	
HIV (cell-free)	6.2
HIV (cell-associated)	6.1
CMV	5.9
Hepatitis B virus	5.5
Hepatitis C virus	4.5
Duck hepatitis B virus	6.2
Bovine viral diarrhea virus	6.0
Human T-cell leukemia virus type I/II	4.7/5.1
West Nile virus	6.0
Gram-negative bacteria	
Escherichia coli	6.4
Serratia marcescens	6.7
Klebsiella pneumoniae	5.6
Pseudomonas aeruginosa	4.5
Salmonella choleraesuis	6.2
Yersinia enterocolitica	5.9
Enterobacter cloacae	5.9
Gram-positive anerobic bacteria	
Lactobacillus species	6.9
Non-enveloped viruses	
Propionibacterium acnes	6.7
Clostridium perfringens	7.0
Bifidobacterium adolescentis	6.5
Protozoa	
Trypanosoma cruzi	5.3
Plasmodium falciparum	7.0
Leishmania mexicana	5.2

[a] Preliminary data: inactivation was performed in 35% B19-infected plasma and 65% PAS III (platelet additive solution III) in the absence of platelets. Studies included a 15- or 30-minute rest between addition of amotosalen and UVA treatment. Adapted from Ref. 79.

the pyrimidine bases thymidine, cytidine, and uridine and forms a monoadduct. The monoadduction causes the helix to unwind slightly and, with continued exposure to UVA light, allows a second adduction to form, which results in cross-linkage. The nucleic acid then becomes non-functional because the cross-linkage is permanent and replication can no longer occur. The same process occurs in single-stranded nucleic acid structures that form hairpin turns and loops that allow for close proximity of pyrimidine bases, thus making them available for cross-linkage.[72,73] Thus, pathogens and white blood cells contained in the blood products are inactivated (Figure 5 and Table I).

The Cerus Corporation that developed S-59 calls this Helinx technology. Combining Helinx technology with a compound adsorption device (CAD) results in a system known as the INTERCEPT Blood System (Figure 6). The CAD is composed of activated charcoal in a diethyl benzene matrix placed in a porous container. The device is located

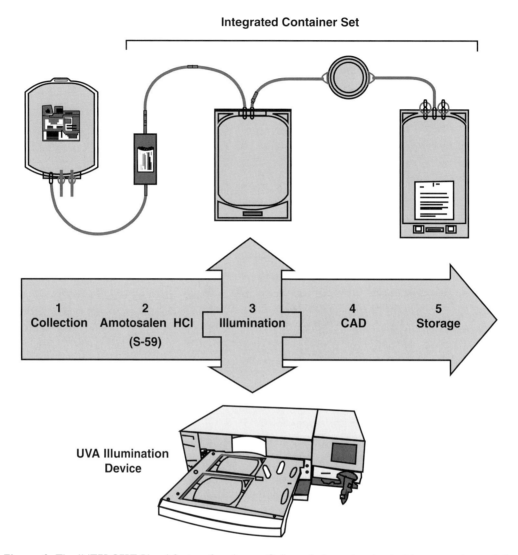

Figure 6. The INTERCEPT Blood System for plasma. Collected plasma is mixed with amotosalen and the mixture is placed in an ultraviolet A (UVA) illumination device. The contents are then passed through a Compound Adsorption Device (CAD) for reduction of amotosalen and free photoproducts. After CAD treatment, the plasma is placed in a final storage container until transfusion (from ref. 72).

in the blood product storage bag where it can scavenge amotosalen and its photoproducts. An additional step is necessary for platelets, as the system works best when the plasma concentration in the platelet bag is lowered to 35% by adding platelet additive solution (PAS III).[73] Amotosalen is added to plasma or platelets at a concentration of 150 μM/mL (50 μg/mL) and, while agitating, the bag is illuminated with 3 J/cm^3 of UVA light. The plasma and/or platelets are subsequently exposed to the CAD, which adsorbs the excess amotosalen and its photoproducts. The product is then ready for storage and transfusion.[74]

Toxicology

Toxicology studies for amotosalen involved evaluation of the chemical itself and the photoproducts present in plasma after exposure to UVA light. These studies, reported by Ciaravino et al[72,73], included evaluations for reproductive, geno-, carcino-, and photo-toxicity, as well as acute and repeated dosing toxicity.

Photochemically treated plasma did not result in any reproductive changes. Genotoxicity was not identified in the in vitro assays (the bacterial mutagenicity assay, chromosome aberration assay, and mouse lymphoma assay) or the following in vivo assays: mouse micronucleus assay and unscheduled DNA synthesis assay, when using photochemically treated plasma without the CAD. However, when photochemically processing a single unit 25 times without a CAD, two of six assays were positive for genotoxicity. The authors attributed this to the abundant excess of amotosalen present in high concentrations, which was much higher than in any expected clinical dose. That part of the study evaluating carcinogenesis used heterozygous p53 transgenic mice.[72] Unlike the homozygous p53 transgenic mice, 50% of which develop tumors by 4–5 months of age, 50% of the heterozygous mice do not develop tumors until 18 months. The heterozygous mice were exposed to high doses of amotosalen and its photoproducts intravenously over 6 months. There was no increase in tumors in the heterozygous p53 transgenic mice.[72] Phototoxicity was not demonstrated, despite residual amotosalen levels of (10 μg/kg). In addition, studies to assess vein irritation and neoantigenicity were negative.

Amotosalen alone produced CNS effects at concentrations 6250-fold greater than the estimated clinical exposure of 4 μg/kg. Electrocardiogram changes were identified at doses 10 000-fold higher, and phototoxicity occurred at doses 250-fold higher than the estimated clinical dose. Genotoxicity occurred in three of the six assays, as expected in in vitro assays, due to the intercalating behavior of the amotosalen.[73,74] Based on these studies, amotosalen appears to be safe when used in blood components in the manner and dosages intended.

Effect on platelets

In addition to toxicology studies, determination of any adverse effects of amotosalen on the blood products, both in vitro and in vivo, is required. Numerous studies have been performed on platelet concentrates using various endpoints to determine the viability of the photochemically treated platelets.

In vitro studies have found that after processing through the INTERCEPT Blood System, there is a not insignificant drop—in the range of 8–10%—in the number of platelets present in the bag. This was due both to the increased amount of platelet sampling necessary to meet the demands of the studies and to the requirements of processing the platelets through the photochemical treatment, which involves manipulation of platelets through three different bags, and agitation needed to mix the amotosalen with platelets and to expose amotosalen and photoproducts to the compound absorption device. In the Moog et al study, single-donor platelet concentrates contained mean platelet counts of $3.06 \pm 0.27 \times 10^{11}$.[74] On completion of the photochemical treatment (PCT), the mean platelet count was $2.62 \pm 0.27 \times 10^{11}$, representing a loss of 9.7%.[74] Also in the Moog study, significant decreases in pH were identified after PCT, with a mean drop to 6.98 ± 0.08. Compared to the control, however, this pH level was well above the required 6.8 limit required in Europe, and the pH remained above 6.8 until the end of the study, at 5 days of storage.[74]

Glucose decreased from 354 ± 34 to 119 ± 32 mg/dL after separation from plasma and following the addition of Intersol (PAS III) and remained essentially the same post-PCT at 122 ± 10 mg/dL. As expected during storage, glucose continued to decrease and lactate dehydrogenase (LDH) to rise. A significant increase in LDH was evident after PCT, indicative of platelet lysis and activation. Subsequently, however, the LDH level remained stable throughout storage. The HSR decreased both after preparation and after PCT; however, the platelets appeared to achieve normal hemostasis upon transfusion.[74]

Parameters for apoptosis, function, and activation of platelets examined by Jansen et al[75] included P-selectin, aggregation studies, hypotonic shock response, annexin V, and caspase 3 activity. PCT did not cause elevation of P-selectin, although the levels did rise over time during storage similar to control. Changes in HSR were not significant in this study compared with controls and caspase 3 activity and annexin V expression were unchanged, suggesting that apoptosis was not stimulated.[75] Decreases in platelet aggregation were not significant after PCT. However, after storage, compared to controls, aggregation studies using collagen and thrombin were decreased, but not in those using ADP.[75] These changes vary in extent from study to study and, to some extent, by technique. The results of a French validation study are consistent with the findings above.[76] This study also investigated longer storage times, finding that the in vitro platelet parameters remained within satisfactory ranges for up to 8 days. The authors suggest that it might be possible to extend the expiration date of PCT platelets to 7 days.[76]

The changes that are induced by the PCT process might not always be significantly different from controls. In vitro platelet parameters remain within the guidelines set by various regulatory agencies and appear to be adequate for clinical use.

One in vivo study looked at PCT platelet survival following indium-111 radiolabeling of the treated autologous platelets. The normal span of platelet survival is broad, ranging from 5 to 7.3 days with 33–66% recovery. Recovery in PCT–CAD platelets was $43\% \pm 8.7$ and lifespan was 4.8 ± 1.3 days. Although within the lower range of normal and significantly lower than controls, the findings are consistent with those of the other studies. In addition, the authors found that, in in vitro studies, the label dissociation was higher in PCT platelets than in control platelets.[77]

Other in vivo studies have yielded similar data, with results showing small changes that might or might not be significant compared to controls, although the performance was still within regulatory guidelines and medically acceptable ranges. Endpoints in these studies included post-platelet counts at various time periods, number of transfusions required over a given time period, number of adverse reactions, platelet refractoriness, and bleeding episodes. Most studies also looked for possible antibodies to amotosalen neoantigens. Two large in vivo studies from the euroSPRITE (S-59 Platelet Recovery In Thrombocytopenia in Europe) and SPRINT (S-59 Platelet Recovery In Thrombocytopenia in the USA) trials have reported similar results.[78,79]

The SPRINT trial was a nationwide study that enrolled 645 thrombocytopenic patients who were randomized to PCT–CAD-treated platelets or standard platelets. The platelets were single donor units collected by apheresis. The euroSPRITE trial was designed similarly. Both studies found that CCIs (corrected count increments) were lower in patients treated with PCT platelets. This finding in both studies is explained by the lower platelet number in the PCT units. In the SPRINT trial, however, after correcting for the lower dose per unit infused, investigators found no significant difference between PCT–CAD platelet and standard platelet units. For the same reasons, patients treated with PCT platelet units required more transfusions over time. Bleeding and refractoriness were essentially the same for controls and patients treated with PCT units in both trials. In the SPRINT trial, transfusion reactions were fewer in patients treated with PCT–CAD platelets (3 versus 4.4%, $p = 0.02$). No antibodies to any amotosalen neoantigens were identified. Therefore, the PCT–CAD treated platelets were considered to be functionally as safe and effective as control platelets for patients.[79,80]

In summary, the platelet studies as a whole demonstrated that the PCT–CAD platelets appear to be an acceptable alternative to untreated platelets given the added safety measure from PR process. Due to the loss of a fraction of the platelets during processing, the number of platelet transfusions required for each patient may be slightly higher.

Fresh frozen plasma

The function of FFP after PCT–CAD has also been validated in phase III trials in Norway and Germany.[80] To support large-scale processing, FFP was pooled to a maximum quantity of 650 mL, allowing up to three units of FFP to be produced per PCT–CAD process. Assays of factors II, V, VII, VIII, IX, X, XI, XIII, proteins C and S, anti-thrombin III, alpha2-antiplasmin, and fibrinogen were assayed in the manufacturers own laboratory. Fibrinogen and factor VIII levels were maintained at 78–79% of pre-PCT–CAD levels. Factors II, V, VII, IX, X, XI, XIII, proteins C and S, anti-thrombin III, and alpha2 antiplasmin were maintained at 85–95% of pre-PCT–CAD levels. Thus, the quantity of anticoagulant and procoagulant factors declined minimally. This recalls the decline seen in PCT platelet numbers. However, clinical trials have demonstrated that PCT–CAD-treated plasma factors function adequately in vivo in patients with acquired and congenital coagulopathies and TTP, as well as those requiring warfarin reversal.[81] Hambleton et al[82] studied healthy volunteers who donated apheresis plasma. Half of the group was treated with PCT–CAD and the other half was processed in the usual fashion. Subsequently, subjects took warfarin for 4 days until factor VII levels were lowered to a mean concentration of 0.33 IU/mL. They were then infused with 1 L of either PCT-treated or untreated plasma. Two weeks later, the process was repeated and the subject received the other type of FFP. Mean peak increments of 0.10–0.12 IU/mL of factor VII were identified for both PCT–CAD-treated and standard FFP. The results reveal that, despite the mild decreased level of factors in PCT-treated FFP, the factor VII level increased to the same level in patients with either PCT-treated or untreated plasma. In addition, the study measured the PT to determine coagulation factor function. The change in PT levels closely reflected the drop in factor VII levels in the first 8 hours and decreased similarly in both control and test patients. At 24 hours after FFP infusions, however, the PT rebounded to above pre-infusion levels, more so in the PCT–CAD-treated FFP patients than in the patients treated with standard FFP.[82]

Another study reported in an abstract reviewed the effect of PCT–CAD-treated FFP on patients with an acquired coagulopathy due to liver disease requiring treatment with FFP. Several factor levels were evaluated but only the PT and PTT were reported. No adverse events were described and the PT and PTT decreased similarly both in controls and in treated patients. Active bleeding stopped in one patient given PCT–CAD-treated FFP.[83] Von Willebrand factor was studied separately in another study, which again was reported in an abstract. Similarly, there was no statistical difference between PCT–CAD-treated plasma and conventional FFP.[84] A more recent abstract reported by Mintz et al examined the efficacy of PCT–CAD plasma in TTP patients.[85] The mean time to remission, remission rates, mean number of exchanges, and relapse rates were not significantly different than controls, with p values ranging from 0.58 to 1.0. No patients developed new antibodies, although one patient had a serious adverse event after 12 days of therapeutic plasma exchanges, which was not further described in the abstract. The patient was removed from the study and recovered without sequelae. Despite this event, the authors concluded that the PCT–CAD-treated FFP performed similarly to the control plasma in terms of efficacy and safety. Therefore, it is likely that the adverse event could have occurred with untreated plasma as well.[85] Thus, numerous clinical trials have demonstrated that FFP treated with PCT–CAD appears to be as effective as standard FFP.

Pathogen inactivation

The ability of amotosalen to reduce pathogens contained in a unit of blood platelets or plasma is in little doubt. Numerous studies have demonstrated a minimum of a greater than 5 log reduction in most viruses, bacteria, and protozoan tested, whether extra- or intracellular. Experiments reported by Lin et al[86] are typical. These researchers added high levels of pathogens to single-donor platelet units. In the case of HIV, they evaluated cell-free and cell-associated virus, as well as pro-viral HIV. Duck hepatitis B (DHBV) and bovine viral diarrhea virus (BVDV) were used as surrogates for human strains of hepatitis B and hepatitis C. A representative of Gram-positive *Staphylococcus epidermidis* and Gram-negative *Klebsiella pnemoniae* bacteria were studied by inoculating 10^4 colony-forming units (CFU)/mL into the platelet units. Before treatment, the bags were sampled in order to determine the viral or bacterial titer. Different levels of UVA light were used to determine the appropriate level of pathogen inactivation. Based on these studies, the UVA frequency is now set at 3 J/cm^2. Starting with small doses allowed the authors to differentiate the speed and effectiveness of the process. HIV was readily eliminated and proviral HIV was even more sensitive to the process than the cell-free or cell-associated HIV. High levels of BVDV and DHBV were also readily inactivated at 3 J/cm^2. Klebsiella bacteria, however, were more resistant, as two of four units were still infective after PCT with 3 J/cm^2. When the experiment was repeated, all four units were negative. Gram-negative bacteria are known to be more resistant to PCT due to the lipopolysaccharide outer membrane, which serves to inhibit small organic molecules such as amotosalen. However, the authors concluded that the ability of the process to reduce the bacteria by a factor of greater than 10^5 was considered a success as clinically the presence of such high titers in blood products would be highly unlikely. *S. epidermidis* was readily inactivated by the process with as few as 0.5 J/cm^2. Van Voorhis et al[87] conducted similar experiments with *T. cruzi* and demonstrated the effectiveness of PCT–CAD in inactivating this parasite, which is likely to become a more of a concern in the future. Lin et al[88] and Jordan et al[89] demonstrated effective pathogen reduction of latent and free CMV in mice. Another experiment by Lin et al[90], looked at several types of bacteria, including Gram-negative, Gram-positive, anaerobic, aerobic, and spirochetes (specifically *Treponema pallidum* and *Borellia burgdorferi*). The spirochetes were very sensitive to the PCT–CAD process and, again, the various other bacteria examined were effectively inactivated by the process.

Summary

As described above, the ability of the psoralen amotosalen (S-59) to reduce pathogens is excellent. However, further studies are needed to more fully explore the upper limit of the capacity of PCT–CAD (150 μg dose of amotosalen plus 3 J/cm^2) to reduce pathogen activity. This might be most important for those pathogens more resistant to the process, such as *Klebsiella pneumoniae* and parvovirus B19. The safety of the amotosalen-based PCT–CAD process has been well demonstrated in the short-term in several phase III clinical trials. Long-term studies will be necessary to determine the risk, particularly of carcinogenesis. The amotosalen-based process for platelets is currently under review in the US by the FDA. In Europe, the process for platelets has received the CE mark and has been validated and implemented in some countries, including France and Norway. Cost-benefit analyses have begun and initial findings have been reported by the Netherlands and Germany, which conclude that the cost of INTERCEPT Blood System for platelets is comparable to that of other blood safety interventions, such as nucleic acid testing.[91,92] Currently, the INTERCEPT Blood System and its programs are in various stages of the development and regulatory approval process.

FRALE

Numerous obstacles have beset the development of photochemical systems for red cells, including problems caused by the absorption of UVA light by hemoglobin. Further, the photochemically treated red cells often sustain damage that results in hemolysis and potassium leakage during storage. New methods are in the process of development. One of these methods, developed by the same manufacturer as amotosalen, is based on a compound known as S-303.[93]

Mechanism of action

S-303 is a part of class of compounds known as Frales (Frangible Anchor Linker Effectors). These tripartite molecules are composed of a nucleic acid anchor, an effector moiety, and a frangible linker. The effector moiety binds nucleic acids covalently, and the frangible linker breaks down forming an inactive negatively charged species (S-300). This prevents further binding to the nucleic acid, thus rendering the DNA or RNA non-functional.[73] The completely light-independent reaction proceeds due to a shift in pH, which occurs as the S-303 is added to red blood cell concentrates. The process as developed requires the addition of S-303 to red cells at a concentration of 150 μg/mL, which is then incubated for 12 hours at room temperature. The red cells are incubated with a compound absorption device (CAD) for an additional 8 hours after transfer to a storage container to remove any residual S-303 and S-300. The CAD remains in the red cells throughout storage.[73]

Red blood cells

Most information published about S-303 pathogen reduction is in abstract form. The earliest abstract by Cook et al reported no biologically significant differences in S-303-treated red cells stored for 42 days, although the degree of hemolysis appeared to vary significantly among treated units.[94] The same study evaluated S-303-treated RBC recovery in dogs and mice using a biotin recovery technique. The results were comparable with controls. A year later, Cook et al reported the results of another S-303-treated red cell study where recovery in dogs was not significantly different than controls. In addition, they conducted two further experiments. One involved replacing 80% of a dog's blood volume with S-303-treated cells and the other involved dogs receiving twelve 10-mL/kg transfusions over a month. The concentration of S-303 in each experiment reached 500 μg/mL, which was thought to be five times what a human would receive; no toxicity was identified. Flow cytometry was used to evaluate immunogenicity, which did not identify any antibodies specific to S-303.[95]

In early human studies, the findings have been similar. In 1999, Hambleton et al found greater than 75% RBC recovery in humans transfused with S-303-treated autologous blood. The study performed one clinical trial then re-enrolled the same subjects in a second trial. The subjects thus received more than one consecutive transfusion and evaluated the DAT antibody screen and cross-match data, all of which remained the same, as did in vivo recovery.[96] Hambleton et al subsequently performed a cross-over study in 2002 and, again, found no statistical differences from controls in 24-hour red cell recovery after treatment with S-303.[97]

Phase III clinical trials were initiated based on these preliminary data. Despite promising results regarding the efficacy of S-303-treated red cells in patients[98,99], these trials have been halted due to antibody formation to S-303-treated cells. Patients requiring chronic transfusion for thalassemia or sickle-cell anemia were entered into a randomized, double-blinded, cross-over study. Each patient was to receive a total of six transfusions. The number of units per transfusion, as well as the frequency of transfusion, was determined by the treating physician. Two asymptomatic pediatric patients developed antibodies to S-303-treated red cells after transfusion; pre-transfusion IAT cross-matches were negative. Despite the antibody, there was no evidence of reduced red cell survival and a monocyte monolayer RBC phagocytic assay was negative, suggesting the antibody was not likely to have been clinically significant. The DAT in both patients was negative.[99] In hapten inhibition assays, the S-303, but not glutathione, exhibited inhibition. The latter is used as the buffer during processing.[99] Alterations in the pathogen-reduction process were made in an attempt to eliminate the antibody problem. In the original protocol, 200 μM of S-303 was added to 2 mM unbuffered GSH. Stassinopoulos et al[100] altered the process by adding 20 mM GSH, which significantly reduced the presence of S-303 on the red cells. Sera from the patients who developed the antibodies was added to the modified treated S-303 red cells, and the IAT was negative. Pathogen reduction using the modified process remained effective.[101] The modification essentially dilutes, rather than eliminates, the neo-antigen presence on the S-303-treated red cells. Further research will be required to determine if dilution alone will be adequate to prevent alloimmunization in red cells processed with S-303-treated red cells.

Pathogen inactivation

With regard to pathogen reduction, the S-303 system appears effective. In 1997, Cook et al reported that log inactivation depended linearly on the dose of S-303 added. In this study, they evaluated pathogen reduction of cell-free HIV, cell-associated HIV, duck hepatitis B virus, bovine viral diarrhea virus, herpes simplex virus-1, vesicular stomatitis virus, and *Yersinia enterocolitica*. Log_{10} inactivation ranged from > 4.7 to > 6.1. Whether the level of inactivation was related to the level of detection or not was not reported.[94] In a second study, Cook et al again looked at cell-free HIV, duck hepatitis B virus, bovine viral diarrheal virus, and *Y. enterocolitica* and found even higher levels of inactivation ranging from 4.2 ± 0.5 for the Yersinia to > 7.3 for bovine viral diarrheal virus. The viruses were reduced to the level of detection of the assay.

Summary

Overall, the literature with regard to Frale technology is minimal due to the early phases of technological development. It appears to be effective as a pathogen-reduction agent, and the red cells function within the necessary clinical parameters both in vitro and in vivo. The phase III trials are now on hold due to the immune reactions of two patients as reported above. Even if the problem of antibody formation against S-303 is diminished, the level of risk for antibody production must be vanishingly small. The side effects of any pathogen-reduction process must be less than the risk of contracting the infectious diseases that it eradicates.

PEN110

PEN110 is another PR/PI compound that also disrupts nucleic acids. Like S-303, light is not required for the reaction and it can therefore be used to treat red cells. PEN110 is a compound chemically related to binary ethyleneimine and is known as an ethyleneimine oligomer. The altered molecule is a cation, selective for nucleic acids, and highly water soluble. As the molecule is very small, it readily diffuses through cell membranes, which, the manufacturer claims, makes it more effective against non-lipid enveloped viruses, such as parvoviruses, which are more resistant to heterocyclic compounds (see amotosalen, above). PEN110 forms ionic bonds with nucleic acids, activating the molecule by protonation of the aziridino nitrogen. The active form can then alkylate a proximal nucleophilic center such as the N7 position of guanine in DNA. This results in the opening of the imidazole ring structure of guanine, which creates a break in the strand and creates a stop message. The nucleic acid is thus inactivated and becomes useless as a template. Binary ethyleneimines, like psoralens, have been used in nucleic acid research since the 1980s. The development and use of PEN110 for pathogen reduction of blood products, however, has occurred only over the past 15 years. In the process known as INACTINE treatment, PEN110 is added to create a 0.1% (vol/vol) concentration and incubated at room temperature for 6 hours. PEN110 is then removed by washing with unbuffered saline to levels below the limit of detection when using HPLC (30 ng/mL). The units are then ready for storage.[101,104]

Toxicology

Two main studies by Chapman, Butterwork, and Moore[101,102] describe the toxicology of PEN110. The PEN110 compound reacts with nucleic acids, and the Ames and mouse lymphoma assays are both positive, indicative of genotoxicity.[102] PEN110 also induced unscheduled DNA synthesis (UDS) in rat hepatocyte cultures. However, chromosomal assays and whole animal toxicity assays were negative. PEN110 given to rats intravenously at high blood concentrations did not induce UDS in their hepatocytes suggestive of an effective clearance pathway.[102] The compound appeared to be excreted quickly in the urine.[102] The second study[103], focusing on reproductive effects, was conducted on rats and rabbits. Male and female rats were regularly dosed with various quantities of PEN110 before and after mating. The animals were then killed after gestational day 14 or 16 and examined. Before euthanasia of the males, sperm analysis was conducted. As rabbits are known to be a more sensitive model for reproductive toxicology than rats, a second study arm was initiated using mated female rabbits dosed with PEN110 and killed on gestational day 29.[102] The ability of PEN110-treated rats to become pregnant was not impaired. Further, the number of implantation sites, number of fetuses, and number of fetal losses were not significantly different from those found in controls. Fetal abnormalities were not identified. Numerous sperm characteristics were evaluated in males, none of which was significantly different than controls. Only female rats and rabbits receiving the highest doses of PEN110 demonstrated toxicity characterized by significantly decreased food consumption and decreased weight gain. The fetuses of rabbit mothers receiving high-dose PEN110 had significantly increased skeletal variations; however, these variations were not clinically significant and did not affect the viability to the fetuses. These effects were identified at dosing regimens of 0.1, 0.3, and 1.0 mg of PEN110 per kilogram of weight in rabbits and 0.05, 0.25, and 0.5 mg/kg in the rats. After washing, PEN110-treated blood (350 mL) contained 0.0175 mg of PEN110, which is equivalent to 0.00025 mg/kg of body weight for a 70-kg person. This level is 2000 times lower than the 0.5 mg/kg dose given the rats and, based on cumulative mg per kg figures, the dose is 48 000 times less. Therefore, even given that an individual human might receive multiple units at once or over time, the dose is believed to be far less than that required to induce reproductive or genotoxicity.[102]

Red blood cells

The majority of research thus far has been on the use of PEN110 for the inactivation of pathogens in units of red blood cells. In a preclinical trial, Purmal et al studied the effect of PEN110 pathogen inactivation, using 6- and 24-hour incubations, on a number of red cell parameters including hemolysis, RBC ATP, intracellular potassium, and red cell surface antigens.[104] RBC ATP was significantly reduced in the PEN110-treated red cells compared to controls whether 6- or 24-hour incubations were used. However, the level of ATP was still within the clinically acceptable range. Hemolysis out to day 42 was not significantly increased compared to controls in the cells incubated for 24 hours with PEN110. The inactive PI/PR process had no effect on intracellular potassium.[104] Snyder et al[105] had similar results with lowered ATP in treated cells but no clinically significant difference in hemolysis for PEN110-treated versus control red cells. This group also studied 2,3-diphosphoglycerate (2,3-DPG), P50, sodium, methemoglobin, complete blood count (CBC), lactate, and glucose. Again, there was no significant difference between controls and PEN110-treated cells.[105] ATP levels were also lower in a study by AuBuchon et al. The authors also noted lower levels of lactate and decreased glucose consumption in the PEN110-treated cells. These changes were interpreted as a 'metabolic slowing', although no further explanation was provided. Again, the changes were within acceptable ranges and clinically were not significantly different when compared with the control results.[106]

 All three of these studies included in vivo study arms evaluated after 28 or 42 days of storage. Purmal et al[104] removed red blood cells from baboons, double labeled them with $^{51}Cr/^{125}I$, and re-infused them into the autologous animals. Red cell survival after 28 days of storage ranged from 66 to 76% in controls and from 72 to 80% in PEN110-treated cells. After 42 days of storage, red cell survival ranged from 39 to 61% in controls and 16 to 77% in PEN110-treated cells. The differences in survival time were not statistically significant. The Snyder et al study[105] was a phase II clinical trial using healthy human volunteers who were re-infused with ^{51}Cr-radiolabeled blood following treatment with PEN110 and 42 or 35 days of storage. Control units were processed in a similar manner. In vivo 24-hour survival in PEN110-treated cells stored for 42 days was $82.9 \pm 5.7\%$ and for 35 days of storage was $84.7 \pm 4.8\%$. The 24-hour survival in controls was statistically similar; after 42 days storage it was $86.3 \pm 8.7\%$, and after 35 days storage, $85.7 \pm 3.5\%$. The mean rise in hemoglobin at 24 hours and 7 days after infusion of the remaining unlabeled autologous units of red blood cells was also evaluated and the PEN110-treated results were not statistically different from control, with 24-hour values of 0.8 versus 0.5 g/dL and 7-day values of 0.8 versus 0.9 g/dL. The in vivo portion of the AuBuchon et al study[106] evaluated the survival of red cells in humans after 28 days of storage and determined T_{50} values. Again, there was no statistical difference between PEN110-treated cells in 24-hour survival. The T_{50} values also were similar to controls.

None of these studies found evidence of PEN110 induced neoantigenicity in any of their subjects (baboons or humans) who were monitored for 21 days[104], 28 days[105], and 56 days.[106] Based on these results, PEN110 appears to be safe in animals and people, at least in the short term, and the PEN110-induced changes in red cell parameters are within acceptable ranges.

Pathogen inactivation

Extensive research has been conducted with regard to the pathogen inactivation capacity of PEN110. These studies are very specific in demonstrating the exact nature of the action of PEN110 on the virus and the kinetics of inactivation, as well as demonstrating activity in the presence of high and low titers of viruses.

One of the initial studies evaluated the effect of PEN110 on four enveloped viruses, six non-enveloped viruses, and cell-associated HIV.[107] The viruses were chosen to include a wide array of physiological characteristics such as size, structure, biochemical composition, and whether the virus was cell associated or cell free. Of the enveloped types, BVDV and pseudorabies virus (PRV) are recognized models for HCV and herpes virus. Other enveloped viruses included in the study were sinbis (SV) virus and vesicular stomatitis Indiana virus (VSIV). The non-enveloped viruses included porcine parvovirus (PPV), which is a model for B19 virus, and vesicular exanthema of swine virus (VESV), which is a model for hepatitis E and Norwalk viruses. The remaining viruses included were used to demonstrate the wide spectrum of activity of PEN110. In these studies, the inactivation process was altered by using 1 M sodium thiosulphate (STS) and 1 M 3-morpholinopropanesulphonic acid (MOPS) to chemically stop the PEN110 reaction (rather than washing) to ensure that the decreased viral cytotoxic effect was due to PEN110 alone and not washing. In addition, red cell units were collected in three different additive solution storage media CPD/AS-1, CP2D/AS-3, and CPD/AS-5. Virus titers were determined by tissue culture infectious dose 50% ($TCID_{50}$) assay and plaque-forming units assay. The kinetics of viral reduction were determined by collecting samples at 3, 6, 12, 18, and 22 hours during incubation with PEN110. The results from these studies are seen in Figures 7 and 8.

Three of the non-enveloped (VESV, foot and mouth disease virus [FMDV], and bluetongue virus [BTV]) and two of the enveloped viruses (SV and VSIV) were reduced to the level of detection of the assay within 3 hours of incubation. These viruses were reduced by factors ranging from 5.4 to 7.5 $\log_{10}$ $TCID_{50}$ per milliliter.[107] BVDV and PRV

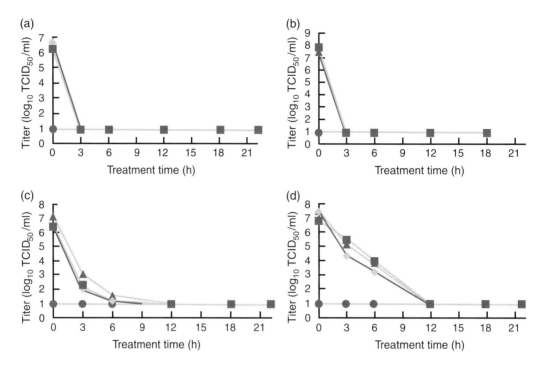

Figure 7. PEN110 kinetics of viral reduction of four enveloped viruses in CPD/AS-1, CP2D/AS-3 or CPD/AS-5 red blood cell concentrate (RBCC) units at 22 ± 2 °C for up to 22 ± 2 h. ♦, CPD/AS-1; ■, CP2D/AS-3; ▲, CPD/AS-5; ●, limit of detection. (a) Inactivation kinetics of sindbis (SIN) virus; (b) inactivation kinetics of vesicular stomatitis Indiana virus (VSIV); (c) inactivation kinetics of bovine viral diarrhoea virus (BVDV); (d) inactivation kinetics of pseudorabies virus (PRV) (from ref. 107).

took longer—12 hours—to be reduced to the level of detection. Three of the non-enveloped viruses—PPV, Reo-3, and Adeno-2—took 18 hours to be reduced to the level of detection. The reduction factors for these viruses were $>6.2 \log_{10} TCID_{50}$ per milliliter, >5.3 and $>5.6 \log_{10}$ PFU per milliliter, respectively. For cellular HIV, the reduction to the level of detection took 6 hours.

The same group of researchers conducted a series of experiments investigating PEN110 inactivation of HIV.[108] They evaluated the effect of PEN110 on the structure of the virus by EM, the ability of the virus to enter cells after PEN110 treatment, and the reverse transcriptase activity after PEN110 treatment, in addition to the usual demonstration of the PEN110 treatment effect via the $TCID_{50}$ assay. The structure of the virus did not change and the ability of the virus to infect cells remained intact after PEN110 treatment. However, the viral reverse transcriptase did not function, consistent with the alteration of nucleic acid by PEN110. The HIV reduction took place primarily in the first 6 hours and decreased to the level of detection after 12 hours. Large-volume infection required 18 hours to decrease to the level of detection. The reduction factors varied from 5.35 to 5.96 log $TCID_{50}$ after 18 hours. Another study demonstrated that PEN110 was effective against HBV.[109]

In a study of West Nile virus, Mather et al[110] explored the survival of the virus in PEN110-treated blood stored under the usual blood bank conditions and found that although the viral population decrease over time, the units remain 'infectious' throughout the 42 days of storage when spiked with high-titer viral concentrates; low-titer spiked units were non-infectious by 42 days. The doses chosen for high and low titers were based on the limited data available from donors with natural WNV

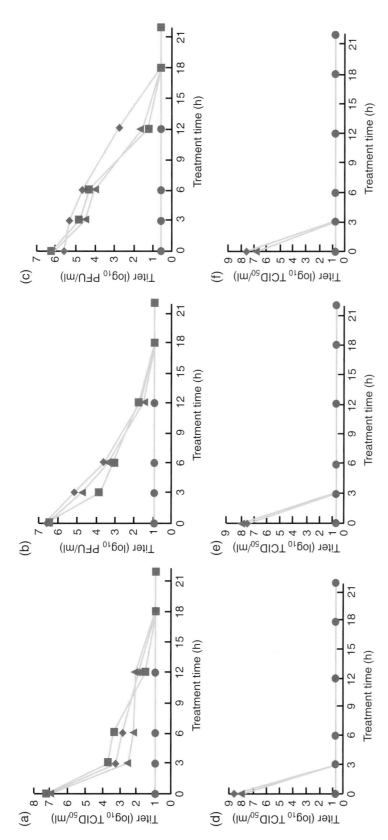

Figure 8. PEN110 kinetics of viral reduction of six non-enveloped viruses in CPD/AS-1, CP2D/AS-3, or CPD/AS-5 red blood cell concentrate (RBCC) units at $22 \pm 2\,^{\circ}C$ for up to 22 ± 2 hours. ◆, CPD/AS-1; ■, CP2D/AS-3; ▲, CPD/AS-5; ●, limit of detection. (a) Inactivation kinetics of porcine parvovirus (PPV); (b) inactivation kinetics of reovirus 3 (Reo-3); (c) inactivation kinetics of human adenovirus 2 (Adeno-2); (d) inactivation kinetics of vesicular exanthema of swine virus (VESV); (e) inactivation kinetics of foot and mouth disease virus (FMDV); (f) inactivation kinetics of bluetongue virus (BTV) (from ref. 107).

infection. Infectivity was determined by PFU assays. Although, the study demonstrated viral survival, whether the dose present would be sufficient to cause infection in humans is not known. In addition, the same study demonstrated that the WNV was distributed in all blood components—red blood cells, plasma, and platelets—and that the virus can infect monocytes and may be harbored in these cells in vivo. PEN110 treatment reduced WNV to the level of detection of the assay within 3 hours and, after 24 hours, reduced the virus by a factor of 5.0 log $TCID_{50}$ per milliliter. In another study[111], the group compared the effect of PEN110 to gamma radiation on CMV-infected THP-1 cells, which are used to model latently infected white cells. In addition to demonstrating the efficiency of PEN110 against CMV-infected cells, the experiments demonstrated that gamma irradiation, despite inactivating white cells, has the capacity to actually increase CMV replication.

PEN110 inactivation of bacteria has been successful, although limitations are evident. Bacterial contamination of blood generally occurs due to organisms on the skin of donors at the time of collection. The most common organisms are therefore skin contaminants, such as *Staphylococcus epidemidis* and *Propionibacterium acnes*. Other organisms ubiquitous in the environment are also common, such as *Clostridium perfringens*, *Pseudomonas fluorescens*, *Pseudomonas putida*, and *Acinetobacter* species. *Yersinia entercolitica* is also associated with transfusion-related sepsis and is thought to come from bacteremia in a donor with Yersinia gastroenteritis. In studies using various titers of these organisms to infect red blood cell units, PEN110 successfully inactivated the majority of the organisms.[112–114] However, some studies revealed that high titers of organisms could not be inactivated. *Acinetobacter iwoffii* and *A. johnsonii* were inactivated when the titer was less than 10^4 CFU/mL, but the bacteria persisted when units were infected with higher titers.[112] *Y. enterocolitica* and *P. fluorescens* have demonstrated similar resistance to inactivation at higher titers in other studies.[112] However, in an earlier study by the same group[115], the titers (10–100 CFU) were chosen to simulate a worse-case scenario based on reported clinical levels detected in donated blood for *Yersinia* of 1 CFU/mL or lower.[115] If this level of bacteremia is the norm clinically, the lack of pathogen reduction at levels above 10^4 CFU/mL is not relevant. However, the question of an upper limit of effectiveness for this pathogen-reduction technology remains a concern. Importantly, the concentration level of pathogens in the blood may be dependent on the organism involved. PEN110 was able to inactivate *Mycoplasma pneumonia* and *M. arthritidis* by more than 10^7 CFU/mL.[113] Even if all of the organisms appear to be removed, however, they are only 'removed' to the level at which they can be detected. In protozoa studies, *B. microti* was eliminated below the level of detection by PEN110 and hamsters given the blood did not develop identifiable infection even by PCR testing. However, the hamsters did mount an IgG antibody response. This is not too surprising given that the inactivation occurs only on the nucleic acid level, leaving organism antigens in place. Other protozoa tested included *P. falciparum* and *T. cruzi*, which were effectively reduced by PEN110.[114]

Summary

PEN110 demonstrates robust viral and bacterial inactivation capacity. Using more sensitive PCR methods and high- and low-titer infections, investigators have revealed the higher and lower limits of this pathogen-reduction process. Given the cost of implementing any pathogen-reduction process, the hope would be that the process would reduce all pathogens to a non-infectious level despite the initial titer. Additional studies are needed to evaluate the pathogen-reduction process in clinical settings and under conditions involving mixtures of pathogens at clinically relevant levels in combination with the white cells present at different concentrations to determine the true capacity of these pathogen-reduction processes. The two phase III PEN110 studies involving patients requiring acute transfusion therapy for surgical support and chronic transfusion involving sickle-cell and thalassemia patients has been halted due to development of an immune response to PEN110-treated RBC and associated clinical findings.[112] Immunogenicity is thus a problem for the pathogen-reduction chemicals. Even if the number of events is very small, because the risk of immunogenicity must be smaller than the risk of infection by untreated blood which is very small, it will take more research over time to determine how safe and effective PR/PI technologies really are.

RIBOFLAVIN

Riboflavin, also known as vitamin B2, has been widely investigated from a number of different perspectives for the past 70 years.[116] Because of the extensive knowledge of this compound, much of the background work required for the development of riboflavin as a pathogen-reducing agent for blood has already been reported.

Toxicology and mechanism of action

Numerous nutritional studies have already been performed. In 1942, Unna et al investigated the toxicity of riboflavin in rats and found that excessive amounts of riboflavin taken by mouth were not toxic due to the inability of the gastrointestinal system to absorb sufficient quantities of the vitamin.[117] Toxicity was observed in rats after intraperitoneal injections of 300 mg/kg, which resulted in renal failure due to yellow concretions that accumulated in the kidneys. Intravenous toxicity could not be determined due to the low solubility of riboflavin.

In 1996, Zempleni et al defined the pharmacokinetics of oral and intravenous riboflavin in humans using oral doses of 20, 40, and 60 mg and intravenous doses of 11.6 mg.[118] Based on these and the numerous other studies performed over the years, riboflavin is now classified as a GRAS, or 'generally regarded as safe' compound. Also known for many years is the response of riboflavin to light, and the damage this reaction has on nucleic acids.

In 1965, Tsugita et al determined that the light reaction with riboflavin-inactivated s-RNA required the presence of oxygen to inactivate tobacco mosaic virus[119] and they demonstrated that the inactivation was localized to guanine and adenine nucleotides. In addition, they compared riboflavin to lumichrome and MB and found riboflavin to be the most efficient sensitizer.[119]

The mechanism of action of the phototoxicity of riboflavin was described by Joshi in 1983. At that time, the photodynamic reaction of riboflavin and light was known to generate superoxide anion radicals O_2^- and HO_2, which damaged nucleic acids. Joshi demonstrated that singlet oxygen is also generated by these reactions, leading to photo-oxidation of the nucleotide guanine thus damaging nucleic acids.[120] Two types of photoreactions can occur. Type 1 is a photoreaction between an electronically excited photosensitizer and a biological substrate. This reaction is oxygen independent and the substrate of concern is nucleic acids, although other biologic molecules can be affected, as well. Type II is a reaction of an activated photosensitizer molecule with oxygen resulting in the formation of oxygen radicals.[120] The singlet oxygen radical is responsible for the majority of the damage to nucleic acids and results in strand breaks and fragmentation.

Kumar et al demonstrated the effectiveness of this process over UV light alone on bacteria, viruses, and white cells in 2004.[121] In addition to the generation of oxygen radicals, the photoreaction of riboflavin also generates breakdown photoproducts of lumichrome, lumiflavin, 2'ketoflavin, 4'ketoflavin, flavin mononucleotide, and formyl-methylflavin. Lumichrome and lumiflavin are the most abundant of these products; the others are present in small amounts best detected by HPLC.[118]

Lumichrome toxicity and genotoxicity were evaluated in in vitro and in vivo experiments by Piper et al, in 2002.[122] In vitro genotoxicity was evaluated using the Ames assay[72,122] and was negative. Mouse fibroblasts were incubated with various concentrations of lumichrome, the highest of which was 90 μM (the limit of solubility). Cytotoxicity was not identified. The in vivo portion of the study involved injecting mice with 900 μg/kg of lumichrome IV. No acute toxicity was identified.[122] The other major photo-product of riboflavin—lumiflavin—was evaluated by the Ames Salmonella assay, umu test, and SOS chromotest. The Ames and umu tests are bacterial genotoxicity test systems[123,124] and the SOS chromotest is a bacterial colorimetric assay for genotoxins.[124] In this study, both riboflavin and lumiflavin were negative for genotoxicity. However, when lumiflavin was exposed to metabolic enzymes of the colon and liver, significant mutagenicity was identified by all three assays. The study was performed in order to ascertain the danger posed by riboflavin in food products.[125] Investigation of mutagenicity of lumiflavin has not yet been investigated in blood products. The remaining photoproducts are present in small concentrations and often react to reform riboflavin and thus they are less likely to have an effect.

Platelets

Riboflavin and light (which can be visible light or light within the UV spectrum) can be used to pathogen-reduce all blood products; however, the majority of the studies reported thus far involve platelets. Platelet units subjected to the riboflavin light process have a decreased concentration due to dilution with the 500-μM riboflavin solution. The total platelet count is unchanged and is similar to controls, remaining stable throughout storage. In one study, some in vitro performance characteristics in treated units were significantly different after 5 days of storage.[126] This difference appears to be due to metabolic changes, as the only parameter that changed significantly after photochemical treatment was a marked reduction in pO_2 and a mild increase in P-selectin expression. The treatment also appears to increase glucose consumption. Despite these differences, the parameters were still within the clinically relevant limits for use. In vivo studies will be necessary to determine the significance of the in vitro findings.[126]

A recent study looked solely at the effect of the riboflavin and light process on platelets produced by the buffy coat method used commonly in Europe and platelets acquired via apheresis. Numerous platelet parameters including platelet integrity, morphology, and biological activity were examined. The results were similar to those of previous studies.[127] Again, there was a marked decrease in pO_2 after photochemical treatment, as expected given the mechanism of action of riboflavin and light. Glucose was decreased and P-selectin expression and lactate were increased after storage. pH was decreased over the storage period but remained above 7.0. Overall, there were changes in parameters compared to controls, but the numbers were still within defined clinical limits and suggested the platelets would be functional.[127]

Pathogen inactivation

Investigations of the capacity of riboflavin and light to reduce pathogens without harming the product are in the early stages and have primarily involved use of the technology in platelet concentrates. One of the initial studies placed 10 mM riboflavin into the storage media and exposed them to 419 nm of visible light at 40 and 80 J/cm^2 energy dose. Bovine viral diarrheal virus (BVDV), a model for HCV, was used to infect the platelets. A 3.1 log reduction to the limit of detection was accomplished when the infection dose was 4.4 log (using 40 J/cm^2 energy dose), and a 6.6 log reduction was identified when the initial infection dose was 6.8 log (using 180 J/cm^2 energy dose). The platelet parameters in this study were minimally affected compared to controls.[128]

Goodrich et al looked at bacterial pathogen reduction in platelets in 2002.[129] Riboflavin (50 μM) was added, and the units were spiked to 5–6 log/mL titers with *S. epidermidis*, *Escherichia coli*, *S. aureus*, *B. cereus*, and *K. pneumoniae*. Illumination this time was with 6–7 J/cm^2 of UV light. A low-titer experiment paralleled the above, spiking the units to 2 log/mL titers and using 7 J/cm^2 of UV light. Significant reduction occurred ranging from 3.1 to 5.5 log/mL reduction. Even the low titers were 100–1000 times higher than levels expected in platelets at the time of donation. Thus, the photoactivation of riboflavin appears to be adequate for pathogen reduction in blood products.[129] At the same time, an experiment investigated riboflavin and light in red blood cell units. Using a 500-μM riboflavin solution and 447 nm of visible light for illumination, the red cells spiked with HIV, BVDV, and PSR were treated. Again, significant pathogen reduction occurred. The only red cell parameter examined, hemolysis, was not observed in this experiment.[130]

More extensive studies have been performed with a riboflavin level of 500 μm, which reaches 50 μM on dilution in the platelet concentrate. The light parameters chosen were UV light at 6.2 J/cm^2 with an output ranging from 265 to 370 nm. Porcine parvovirus (PPV) was added to achieve a titer of 6.68 ± 0.20 log $TCID_{50}$. Cell-associated and cell-free HIV were added to a titer of 7.93 ± 0.27 log $TCID_{50}$ per milliliter, and intracellular HIV was added to a titer of 6.64 ± 0.27 $TCID_{50}$ per milliliter. WNV was added to achieve an initial titer of 7.06 ± 0.26 $TCID_{50}$ per milliliter. Interference and cytotoxicity were determined and factored into the results. Gram-negative bacteria represented by *E. coli* and Gram-positive bacteria represented by *S. epidermidis* were used to spike units to an initial titer of 5–6 CFUs/mL for the high-titer arm and 0.5–2 CFUs/mL for the low-titer arm. In vitro platelet parameters were measured and included pH, lactate, pO_2, pCO_2, platelet count, HSR, swirl scores, and P-selectin expression. The viral reduction levels observed exceeded the levels required to close the window period for HIV and reduced the titers of intracellular and free- and cell-associated HIV to below the levels of detection. The reduction in WNV occurred to an extent believed to close the total viremic period for WNV, due to inactivation of 5.11 ± 0.5 log $TCID_{50}$ per milliliter. Parvovirus was also reduced to the level of detection with a reduction factor of > 5.03 log $TCID_{50}$. This amount of reduction could close the chronic phase transmission window for some human parvovirus B19 infections. This last virus is difficult to eradicate, as titers in infected donors can exceed 10^{13} genome equivalents per milliliter. However, levels of B19 below 3.5 log/mL are thought not to be infectious. Both bacterial strains were reduced to below the level of detection in the high titer arm of the study. In the low titer arm, the concentrates remained culture negative after 5 days of storage.[126]

Summary

Riboflavin is photochemically activated by light and produces marked and robust pathogen reduction in platelets and red blood cells. The compound riboflavin is generally considered safe. Questions remain, however, regarding the photoproducts produced by this process; studies of the photoproducts are limited. Lumichrome appears to be safe in studies thus far, but more research is required. Lumiflavin is questionable and additional research will also be necessary. The early studies indicate that the effect of the process on platelets and red blood cells are clinically acceptable. More research on pathogen-reduction technology using riboflavin is needed.

TRANSFUSION-ASSOCIATED GRAFT-VERSUS-HOST DISEASE

Leukocyte inactivation

An unintended, but beneficial, result of nucleic-acid-altering pathogen-reduction technologies is that the processes also inactivate white blood cells, which can cause transfusion-associated graft-versus-host disease (TA-GVHD). Several studies using mice have demonstrated the efficiency of pathogen-reduction technologies in preventing GVHD. Grass et al[131] compared amotosalen PCT and gamma irradiation in an experiment using strain A and B6AF1 mice. Strain A mice are homozygous at the H-2 locus whereas B6AF1 mice are heterozygous. Spleens from the donor mice were collected, processed to produce a splenocyte suspension, and treated in one of three ways. One-third of the suspension was treated with gamma irradiation, one-third was treated with amotosalen PCT, and one-third was untreated. The recipient mice (B6AF1 strain) each received transfusions of one of three suspensions or a suspension of splenocytes from another B6AF1 mouse, which were the controls. Several features of GVHD were followed over several weeks. Those that received untreated cells developed GVHD characterized by splenomegaly, decreased body weight, decreased skin integrity, and pancytopenia. After the animals were killed, the organs were examined histologically for evidence of GVHD. In addition, donor T cell engraftment was demonstrated by flow cytometry. None of the mice that received products treated by gamma irradiation or amotosalen PCT developed GVHD. All six mice that received the untreated product developed GVHD.[131] Additional mouse-based studies[132–134] demonstrated the efficiency of PEN110 in preventing GVHD. Riboflavin was demonstrated to be effective using a cell culture of Jurkat cells.[135] Thus, based on existing data, pathogen-reduction technologies that disrupt nucleic acids also appear to prevent TA-GVHD.

CONCLUSION

Pathogen-reduction technologies show great promise for making the blood supply safer. Indeed, some PR-treated products are in use clinically. However, no PR technology is risk free. As we learn more about the pathogens that infect the blood supply, we realize that not all pathogens will be fully inactivated. Accordingly, it is unlikely that current practices testing for pathogens can be eliminated. The full clinical role of PR technologies in the field of transfusion medicine remains to be determined.

REFERENCES

1. Teitel JM. Viral safety of haemophilia treatment products. *Annals Medicine* 2000; **32**(7): 785.
*2. Epstein JS & Vostal JG. FDA approach to evaluation of pathogen reduction technology. *Transfusion* 2003; **43**: 1347.
3. Katz L. Blood bags for diversion of the initial collection: a statement of the American Association of Blood Banks before the Blood Products Advisory Committee; March 15, 2001.
4. Rossi EC & Simon TL. Transfusion in the new millennium. In Simon TL et al (ed.) *In: Rossi's Principles of Transfusion Medicine*, third edn. Philadelphia, PA: Lippincott Williams and Wilkins, 2002.
5. *Technical Manual*. 14th edn. Bethesda, MD: American Association of Blood Banks; 2002.
6. Update on WNV-related activities and recommendations, American Association of Blood Banks, Bulletin 03–11; September 12 2003.
7. Biggeerstaff BJ & Petersen LR. Estimated risk of transmission of the West Nile Virus through blood transfusions in the US, 2002. *Transfusion* 2003; **43**(8): 1007.
8. Yoto Y. Incidence of human parvovirus B19 DNA detection in blood donors. *British Journal of Haematology* 1995; **91**: 1017.
9. Wu YY & Snyder EL. Safety of the blood supply: role of pathogen reduction. *Blood Reveiws* 2003; **17**: 111.
10. Hirayama J, Wagner SJ, Abe H et al. Involvement of reactive oxygen species in hemoglobin oxidation and virus inactivation by 1,9-dimethylmethylene blue photo-treatment. *Biological Pharmacy Bulletin* 2001; **24**(4): 418.
11. Wagner SJ, Skripchenko A & Thompson-Montgomery D. Quinacrine enhances vesicular stomatitis virus inactivation and diminishes hemolysis of dimethylene blue-photo-treated red cells. *Photochemistry and Photobiology* 2002; **76**(5): 514.
12. van der Poel CL. Hepatitis C virus and blood transfusion: past and present risks. *Journal of Hepatology* 1999; **31**(S1): 101.
13. Rollag H, Solheim BG & Svennevig JL. Viral safety of blood derivatives by immune neutralization. *Vox Sanguinis* 1998; **74**(S1): 213.
14. Horowitz B & Ben-Hur E. Efforts in minimizing risk of viral transmission through viral inactivation. *Annals of Medicine* 2000; **32**: 475.
15. Dodd RY. Current viral risks of blood and blood products. *Annals of Medicine* 2000; **32**: 469.
16. Haubelt H, Blome M, Kiessling AH et al. Effects of solvent/detergent-treated plasma and fresh-frozen plasma on haemostasis and fibrinolysis in complex coagulopathy following open-heart surgery. *Vox Sanguinis* 2002; **82**: 9.
17. Snyder EL & Dodd RY, Reducing the risk of blood transfusion. In Schecuter GP, Broudy VC & Williams ME (eds.) *Hematology, 2001 American Society of Hematology Education Program Book*; 2001, 2001, . 433.
18. FDA. Workshop on safety and efficacy of methods for reducing pathogens in cellular products used in transfusion, Bethesda, MD; 7 August 2002. Available at: http://www.fda.gov/cber/minutes/path-trans080702.pdf
19. Cazenave JP, Aleil B, Wiesel ML et al. In vitro evaluation of pooled buffy coat platelets treated with photochemical pathogen inactivation using amotosalen. *Vox Sanguinis* 2004; **86**: 201–202.
20. Roberts P. Resistance of Vaccinia virus to inactivation by solvent/detergent treatment of blood products. *Biologicals* 2000; **28**: 29.
21. Mohr H. Virus inactivation of fresh plasma. *Vox Sanguinis* 1998; **74**(S2): 171.
22. Delipidation treatments for large scale protein purification process. From http://scholar.lib.vt.edu/theses/public/etd-1454132679612381/etd-title.html
23. Pamphilon D. Viral inactivation of fresh frozen plasma. *British Journal of Haematology* 2000; **109**: 680.

24. Horowitz B, Lazo A, Grossberg H et al. Virus inactivation by solvent/detergent treatment and the manufacture of SD-plasma. *Vox Sanguinis* 1998; **74**(S1): 203.

25. Pehta JC. Clinical studies with solvent detergent-treated products. *Transfusion Medicine Reviews* 1996; **10**(4): 303.

26. Letter to providers from V.I. Technologies Inc. (VITEX). Important prescribing information October 20, 2000.

27. Horowitz B, Klein HG, Cable R. Preparing for pathogen reduction. AABB Annual Meeting News; 2003, 7.

28. Williamson LM, Llewelyn CA, Fisher NC et al. A randomized trial of solvent/detergent-treated and standard fresh-frozen plasma in the coagulopathy of liver disease and liver transplantation. *Transfusion* 1999; **39**: 1227.

29. Beisert L & Suhartono H. Solvent/detergent treatment of human plasma—a very robust method for virus inactivation. Validation virus safety of OCTAPLAS®. *Vox Sanguinis* 1998; **74**(S1): 207.

30. AuBuchon JP & Birkmeyer JD. Safety and cost-effectiveness of solvent-detergent-treated plasma: in search of a zero risk blood supply. *JAMA* 1994; **272**(15): 1210.

31. Fricke W. FDA perspective on and response to risk of hepatitis A from blood products. *Vox Sanguinis* 1994; **67**(S4): 16.

32. Beisert L. Virus validation studies of immunoglobulin preparations. *Clinical and Experimental Rheumatology* 1996; **14**(S15): S47.

*33. Wagner SJ, Skripchenko A, Robinette D et al. The use of dimethylene blue for virus photo-inactivation of red cell suspensions. *Development in Biological Standardization* 1999; **102**: 125.

*34. Summary of basis for approval: 93-0253 and 97-0141, plasma, solvent/detergent treated. VIPLAS/SDTM V.I. Technologies (VITEX). From www.fda.gov/cber/sba/sdplvit050698s.pdf

35. Chandra S, Groener A & Feldman F. Effectiveness of alternative treatments for reducing potential viral contaminants from plasma derived products. *Thrombosis Research* 2002; **105**: 391.

36. Horowitz MS & Pehta JC. SD plasma in TTP and coagulation factor deficiencies for which no concentrates are available. *Vox Sanguinis* 1998; **74**(S1): 231.

*37. Breek H & Hellstern P. In vitro characterization of solvent/detergent-treated human plasma and of quarantine fresh frozen plasma. *Vox Sanguinis* 1998; **74**(S1): 219.

38. Freeman JW, Williamson LM & Llewelyn C. A randomized trial of solvent/detergent and standard fresh frozen plasma in the treatment of coagulopathy seen during orthotopic liver transplantation. *Vox Sanguinis* 1998; **74**(S1): 225.

39. Williamson LM & Allain JP. Virally inactivated fresh frozen plasma. *Vox Sanguinis* 1995; **69**(3): 159.

40. Sarode R & Yomtovian R. Efficacy of SD-treated plasma during liver transplantation. *Transfusion* 2000; **40**: 886.

41. Fischer G, Hoots WK & Abrams C. Viral reduction techniques: types and purpose. *Transfusion Medicine Reviews* 2001; **15**(2 supplement 1): 27.

42. Material safety datae sheet for Triton-X. From: http://www.genomicsolutions.com/files/80-0178%20Triton%20X-100.pdf

43. FDA approves alternative to fresh frozen plasma. May 6, 1998. From: http://www.fda.gov/bbs/topics/ANSWERS/ANS00868.html

44. Piquet Y, Janvier G, Selosse P et al. Virus inactivation of fresh frozen plasma by a solvent detergent procedure: biological results. *Vox Sanguinis* 1992; **63**(4): 251.

45. Riedler GF, Haycox AR, Duggan AK & Dakin HA. Impact of TRALI on the cost-effectiveness of solvent-detergent-treated fresh-frozen plasma (Octaplas®). *British Journal of Haematology* 2003; **121**(supplement 1): 81.

46. Pereira A. Cost-effectiveness of transfusing virus-inactivated plasma instead of standard plasma. *Transfusion* 1999; **39**: 479.

47. Jackson BR, AuBuchon JP & Birkmeyer JD. Update of cost-effectiveness analysis for solvent-detergent-treated plasma. *JAMA* 1999; **282**(4): 329.

48. Tollofsrud S, Noddeland H & Svennevig JL. Universal fresh frozen plasma (Uniplas®): a safe product in open heart surgery. *Intensive Care Medicine* 2003; **29**: 1736.

49. Noddeland H, Tollofsrud S, Svennevig JL et al. Universal solvent/detergent-treated fresh frozen plasma (Uniplas®)—rationale and clinical properties. *Thrombosis Research* 2002; **107**: S33.

*50. Wainwright M. The use of dyes in modern medicine. *Biotechnic and Histochemistry* 2003; **78**(3-4): 147.

*51. OhUigin C, McConnell DJ, Kelly JM & van der Putten WJM. Methylene blue photosensitized strand cleavage of DNA: effects of dye binding and oxygen. *Nucleic Acid Research* 1987; **15**(18): 7411.

52. Floyd RA, Schneider JE & Dittmer DP. Methylene blue photo-inactivation of RNA viruses. *Antiviral Research* 2004; **61**: 141.

53. Wainwright M. Methylene blue derivatives-suitable photomicrobials for blood product disinfection? *International Journal of Antimicrobial Agents* 2000; **16**: 381.

54. Wainwright M. Pathogen inactivation in blood products. *Current Medicinal Chemistry* 2002; **9**: 127.

55. Hornsey VS, Drummond O, Young D et al. A potentially improved approach to methylene blue virus inactivation of plasma: the Maco Pharma Maco-Tronic system. *Transfusion Medicine* 2001; **11**: 31.

56. Wagner SJ & Skripchenko A. Investigation of photosensitizing dyes for pathogen reduction in red cell suspensions. *Biotechnic and Histochemistry* 2003; **78**(3-4): 171.

57. Kelner MJ & Alexander NM. Methylene blue directly oxidizes glutathione without the intermediate formation of hydrogen peroxide. *The Journal of Biological Chemistry* 1985; **260**(28): 15168.

58. Mohr H, Bachmann B, Klein-Struckmeier A & Lanbrecht B. Virus inactivation of blood products by phenothiazine dyes and light. *Photochemistry and Photobiology* 1997; **65**(3): 441.

59. Karl-Freidrich Bopp K, Morell A, Parkkinen J et al. Pathogen inactivation of labile blood products. *Transfusion Medicine* 2001; **11**(3): 149.

60. Material safety data sheet for methylene blue from http://ptcl.chem.ox.ac.uk/MSDS/ME/methylene_blue.html

61. Material safety data sheet: methylene blue from http://www.jtbaker.com/msds/englishhtml/m4381.htm

*62. Wollowitz S. Fundamentals of the Psoralen-based helinx technology for inactivation of infectious pathogens and leukocytes in platelets and plasma. *Seminars in Hematology* 2001; **38**(supplement 11): 4–11.

63. Dardare N & Platz MS. Binding affinities of commonly employed sensitizers of viral inactivation. *Photochemistry and Photobiology* 2002; **75**(6): 561.

64. Allain J & Seghatchain J. Current strategies on pathogen removal/inactivation: an overview. *Transfusion and Apheresis Science* 2001; **25**: 195.

65. Detty MR, Gibson SL & Wagner SJ. Current clinical and pre-clinical photosensitizers for use in photodynamic therapy. *Journal of Medicinal Chemistry* 2004; **47**(16): 3897–3915.

66. Skripchenko AA & Wagner SJ. Inactivation of WBCs in RBC suspensions by photoactive phenothiazine dyes: comparison of dimethylene blue and MB. *Transfusion* 2000; **40**: 968.

67. Wieding JU, Hellstern P & Kohler M. Inactivation of viruses in fresh frozen plasma. *Annals of Hematology* 1993; **67**(6): 259.

68. Pereira A. Methylene-blue photo-inactivated plasma and its contribution to blood safety. *Transfusion* 2004; **44**: 948.

69. Aznar JA, Bonanad S, Montoro JM et al. Influence of Methylene blue photoinactivation treatment on coagulation factors from fresh frozen plasma, cryoprecipitates, and cryosupernatants. *Vox Sanguinis* 2000; **79**: 156.

70. Wollowitz S. Fundamentals of the Psoralen-based helinx technology for inactivation of infectious pathogens and leukocytes in platelets and plasma. *Seminars in Hematology* 38(supplement 11): 4–11.

71. Wu YY & Snyder EL. Safety of the blood supply: role of pathogen reduction. *Blood Reviews*172003;: 111–122.

72. Ciaravino V, McCullough T, Cimino G & Sullivan T. Preclinical safety profile of plasma prepared using the INTERCEPT Blood System. *Vox Sanguinis* 2003; **85**: 171–182.

*73. Ciaravino V, McCullough T & Cimino G. The role of toxicology assessment in transfusion medicine. *Transfusion* 2003; **43**: 1481–1492.

*74. Moog R, Frohlich A, Mayaudon V & Lin L. In vitro evaluation of COM.TEC apheresis platelet concentrates using a preparation set and pathogen inactivation over a storage period of five days. *Journal of Clinical Apheresis* 2004; **19**: 185–191.

75. Jansen G, VanVliet H, Vermeij H et al. Functional characteristics of photochemically treated platelets. *Transfusion* 2004; **44**: 313–319.

*76. Cazenave J, Aleil B, Wiesel M et al. In vitro evaluation of pooled buffy-coat platelets treated with photochemical pathogen inactivation using amotosalen. Letters. *Vox Sanguinis* 2004; **86**: 201–202.

77. Snyder E et al. Recovery and life span of 111 indium-radiolabeled platelets treated with pathogen inactivation with amotosalen HCL (S-59) and ultraviolet A light. *Transfusion* 2004; **44**: 1732–1740.

78. van Rhenen V et al. Transfusion of pooled buffy coat platelet components prepared with photochemical pathogen inactivation treatment: the euroSPRITE trial. *Blood* 2003; **101**(6): 2426–2433.

*79. McCullough J et al. Therapeutic efficacy and safety of platelets treated with a photochemical process for pathogen inactivation: the SPRINT Trial. *Blood* 2004; **104**: 1534–1541.

*80. Pinkoski T, et al. The INTERCEPT Blood System for plasma: process validation studies of coagulation factor activity and yield in two European blood centers. Abstract presented at American Society of Hematology Annual Meeting, San Diego, CA; December 4–7, 2004.

81. Corash L. Helinx technology for inactivation of infectious pathogens and leukocytes in labile blood components: from theory to clinical application. *Transfusion and Apheresis Science* 2001; **25**: 179–181.

*82. Hambleton J et al. Pharmacokinetic study of FFP photochemically treated with amotosalen (S-59) and UV light compared to FFP in healthy volunteers anticoagulated with warfarin. *Transfusion* 2002; **42**: 1302–1307.

83. Wages D et al. Treatment of acquired coagulopathy by transfusion of fresh frozen plasma (FFP) prepared using a novel, single unit photochemical pathogen inactivation (P.I.) process. *Blood* 1999; **Nov. 15**(supplement 1): 247a.

84. Hillyer KL, et al. von Willebrand factor-cleaving protease (vWF-CP) in S-59 treated donor plasma. Abstract Presented at the American Society of Hematology, 42nd Annual Meeting; December 2000.

85. Mintz PD et al. Theraputic plasma exchange for thrombotic thrombocytopenic purpura using plasma prepared with photochemical treatment (INTERCEPT Plasma). *Blood* 2004; **104**: 239a.

86. Lin L et al. Photochemical inactivation of viruses and bacteria in platelet concentrates by use of a novel psoralen and long-wavelength ultraviolet light. *Transfusion* 1997; **7**: 423–435.

87. van Voorhis WC et al. *Trypanosoma cruzi* inactivation in human platelet concentrates and plasma by a psoralen (amotosalen HCL) and long-wavelength UV. *Antimicrobial Agents of Chemotherapy* 2003; **47**(2): 475–479.

88. Lin L et al. Inactivation of cytomegalovirus in platelet concentrates using Helinx™ technology. *Seminars in Hematology* 2001; **38**(4): 27–33.

89. Jordan CT. Photochemical treatment of platelet concentrates with amotosalen hydrochloride and ultraviolet A light inactivates free and latent cytomegalovirus in a murine transfusion model. *Transfusion* 2004; **44**: 1159–1165.

90. Lin L et al. Photochemical treatment of platelet concentrates with amotosalen and longwavelength ultraviolet light inactivates a broad spectrum of pathogenic bacteria. *Transfusion* 2004; **44**: 1496–1504.

91. Bell CF, et al. Cost effectiveness of pathogen inactivation in blood platelet transfusion-a German model. Abstract presented at 27th Annual Congress of the International Society of Blood Transfusion, Vancouver, BC; August 2002.

92. van Hulst M, et al. Cost effectiveness of pathogen inactivation for platelet transfusions in Dutch cardiac surgery. Abstract presented at 27th Annual Congress of the International Society of Blood Transfusion, Vancouver, BC; August 2002.

93. Corash L. Inactivation of viruses, bacteria, protozoa, and leukocytes in platelet and red cell concentrates. *Vox Sanguinis* 2000; **78**(supplement 2): 205–210.

*94. Cook D, Stassinopoulos A et al. Inactivation of pathogens in packed red cell concentrates using S-303. *Blood* 1997; **90**(supplement 1): 409a.

*95. Cook D et al. In vivo analysis of packed red blood cells treated with S-303 to inactivate pathogens. *Blood* 1998; **92**(supplement 1): 503a.

96. Hambleton J et al. Post transfusion recovery after multiple exposures to red cell concentrates treated with a novel pathogen inactivation process. *Blood* 1999; **94**(supplement 1): 376a.

97. Hambleton J, et al. RBCs treated with Helinx™ pathogen inactivation have recovery and half-life comparable to conventional RBCs in a randomized cross-over trial. Presented at the Seventh Annual Congress of the European Hematology Association, Florence, Italy; June 2002.

*98. Benjamin RJ et al. Transfusion of S-303 treated RBCs to treat acute anemia during or following cardiac surgery: results of a phase III trial. Abstract No. 381. *Blood* 2004; **104**: 112a.

*99. Conlan MG et al. Antibody formation to S-303 treated RBCs in the setting of chronic RBC transfusion. Abstract No. 382. *Blood* 2004; **104**: 112a.

100. Stassinopoulos A et al. Elimination of immunoreactivity of red cells treated with a modified S-303 pathogen inactivation process. Abstract No. 2703. *Blood* 2004; **104**: 738a.

101. Chapman J. Progress in improving the pathogen safety of red cell concentrates. *Vox Sanguinis* 2000; **78**(supplement 2): 203–204.

*102. Chapman J et al. Pathogen inactivation of RBCs: PEN110 reproductive toxicology studies. *Transfusion* 2003; **43**: 1386–1393.

103. Chapman J & Butterworth BE. Genetic toxicology profile of Inactine PEN110. *Toxicologist* 2000; **66**: 73.

104. Purmal A et al. Process for the preparation of pathogen-inactivated RBC concentrates by using PEN110 chemistry: preclinical studies. *Transfusion* 2002; **42**: 139–145.

*105. Snyder E, et al. Pathogen inactivated red blood cells using INACTINE™ technology demonstrate 24 hours post transfusion recovery equal to untreated red cells after 42 days of storage. Presented at the American Society of Hematology, 43rd Annual Meeting, Orlando, FL; December 2001.

*106. AuBuchon J et al. Production of pathogen-inactivated RBC concentrates using PEN110 chemistry: a phase I clinical study. *Transfusion* 2002; **42**: 146–152.

107. Lazo A et al. Broad-spectrum virus reduction in red cell concentrates using INACTIME™ PEN110 chemistry. *Vox Sanguinis* 2002; **83**: 313–323.

108. Ohagen A et al. Inactivation of HIV in blood. *Transfusion* 2002; **42**: 1308–1317.

*109. Aytay S et al. Development of a sensitive PCR inhibition method to demonstrate HBV nucleic acid inactivation. *Transfusion* 2004; **44**: 476–484.

110. Mather T et al. West Nile virus in blood: stability, distribution, and susceptibility to PEN110 inactivation. *Transfusion* 2003; **43**: 1029–1037.

111. Ohagen A et al. Induction of latent human cytomegalovirus by conventional gamma irradiation and prevention by treatment with INACTINE PEN110. *Vox Sanguinis* 2004; **87**: 1–9.

*112. Zavizion B et al. Inactivation of Gram-negative and Gram-positive bacteria in red cell concentrates using INACTINE PEN110 chemistry. *Vox Sanguinis* 2004; **87**: 143–149.

*113. Zavizion B et al. Inactivation of mycoplasma species in blood by Inactine PEN110 process. *Transfusion* 2004; **44**: 286–293.

*114. Zavizion B et al. Inactivation of protozoan parasites in red blood cells using Inactine PEN110 chemistry. *Transfusion* 2004; **44**: 731–738.

115. Zavizion B et al. Prevention of *Yersinia enterolitica*, *Pseudomonas fluorescens*, and *Pseudamonas putida* out growth in deliberately inoculated blood by a novel pathogen-reduction process. *Transfusion* 2003; **43**: 135–142.

*116. Hardwick C et al. Separation, identification, and quantification of riboflavin and its photoproducts using high-performance liquid chromatography with fluorescence detection: a method to support pathogen reduction technology. *Photochemistry and Photobiology* 2004; **80**: 609–615.

117. Unna K & Greslin J. Studies on the toxicity and pharmacology of riboflavin. *The Journal of Pharmacology and Experimental Therapeutics* 1942; **75**: 75–80.

118. Zempleni J et al. Pharmacokinetics of orally and intravenously administered riboflavin in health humans. *American Journal of Clinical Nutrition* 1996; **63**: 54–66.

*119. Tsugita A, Okada Y & Uehara K. Photosensitized inactivation of ribonucleic acid in the presence of riboflavin. *Biochemica et Biophysica Acta* 1965; **103**: 360–363.

*120. Joshi P. Comparison of the DNA-damaging property of photosensitized riboflavin via singlet oxygen and superoxide radical mechanisms. *Toxicology Letters* 1985; **26**: 211–217.

121. Kumar V et al. Riboflavin and UV-light based pathogen reduction: extent and consequence of DNA damage at the molecular level. *Photochemistry and Photobiology* 2004; **80**: 15–21.

122. Piper J et al. Assessment of the acute toxicity and genotoxicity risks associated with lumichrome, the primary photoproduct of riboflavin. Abstract No. P575. *Vox Sanguinis* 2002; **83**: 192.

123. Maron DM & Ames BN. Revised methods for the Salmonella mutagenicity test. *Mutation Research* 1983; **113**: 173–215.

124. Quillardet P & Hofnung M. The SOS chromotest, a calorimetric bacterial assay for genotoxins: procedures. *Mutation Research* 1985; **147**: 65–78.

125. Kale H et al. Assessment of the genotoxic potential of riboflavin and lumiflavin. A. Effect of metabolic enzymes. *Mutation Research* 1992; **298**: 9–16.

126. Ruane PH et al. Photochemical inactivation of selected viruses and bacteria in platelet concentrates using riboflavin and light. *Transfusion* 2004; **44**: 855–877.

127. Li J et al. Pathogen reduction of buffy coat platelet concentrates using riboflavin and light: comparisons with pathogen-reduction technology-treated apheresis platelet products. *Vox Sanguinis* 2004; **87**: 82–90.

128. McBurney LL et al. The use of riboflavin for the viral inactivation of platelets. Abstract No. 136-0401. *Transfusion* 2000; **40S:** 37S.

129. Goodrich L et al. Riboflavin photoinactivation procedure inactivates significant levels of bacteria and produces a culture negative product. Abstract No. S58-030J. *Transfusion* 2002; **42:** 16S.

130. Reddy H et al. Reduction of virus in red blood cell suspensions with riboflavin and light. Abstract No. S57-030J. *Transfusion* 2002; **42:** 16S.

131. Grass J et al. Prevention of transfusion associated graft versus host disease by photochemical treatment. *Blood* 1999; **93:** 3140–3147.

132. Fast L et al. Inhibition of xenogeneic GVHD by PEN 110 treatment of donor human PBMNCs. *Transfusion* 2004; **44:** 282–285.

*133. Fast L et al. Inhibition of murine GVHD by PEN 110 treatment. *Transfusion* 2002; **42:** 1326–1332.

*134. Fast L et al. PEN 110 treatment functionally inactivates the PBMNCs present in RBC units: comparison to the effects of exposure to gamma irradiation. *Transfusion* 2002; **42:** 1318–1325.

135. Reddy H, et al. Inactivation of T-lymphocytes with riboflavin and visible light. Abstract presented at the 27th Congress of the International Society of Blood Transfusion, Vancouver, BC, Canada; August 24–28, 2002.

Hereditary angioedema: Safety of long-term stanozolol therapy

David E. Sloane, MD, Chyh Woei Lee, MD, and Albert L. Sheffer, MD *Chestnut Hill, Mass*

Background: Attenuated androgens control attacks of hereditary angioedema. Short-term studies of such patients treated at our institution with attenuated androgens demonstrated no adverse effects. However, the side-effect frequencies in patients receiving long-term treatment are relatively less well characterized.

Objective: To assess the frequencies of various side effects of the attenuated androgen stanozolol in a population of patients with hereditary angioedema treated for 20 to 40 years.

Methods: Data on side effects in patients who continued stanozolol therapy since 1987 were obtained by means of questionnaire. Patients were evaluated by physical examination; biochemical assays of hepatic function, serum lipids, and prostate specific antigen; and liver ultrasound.

Results: The minimal initial effective dosage of stanozolol was 0.5 to 2.0 mg daily, although most patients achieved symptomatic control and decreased the dose and frequency as the frequency of attacks decreased. Treatment-related symptoms developed in 10 of 21 patients. No interruption in stanozolol therapy was required because symptoms subsided with a reduction in the stanozolol dosage. Adverse side effects included hirsutism, weight gain, menstrual irregularities or postmenopausal bleeding, acne, and mood changes. Liver enzyme assays revealed no persistent abnormalities. Liver ultrasounds in 8 patients revealed 3 abnormalities deemed unrelated to therapy. Five patients had a reduced high-density lipoprotein, and 2 patients had elevated triglycerides.

Conclusion: Stanozolol is a safe and effective drug for the long-term management of hereditary angioedema.

Clinical implications: Stanozolol may be used in the long-term treatment of patients with hereditary angioedema provided such patients are closely supervised with routine clinical, biochemical, and radiologic assessments. (J Allergy Clin Immunol 2007;120:654-8.)

Key words: *Hereditary angioedema, attenuated androgens, stanozolol, side effects*

From Harvard Medical School/Brigham and Women's Hospital.

Disclosure of potential conflict of interest: A. L. Sheffer has consulting arrangements with Genentech and Pharming and has received grant support from Dyax. D. E. Sloane has received grant support from GlaxoSmithKline and Dyax and is on the speakers' bureau for Genentech and Novartis. C. W. Lee has declared no conflict of interest.

Received for publication March 22, 2007; revised June 5, 2007; accepted for publication June 29, 2007.

Reprint requests: Albert L. Sheffer, MD, Harvard Medical School/Brigham and Women's Hospital, Division of Rheumatology, Immunology, and Allergy, 850 Boylston Street, Suite 540, Chestnut Hill, MA 02467. E-mail: asheffer@partners.org.

0091-6749/$32.00

© 2007 American Academy of Allergy, Asthma & Immunology

doi:10.1016/j.jaci.2007.06.037

Abbreviations used
HAE: Hereditary angioedema
PSA: Prostate specific antigen

Prophylactic administration of androgens[1,2] or anabolic agents with impeded androgenic effects[3-5] clearly prevents spontaneous as well as soft tissue trauma (dental and surgical)–induced episodes of angioedema in patients with hereditary angioedema (HAE). Since Spaulding's[1] original report of the efficacy of methyltestosterone in HAE, several anabolic agents with impeded androgenic effect have been used in the treatment of this disorder.[3-5] Biochemical evidence in support of therapy with such agents includes the partial correction of the decreased inhibitor to the first complement component (C 1 INH) serum concentration and reversal of the secondarily depressed C4 serum levels.[3] Attenuated androgens probably enhance hepatic C 1 INH production. Because these drugs act on the liver, hepatic dysfunction as a result of treatment is a concern.[6-8]

With close supervision of patients with HAE treated with attenuated androgens, the anticipated adverse side effects such as retarded growth in children, virilization, hepatic dysfunction, and lipid abnormalities have not been observed in short-term assessments.[8,9] A previous study determined the lowest and safest dosage, which controlled the symptoms of patients with HAE by using oxymetholone and then stanozolol.[9] The current study retrospectively ascertained the clinical status of patients with biochemically proven HAE who continued androgen therapy since our last report[9,10] and also evaluated the frequency of adverse effects of such therapy. Along with assessment of treatment-related symptoms, biochemical assays of hepatic function, serum lipids, liver ultrasound, and prostatic assessment by prostate specific antigen (PSA) were performed. The patients had been followed by the investigators for at least 20 and in some instances for nearly 40 years.[10]

METHODS

A previous study from this institution documented a decade of experience with stanozolol in the treatment of 37 patients with HAE.[10] The purpose of the current study was to evaluate those patients in follow-up, including physical and biochemical assessment, to define any long-term toxicity of therapy with attenuated androgens. Of the original group, 2 patients with HAE have died (1 of natural

Food allergy, anaphylaxis, dermatology, and drug allergy

TABLE I. Population data for patients with HAE*

Patient no.	Sex	Current age (y)	C1INH (functional/nonfunctional)	MT	Oxy	Stan	Years on stanozolol
1	F	57	Functional		1976	1977	29
3	M	73	Functional	1974	1976	1977	29
4	F	61	Functional		1976	1977	29
5	F	48	Functional		1976	1977	29
6	F	55	Functional		1976	1977	29
7	F	48	Functional		1976	1977	29
8	M	72	Nonfunctional	1968	1976	1977	29
9	M	66	Nonfunctional	1973	1976	1977	29
10	F	72	Functional	1968		1977	29
14	M	63	Functional		1976	1977	29
15	M	54	Functional		1976	1977	29
16	F	58	Functional			1977	29
17	F	31	Functional			1983	23
18	F	42	Functional			1979	27
19	M	70	Functional		1976	1977	29
21	M	58	Functional	1967	1976	1977	29
22	F	59	Functional		1976	1977	29
26	F	84	Functional			1977	29
28	F	45	Functional			1977	29
30	F	62	Functional			1977	29
36	M	88	Functional		1976	1977	29

F, Female; *M*, male.

*Patients with HAE from our institution treated with attenuated androgens participated in the current study on the safety of stanozolol. Patient numbers are not consecutive because they are carried over from reference 9 and experience summarized in reference 10. Before the initiation of stanozolol *(Stan)*, 5 patients had been taking methyltestosterone *(MT)*, and 14 had been taking oxymethalone *(Oxy)*.

causes unrelated to HAE and the other of esophageal carcinoma), 2 brothers were lost to follow-up, and 5 were using a drug other than stanozolol (danazol). As previously reported, a significant proportion of patients with HAE whose disease is controlled with attenuated androgens see a decrement in the frequency and/or severity of their attacks. In keeping with this, 6 of the 37 patients no longer required pharmacologic treatment for HAE. The remaining 22 patients reported on are those who have been treated with stanozolol since 1977. They received a questionnaire approved by the Brigham and Women's Hospital Human Study Committee (Table I). Of the 22 reported patients, 2 patients had biochemical documentation of a nonfunctional C 1 INH, whereas the remaining 20 had subnormal concentrations of C 1 INH.

The reported population consisted of 9 men and 13 women from 31 to 88 years of age, mean 60.3 years, who without treatment experienced at least monthly attacks of HAE. Most of the patients had been asymptomatic for several months to years on stanozolol therapy. Fifteen patients were followed at the Brigham and Women's Hospital Allergy Section every 6 months. The other 7 patients had returned to their respective primary care physicians or had moved from the area, but they responded to the study questionnaire. Patients were evaluated by the investigator every 6 months unless abnormalities were detected on assessment, in which case the patient was asked to return in a month. The objective was to maintain the patients with HAE attack-free at a dosage of stanozolol that did not cause hepatic enzyme elevation. Patients receiving stanozolol (usually at 2 mg per day or less) had a complete blood count, liver enzyme measurement, lipid profile, and PSA for men measured every 6 months. Patients underwent routine breast and prostate examination by their primary care physician, gynecologist, or urologist. This and all previous protocols were approved by the Brigham and Women's Hospital Committee for the Protection of Human Subjects from Research Risks. Informed consent was obtained from each participant.

RESULTS

Clinically relevant treatment-related symptoms occurred in 10 patients, but these adverse reactions (symptoms) required no interruption in stanozolol therapy and subsided with a reduction in the dosage of stanozolol (Table II). The most commonly reported adverse effects included hirsutism (7 patients), weight gain (3 patients), menstrual irregularities (oligomenorrhea in 2 patients and menorrhagia in a third patient) or postmenopausal bleeding (4 women), acne (3 patients), and mood changes (2 patients). None of these effects was long-lasting or required specific treatment. As patients achieved improved control of their HAE and were able to decrease the dosage of stanozolol, these symptoms resolved without permanent sequelae. There were 11 patients who experienced no adverse effects with stanozolol therapy (Table II).

Measurement of liver enzymes (alanine aminotransferase, aspartate aminotransferase) within the past year revealed no persistent abnormalities (Table III). Hepatic ultrasound recently has been suggested as an additional parameter for routine assessment of adverse effects of attenuated androgens involving the liver, because hepatic function and transaminase levels may be preserved in some patients with hepatocellular adenoma.[11] A recent HAE consensus report supports this position.[12] Therefore, liver ultrasound evaluation was performed after this recommendation was published. Recent scans in 8 patients revealed 3 with abnormalities. One occurred in a patient with esophageal carcinoma, but this patient

TABLE II. Patient-reported side effects of stanozlol*

Patient no.	Sex	Current stanozolol dose	Menstrual cycle	Hair growth	Skin	Weight gain	Psychiatric	Voice	Other	None reported	No survey
1	F	2 mg Q4 d								Yes	
3	M	1-2 mg QD								Yes	
4	F	1 mg QOD		Yes							
5	F	PRN								Yes	
6	F	PRN		Yes	Yes						
7	F	2 mg QD		Yes (thinner)	Yes (oily)		Loss of libido	Deeper			
8	M	PRN								Yes	
9	M	1-2 mg Q3 d				Yes					
10	F	2 mg QOD		Yes		Yes					
14	M	1 mg QD								Yes	
15	M	2 mg × 2 d, off for 1 d		Yes		Yes	"Short temper, anger"				
16	F	PRN								Yes	
17	F	1 mg QD	Yes	Yes							
18	F	1 mg QOD vs 2 mg QOD	Yes		Yes (acne)						
19	M	PRN								Yes	
21	M	2 mg QOD								Yes	
22	F	PRN	Yes								
26	F	2 mg QD		Yes							
28	F	PRN									X
30	F	PRN								Yes	
36	M	PRN								Yes	
Total patients		**Totals**	3	7	3	3	2	1	0	10	
21			13	21	21	21	21	21	21	21	
Men	Women										
8	13										

F, Female; *M*, male; *Q4 d*, every 4th day; *QD*, daily; *QOD*, every other day; *PRN*, as necessary; *Q3 d*, every 3rd day; *2 d*, daily for 2 days; *1 d*, off the 3rd day.
*Patients with HAE reported the side effects of stanozolol treatment via standardized questionnaire. See text for details. Patient numbers are not consecutive because they are carried over from reference 9 and experience summarized in reference 10.

subsequently had a normal abdominal computed tomography (CT) scan, suggesting that the liver lesion was inconsequential. A second patient had fatty infiltration of the liver, and a third had evidence of slight steatosis without a mass. A fourth patient had a small hemangioma that was considered unrelated to therapy.

Lipid profiles demonstrated no patient with either elevated total cholesterol or low-density lipoprotein (LDL) cholesterol. There was a reduced high-density lipoprotein (HDL) in 5 patients and elevated triglycerides in 2. Clinical evidence of cardiovascular complications was not observed in this study. An elevated PSA occurred in 1 of the 5 men tested.

Decisions regarding stanozolol dosage were based on the frequency and severity of a patient's HAE attacks according to an empirically successful weaning protocol (Fig 1). The initial dosage of stanozolol was 2 mg once daily. At the time of this assessment, 5 patients were on stanozolol therapy (1-2 mg) daily, 4 were on alternate day therapy, 3 patients were on less frequent but regular therapy, and 9 patients were no longer taking stanozolol regularly after being asymptomatic for at least a 3-month period. These patients used stanozolol only as needed preoperatively or for cutaneous or gastrointestinal attacks (as

necessary). For dental extraction and for other procedures involving soft tissue trauma and/or general anesthesia, stanozolol 4 mg was administered every 6 hours for 5 days before to the procedure.[10] To break an acute attack, 2 units of fresh frozen plasma were administered (as has recently been reviewed[13]), and the patient was told to take stanozolol 4 mg 3 times daily if it was early in an attack. Thereafter, the 2 mg per day schedule was resumed and a reduction in dosage schedule attempted according to the weaning protocol (Fig 1). The severity of the attacks was clearly reduced while on stanozolol and even after regular stanozolol therapy was discontinued.[10] As noted previously, the mean concentration for C4 rose when the patients were receiving a maintenance dosage.[9] In some cases, the C4 reached the normal range, but the C 1 INH levels did not reach the lower range of normal on maintenance therapy.[2]

DISCUSSION

The objectives in treating HAE include the amelioration of acute attacks and the prevention of spontaneous

TABLE III. Biochemical data*

| Sex | Hepatic enzymes (U/L) | | Lipids (mg/dL) | | | |
	ALT (normal = 7-52)	AST (normal = 9-30)	Total cholesterol (normal = 140-240)	LDL (normal = 50-160)	HDL (normal = 35-60)	Triglycerides (normal = 40-160)
F	14	18	209	ND	ND	176
M	30	30	136	79	21	182
F	29	27	215	159	44	60
F	15	18	146	ND	ND	57
F	24	24	191	125	47	96
F	13	16	226	ND	ND	133
M	ND	ND	ND	ND	ND	ND
M	ND	ND	ND	ND	ND	ND
F	15	18	109	42	42	127
M	56	28	171	120	25	129
M	25	20	144	89	41	69
F	20	22	178	110.2	59	44
F	29	24	130	76.4	47	33
F	19	39	130	82	31	23
M	29	25	ND	ND	ND	ND
M	30	29	224	155	38	160
F	14	19	191	88	57	126
F	23	19	158	112	22	118
F	8	13	192	ND	ND	70
F	15	16	167	ND	ND	53
M	16	28	148	97	32	135
No. elevated	1/19	1/19	0/18	0/13	5/13	1/18

F, Female; *M*, male.

*The most recent laboratory results for the patients with HAE using stanzolol. *ND* indicates that the test was not done or that no documented results could be obtained. See text for details. Patient numbers are not consecutive because they are carried over from reference 9 and experience summarized in reference 10.

episodes as well as attacks induced by soft tissue trauma (eg, dental extraction or surgery). Several drugs are currently available for such therapy. These include antifibrinolytic agents (ε-amino caproic acid), fresh frozen plasma, and anabolic steroids (stanozolol, danazol). Other agents such as a kallikrein inhibitor, a bradykinin 2-receptor antagonist, recombinant rabbit C 1 INH, and pasteurized human C 1 INH are being studied and may be available in the United States in the near future.

The administration of methyltestosterone[1,2] and attenuated androgens such as oxymetholone,[4] danazol, and stanozolol[5,9,10] reduces the incidence and severity of spontaneous attacks of HAE. Although the efficacy of the anabolic steroids in the treatment of HAE is well established, the mechanism for this effect remains unclear. Stanozolol is metabolized in the liver and with its administration, there appears to be an enhancement of C 1 INH protein production.[9] However, the therapeutic dose, usually 0.5 to 2 mg daily, is one that reduces the frequency and intensity of episodic attacks, which seldom achieves correction of the biochemical complement abnormalities, and therefore it is not necessary to correct the biochemical abnormality completely. In fact, attempting to do so by increasing the stanozolol dose may be associated with significant hepatic dysfunction.[8-10] Although stanozolol is no longer marketed, it is generally easily obtainable through a compounding pharmacy.

Adverse side effects of these drugs are a concern. Hepatic toxicity with the use of anabolic steroids with an impeded androgenic effect is well established.[7,11] Peliosis hepatis is a life-threatening experience caused by the abuse of such drug therapy.[14] In a detailed study in which liver status was evaluated by hepatic enzyme determination as well as by technetium scanning and percutaneous liver biopsy, the use of anabolic steroids in the treatment of HAE did not cause hepatotoxicity.[8] At the minimal effective dosage of 0.5 to 2 mg stanozolol daily, the mean maximum values for liver function were within the normal range. Consistent with our experience, the values for hepatic transaminases were elevated when higher daily dosages were administered for attacks or preoperative prophylaxis. Data from the current study suggest that this dose (0.5-2 mg daily) is associated with minimal adverse drug effects in both the short-term and the long-term. When biochemical clinical abnormalities occurred, there was reversal with the reduction of stanozolol dosage without persistent or long-term abnormalities. We were aggressive in minimizing the stanozolol dosage by tapering according to our protocol, and we acknowledge that danazol therapy frequently causes some side effects, such as menstrual irregularities in women with HAE.[15]

Since 1966, 42 patients at the Brigham and Women's Hospital have been administered steroids with impeded androgenic effect (17-α alkylated anabolic agents). Four received methyltestosterone and subsequently received,

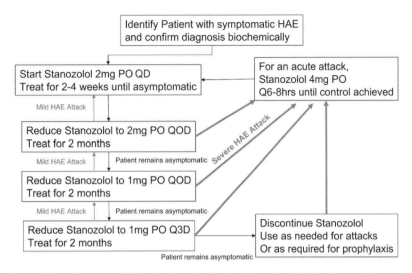

FIG 1. Stanozolol tapering protocol. The flowchart details the scheme by which the dosage of stanozolol was adjusted after the initiation of treatment and the control of symptoms. Patients who remained attack-free were followed closely and the dosage of stanozolol decreased as indicated *(thin black arrows)*. If at any time a patient experienced a severe, acute HAE attack, the attack was treated with fresh frozen plasma and the stanozolol was increased to 4 mg by mouth every 6-8 hours *(bold red arrows)* until resolution of the attack. Thereafter, the tapering protocol was restarted. Milder attacks were managed with temporary increases in the dose *(thin red arrows)*, and resumption of tapering after control was re-established. *QD*, daily; *Q*, every; *PO*, by mouth; *QOD*, every other day; *Q3D*, every 3rd day.

with 33 other patients, oxymetholone. All have subsequently been administered stanozolol over a period of nearly 40 years for long-term chronic prophylaxis. Over this period, we have made 2 important clinical observations about the use of stanozolol in addition to its efficacy and safety. First, most patients can achieve symptomatic control and decrease the dose of stanozolol according to our weaning protocol, increasing and decreasing the dose as circumstances dictate. Second, as the frequency of attacks decreases, most patients with HAE effectively autoregulate, adjusting the dosage of stanozolol themselves.

Nevertheless, long-term monitoring of such patients is essential. At a minimum, patients should be clinically evaluated every 6 to 12 months, including age-appropriate cancer screening. In addition, blood studies (lipid profile, PSA for men, and hepatic transaminases) should be performed, and patients who continue taking stanozolol should have an annual ultrasound.

This drug ensures that patients with HAE a convenient, safe mechanism for self-administration of drug therapy to control their disease. In some instances, patients are able to wean themselves from chronic anabolic steroid therapy.

In conclusion, stanozolol is a safe and an effective drug for the chronic, long-term treatment of patients with HAE, provided such affected patients are closely supervised with routine clinical, biochemical, and radiographic assessment.

We acknowledge with gratitude the advice and suggestions regarding this study and manuscript from K. Frank Austen, MD.

REFERENCES

1. Spaulding W. Methyltestosterone therapy for hereditary episodic edema (hereditary angioneurotic edema). Ann Intern Med 1960;53:139-45.
2. Sheffer AL, Fearon DT, Austen KF. Methyltestosterone therapy in hereditary angioedema. Ann Intern Med 1977;86:306-8.
3. Gelfand JA, Sherins RJ, Alling DW, Frank MM. Treatment of hereditary angioedema with danazol: reversal of clinical and biochemical abnormalities. N Engl J Med 1976;295:1444-8.
4. Sheffer AL, Fearon DT, Austen KF. Clinical and biochemical effects of impeded androgen (oxymetholone) therapy of hereditary angioedema. J Allergy Clin Immunol 1979;64:275-80.
5. Agostoni A, Cicardi M, Martignoni GC, Bergamaschini L, Marasini B. Danazol and stanozolol in long-term prophylactic treatment of hereditary angioedema. J Allergy Clin Immunol 1980;65:75-9.
6. Farrell GC, Joshua DE, Uren RF, Baird PJ, Perkins KW, Kronenberg H. Androgen-induced hepatoma. Lancet 1975;1:430-2.
7. Johnson FL, Lerner KG, Siegel M, Feagler JR, Majerus PW, Hartmann JR, et al. Association of androgenic-anabolic steroid therapy with development of hepatocellular carcinoma. Lancet 1972;2:1273-6.
8. Cicardi M, Castelli R, Zingale LC, Agostoni A. Side effects of long-term prophylaxis with attenuated androgens in hereditary angioedema: comparison of treated and untreated patients. J Allergy Clin Immunol 1997;99:194-6.
9. Sheffer AL, Fearon DT, Austen KF. Clinical and biochemical effects of stanozolol therapy for hereditary angioedema. J Allergy Clin Immunol 1981;68:181-7.
10. Sheffer AL, Fearon DT, Austen KF. Hereditary angioedema: a decade of management with stanozolol. J Allergy Clin Immunol 1987;80:855-60.
11. Bork K, Pitton M, Harten P, Koch P. Hepatocellular adenomas in patients taking danazol for hereditary angio-oedema. Lancet 1999;353:1066-7.
12. Bowen T, Cicardi M, Farkas H, Bork K, Kreuz W, Zingale L, et al. Canadian 2003 international consensus algorithm for the diagnosis, therapy, and management of hereditary angioedema. J Allergy Clin Immunol 2004;114:629-37.
13. Prematta M, Gibbs JG, Pratt EL, Stoughton TR, Craig TJ. Fresh frozen plasma for the treatment of hereditary angioedema. Ann Allergy Asthma Immunol 2007;98:383-8.
14. Cicardi M, Bergamaschini L, Tucci A, Agostoni A, Tornaghi G, Coggi G, et al. Morphologic evaluation of the liver in hereditary angioedema patients on long-term treatment with androgen derivatives. J Allergy Clin Immunol 1983;72:294-8.
15. Zurlo JJ, Frank MM. The long-term safety of danazol in women with hereditary angioedema. Fertil Steril 1990;54:64-72.

Hereditary angioedema: A decade of human C1-inhibitor concentrate therapy

Henriette Farkas, MD, PhD, DSc,[a] László Jakab, MD,[a] György Temesszentandrási, MD,[a]
Beáta Visy, MD,[b] György Harmat, MD, PhD,[b] George Füst, MD, PhD, DSc,[a]
Gábor Széplaki, MD,[a] Béla Fekete, MD, PhD, DSc,[a] István Karádi, MD, PhD, DSc,[a]
and Lilian Varga, PhD[a] *Budapest, Hungary*

Background: C1-inhibitor (C1-INH) is a serine protease
inhibitor regulating the complement, kinin-kallikrein,
coagulation, and fibrinolytic systems. Hereditary angioedema
(HAE) is caused by an inherited deficiency of C1-INH
characterized by sudden, recurrent edematous swellings of the
subcutaneous or submucosal tissues. The optional therapy for
the acute management of HAE is administration of human
C1-INH (hC1-INH) concentrate. However, hC1-INH is not
available in many countries, in which case fresh frozen plasma
is an alternative.
Objective: To summarize our experience with hC1-INH
concentrate in patients with HAE.
Methods: Clinical and laboratory information on the
effectiveness and safety of hC1-INH administered to relieve 468
acute edematous attacks in 61 patients with HAE was analyzed.
Results: Severe abdominal or subcutaneous attacks and
laryngeal edema were consistently relieved by the
administration of 500 U hC1-INH concentrate. Symptoms
improved within 15 to 60 minutes of administration.
Progression of the attacks was never observed, and there were
no recurrent attacks within 72 hours. hC1-INH concentrate
requirements did not change after repeated use. hC1-INH
concentrate proved effective in the management of 94 attacks in
22 children and 6 attacks in 4 pregnant women. Adverse
reactions, viral infections, and antibody formation against the
purified protein did not occur.
Conclusion: The administration of hC1-INH concentrate in
HAE is highly effective and safe for the treatment of acute
attacks and short-term prophylaxis and in pediatric patients
and pregnant women.
Clinical implications: Human C1-INH concentrate is effective
and safe for the treatment of acute HAE attacks as well as for
short-term prophylaxis. (J Allergy Clin Immunol 2007;120:
941-7.)

Key words: *Human C1-inhibitor concentrate, treatment, hereditary
angioneurotic edema, hereditary angioedema*

From [a]Semmelweis University, 3rd Department of Internal Medicine; and [b]the
   Madarász Street Hospital of the "Heim Pál" Pediatric Hospital.
Disclosure of potential conflict of interest: The authors have declared that they
   have no conflict of interest.
Received for publication September 14, 2006; revised June 18, 2007; accepted
   for publication June 19, 2007.
Available online August 30, 2007.
Reprint requests: Henriette Farkas, MD, PhD, DSc, Semmelweis University,
   Faculty of Medicine, 3rd Department of Internal Medicine, H-1125
   Budapest, Kútvölgyi út 4, Hungary. E-mail: farkash@kut.sote.hu.
0091-6749/$32.00
© 2007 American Academy of Allergy, Asthma & Immunology
doi:10.1016/j.jaci.2007.06.026

Abbreviations used
C1-INH: C1-inhibitor
HAE: Hereditary angioedema
hC1-INH: Human C1-inhibitor
HCV: Hepatitis C virus

Hereditary angioneurotic edema (hereditary angioedema; HAE) results from a deficiency of C1-inhibitor (C1-INH). This protein regulates the complement and coagulation cascade as well as the fibrinolytic and kinin pathways. Deficiency of C1-INH allows activation of these cascade systems and the release of bradykinin, which induces edema formation.[1-7] Clinical manifestations are associated with recurrent, paroxysmal, circumscribed edema formation in the subcutis and in the submucosa. Laryngeal edema may lead to suffocation, which is responsible for the strikingly high 20% to 30% mortality of HAE. Fatal outcome is related to delays in establishing an accurate diagnosis and introducing appropriate therapy. Edematous episodes can be precipitated by a variety of factors.[8-10] Because of its unique pathomechanism, the management of HAE is essentially different from the therapy of other angioedemas with similar clinical manifestations, albeit with a different etiology.[11-14] Although other angioedemas respond to antihistamines, glucocorticoids, and epinephrine, these agents are ineffective in angioedema caused by C1-INH deficiency. Although it is currently indicated only for acute attacks and short-term prophylaxis before procedures known to trigger attacks, human C1-INH (hC1-INH) concentrate, because of its long half-life, is ideally suited for long-term prophylaxis.[12-15] In particular, self-administration of hC1-INH concentrate has proven safe and effective for the long-term prophylaxis of severe, frequently recurring attacks not relieved by antifibrinolytics or attenuated androgens.[16,17]

This article summarizes more than 10 years of experience reflecting the effectiveness and safety of hC1-INH concentrate administered to patients treated at the Hungarian HAE Center.

METHODS

Patients

Relevant data of 112 patients treated at the center[18] since 1996 were analyzed (Table I). At the initial visit, patients diagnosed with

Basic and clinical immunology

TABLE I. Descriptive statistics of the patients*

	Ever received hC1-INH concentrate	Never received hC1-INH concentrate	P value	All patients
N	61	51		112
Age (y)‖	33 (20-47)	33 (20-47)	.770	33 (20-47)
Children/adult patients¶	22/39	20/31	.730†	42/70
Male/female	24/37	24/27	.410†	48/64
HAE I/HAE II	55/6	46/5	.990†	101/11
Age at diagnosis (y)	17 (8-25.5)	27 (11-42)	.012	21 (10-33)
Onset of symptoms (y)	9 (5-16)	12 (7-18.5)	.076	10 (5-18)
Duration of follow-up (y)	13.6 (7.35-20.15)	5.9 (3.9-8.2)	<.0001	8 (5.5-15.75)
HAE severity at diagnosis				
Class I (severe)	27	4	<.0001‡	31
Class II (moderate)	20	11		31
Class III (mild)	6	3		9
Class IV (minimal)	4	17		21
Class V (asymptomatic)	4	16		20
C1-INH concentration (%)§	21.0 (11.0-29.0)	19.5 (11-27.5)	.679	20.0 (11.0-28.5)
C1-INH activity (%)	38.4 (18.45-50.95)	47.6 (30-57)	.036	43.05 (25.9-55)
C4 (g/L)	0.04 (0.01-0.08)	0.06 (0.01-0.13)	.210	0.05 (0.01-0.10)

C4, The fourth component of complement.
*Values are presented as absolute numbers or medians (25% to 75% percentiles).
P values were calculated with the Mann-Whitney nonparametric test, the †Fisher exact test, and ‡χ^2 test for trend.
§Patients with HAE type II were excluded from the analysis.
‖Age was determined at the end of the study period.
¶Children were defined as <18 years of age at the first administration of hC1-INH.

HAE—established by clinical manifestations and complement screening—were invited by mail to attend control visits, scheduled at 1-year intervals at least. The disease severity class of patients was determined according to the criteria for evaluating disease severity, developed by experts from the Novel Methods for Predicting, Preventing, and Treating Attacks in Patients with Hereditary Angioedema (PREHAET) group, and as described by Agostoni et al[12] in the first year of treatment.

Treatment with hC1-INH concentrate

A single brand of highly purified, lyophilized, human plasma–derived C1-INH concentrate (Berinert P; ZLB Behring GmbH, Marburg, Germany) was used[12] in an initial dose of 500 U. Berinert P is produced from pooled human plasma, and the final product goes through 2 viral reduction steps (pasteurization and chromatography). Hence, the transmission of viruses has never been reported.[19,20] Because the preparation is stored in the refrigerator (at 2°C to 8°C), it should be allowed to warm up to room temperature after reconstitution before it can be administered by slow intravenous injection (after approximately 5 minutes).

The indications for administering hC1-INH concentrate (Table II) were defined in conformity with pertinent international recommendations,[12,13] as well as in observance of domestic experience and capabilities.

On enrollment, patients were supplied with an ampoule (500 U) of hC1-INH concentrate. The injection was intended for administration in the patient's home by the medical professional. The time to administration of hC1-INH concentrate is approximately 20 minutes in an emergency, and the patient can be hospitalized if a further ampoule of hC1-INh is required.

Follow-up

Laboratory analysis. At control visits, changes of hematologic and urinary parameters as well as of liver and renal function were monitored by routine laboratory methods. Complement measurements (C1q, C4 and C1-INH levels, C1-INH activity, and anti–C1-INH antibody titers) were taken as previously described.[21] Virus serology (screening for hepatitis B surface antigen [HBsAg], anti-hepatitis C virus [HCV], and anti-HIV antibodies) was performed on enrollment and at every subsequent control visit.

Clinical follow-up. The following were recorded at control visits: the occurrence of HAE attacks that have occurred since the previous visit, information on triggering factors and the management of related attacks, as well as on accompanying disorders. Notes from patient diaries and information contributed by the patients themselves were used to collect data. These were localization/body region of the attack treated with hC1-INH concentrate, the number of C1-INH units administered, attack duration, time to the onset of symptomatic relief and to complete resolution of symptoms, potential adverse reactions and accompanying symptoms, and the initiation of short-term or long-term prophylaxis (along with the type of intervention, condition, or disorder warranting its use).

Statistical analysis

Statistical analysis was performed by using Prism for Windows 4.02 (GraphPad Software, San Diego, Calif) software. Because many of the variables had non-Gaussian distributions, we used nonparametric tests. The Mann-Whitney *U* test was used to compare 2 independent groups, whereas the Fisher exact test and the χ^2 test for trend were performed to compare categorical variables. All statistical analyses were 2-tailed, and *P* < .05 was considered significant.

RESULTS

Of the 112 individuals managed at the center, 61 (including 22 children) had received hC1-INH concentrate intravenously during their life. Fifty-one patients had

TABLE II. Indications for hC1-INH concentrate administration

Treatment of acute attacks		
Localization	Specific conditions	Dose
Pharyngeal, laryngeal edema	Always	Initial dose, 500 U, repeated when required
Severe edematous abdominal attack*	Always	
Subcutaneous only localization	Edema always occurred on the face and neck. If other body regions were involved, treatment was indicated only if edema caused additional symptoms, eg, pain and circulatory abnormalities in the extremities, dyspnea (from edema of the torso), pain, or micturition problems (related to edema of the genitals).	
Prophylaxis		
Duration	Specific conditions	Dose
Long-term	First trimester of pregnancy if attack frequency increases because of the pregnancy (1) spontaneously or (2) as a rebound effect of discontinuing long-term prophylaxis.	500 U at 5-d intervals
Short term	Before diagnostic and surgical interventions on the head and neck, endotracheal narcosis, childbirth, induced abortion—if the patient has not received long-term drug prophylaxis or the history contains edematous attacks in relation to diagnostic or surgical procedures.	500 U 1 h before the procedure

*Severe edematous abdominal attack: intense, colicky abdominal pain, recurrent vomiting, accompanied by watery diarrhea and fainting.

never been treated with this agent, and 5 had never had an edematous episode. These 2 subsets (ie, patients treated vs not treated with hC1-INH concentrate) were similar with regard to age, sex, ratio of children/adults, type of HAE, and the time of onset of initial symptoms. In the subset treated with hC1-INH concentrate, HAE was diagnosed at a younger age, and consequently, the duration of follow-up was longer in these patients (Table I). Moreover, these patients were categorized according to disease severity at the time of diagnosis[12]—HAE was more severe in these patients than in those not requiring treatment with hC1-INH concentrate. The functional activity of C1-INH was lower at the time of diagnosis than in untreated patients (Table I).

Localization of treated attacks

Human C1-inhibitor concentrate was administered to control 468 attacks (occurring in 22 children and 39 adults). Although the majority of attacks occurred in adults, 20% of treated attacks (94/468) occurred in children. As shown by medication use, the occurrence of an abdominal attack was the most common indication for treatment (49.2% or 230 attacks in 35 adults and 15 children). Laryngeal edema necessitated treatment in 28.4% of cases (133 attacks; 27 adults and 9 children). In 13.1% of cases, subcutaneous edema requiring intravenous C1-INH supplementation was accompanied by laryngeal or gastrointestinal edema. Only 20% of attacks requiring C1-INH supplementation were confined to the subcutis (20 adults and 9 children). Treatment for

subcutaneous attacks was more common in children than in adults (28/94 vs 67/374; $P = .0105$; Table III).

Number of treated attacks

On average, 8 ampoules of hC1-INH concentrate were administered for the treatment of HAE attacks over the follow-up period of a patient ever treated with the concentrate. Eighty percent of the 61 treated patients received 10 ampoules at the most. This corresponds to 10 treatments, because in general, a single ampoule was sufficient to control the attack in the majority of cases. Only 11 patients required more than 10 treatments during follow-up (Fig 1, A). Mean age at the time of the first treatment was 27 years (range, 6-51 years). Because the study population varied in age and time since recruitment to follow-up care, the number of injections administered annually was worth analyzing. Mean annual dose requirement was 1.3 ampoules; the majority of patients (77%) received hC1-INH concentrate for an attack on 0.5 to 2 occasions per year. Severe attacks recurred more frequently in a few patients only; these subjects received 4 to 5 ampoules each year (Fig 1, B).

Effectiveness of C1-INH supplementation

As a rule, the 468 attacks of HAE were controlled by a single ampoule (500 U) of C1-INH. In 9 cases (5 children and 4 adults), symptomatic relief afforded by the initial dose of 500 U was insufficient; clinical manifestations persisted without further regression or progression. This warranted repeating the 500-U dose within 2 hours, which elicited the expected response.

Basic and clinical immunology

TABLE III. Localization of HAE attacks treated with hC1-INH concentrate*

	Children	Adults	All patients
No. of patients treated (n)	22	39	61
GI tract	15	35	50
Larynx	9	27	36
Subcutaneous tissues only	9	20	29
No. of HAE attacks treated (n)	94	374	468
Localization of treated attacks, n (%)			
GI tract (total)	41 (43.6%)	189 (50.5%)	230 (49.2%)
GI tract	39 (41.5%)	179 (47.9%)	218 (46.6%)
GI tract + extremities	2 (2.1%)	10 (2.7%)	12 (2.6%)
Larynx (total)	25 (26.6%)	108 (28.9%)	133 (28.4%)
Larynx	14 (14.9%)	70 (18.7%)	84 (17.9%)
Larynx + extremities	11 (11.7%)	38 (10.2%)	49 (10.5%)
Subcutaneous tissues only (total)	28 (29.8%)	67 (17.9%)	95 (20.3%)
Face/neck	17 (18.1%)	44 (11.8%)	61 (13.0%)
Face/neck + extremities	5 (5.3%)	8 (2.1%)	13 (2.8%)
Extremities/trunk	6 (6.4%)	12 (3.2%)	18 (3.8%)
Genitals	0 (0.0%)	3 (0.8%)	3 (0.6%)
Unknown†	0 (0.0%)	10 (2.7%)	10 (2.1%)

GI, Gastrointestinal.

*Values are presented as absolute numbers (percentages).

†hC1-INH concentrate was administered under unknown circumstances.

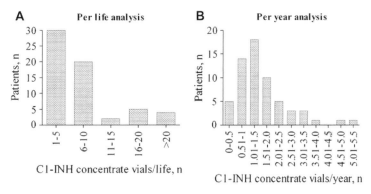

FIG 1. Number of ampoules of hC1-INH concentrate used for the treatment of the patients with HAE during follow-up. **A,** Number of ampoules received over the lifetime of a patient. **B,** Average number of ampoules per year (corrected for the duration of follow-up).

Time to the onset of relief, as well as to the complete resolution of symptoms, was analyzed by using the data in patient diaries on 128 severe abdominal, 32 laryngeal, and 18 facial-cervical attacks. Time to the onset of symptomatic relief was the shortest in laryngeal edema (within 15 minutes on average). Improvement of abdominal attacks ensued within 30 minutes, whereas this took more than 30 minutes in subcutaneous edema. Time to complete resolution of symptoms followed a similar trend (Fig 2). Repeated administration of hC1-INH concentrate did not lead to any decrease in therapeutic efficacy.

Short-term prophylaxis

C1-inhibitor was administered as short-term prophylaxis in 19 cases: to 8 patients undergoing endotracheal intubation for general anesthesia, 6 patients undergoing gastroscopy, 6 patients undergoing dental interventions (extraction and minor dental surgeries), and 1 woman undergoing induced abortion. In all of these cases, 1 ampoule hC1-INH concentrate prevented angioedema.

Safety of C1-INH supplementation

Side effects. During observation over the period of a decade, none of the patients or their doctors reported any drug-related adverse reactions.

Anti–C1-INH antibodies. Abnormally high antibody titers characteristic of patients with acquired C1-INH deficiency were not observed. Changes in anti–C1-INH antibody levels were analyzed longitudinally by comparing antibody titers measured in the first and last blood samples obtained between 2002 and 2006. Four of the 61 patients required treatment with hC1-INH concentrate on 1 to 15 occasions over this 4-year period. The actual difference in the duration of follow-up ranged from 1.5 to 4.5 years (median, 3 years). The titers of anti–C1-INH antibodies of either class (ie, IgG, IgA, and IgM) were

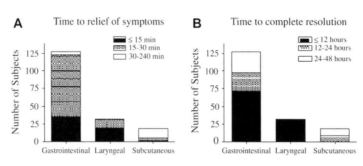

FIG 2. Time to relief and complete resolution of symptoms after treatment with hC1-INH concentrate. Laryngeal edema responded most rapidly to the treatment and the time for complete resolutions was the shortest compared with gastrointestinal and subcutaneous edema. Both time to relief and complete resolution of symptoms were longest in patients with subcutaneous edema. *P* values were calculated with the χ^2 for trend.

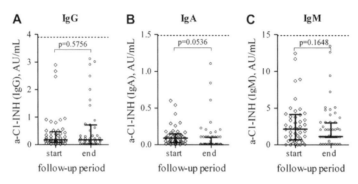

FIG 3. Changes of anti–C1-INH autoantibody titers during follow-up. No significant increase or decrease was observed in anti-C1-INH titers during the follow-up of patients with HAE who ever received hC1-INH concentrate. *Lines* indicate medians and 25th to 75th percentiles. *P* values were calculated with the Wilcoxon signed-rank test.

similar in paired serum samples (Fig 3). Elevation of antibody titers could not be demonstrated even by restricting the analysis to the 36 patients who had received hC1-INH concentrate on several occasions. Similarly, no correlation was found between the number of C1-INH injections administered and the difference of titers measured at the 2 time points (data not shown).

Viral infection. Subclinical anti-HCV positivity (without the appearance of biochemical markers) was detected in a single patient before the initiation of C1-INH supplementation. Viral activity was ruled out by HCV-RNA-PCR and accordingly, treatment was not necessary. HBV, HIV-1, or HIV-2 positivity was not demonstrated in any of the patients (Table IV).

Pregnancy. Four pregnant women received hC1-INH concentrate on 6 occasions for acute abdominal attacks. Treatment proved effective in all instances. Adverse reactions were not observed, and every treated woman delivered a healthy neonate. Long-term prophylaxis with danazol had to be suspended in another woman contemplating pregnancy. During the first trimester, increasing attack frequency warranted the prophylactic use of 500 U hC1-INH concentrate once a week. No attacks occurred during treatment.

DISCUSSION

In many countries, C1-INH concentrate is still unavailable; therefore, patients with HAE receive either symptomatic treatments[22] or fresh frozen plasma.[23-25] However, the use of fresh frozen plasma is associated with a relatively high risk of alloimmunization,[26] anaphylactoid reactions,[27] transfer of viral infections,[28] and transfusion-related acute lung injury.[29] Moreover, human plasma contains a variety of components that are undesirable during use for this purpose. Administration of a relatively large volume of plasma is necessary; this takes time, which might prove a critical setback in an emergency.[30,31] Patients with HAE benefited from the introduction of C1-INH supplementation in many ways. These achievements improved their quality of life substantially. Previously, 6 patients died from suffocation caused by laryngeal edema, whereas no lives have been lost during the last 17 years; similarly, neither emergency tracheotomy nor unwarranted abdominal surgery has been performed. Thanks to the proper information and education of patients, the onset of prodromal symptoms (dysphagia, lump sensation in the throat, feeling of tightness, voice changes) prompted

Basic and clinical immunology

Basic and clinical immunology

TABLE IV. Viral serology screening results before and after the use of hC1-INH concentrate

	Before treatment (no. of patients)		After treatment (no. of patients)	
	Negative	Positive	Negative	Positive
HBV	60	0	60	0
HCV	59	1	59	1
HIV-1, HIV-2	60	0	60	0

HBV, Hepatitis B virus.

patients to seek medical help instantly, and therefore, C1-INH concentrate could be administered immediately. Treatment with this agent halted the progression of clinical manifestations within 10 to 20 minutes and achieved complete resolution of symptoms within 4 to 12 hours. These findings are in agreement with the experience published by other authors.[32-34] Although a single dose of 500 U C1-INH almost invariably elicited a therapeutic effect, repeated administration was necessary in 9 cases. This emphasizes the need for keeping the patient under observation until symptomatic improvement ensues. In general, an insufficient therapeutic effect may be expected when treatment is belated—that is, several hours after the onset of initial symptoms.[33,34] Importantly, administering hC1-INH as early as possible is the key to the success of the emergency management of HAE. Interestingly enough, when repeated administration of hC1-INH concentrate was necessary in 8 of 9 cases, airway infection was the triggering factor of laryngeal edema.

In addition to mitigating life-threatening laryngeal edema, hC1-INH concentrate is an invaluable remedy for severe abdominal attacks, which represent a more common localization of edema formation. The regression of the clinical manifestations of severe abdominal attacks was slower than that of laryngeal edema. This finding is similar to the data published by Bork et al.[35] As shown by our abdominal ultrasound follow-up study conducted earlier, free intraperitoneal fluid disappears completely within 48 hours.[36] The manifestations of subcutaneous edema began to improve within 30 to 60 minutes, but their regression became complete over a period of 24 to 48 hours. Likely explanations for this difference include the different structure, vascularization, and functions of subcutaneous and submucosal tissues, as well as the extent of edema formation (which is small in the larynx, for example). Furthermore, it is reasonable to presume that patients with laryngeal edema sought medical attention as soon as early, mild manifestations occurred, whereas those with facial-cervical or abdominal attacks sought treatment only when the symptoms of edema formation became more severe and perceptible. In children, treatment was more frequently indicated for subcutaneous edema involving the face and neck, which was probably triggered by airway infections (more prevalent in the pediatric population) and mechanical trauma.

Short-term prophylaxis implemented by administering 500 U hC1-INH concentrate was consistently effective. These results are in agreement with the observations of other authors.[33,37,38] Although it was tested in a single case only, long-term prophylaxis with hC1-INH concentrate proved similarly effective and safe during the first trimester of pregnancy. The use of hC1-INH concentrate for long-term prophylaxis was also restricted for financial reasons. Since the introduction of C1-INH supplementation, the average dose requirement was 1 ampoule per year and per patient. In general, this was sufficient for the management of acute attacks only. Almost all patients treated with C1-INH supplementation received prophylaxis with antifibrinolytics or attenuated androgens.

The use of hC1-INH concentrate has been associated with a few adverse reactions only. A proportion of these was related either to too rapid injection or to insufficient warming of the solution.[35] Importantly, no side effects occurred in our patients, who had received 477 ampoules altogether; hC1-INH concentrate was well tolerated by the subjects. The effectiveness of this agent did not decline during repeated use.

Human C1-inhibitor concentrate is also a safe drug for children and pregnant women.[14,39] This is supported both by our previous experience[40] and by the results of this study. Similarly, the transmission of hepatitis B virus, HCV, HIV-1, or HIV-2 virus was not observed in our series. Thus, it seems that viral inactivation and elimination during the production of hC1-INH concentrate makes the drug safe and virus-free, as reported by Agostoni et al.[12]

Donaldson et al[21] documented the formation of anti–C1-INH antibodies in a patient with HAE complicated by systemic lupus erythematosus and presumed that treatment with C1-INH concentrate could induce antibody formation. This hypothesis was not confirmed by our previous follow-up study.[21] Moreover, the study reported herein failed to show any elevation of antibody titers, even after repeated administration of C1-INH, despite using the most sensitive detection methods.

In conformity with data published in the literature, our experience accumulated over a period of 10 years confirms that hC1-INH concentrate is currently the treatment of choice for controlling severe HAE attacks. In addition, it proves highly effective and safe for short-term prophylaxis, as well as for the treatment of children and pregnant women; hC1-INH concentrate has no contraindications. It would be highly desirable if this treatment could be made available to all patients with HAE to reduce mortality, avoid unsubstantiated surgical interventions, and improve the patients' quality of life.

We thank Éva Németh, MD, and Réka Felvinci, MD, for the uninterrupted maintenance of the HAE Registry, as well as for their assistance in processing the accumulated data. We are also indebted to ZLB Behring Co for producing and supplying a sufficient quantity of patient diaries in the Hungarian language, year after year.

REFERENCES

1. Nussberger J, Cugno M, Amstutz C, Cicardi M, Pellacani A, Agostoni A. Plasma bradykinin in angio-oedema. Lancet 1998;351:1693-7.

2. Kaplan AP. C1 inhibitor deficiency: hereditary and acquired forms. J Investig Allergol Clin Immunol 2001;11:211-9.

3. Agostoni A, Cicardi M. Hereditary and acquired C1-inhibitor deficiency: biological and clinical characteristics in 235 patients. Medicine (Baltimore) 1992;71:206-15.

4. Donaldson VH, Evans RR. A biochemical abnormality in hereditary angioneurotic edema: absence of serum inhibitor of C' 1-esterase. Am J Med 1963;35:37-44.

5. Farkas H, Harmat G, Füst G, Varga L, Visy B. Clinical management of hereditary angio-oedema in children. Pediatr Allergy Immunol 2002;13:153-61.

6. Farkas H, Varga L, Széplaki G, Visy B, Harmat G, Bowen T. Management of hereditary angioedema in pediatric patients. Pediatrics 2007. In press.

7. Bork K, Meng G, Staubach P, Hardt J. Hereditary angioedema: new findings concerning symptoms, affected organs, and course. Am J Med 2006;119:267-74.

8. Agostoni A, Cicardi M. Drug-induced angioedema without urticaria. Drug Saf 2001;24:599-606.

9. Bouillet L, Ponard D, Drouet C, Jullien D, Massot C. Angioedema and oral contraception. Dermatology 2003;206:106-9.

10. Visy B, Fust G, Varga L, Szendei G, Takacs E, Karadi I, et al. Sex hormones in hereditary angioneurotic oedema. Clin Endocrinol (Oxf) 2004;60:508-15.

11. Kaplan AP, Greaves MW. Angioedema. J Am Acad Dermatol 2005;53:373-88; quiz 89-92.

12. Agostoni A, Aygoren-Pursun E, Binkley KE, Blanch A, Bork K, Bouillet L, et al. Hereditary and acquired angioedema: problems and progress: proceedings of the Third C1 Esterase Inhibitor Deficiency Workshop and beyond. J Allergy Clin Immunol 2004;114:S51-131.

13. Bowen T, Cicardi M, Farkas H, Bork K, Kreuz W, Zingale L, et al. Canadian 2003 international consensus algorithm for the diagnosis, therapy, and management of hereditary angioedema. J Allergy Clin Immunol 2004;114:629-37.

14. Gompels MM, Lock RJ, Abinun M, Bethune CA, Davies G, Grattan C, et al. C1 inhibitor deficiency: consensus document. Clin Exp Immunol 2005;139:379-94.

15. Kreuz W, Fischer D, Martinez-Saguer I, Heller C, Klarmann D. C1-esterase inhibitor substitution in hereditary angioedema. Biomed Prog 1999;12:1-7.

16. Levi M, Choi G, Picavet C, Hack CE. Self-administration of C1-inhibitor concentrate in patients with hereditary or acquired angioedema caused by C1-inhibitor deficiency. J Allergy Clin Immunol 2006;117:904-8.

17. Bork K, Witzke G. Long-term prophylaxis with C1-inhibitor (C1 INH) concentrate in patients with recurrent angioedema caused by hereditary and acquired C1-inhibitor deficiency. J Allergy Clin Immunol 1989;83:677-82.

18. Farkas H, Varga L. The Hungarian HAE experience. Transfus Apher Sci 2003;29:229-33.

19. De Serres J, Groner A, Lindner J. Safety and efficacy of pasteurized C1 inhibitor concentrate (Berinert P) in hereditary angioedema: a review. Transfus Apher Sci 2003;29:247-54.

20. Donaldson VH, Bissler JJ, Welch TR, Burton MF, Davis AE 3rd. Antibody to C1-inhibitor in a patient receiving C1-inhibitor infusions for treatment of hereditary angioneurotic edema with systemic lupus erythematosus reacts with a normal allotype of residue 458 of C1-inhibitor. J Lab Clin Med 1996;128:438-43.

21. Varga L, Szeplaki G, Visy B, Fust G, Harmat G, Miklos K, et al. C1-inhibitor (C1-INH) autoantibodies in hereditary angioedema: strong correlation with the severity of disease in C1-INH concentrate naive patients. Mol Immunol 2007;44:1454-60.

22. Zuraw BL. Current and future therapy for hereditary angioedema. Clin Immunol 2005;114:10-6.

23. Pickering RJ, Good RA, Kelly JR, Gewurz H. Replacement therapy in hereditary angioedema: successful treatment of two patients with fresh frozen plasma. Lancet 1969;1:326-30.

24. Sim TC, Grant JA. Hereditary angioedema: its diagnostic and management perspectives. Am J Med 1990;88:656-64.

25. Jaffe CJ, Atkinson JP, Gelfand JA, Frank MM. Hereditary angioedema: the use of fresh frozen plasma for prophylaxis in patients undergoing oral surgery. J Allergy Clin Immunol 1975;55:386-93.

26. Ching EP, Poon MC, Neurath D, Ruether BA. Red blood cell alloimmunization complicating plasma transfusion. Am J Clin Pathol 1991;96:201-2.

27. Gilstad CW. Anaphylactic transfusion reactions. Curr Opin Hematol 2003;10:419-23.

28. MacLennan S, Williamson LM. Risks of fresh frozen plasma and platelets. J Trauma 2006;60:S46-50.

29. Gajic O, Moore SB. Transfusion-related acute lung injury. Mayo Clin Proc 2005;80:766-70.

30. Hashim SW, Kay HR, Hammond GL, Kopf GS, Geha AS. Noncardiogenic pulmonary edema after cardiopulmonary bypass: an anaphylactic reaction to fresh frozen plasma. Am J Surg 1984;147:560-4.

31. Sonntag J, Stiller B, Walka MM, Maier RF. Anaphylatoxins in fresh-frozen plasma. Transfusion 1997;37:798-803.

32. Cicardi M, Bergamaschini L, Marasini B, Boccassini G, Tucci A, Agostoni A. Hereditary angioedema: an appraisal of 104 cases. Am J Med Sci 1982;284:2-9.

33. Bork K, Barnstedt SE. Treatment of 193 episodes of laryngeal edema with C1 inhibitor concentrate in patients with hereditary angioedema. Arch Intern Med 2001;161:714-8.

34. Kunschak M, Engl W, Maritsch F, Rosen FS, Eder G, Zerlauth G, et al. A randomized, controlled trial to study the efficacy and safety of C1 inhibitor concentrate in treating hereditary angioedema. Transfusion 1998;38:540-9.

35. Bork K, Meng G, Staubach P, Hardt J. Treatment with C1 inhibitor concentrate in abdominal pain attacks of patients with hereditary angioedema. Transfusion 2005;45:1774-84.

36. Farkas H, Harmat G, Kaposi PN, Karadi I, Fekete B, Fust G, et al. Ultrasonography in the diagnosis and monitoring of ascites in acute abdominal attacks of hereditary angioneurotic oedema. Eur J Gastroenterol Hepatol 2001;13:1225-30.

37. Leimgruber A, Jaques WA, Spaeth PJ. Hereditary angioedema: uncomplicated maxillofacial surgery using short-term C1 inhibitor replacement therapy. Int Arch Allergy Immunol 1993;101:107-12.

38. Mohr M, Pollok-Kopp B, Gotze O, Burchardi H. [The use of a C1-inhibior concentrate for short-term preoperative prophylaxis in two patients with hereditary angioedema]. Anaesthesist 1996;45:626-30.

39. Abinun M. Hereditary angio-oedema in children. Lancet 1999;353:2242.

40. Farkas H, Harmat G, Fust G, Varga L, Visy B. Clinical management of hereditary angio-oedema in children. Pediatr Allergy Immunol 2002;13:153-61.

Hereditary angiodema: a current state-of-the-art review, VII: Canadian Hungarian 2007 International Consensus Algorithm for the Diagnosis, Therapy, and Management of Hereditary Angioedema

Tom Bowen, MD, FRCPC; Marco Cicardi, MD; Konrad Bork, MD; Bruce Zuraw, MD; Mike Frank, MD; Bruce Ritchie, MD, FRCPC; Henriette Farkas, MD, PhD, DSc; Lilian Varga, PhD; Lorenza C. Zingale, MD; Karen Binkley, MD, FRCPC; Eric Wagner, PhD; Peggy Adomaitis; Kristylea Brosz, BSc; Jeanne Burnham; Richard Warrington, MB, PhD, FRCPC; Chrystyna Kalicinsky, MD, FRCPC; Sean Mace, MD, FRCPC; Christine McCusker, MD, FRCPC; Robert Schellenberg, MD, FRCPC; Lucia Celeste; Jacques Hebert, MD, FRCPC; Karen Valentine, MD, FRCPC; Man-Chiu Poon, MD, FRCPC; Bazir Serushago, MD, FRCPC; Doris Neurath, BSc, PharmART; William Yang, MD, FRCPC; Gina Lacuesta, MD, FRCPC; Andrew Issekutz, MD, FRCPC; Azza Hamed, MD, FRCPC; Palinder Kamra, MD, FRCPC; John Dean, MBBS, FRCPC; Amin Kanani, MD, FRCPC; Donald Stark, MD, FRCPC; Georges-Etienne Rivard, MD, FRCPC; Eric Leith, MD, FRCPC; Ellie Tsai, MD, FRCPC; Susan Waserman, MD, FRCPC; Paul K. Keith, MD, FRCPC; David Page; Silvia Marchesin; Hilary J. Longhurst, MA, MRCP, PhD, MRCPath; Wolfhart Kreuz, MD, PhD; Eva Rusicke, MD; Inmaculada Martinez-Saguer, MD; Emel Aygören-Pürsün, MD; George Harmat, MD, PhD; George Füst, MD, PhD, DSc; Henry Li, MD, PhD; Laurence Bouillet, MD, PhD; Teresa Caballero, MD, PhD; Dumitru Moldovan, PhD, MD; Peter J. Späth, PhD; Sara Smith-Foltz; Istvan Nagy; Erik W. Nielsen, MD, PhD; Christoph Bucher, MD; Patrik Nordenfelt, MD; and Zhi Yu Xiang, MD

Background: We published the Canadian 2003 International Consensus Algorithm for the Diagnosis, Therapy, and Management of Hereditary Angioedema (HAE; C1 inhibitor [C1-INH] deficiency) in 2004.

Objective: To ensure that this consensus remains current.

Methods: In collaboration with the Canadian Network of Rare Blood Disorder Organizations, we held the second Canadian Consensus discussion with our international colleagues in Toronto, Ontario, on February 3, 2006, and reviewed its content at the Fifth C1 Inhibitor Deficiency Workshop in Budapest on June 2, 2007. Papers were presented by international investigators, and this consensus algorithm approach resulted.

Results: This consensus algorithm outlines the approach recommended for the diagnosis, therapy, and management of HAE, which was agreed on by the authors of this report. This document is only a consensus algorithm approach and continues to require validation. As such, participants agreed to make this a living 2007 algorithm, a work in progress, and to review its content at future international HAE meetings.

Conclusions: There is a paucity of double-blind, placebo-controlled trials on the treatment of HAE, making levels of evidence to support the algorithm less than optimal. Controlled trials currently under way will provide further insight into the management of HAE. As with our Canadian 2003 Consensus, this 2007 International Consensus Algorithm for the Diagnosis, Therapy, and Management of HAE was formed through the meeting and agreement of patient care professionals along with patient group representatives and individual patients.

Ann Allergy Asthma Immunol. 2008;100(Suppl 2):S30–S40.

INTRODUCTION

Disclosures: Dr Bowen either has consultancy with or has been involved in educational programs and their organization that have required fundraising from Pharming, Jerini, Dyax-Genzyme, CSL Behring, and KOS. Dr Cicardi has consultancies with Jerini, Dyax, Lev Pharma, CSL Behring, and Pharming. Dr Zingale has consultancies with Pharming and Jerini.

Received for publication May 30, 2007; Received in revised form August 26, 2007; Accepted for publication September 5, 2007.

C1 inhibitor (C1-INH) deficiency (congenital or hereditary angioedema [HAE]) was first described by Quincke in 1882[1]; its inheritance nature was evidenced by Osler in 1888[2] and further defined as autosomal dominant by Crowder and Crowder in 1917. The protein defect was described by Donaldson in 1963.[3] An acquired form (acquired angioedema [AAE]) was described in 1972.[4] The approach to patients who present with angioedema without urticaria was recently presented by Zingale et al.[5] The incidence of HAE is estimated at 1:10,000 to 1:150,000, with most authors quoting 1:10,000 to 1:50,000 (with most agreeing that 1:50,000 is the closest estimate), no ethnic group differences have been reported, 25% of patients present with new mutations and no family history, and the *C1-INH* gene maps to chromosome 11q12-q13.1.[5-9] There appears to be little phenotype genotype correlation.[10] The gene for C1-INH has been expressed in recombinant systems, a knockout mouse model created, and much of the pathophysiology of HAE worked out, with the most likely candidate molecule resulting in angioedema being bradykinin.[5,8] Three variants of HAE have been described: HAE type 1, with low C1-INH antigenic protein and functional activity (85% of cases; autosomal dominant); HAE type 2, with normal or elevated protein level but low C1-INH function (15% of cases; autosomal dominant); and the recently described types of HAE (sometimes called HAE type 3 or estrogen-dependent angioedema), with normal C1-INH protein level and function occurring mainly in women, including HAE due to mutations in the coagulation factor XII gene and other defects yet to be identified.[8,11-13] AAE differs from HAE because it has an absent family history, late onset of symptoms, and different response to therapy (sometimes markedly higher doses of C1-INH required with rapid C1-INH catabolism and prophylactic response to antifibrinolytics often better than to androgens) and usually low C1q antigen levels.[5,8] AAE has been found with some B-lymphocyte disorders from monoclonal gammopathies of unknown significance to B-cell malignancies (AAE type 1) and in persons with acquired anti–C1-INH antibodies (AAE type 2).[5,8,14] Angioedema has been seen with some medication use (eg, angiotensin-converting enzyme inhibitors [ACE-Is]).[5] Patients with HAE may experience recurrent edema of subcutaneous tissues (extremities, genitals, face, trunk, or elsewhere); intestinal swellings and abdominal pains, nausea, vomiting, or diarrhea; and life-threatening swellings of the airway.[8] Risk of dying from airway obstruction if left untreated has been estimated at 30%.[10,15]

Approaches to the diagnosis, therapy, and management of HAE vary among countries, with C1-INH replacement therapy being standard in many countries but not available or with limited availability in others (licensed in Germany and Holland, available under the Special Access Program of Health Canada, not available in countries such as the United States). The Canadian Hereditary Angioedema Society (CHAES)/Société d'Angioédème Héréditaire du Canada (SAHC; www.haecanada.com) held a Canadian International Consensus Conference on HAE in Toronto, Ontario, Canada, in October 2003 and held the follow-up second Canadian Consensus Conference in conjunction with the meeting on Comprehensive Care for Rare Blood Disorders hosted by the Network of Rare Blood Disorder Organizations (NRBDO) in Toronto, Ontario, Canada, on February 3, 2006. Proceedings and the PowerPoint presentations from this conference are available on the Canadian Hemophilia Society Web site[16]

(http://www.hemophilia.ca/nrbdo/en/home.php). This meeting was patterned after the European C1-INH Deficiency Workshops organized by the European C1-INH Deficiency Working Group Hungarian HAE Working Group and after the first Canadian Consensus Conference that brought together government agencies; blood product suppliers; comprehensive care treatment team members, including nurses and physicians (family physicians and specialists, including hematologists, dermatologists, allergists, immunologists, pediatricians, and internists); HAE patient group representatives; and industry sponsors.[8,16-21] The consensus was reviewed at the Fifth C1 Inhibitor Deficiency Workshop held in Budapest on May 31 through June 3, 2007.[16]

Papers for discussion at the first Canadian Consensus meeting were published in the December 2003 edition of *Transfusion and Apheresis Science,* a special issue dedicated to HAE.[18,19] The consensus was, therefore, an agreement among patients, patient groups, and treatment team members on how to approach the diagnosis, therapy, and management of HAE. That final first Canadian Consensus was reviewed by the patient groups and treatment teams listed on the authorship and was presented as a living algorithm approach[17] for the management of HAE types 1 and 2 with a comprehensive review of HAE guest edited by Henriette Farkas and published in supplement form in the same journal issue.[8] Since that time, another consensus was published by the UK Primary Immunodeficiency Association.[22] We have not attempted to include approaches to AAE or type 3 HAE but offer our updated algorithm for the diagnosis, therapy, and management of types 1 and 2 HAE. We hope that the algorithm will be validated by treatment teams and await with interest the results on ongoing phase 3 clinical trials in HAE.[16] The program and abstracts from the Fifth C1 Inhibitor Deficiency Workshop are available at www.haenet.hu.[16] We hope that this approach will be openly discussed and modified at upcoming international HAE conferences and by patient groups and treatment teams and encourage changes in the proposed approach as new evidence comes to light. Exciting investigational therapies were discussed at the 2 meetings, but the algorithm is limited to the treatments available in 2007 in most countries. This dynamic algorithm (a revision of the first 2003 Canadian Consensus published in the *Journal of Allergy and Clinical Immunology*[17] and presented herein with the minor revisions based on the February 3, 2006, Toronto Canadian Consensus Conference and the Budapest Fifth C1 Inhibitor Deficiency Workshop on June 2, 2007[16]) recognizes that there are many different and possibly equally valid approaches to management of HAE and is meant to be a recommendation for an approach that needs ongoing validation. We agree that Consensus Conferences are a poor replacement for double-blind, placebo-controlled trials. Until the results of such trials are available, consensus may provide some guidance and stimulate research that will encourage undertaking further clinical trials.[16]

PATIENT GROUP PERSPECTIVE

The HAE patient societies, including the CHAES/SAHC, have proposed establishment of comprehensive care clinics for the diagnosis, therapy, and management of HAE, including the development of home infusion and home care programs.[16,21] Similar to the presentation by Hungarian-sponsored HAE workshops in their publication,[8] we think it appropriate to share the patient perspective of HAE management to help administrators reflect on the development of comprehensive care clinics for HAE. The perspective of one Canadian patient with HAE is presented on the Canadian HAE Network Web site (http://www.haecanada.com, "Patient Perspective" section).

CLINICAL CHARACTERISTICS

HAE may present as recurrent angioedema (swelling) without urticaria (without hiving) and usually nonpruritic (without itch).[23] Sometimes there is a nonpruritic serpentine erythematous rash.[24] Distinguishing features of HAE are reviewed by Zingale et al[5] and Bork et al.[24] Swelling may affect any part of the body, including the extremities, face, trunk, gastrointestinal tract, genitourinary regions, or upper airways. Abdominal symptoms may mimic infantile colic, acute appendicitis, or other forms of acute abdomen, and symptoms may include nausea, vomiting, abdominal pains, and postattack diarrhea.[23–26] In patients with known HAE and a strong indication that the abdominal attack may be HAE related, infusion with C1-INH replacement therapy can be used to differentiate acute abdomen from an HAE attack.[26] Age of onset is variable, and patients may present at younger than 1 year with colic or rarely swelling.[27] Laryngeal attacks are uncommon before the age of 3 years and tend to occur later than other symptoms.[23,27] Attacks frequently worsen around puberty.[23,27,28] Symptoms often worsen with estrogen-containing birth control pills or hormone replacement therapy.[28,29] Untreated attacks tend to be prolonged, typically increasing during the first 24 hours and then slowly and spontaneously subsiding at more than 48 to 72 hours. However, some attacks may last longer than 72 hours as the swelling migrates from site to site. Attack triggers may include stress, minor trauma (such as dental procedures), menstruation, pregnancy, some drugs (eg, oral contraceptives, ACE-Is), or infections.[5,16,23] However, triggers are often unidentified. Attacks tend to be periodic, sometimes coming in clusters, and often followed by several weeks of remission. Attacks may not respond to treatment with epinephrine, antihistamines, or glucocorticoids.[5,16,23,30]

DIAGNOSIS

Indications for testing include clinical suspicion at any age or, if the family history is positive, test at any age. Tests may not be reliable in patients younger than 1 year (false-negative and false-positive testings may occur unless using genetic typing). Testing performed in patients before the age of 1 year should be confirmed after the age of 1 year.[31] A serpiginous rash is sometimes seen with the prodrome of HAE, but clinical urticaria (hives) usually make the diagnosis of HAE unlikely.[24] An algorithm approach to angioedema has been presented by Zingale et al.[5] Figure 1 shows the HAE diagnostic algorithm.

DIAGNOSTIC TESTING

If C1-INH deficiency is clinically suspected, we recommend screening with serum C4 and C1-INH proteins. C4 is normal between swelling events in only 2% of cases, so a normal C4 level should make one question the diagnosis of HAE. If there is a low index of suspicion, it may be more cost effective to screen with C4 alone (it is not necessary to screen with CH_{50} or C3).[32] If serum C4 and C1-INH antigenic protein levels are both low and AAE not suspected, then the diagnosis is compatible with type 1 HAE (we suggest repeating testing once to confirm). If AAE is possible (ie, no family history and later onset of symptoms, such as age older than 40 years), then serum C1q antigenic protein testing is required, and if levels are low, the diagnosis is highly compatible with AAE (C1q antigenic protein is reduced in 75% of AAE but normal in HAE). If the C4 level is normal or low and the C1-INH antigenic protein level normal but clinical suspicion is strong, HAE is NOT ruled out. We recommend obtaining a C1-INH functional assay. If the C1-INH functional activity is low with normal or elevated C1-INH antigenic protein and normal C1q levels, this finding is compatible with type 2 HAE. Testing should be repeated at least once more to confirm the diagnosis. If C4 antigenic protein and C1-INH functional assays are both normal, types 1 and 2 HAE can be ruled out. However, this does not rule out the recently described types of HAE (sometimes called type 3 HAE or estrogen-dependent angioedema), with normal C1-INH protein and function occurring mainly in women, including HAE due to mutations in the coagulation factor XII gene and other defects yet to be identified.[8,11–13,16] The same is true for ACE-I–related angioedema. If C4 and C1-INH protein levels are normal, these tests should be repeated during an acute attack (Fig 1).

Genetic testing is not necessary to confirm the diagnosis of types 1 and 2 HAE, and similar to other autosomal dominant disorders, approximately 25% of patients may represent de novo mutations.[16] However, genetic testing may be necessary to investigate type 3.[16] C1-INH functional assays vary, and we recommend standardizing the functional assays and establishing specialized laboratories capable of accurately measuring C1-INH function and establishing an international set of reference patient samples to facilitate independent quality assurance programs for laboratories claiming to test for HAE. (For example, one of our authors, E. Wagner, surveyed Canadian laboratories testing for HAE, with results of the survey summarized in http://www.haecanada.com - diagnosis section Canadian testing facilities.) Physicians are reminded that patient sample handling for complement testing must be strictly adhered to obtain reliable results (http://www.haecanada.com – diagnosis section – sample handling).

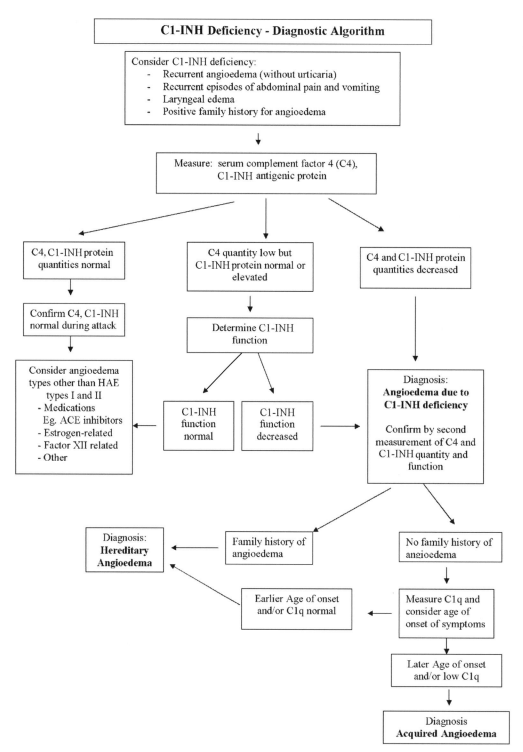

Figure 1. C1 inhibitor (C1-INH) deficiency diagnostic algorithm. This Figure is reprinted with permission from the American Academy of Allergy, Asthm and Immunology from Bowen et al.[17] HAE indicates hereditary angioedema; ACE, angiotensin-converting enzyme.

BASELINE LABORATORY TESTING AT DIAGNOSIS AT ANY AGE

Baseline bloodborne pathogen surveillance (hemovigilance) samples should be collected and stored at baseline and annually through national programs similar to the Canadian hemophilia hemovigilance program (Dr Bruce Ritchie: bruce.ritchie@ualberta.ca; http://www.ahcdc.ca/BBPSP; baseline sample storing for testing for human immunodeficiency virus; human T-cell lymphoma; hepatitis B, C, and G; and future testing for possible emerging pathogens).[16,17,22,33] C1-INH hormone replacement (C1INHRP) therapy may have to be administered at any time on an emergency basis. Therefore, hemovigilance and baseline chemical analysis and urinalysis are best performed at diagnosis. Methods of production for C1-INH replacement therapy may differ, and risk of bloodborne pathogen transmission may differ among products. CSL Behring safety data collected since 1985 on Berinert P (pasteurized C1-INH replacement material) have shown no viral transmission to date (including enveloped and nonenveloped viruses, such as hepatitis B and C and human immunodeficiency virus 1 and 2).[16,17,22,34]

Attenuated androgens and antifibrinolytics may predispose patients to atherogenesis and liver disorders.[16,17,22,35,36] Serum lipid profile should be obtained before androgen administration. Abdominal liver spleen ultrasonography can be considered before continuous androgen administration and performed every 2 years if receiving regular androgen therapy and annually if treated for more than 10 years with androgens. Liver function studies, including alanine aminotransferase, total bilirubin, alkaline phosphatase (prothrombin time, partial thromboplastin time, and albumin could be included), creatine kinase, lactic dehydrogenase, blood urea nitrogen, creatinine, complete blood cell count, and differential, and urinalysis should be performed at diagnosis.

VACCINATION RECOMMENDATIONS

It is recommended that patients who may need to receive blood products receive vaccination to hepatitis B (may be in combination with a hepatitis A vaccine such as Twinrix).

MEDICATIONS TO AVOID IN PATIENTS WITH HAE

Some medications may trigger or worsen angioedema events in patients with HAE and should be avoided, including ACE-Is[5,16] and estrogen contraceptives.[8,16,28,29] Plasminogen activators are a theoretical risk, but the benefit may outweigh the risk.[37–39]

SHORT-TERM PROPHYLAXIS: MINOR MANIPULATIONS

If only mild manipulation, such as mild dental work, is required or if C1INHRP therapy is immediately available, then no prophylaxis is required. If C1INHRP therapy is not available, then danazol prophylaxis is required. Injection of local anesthetic may precipitate an attack. Figure 2 shows the HAE prophylaxis algorithm.

If considering more than mild manipulation such as dental work, danazol is recommended (even in children and in women in the last trimester of pregnancy; avoid in the first 2 trimesters of pregnancy[16,17,22,27]). The recommended dosage is 2.5 to 10 mg/kg daily, with a maximum of 600 mg/d, for 5 days before and 2 days after the event. C1INHRP therapy should be immediately available when possible.

Tranexamic acid is much less predictable for acute prevention compared with danazol but more often recommended than ε-aminocaproic acid (EACA).[8,16,17,22,27,35] Because of the safety of danazol given in the short term, we do not recommend use of tranexamic acid or EACA for short-term prophylaxis. C1INHRP therapy should be immediately available when possible.

SHORT-TERM PROPHYLAXIS: INTUBATION OR MAJOR PROCEDURES

C1INHRP therapy 1 hour before surgery (to be used if intubation is used; not available in all countries and currently not available in the United States). The recommended dosage is 500 U up to a weight of 50 kg (110 lb), 1,000 U for weight greater than 50 kg (110 lb) and less than 100 kg (220 lb), and 1,500 U if weight is greater than 100 kg (>220 lb). A second dose of an equal amount should be immediately available at time of surgery.[8,16,17,40] Repeat daily or as needed until there is no further risk of angioedema.

If C1INHRP therapy is not available, then danazol is recommended. Solvent- or detergent-treated fresh frozen plasma is another option 1 or more hours before surgery. If solvent- or detergent-treated fresh frozen plasma is not available, regular fresh frozen plasma is a less safe alternative. The dose has not been studied but is usually 2 U per adult infusion (200 mL per unit). For coagulopathies, 10 mL/kg of solvent- or detergent-treated fresh frozen plasma has been used,[41] which may be appropriate for HAE, but neither the dose nor timing before the procedure have been studied.

C1 INH prophylaxis is the safest prophylactic agent during pregnancy.

LONG-TERM PROPHYLAXIS

If a patient experiences more than 1 severe event per month or is disabled more than 5 days per month or if the patient has a history of previous airway compromise, then consider prophylaxis with tranexamic acid, androgens, or C1INHRP therapy on demand. The number of events per year does not predict severity of the next event or whether the first or next event will be an airway event.

Attenuated androgens danazol and stanozolol (stanozolol is available in the United States through pharmacies that compound the drug) are the usual agents, with methyltestosterone and oxandrolone as alternatives.[16,17,22,36] These agents may be more effective than antifibrinolytic agents.[35] Contraindications usually include pregnancy and lactation, cancer, and childhood (until finished growing). Adverse effects may in-

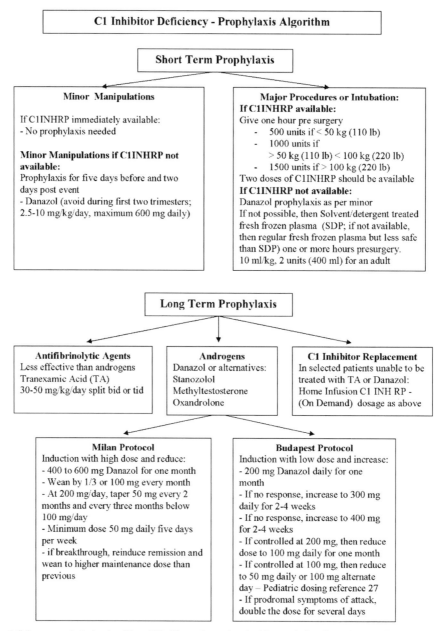

Figure 2. C1 inhibitor deficiency prophylaxis algorithm. This Figure is reprinted with permission from the American Academy of Allergy, Asthma and Immunology from Bowen et al.[17] C1INHRP indicates C1 inhibitor hormone replacement.

clude hair growth, weight gain, acne, voice deepening, vasomotor symptoms, decreased breast size, menstrual irregularities, decreased libido, hepatic necrosis or cholestasis, altered liver enzymes, liver neoplasms (hepatocellular adenomas or carcinomas), hypertension, atherogenesis with altered lipid metabolism, polycythemia, and hemorrhagic cystitis.[16,17,22,36,42–51]

According to the Milan protocol,[52] induction with high-dose danazol of 400 to 600 mg daily for 1 month should be

initiated. The patient should be weaned off the drug by one-third or 100 mg every month as long as there is no breakthrough. At 200 mg/d, slow the tapering with reductions of 50 mg every 2 months, and every 3 months, the dose should be less than 100 mg/d. The usual minimum dose is 50 mg/d 5 days per week. If breaking through with more than 6 attacks per year, then increase the dose to reinduce remission and then wean again to a higher dose than previous.

According to the Budapest protocol,[27,53] induction with low-dose danazol of 2.5 mg/kg daily up to 200 mg daily for 1 month should be initiated. If no response, then increase the dose to 300 mg/d for 2 weeks to 1 month (maximum of 200 mg for children[27]). If no response, then increase to 400 mg daily for 2 weeks to 1 month. If controlled at 200 mg, then reduce the dose to 100 mg/d for 1 month. If still controlled, then reduce to 50 mg/d or try 100 mg on alternate days. Androgen therapy is not recommended for children but has been used in the prepubertal setting.[27,53] If the sensation of prodromal attack symptoms or mild clinical manifestations develop or if patients are exposed to a precipitating factor (eg, upper airway infection), the dose should be doubled for several days.

To monitor androgen levels, every 6 months a complete blood cell count, measurement of liver enzymes (alanine aminotransferase, aspartate aminotransferase, alkaline phosphatase), lipid profile, and urinalysis should be performed. For adults with a dose of 200 mg/d or less of androgens, suggest annual liver spleen ultrasonography. In adults with doses higher than 200 mg/d or in prepubertal patients, suggest 6 months of liver spleen ultrasonography for the detection of focal lesions.

Tranexamic acid (not available in the United States) has mostly replaced EACA.[35] Tranexamic acid may not be as effective as androgen therapy in HAE[54] but may be useful in AAE.[14] Tranexamic acid is mostly used when prophylaxis is indicated before Tanner V puberty stage. Adverse effects may include myalgia, elevated serum creatine phosphokinase or aldolase level, rhabdomyolysis, muscle weakness, hypotension, and fatigue.[35,55–63] The tranexamic acid dosage recommended is 30 to 50 mg/kg daily (split 2 to 3 times daily).[8,16,17,22,27,35,53]

Patients should be allowed to keep a supply of C1INHRP for personal use at home or with travel, to be either self-administered or infused by a caregiver or at a medical facility. To facilitate early infusion for acute HAE events and to facilitate prophylaxis therapy where indicated, home C1INHRP self-infusion programs should be offered to patients[8,16,17,22,27,64,65] (created similarly to hemophilia self-infusion programs, which have existed for 35 years[64]). An example of home infusion technique can be viewed at http://www.haecanada.com, home infusion section.

C1INHRP should be administered at 500 U up to a weight of 50 kg (110 lb), 1,000 U for a weight of more than 50 kg (110 lb) to less than 100 kg (220 lb), and 1,500 U if weight is more than 100 kg (>220 lb).

C1INHRP should be reconstituted and warmed to body temperature before infusion. If a severe event, do not wait to warm the product before administration. DO NOT SHAKE because this will denature the protein. Administration should be via a peripheral vein for more than 10 minutes. Epinephrine is not routinely recommended to have on hand for home C1INHRP administration (systemic reactions uncommon[34]).

Patients are encouraged to carry "alert" identification (such as a wallet card, an example of which is available for downloading from http://www.haecanada.com, wallet card section) and an accompanying letter indicating C1-INH deficiency and outlining instructions for administration of the C1INHRP. HAE organization Web sites should provide infusion instructions for downloading by patients and comprehensive care clinics. Home self-infusion protocols should be available on the patient Web sites (example: http://www.haecanada.com, self infusion section).

If significant angioedema attacks are frequent despite androgen or tranexamic acid prophylaxis and C1INHRP on demand is given more than once per 10 days, then C1-INH prophylaxis at the previously mentioned dosage given every 5 to 7 days (sometimes more frequently for short periods) can be considered.[8,16,17,22]

C1-INH prophylaxis is the safest prophylactic agent during pregnancy.

TREATMENT OF ACUTE HAE ATTACKS

The first-line therapy for treatment of any significant angioedema event is C1INHRP (C1INHRP administered at 500 U up to a weight of 50 kg, 1,000 U for a weight of more than 50 kg to less than 100 kg (220 lb), and 1,500 U if weight is more than 100 kg).[8,16,17,22,27,66]

If C1INHRP is not available, other therapies may include increasing (usually doubling) the androgen (danazol or stanozolol) dose, tranexamic acid (Table 1), early use of adrenaline (if other therapy is not available but treating physicians should be prepared that it may have no benefit[30]), pain management, intravenous fluids, and supportive care. Use of fresh frozen plasma (solvent detergent preferred) could theoretically worsen attacks and remains controversial.[67]

BLOOD PRODUCT RISKS

Blood product infusion risks are reviewed annually by the Canadian Pediatric Society, Infectious Diseases and Immunization Committee,[68] and the safety profile for pasteurized C1INHRP has been previously presented.[34] We recommend patients receiving blood products should undergo annual hemosurveillance similar to the Canadian Hemophilia Program (Dr Bruce Ritchie, bruce.ritchie@ualberta.ca).[33] To date, bloodborne pathogen transmission with pasteurized C1INHRP has not been reported.[16,22,34]

COMPREHENSIVE CARE CLINICS

We recommend that a comprehensive care clinic programs be established for the diagnosis, therapy, and management of HAE similar to the model for comprehensive care of hemophilia in Canada.[8,16,17,19,22,21,27,64] A suggested CHAES/SAHC clinic model for HAE is included in http://www.hemophilia.ca/nrbdo/en/home.php, conference proceedings and conference recommendations,[16,18,19,21] and is outlined in Table 2.

DATABASE REGISTRY FOR HAE

We recommend comprehensive care clinics be encouraged to register HAE patients in national and international database registries to facilitate progress in management of this

Table 1. Treatment of Acute Hereditary Angioedema Attacks[a]

Treatment	Cutaneous swellings		Abdominal attack	Laryngeal attack
	Other than face or neck	Face or neck		
Wait and see (spontaneous resolution)	+	−	−	−
Tranexamic acid[b]	+	+	+	−
C1INHRP concentrate[b]	+/−	+	+	+
ICU (intubation,[c] tracheotomy)	−	−	−	+

Abbreviations: C1INHRP, C1 inhibitor hormone replacement; ICU, intensive care unit.
Symbols: minus sign, negative; plus sign, positive.
[a] Table modified and reprinted with permission from the American Academy of Allergy, Asthma and Immunology from Bowen et al.[17]
[b] Tranexamic acid (oral or intravenous), 15 mg/kg every 4 hours, or C1INHRP concentrate (intravenous), 500 U for those who weigh less than 50 kg, 1,000 U for those who weigh 50 to 100 kg, and 1,500 U for those who weigh more than 100 kg.
[c] Consider intubation early in progressive laryngeal edema.

Table 2. Goals of Comprehensive Care Clinics for Hereditary Angioedema[a]

1. Psychosocial support for patients, their families, and clinic staff.
2. Education regarding responsible self/family care (home care model) and provide home and self-infusion instruction and support, including self-infusion training and guidelines to ensure patient safety and emergency services assistance.
3. An environment conducive to research and clinical trials for improved patient care and outcome.
4. Standards of care and treatment protocols and assess outcome measures and monitoring including quality of life assessments, therapy monitoring including infusion log tracking (to record lot numbers and infusion details for C1 inhibitor product used by each patient), treatment side effect monitoring programs, attack trigger monitoring.
5. Patient information systems: interclinic networking to facilitate product recalls (such as the Patient Notification System), collect data on outcome measures of various therapies and to facilitate participation in clinical trials and encourage participation in provincial/territorial, national, and international data base registries.
6. 24-Hour support and information line for patients and physicians in communities across Canada.
7. Informative wallet cards and letters, including care plans to be carried by all patients and encourage carrying alert materials (such as MedicAlert).
8. Clinical audit with respect to outcome measures.
9. Hemovigilance hemosurveillance protocols.
10. Access to specialized diagnostic facilities.
11. Counseling regarding the risk benefit of therapies including the risks of blood products.
12. A team of specialists, including immunologists/allergists, hematologists, gastroenterologists, genetic counseling, endocrinologists, obstetrics/gynecology, pain management specialists, social workers, nurses, occupational and vocational guidance counselors, emergency physicians, internists, and pediatricians.
13. Decentralization of care through outreach.
14. An advisory or oversight board with patient group representation for each clinic.

[a] Modified by permission from www.haecanada.com, comprehensive care clinics section.

disorder. The European HAE network PREHAEAT chaired by Marco Cicardi established a European HAE Register (www.haeregister.org) and invited international collaboration in this and the International Hereditary Angioedema group (http://www.haei.org/) to facilitate advancement in HAE management. Countries are encouraged to fund database registry for HAE and fund participation in international collaborative efforts, including the HAEI database registry and other international collaborative efforts (similar need for the patients with rare blood disorders, including hemophilia, HAE, and hemoglobinopathies, including sickle cell and thalassemia; discussed at the NRBDO conference of February 3 to 5, 2006, in Toronto and at the Fifth C1 Inhibitor Deficiency Workshop).[8,16,19,21] These database registries share common issues of privacy, confidentiality, and ownership of data and therefore benefit by sharing clinics or at least the

clinic models. Similar to the Canadian hemophilia program, patients own their own data. Consent to share their anonymous data is encouraged and in the HAEI registry is required. Clinicians who contribute to the registries will have access to their own data as individual or group reports.[8,9,16,21]

EMERGING THERAPIES

Double-blind, placebo-controlled clinical trials are under way, including human blood product C1-INH products, kallikrein inhibitor, bradykinin β_2-receptor inhibitor, and recombinant C1-INH. Results of these trials should be available in the near future and should provide expanded options for therapy (http://www.hemophilia.ca/nrbdo/en/home.php, conference presentations; Fifth C1 Inhibitor Deficiency Workshop).[16]

ACKNOWLEDGMENTS

We thank the partners, sponsors, and the NRBDO (Canada) Meeting Organizing committee for participating in and contributing financial support to the meeting held in Toronto, Ontario, Canada, February 3, 2006, and the Fifth C1 Inhibitor Deficiency Workshop at which the consensus described herein was agreed to (listed on the Canadian Hemophilia Society Web site: http://www.hemophilia.ca/nrbdo/en/home. php, NRBDO, final program, and on the program for the Fifth C1 Inhibitor Deficiency Workshop found at www. haenet.hu).[16] We particularly thank the Public Health Agency of Canada (Agence de santé publique du Canada) for sponsoring the Comprehensive Care Meeting of the NRBDO and CSL (ZLB) Behring for their unrestricted educational grant sponsorship for the Medical/Scientific Programme Day, February 3, 2006.

REFERENCES

1. Quincke H. Concerning the acute localized oedema of the skin. *Monatsh Prakt Derm.* 1882;1:129–131.
2. Osler W. Hereditary angio-neurotic oedema. *Am J Med Sci.* 1888;95: 362–367.
3. Donaldson VH, Evans RR. A biochemical abnormality in hereditary angioneurotic edema: absence of serum inhibitor of C'1-esterase. *Am J Med.* 1963;35:37–44.
4. Caldwell JR, Ruddy S, Schur PH, Austen KF. Acquired C1 inhibitor deficiency in lymphosarcoma. *Clin Immunol Immunopathol.* 1972;1: 39–52.
5. Zingale LC, Beltrami L, Zanichellia A, et al. Angioedema without urticaria: a large clinical survey. *CMAJ.* 2006;175:1065–1070.
6. Bock SC, Skriver K, Nielsen E, et al. Human C1 inhibitor: primary structure, cDNA cloning, and chromosomal localization. *Biochemistry.* 1986;25:4292–4301.
7. Theriault A, Whaley K, McPhaden AR, Boyd E, Connor JM. Regional assignment of the human C1-inhibitor gene to 11q11–q13.1. *Hum Genet.* 1990;84:477–479.
8. Agostoni A, Aygoren-Pursun E, Binkley KE, et al. Hereditary and acquired angioedema: problems and progress: proceedings of the third C1 esterase inhibitor deficiency workshop and beyond. *J Allergy Clin Immunol.* 2004;114:S51–131.
9. Roche O, Blanch A, Caballero T, Sastre N, Callejo D, Lopez-Trascasa M. Hereditary angioedema (HAE) due to C1 inhibitor deficiency: registry of the patients and approach to the prevalence in Spain. *Ann Allergy Asthma Immunol.* 2005;94:498–503.
10. Cicardi M, Bergamaschini L, Cugno M, et al. Pathogenetic and clinical aspects of C1 inhibitor deficiency. *Immunobiology.* 1998;199:366–376.
11. Bork K, Barnstedt SE, Koch P, Traupe H. Hereditary angioedema with normal C1-inhibitor activity in women. *Lancet.* 2000;356:213–217.
12. Binkley KE, Davis AE III. Estrogen-dependent inherited angioedema. *Transfus Apheresis Sci.* 2003;29:215–219.
13. Dewald G, Bork K. Missense mutations in the coagulation factor XII (Hageman factor) gene in hereditary angioedema with normal C1 inhibitor. *Biochem Biophys Res Commun.* 2006;343:1286–1289.
14. Cicardi M, Zingale LC, Pappalardo E, Falcioni A, Agostoni A. Autoantibodies and lymphoproliferative diseases in acquired C1-inhibitor deficiencies. *Medicine (Baltimore).* 2003;82:274–281.
15. Bork K, Ressel N. Sudden upper airway obstruction in patients with hereditary angioedema. *Transfus Apheresis Sci.* 2003;29:235–238.
16. Agenda, Proceedings, Recommendations and the PowerPoint presentations from Comprehensive Care for Rare Blood Disorders; February 3–5, 2006; organized by the Canadian Network of Rare Blood Disorder Organizations (NRBDO). http://www.hemophilia.ca/nrbdo/en/home.php. Program and abstracts for the Fifth C1 Inhibitor Deficiency Workshop; Budapest; May 31 to June 3, 2007. www.haenet.hu.
17. Bowen T, Cicardi M, Farkas H, et al. Canadian 2003 International Consensus Algorithm for the Diagnosis, Therapy, and Management of Hereditary Angioedema. *J Allergy Clin Immunol.* 2004;114:629–637.
18. Bowen T, guest editor. Editorial. *Transfus Apheresis Sci.* 2003;29: 193–194.
19. Bowen T, Hebert J, Ritchie B, et al. Management of hereditary angioedema: a Canadian approach. *Transfus Apheresis Sci.* 2003;29: 205–214.
20. Farkas H, Varga L. The Hungarian HAE experience. *Transfus Apheresis Sci.* 2003;29:229–233.
21. Bowen T. Angioedema and the Canadian Network of Rare Blood Disorder Organizations: extending the Canadian hemophilia care model [commentary]. *CMAJ.* 2006;175:1083–1084.
22. Gompels MM, Lock RJ, Abinun M, et al. C1 inhibitor deficiency: consensus document. *Clin Exp Immunol.* 2005;139:379–394.
23. Bork K, Meng G, Staubach P, Hardt J. Hereditary angioedema: new findings concerning symptoms, affected organs, and course. *Am J Med.* 2006;119:267–274.
24. Farkas H, Harmat G, Fay A, et al. Erythema marginatum preceding an acute oedematous attack of hereditary angioneurotic oedema. *Acta Derm Venereol.* 2001;81:376–377.
25. Farkas H, Harmat G, Kaposi NP, et al. Ultrasonography in the diagnosis and monitoring of ascites in acute abdominal attacks of hereditary angioneurotic oedema. *Eur J Gastroenterol Hepatol.* 2001;13: 1225–1230.
26. Bork K, Staubach P, Eckardt AJ, Hardt J. Symptoms, course, and complications of abdominal attacks in hereditary angioedema due to C1 inhibitor deficiency. *Am J Gastroenterol.* 2006;619–27.
27. Farkas H, Varga L, Szeplaki G, Visy B, Harmat G, Bowen T. Management of hereditary angioedema in pediatric patients. *Pediatrics.* In press.
28. Frank MM, Gelfand JA, Atkinson JP. Hereditary angioedema: the clinical syndrome and its management. *Ann Intern Med.* 1976;84:580–593.
29. Bork K, Fischer B, Dewald G. Recurrent episodes of skin angioedema and severe attacks of abdominal pain induced by oral contraceptives or hormone replacement therapy. *Am J Med.* 2003;114:294–298.
30. Trachsel D, Hammer J. A vote for inhaled adrenaline in the treatment of severe upper airway obstruction caused by piercing of the tongue in hereditary angioedema. *Int Care Med.* 1999;25:1335–1336.
31. Nielsen EW, Johansen HT, Holt J, Mollnes TE. C1 inhibitor and diagnosis of hereditary angioedema in newborns. *Pediatr Res.* 1994;35: 184–187.
32. Zuraw BL, Sugimoto S, Curd JG. The value of rocket immunoelectrophoresis for C4 activation in the evaluation of patients with angioedema or C1-inhibitor deficiency. *J Allergy Clin Immunol* 1986;78:1115–1120.
33. Ritchie B. Tissue archives to track blood borne pathogens in people receiving blood products. *Transfus Apheresis Sci.* 2003;29:269–274.
34. DeSerres J, Gröner A, Lindner J. Safety and efficacy of pasteurized C1 inhibitor concentrate (Berinert P) in hereditary angioedema: a review. *Transfus Apheresis Sci.* 2003;29:247–254.
35. Ritchie B. Protease inhibitors in the treatment of hereditary angioedema. *Transfus Apheresis Sci.* 2003;29:259–267.
36. Agostoni A, Cicardi M, Martignoni GC, Bergamaschini L, Marasini B. Danazol and stanozolol in long-term prophylactic treatment of hereditary angioedema. *J Allergy Clin Immunol.* 1980;65:75–79.
37. Ewald GA. Eisenberg PR. Plasmin-mediated activation of contact system in response to pharmacological thrombolysis. *Circulation.* 1995;91: 28–36.
38. Lynch M, Pentecost BL. Littler Was, Stockley RA. Why do patients develop reactions to streptokinase? *Clin Exp Immunol.* 1993;94: 279–285.
39. Francis CW, Brenner B, Leddy JP, Marder VJ. Angioedema during therapy with recombinant tissue plasminogen activator. *Br J Haematol.* 1991;77:562–563.
40. Bork K, Meng G, Staubach P, Hardt J. Treatment with C1 inhibitor concentrate in abdominal pain attacks of patients with hereditary angioedema. *Transfusion.* 2005;45:1774–1784.
41. Hellstern P, Muntean W, Schramm W, Seifried E, Solheim BG. Practical guidelines for the clinical use of plasma. *Thromb Res.* 2002;107(suppl

1):S53–S57.

42. Cicardi M, Castelli R, Zingale LC, Agostoni A. Side effects of long-term prophylaxis with attenuated androgens in hereditary angioedema: comparison of treated and untreated patients. *J Allergy Clin Immunol.* 1997;99:194–196.

43. Farrell GC, Joshua DE, Uren RF, Baird PJ, Perkins KW, Kronenberg H. Androgen-induced hepatoma. *Lancet.* 1975;1:430–432.

44. Johnson FL, Feagler JR, Lerner KG, et al. Association of androgenic-anabolic steroid therapy with development of hepatocellular carcinoma. *Lancet.* 1972;2:1273–1276.

45. Kew MC, Van Coller B, Prowse CM, et al. Occurrence of primary hepatocellular cancer and peliosis hepatis after treatment with androgenic steroids. *S Afr Med J.* 1976;50:1233–1237.

46. Falk H, Thomas LB, Popper H, Ishak KG. Hepatic angiosarcoma associated with androgenic-anabolic steroids. *Lancet.* 1979;2:1120–1123.

47. Andriole GL, Brickman C, Lack EE, et al. Danazol-induced cystitis: an undescribed source of hematuria in patients with hereditary angioneurotic edema. *J Urol.* 1986;135:44–46.

48. Crampon D, Barnoud R, Durand M, et al. Danazol therapy: an unusual aetiology of hepatocellular carcinoma [letter]. *J Hepatol.* 1998;29:1035–1036.

49. Bork K, Pitton M, Harten P, Koch P. Hepatocellular adenomas in patients taking danazol for hereditary angiooedema. *Lancet.* 1999;353:1066–1067.

50. Mantel-Teeuwisse AK, Kloosterman JM, Maitland-van der Zee AH, Klungel OH, Porsius AJ, de Boer A. Drug-induced lipid changes: a review of the unintended effects of some commonly used drugs on serum lipid levels. *Drug Saf.* 2001;24:443–456.

51. Bork K, Schneiders V. Danazol-induced hepatocellular adenoma in patients with hereditary angio-oedema. *J Hepatol.* 2002;36:707–709.

52. Cicardi M, Zingale L. How do we treat patients with hereditary angioedema. *Transfus Apheresis Sci.* 2003;29:221–227.

53. Farkas H, Harmat G, Fust G, Varga L, Visy B. Clinical management of hereditary angio-oedema in children. *Pediatr Allergy Immunol.* 2002;13:153–161.

54. Agostoni A, Cicardi M. Hereditary and acquired C1-inhibitor deficiency: biological and clinical characteristics in 235 patients. *Medicine (Baltimore).* 1992;71:206–215.

55. Theil PL. Ophthalmological examination of patients in long-term treatment with tranexamic acid. *Acta Ophthalmol (Copenh).* 1981;59:237–241.

56. Endo Y, Nishimura S, Miura A. Deep-vein thrombosis induced by tranexamic acid in idiopathic thrombocytopenic purpura. *JAMA.* 1988;259:3561–3562.

57. Woo KS, Tse LK, Woo JL, Vallance-Owen J. Massive pulmonary thromboembolism after tranexamic acid antifibrinolytic therapy. *Br J Clin Pract.* 1989;43:465–466.

58. Davies D, Howell DA. Tranexamic acid and arterial thrombosis [letter]. *Lancet.* 1977;1:49.

59. Rydin E, Lundberg PO. Tranexamic acid and intracranial thrombosis [letter]. *Lancet.* 1976;2:49.

60. Lindoff C, Rybo G, Astedt B. Treatment with tranexamic acid during pregnancy, and the risk of thrombo-embolic complications. *Thromb Haemost.* 1993;70:238–240.

61. Berntorp E, Follrud C, Lethagen S. No increased risk of venous thrombosis in women taking tranexamic acid. *Thromb Haemost.* 2001;86:714–715.

62. Dalmau A, Sabate A, Koo M. Prophylactic use of tranexamic acid and incidence of arterial thrombosis in liver transplantation. *Anesth Analg.* 2001;93:516.

63. Taparia M, Cordingley FT, Leahy MF. Pulmonary embolism associated with tranexamic acid in severe acquired haemophilia. *Eur J Haematol.* 2002;68:307–309.

64. Strawczynski H, Stachewitsch A, Morgenstern G, Shaw ME. Delivery of care to hemophiliac children: home care versus hospitalization. *Pediatrics.* 1973;51:986–991.

65. Levi M, Choi G, Picavet MA, Hack CE. Self-administration of C1-inhibitor concentrate in patients with hereditary or acquired angioedema

caused by C1-inhibitor deficiency. *J Allergy Clin Immunol.* 2006;117:904–908.

66. Waytes AT, Rosen FS, Frank MM. Treatment of hereditary angioedema with a vapor-heated C1 inhibitor concentrate. *N Engl J Med.* 1996;334:1630–1634.

67. Zuraw BL. Diagnosis and management of hereditary angioedema: an American approach. *Transfus Apheresis Sci.* 2003;29:239–245.

68. Canadian Paediatric Society, Infectious Diseases and Immunization Committee. Annual report. *J Paediatr Child Health.* 2006;11:158–162.

Departments of Medicine and Paediatrics, University of Calgary, Calgary, Alberta, Canada (T.B.)

Department of Internal Medicine, Universita degli Studi di Milano, Ospedale L. Sacco, Milan, Italy (M.C., L.C.Z.)

Department of Dermatology, University Hospital of the Johannes Gutenberg-University of Mainz, Mainz, Germany (K.B.)

University of California, San Diego, San Diego, California (B.Z.)

Duke University Medical Center, Durham, North Carolina (M.F.)

Departments of Medicine and Medical Oncology, University of Alberta, Edmonton, Alberta, Canada (B.R.)

Department of Internal Medicine, Kutvolgyi Clinical Center, Semmelweis University, Budapest, Hungary (H.F., L.V., G.F.)

Department of Medicine, University of Toronto, Toronto, Canada (K.B., S.M.)

Department of Pediatrics, CHU Sainte-Justine, University of Montreal, Montreal, Quebec, Canada (E.W.)

The Canadian Hereditary Angioedema Society (CHAES) Société d'angioédème héréditaire du Canada (SAHC), Elk Point, Alberta, Canada (P.A., G.-E.R.)

The Canadian Hereditary Angioedema Society (CHAES)/Société d'angioédème héréditaire du Canada (SAHC), Calgary, Alberta, Canada (K.B.)

The Canadian Hereditary Angioedema Society (CHAES)/Société d'angioédème héréditaire du Canada (SAHC), Claresholm, Alberta, Canada (J.B.)

Department of Medicine, University of Manitoba, Winnipeg, Manitoba, Canada (R.W., C.K.)

Department of Pediatrics, Montreal Children's Hospital, McGill University, Montreal, Quebec, Canada (C.M.)

Department of Medicine, University of British Columbia, Vancouver, British Columbia, Canada (R.S., A.K., D.S.)

The Canadian Hereditary Angioedema Society (CHAES)/Société d'angioédème héréditaire du Canada (SAHC), Montreal, Quebec, Canada (L.C.)

Department of Medicine, Laval University, Quebec City, Quebec, Canada (J.H.)

Department of Medicine, University of Calgary, Calgary, Alberta, Canada (K.V., M.-C.P.)

Departments of Pediatrics and Medicine, University of Calgary, Calgary, Alberta, Canada (B.S.)

Transfusion Medicine, Ottawa Hospital, Ottawa, Ontario, Canada (D.N.)

Department of Medicine, University of Ottawa, Ottawa, Ontario, Canada (W.Y.)

Department of Medicine, Dalhousie University, Halifax, Nova Scotia, Canada (G.L.)

Department of Pediatrics, Dalhousie University, Halifax, Nova Scotia, Canada (A.I.)

Memorial University and Janeway Child Health Centre, St. John's, Newfoundland, Canada (A.H., P.K.)

Department of Pediatrics, University of British Columbia, Vancouver, British Columbia, Canada (J.D.)

Department of Medicine, University of Toronto, Oakville, Ontario, Canada (E.L.)

Kingston, Ontario, Canada (E.T.)

Department of Medicine, McMaster University, Hamilton, Ontario, Canada (S.W., P.K.K.)

Canadian Hemophilia Society and Network of Rare Blood Disorder Organizations (Canada), Montreal, Quebec, Canada (D.P.)

Aplastic Anemia and Myelodysplasia Association of Canada and Network of Rare Blood Disorder Organizations (Canada), Richmond Hill, Ontario, Canada (S.M.)

Barts and the London NHS Trust, London, England (H.J.L.)
Johann Wolfgang Goethe University, Frankfurt/Main, Germany (W.K., E.R., I.M.-S., E.A.-P.)
Heim Pal Pediatric Hospital, Budapest, Hungary (G.H.)
    Institute for Asthma & Allergy, Wheaton and Chevy Chase, Maryland (H.L.)
CHU de Grenoble, Grenoble, France (L.B.)
Hospital Universitario La Paz, Madrid, Spain (T.C.)
4th Medical Clinic, University of Medicine and Pharmacy, Tirgu Mures, Romania (D.M.)
Institute of Pharmacology, University of Bern, Switzerland (P.J.S.)
Asociación Española de Angioedema Familiar por Deficiencia de C1 inhibidor, Madrid, Spain (S.S.-F.)
Hungarian Association of Angioedema Patients, Budapest, Hungary (I.N.)
Nordland Hospital, Bodo, Norway (E.W.N.)
University Hospital, Zurich, Switzerland (C.B.)

Department of Medicine, County Hospital Ryhov, Jonkoping, Sweden (P.N.)
Peking Union Medical College Hospital, Beijing, China (Z.Y.X.)

Requests for reprints should be addressed to:
Tom Bowen, MD, FRCP(C)
Department of Medicine and Paediatrics
University of Calgary
705 South Tower
3031 Hospital Dr NW
Calgary, Alberta
Canada T2N 2T8
E-mail: tbowen@pol.net

RESEARCH

www.AJOG.org

GENERAL GYNECOLOGY

Disease expression in women with hereditary angioedema

Laurence Bouillet, MD, PhD; Hilary Longhurst, MA, MRCP, PhD; Isabelle Boccon-Gibod, MD; Konrad Bork, MD; Christophe Bucher, MD; Anette Bygum, MD; Teresa Caballero, MD, PhD; Christian Drouet, PhD; Henriette Farkas, MD, PhD; Christian Massot, MD; Erik W. Nielsen, MD, PhD; Denise Ponard, PharmD; Marco Cicardi, MD

OBJECTIVE: Fluctuations in sex hormones can trigger angioedema attacks in women with hereditary angioedema. Combined oral contraceptive therapies, as well as pregnancy, can induce severe attacks. The course of angioedema may be very variable in different women.

STUDY DESIGN: Within the PREHAEAT project launched by the European Union, data on 150 postpubertal women with hereditary angioedema were collected in 8 countries, using a patient-based questionnaire.

RESULTS: Puberty worsened the disease for 62%. Combined oral contraceptives worsened the disease for 79%, whereas progestogen-only pills improved it for 64%. During pregnancies, 38% of women had more attacks, but 30% had fewer attacks. Vaginal delivery was usually uncomplicated. Attacks occurred within 48 hours in only 6% of cases. Those more severely affected during menses had more symptoms during pregnancies, suggesting a hormone-sensitive phenotype for some patients.

CONCLUSION: The course of angioedema in women with C1 inhibitor deficiency is affected by physiologic hormonal changes; consequently, physicians should take these into account when advising on management.

Key words: angioedema, estrogens, pregnancies, puberty

Cite this article as: Bouillet L, Longhurst H, Boccon-Gibod I, et al. Disease expression in women with hereditary angioedema. Am J Obstet Gynecol 2008;199:484.e1-484.e4.

Hereditary angioedema (HAE) is a rare disease caused by C1 inhibitor (C1Inh) deficiency with an estimated prevalence between 1 in 10,000 and 1 in 50,000.[1] This disease is characterized by episodic subcutaneous and submucosal edema. It is inherited in an autosomal dominant manner: consequently, both women and men can be affected. HAE attacks appear to depend on bradykinin release[2] and respond to an antagonist of bradykinin receptors.[3]

It is known that HAE is influenced by the fluctuation of female hormones, but individual women vary greatly in their hormone sensitivity. Variations appear in frequency of angioedema symptoms according to the different female life stages of childhood, puberty, menses, pregnancies, and menopause. Reports have noted a close relationship between female hormones and angioedema.[4] Yip et al[5] published the case of a mother and her daughter whose HAE-related symptoms appeared to be sex hormone dependent. Their first attack happened around puberty; angioedema worsened during premenstrual periods and when they took combined oral contraceptives. The report of a woman[6] with HAE and Turner's syndrome is also very interesting: starting physiologic estrogen replacement at the age of 34 years old, this woman experienced a worsening, both in the severity and in the frequency of angioedema attacks. McGlinchey et al[7] described a patient whose symptoms of HAE emerged after starting hormone replacement therapy (HRT). Bork et al[8] reported that women with HAE had more severe disease than men, and that combined oral contraceptives or HRTs can exacerbate HAE: indeed, 63% of women with HAE taking these drugs reported new or worsened angioedema. The women studied had variable numbers of attacks and appeared to show different degrees of estrogen sensitivity.

When a physician takes care of women with a HAE, some issues have to be addressed: the choice of contraception, management of pregnancies and deliveries, and the selection of an effective prophylactic treatment without side effects. Danazol therapy is an effective prophylactic treatment for HAE, but it may be associated with side effects, especially for women. There is a lack of published literature about clinical behavior and man-

From the Department of Internal Medicine (Drs Bouillet, Boccon-Gibod, and Massot) and the Immunology Laboratory (Dr Drouet and Ms Ponard), Grenoble University Hospital, Grenoble, France; Barts and the London NHS Trust (Dr Longhurst), London, England, UK; Department of Dermatology (Dr Bork), Johannes Gutenberg University, Mainz, Germany; University Hospital (Dr Bucher), Zurich, Switzerland; the Department of Dermatology (Dr Bygum), Odense University Hospital, Odense, Denmark; University Hospital La Paz (Dr Caballero), Madrid, Spain; Third Department of Internal Medicine (Dr Farkas), Semmelweis University, Budapest, Hungary; the Department of Anesthesiology, Nordland Hospital, Bodo, and the University of Tromsø, Tromsø, Norway (Dr Nielsen); and Dipartimento di Medicina Interna (Dr Cicardi), Università degli Studi di Milano, University of Milan, Milan, Italy.

Received April 25, 2007; revised April 9, 2008; accepted April 17, 2008.

Reprints not available from the authors.

This project was performed within the framework of the PREHAEAT project (QLG1-CT-2002-01359) of the European Union and was supported by grants from the thematic action 5 of the French 2002 Programme Hospitalier de Recherche Clinique PHRC.

0002-9378/$34.00 • © 2008 Mosby, Inc. All rights reserved. • doi: 10.1016/j.ajog.2008.04.034

agement of HAE with respect to obstetric and gynecologic conditions. Therefore, we undertook a retrospective survey to investigate the associations of HAE-related angioedema with gynecologic events and hormonal changes.

MATERIALS AND METHODS

A retrospective study was conducted. One hundred fifty postpubertal women were enrolled within the framework of the PREHAEAT Project (QLG1-CT-2002601359) of the European Union. The aim of this project was to improve the quality of life of patients with HAE. Hormonal problems in HAE were the subject of the Fifth Work Package of the Project. All women had a C1Inh functional level of 40% or lower, family or personal history of HAE, and/or mutation of the C1Inh gene.

A specific patient-based questionnaire was developed and sent to the principal investigator of each country participating in the project. Anonymous clinical data were collected retrospectively by the patient's physician during a consultation. The data were subjected to statistical analysis (χ^2 test). The study was approved by the individual ethics review boards of each principal investigator and all patients gave written consent.

RESULTS
Characteristics of the sample
Data of 150 postpubertal women from 8 countries: Hungary (32%), Germany

(19%), Denmark (10%), France (10%), Spain (10%), Norway (8%), United Kingdom (6%), and Switzerland (5%), were analyzed. The average age of puberty was 13.5 years (range: 9-17 years). Forty-four women had undergone menopause at an average age of 48.5 years (range: 37-56 years). One hundred seven women had experienced 227 pregnancies.

Puberty and menstrual cycle: Influence on HAE course
Puberty worsened the disease for 62%; the remaining 38% percent of women reported no change. Attacks were triggered by menses for 35% and by ovulation for 14%.

Effect of pregnancy on HAE
Sixty-eight percent of pregnancies influenced the course of HAE. There were more attacks for 38% and fewer for 30%, whereas 32% reported no variation. For almost all women, the effects on HAE symptoms were similar for each subsequent pregnancy. Twelve percent had cesarean deliveries; in the general French population, the rate was 16%. Eighty-nine percent of women had not received a prophylactic treatment during deliveries, but attacks occurred for only 6% of women, just after delivery or within 48 hours.

Contraception
Ninety-one women had used contraception: 59 women had taken combined (estrogen and progestogen) contraceptive pills, 14 women progestogen-only pills, and 18 had used an intrauterine device. Combined oral contraceptives worsened the disease for 80% of women, whereas progestogen pills improved it for 64%. Intrauterine devices were well tolerated in 83% of the cases.

Menopause
Forty-four women had experienced menopause at the time of the questionnaire. For 55%, there was no change in HAE-related symptoms. HAE worsened for 32%. Only 13% had fewer symptoms.

Gynecologic disorders
The frequency of different gynecologic diseases was similar to the general popu-

lation (Table). Fertility was unaffected: the infertility rate was 4% (3-5% for the overall French population). The rate of spontaneous abortion was 12% compared with 10-15% for the overall French population.

Factors predictive of HAE severity
We investigated whether hormonal events could be predictive of future HAE severity. Among the 150 women, 93 experienced more frequent attacks after puberty and 57 experienced the same number of attacks or fewer. Among the 93 women with more frequent attacks, 31% had more attacks during menses, compared with 35% of 57 women who did not have more attacks after puberty. This difference was not statistically significant. Among 107 women who had at least 1 pregnancy, 66 presented with more frequent attacks after puberty and 41 with the same number of attacks or fewer. Among the 66 women with more frequent attacks, 34% had more attacks during their pregnancies compared with 49% for the others. This difference was not statistically significant. Among 44 women who had had their menopause at the time of the questionnaire, we compared 27 women who experienced more frequent attacks after puberty with those who had not: 41% of these had fewer attacks after menopause, compared with only 18% for those who did not experience an increased frequency of attacks at puberty. This difference was not statistically significant. Among the 150 women, 48 experienced more attacks during their menses. Fifty-six percent of the women who had more attacks during their menses experienced more symptoms after puberty compared with 63.7% of women who did not. The difference was not statistically significant. Among 37 women who had more symptoms during their menses, 22 (59%) had more attacks during their pregnancy. In contrast, of 70 women who did not have more attacks during menses, only 17 (24%) had more attacks during pregnancy. This difference was statistically significant ($P < .01$).

COMMENT

This retrospective analysis answers frequently asked questions about puberty, fertility, pregnancies, and contraception in women with HAE. There is no increase in gynecologic events or infertility. Pregnancy is likely to worsen, improve, or to have no effect on disease severity equally. The observation[4] that HAE symptoms improve during the 2 last trimesters was not confirmed in our study. Because of insufficient data, we could not answer the question whether HAE course during pregnancy is affected by the infant's HAE status.

Delivery does not appear to be a major risk factor for attacks, which were rare even in women who did not receive any treatment to prevent angioedema. There were so few reported attacks during delivery that it was not possible to determine events predictive of attacks during delivery. Therefore, prophylactic treatment for vaginal delivery need not be offered routinely but may be considered if the woman is considered to have additional risk factors for an attack.

The disease often worsens at puberty, and attacks are more frequent just before or during menses. Some hormonal events appeared to be associated: women who improved during menses, often improved during pregnancies, suggesting the existence of a group of hormonally sensitive women. It would be interesting to know if this hormonal sensitivity is familial, as for HAE type III. Available information was not sufficient to answer this question. For women requiring contraception, it is very important to avoid combined pills in favor of progestogen-only pills, which may have a favorable effect on HAE.

Angioedema, related to sex hormone therapy, has been reported in absence of HAE. The first cases of angioedema associated with oral contraception were described in 1986 by Warin et al.[9] Two sisters presented with angioedema only after taking combined contraceptive pills and during pregnancy: C1Inh level and complement components were normal. Pichler et al[10] reported angioedema associated with functional C1inh insufficiency in 4 women taking the antiandrogen cyproterone acetate and angioedema in 2 men with hypogonadism, successfully cured by androgen treatment.

In recent years, 3 reports[11-13] have described a new hormone-dependent hereditary angioedema (HAE type III). In these families, only women were affected and in many cases their attacks were precipitated when sex hormonal levels rose, such as pregnancy and use of combined oral contraception. No abnormalities of C1Inh have been reported in these cases. Dewald and Bork[14] recently reported 2 missense mutations in the same codon of the coagulation factor XII gene as the cause of HAE type III in 6 of 20 unrelated German families. One of these 2 mutations has been suggested to be associated with markedly increased factor XIIa levels.[15] We have also reported women who presented with angioedema attacks after starting contraception or during their pregnancies.[16] In these cases, the C1Inh functional studies revealed a lowered C1Inh activity with a marked C1Inh protein cleavage on immunoblot. Clinical and laboratory anomalies disappeared after stopping contraception or after delivery. These women also had mutation of the factor XII gene.

It is well established that HAE symptoms are mediated by bradykinin released from high molecular weight kininogen when it is cleaved at 2 sites by kallikrein generated on activation of the contact system.[17-19] C1Inh regulates this system by inhibiting Hageman factor (90%) and kallikrein (42%). During attacks, local bradykinin levels rise, increasing vascular permeability via the B2 receptors. Specific inhibition of kallikrein or blockade of B2 receptors reverses increased vascular permeability in an animal model of C1Inh deficiency as well as in subjects with HAE.[20-23]

In ovariectomized rats, studies showed that 17β-estradiol increases Hageman factor levels by stimulation of gene transcription.[23-26] This hormone also increases kininogen and kallikrein levels.[27] In addition, estrogens regulate B2 receptor gene expression and function: the vasodepressor response to bradykinin and the B2 receptor messenger RNA (mRNA) levels are reduced in ovariectomized rats and restored by oestrogen substitution.[28] Progesterone does not modify Hageman factor levels but seems to raise kallikrein complementary DNA (cDNA) levels.[27]

In healthy women taking oral contraception, there is an increase of fibrinolytic proteins: elevation of plasmin, factors VII, X, IX, and a decrease of plasminogen activator inhibitor (PAI).[29-31] These effects appear to be estrogen-dependent.[30] The plasma of these women shows enhanced in vitro fibrinolysis.[32] The contact system is also affected, Hageman factor, prekallikrein, kallikrein, and high-molecular weight kininogen increase.[33-35] This results in consumption of C1Inh: the decrease of C1Inh levels correlating with the increase in Hageman factor.[32-34] HRT appears to have the same effect, despite lower estrogen dosage, fibrinolytic proteins (plasminogen and tissue-type plasminogen activator) rise, PAI decreases,[36-38] Hageman factor, prekallikrein, and C3 and C4 levels rise.[31,39,40] Moreover, some studies have shown an influence of HRT on the bradykinin system, angiotensin-converting enzyme activity decreases whereas bradykinin levels increase.[41-43] Visy et al[44] measured serum sex hormone levels in 44 females with HAE, they found a positive correlation between the rate of attacks and estradiol and progesterone levels. However, we do not have detailed information about occurrences of angioedema with clinical events associated with changes in sex hormones for women in this study.

In the case of women with HAE, there is variation in the sex hormone sensitivity, as exemplified by women who have more symptoms after puberty or during menses. One explanation of these different phenotypes may be the presence of mutations or polymorphisms in other potentially relevant genes, such as the Factor XII gene, angiotensin-converting enzyme gene, or bradykinin B2 receptor gene. ∎

REFERENCES

1. Cicardi M, Agostini A. Hereditary angioedema. N Engl J Med 1996;334:1666-7.

2. Nussberger J, Cugno M, Amstutz C, Cicardi M, Pellacani A, Agostini A. Plasma bradykinin in angioedema. Lancet 1998;351:1693-7.

3. Bas M, Bier H, Greve J, Kojda G, Hoffmann TQ. Novel pharmacotherapy of acute hereditary angioedema with bradykinin B2-receptor antagonist icatibant. Allergy 2006;61:1490-2.

4. Nielsen EW, Gran JT, Straume B, Mellbye OJ, Johansen HT, Mollnes TE. Hereditary angio-oedema: new clinical observations and autoimmune screening, complement and kallikrein-kinin analyses. J Intern Med 1996; 239:119-30.

5. Yip J, Cunliffe WJ. Hormonally exacerbated hereditary angioedema. Australas J Dermatol 1992;33:35-8.

6. Fletcher A, Weetman AP. Coexistence of hereditary angioedema and Turner's syndrome. Postgrad Med 1998;74:41-2.

7. McGlinchey PG, McCluskey DR. Hereditary angioedema precipitated by estrogens replacement therapy in a menopausal woman. Am J Med Sci 2000;320:212-3.

8. Bork K, Fischer B, Dewald G. Recurrent episodes of skin angioedema and severe attacks of abdominal pain induced by oral contraceptives or hormone replacement therapy. Am J Med 2003;114: 294-8.

9. Warin RP, Cunliffe WJ, Greaves MW, Wallington TB. Recurrent angioedema: familial and estrogens induced. Br J Dermatol 1986;115: 731-4.

10. Pichler WJ, Lehner R, Spath PJ. Recurrent angioedema associated with hypogonadism or anti-androgen therapy. Ann Allerg 1989;63: 301-5.

11. Bork K, Barnstedt SE, Koch P, Traupe H. Hereditary angioedema with normal C1 inhibitor activity in women. Lancet 2000;356:213-7.

12. Binkley KE, Davis A. Clinical, biochemical, and genetic characterization of a novel estrogen dependent inherited form of angioedema. J Allergy Clin Immunol 2000;106:546-50.

13. Martin L, Degenne D, Toutain A, Ponard D, Watier H. Hereditary angioedema type III: an additional pedigree with autosomal dominant transmission. J Allergy Clin Immunol 2001;107: 747.

14. Dewald G, Bork K. Missense mutations in the coagulation factor XII (Hageman factor) gene in hereditary angioedema with normal C1 inhibitor. Biochem Biophys Res Commun 2006; 343:1286-9.

15. Cichon S, Martin L, Hennies HC, Muller F, Van Driessche K, Karpushova A, et al. Increased activity of coagulation factor XII (Hageman factor) causes hereditary angioedema type III. Am J Human Genet 2006;79:1098-104.

16. Bouillet L, Ponard D, Drouet C, Jullien D, Massot C. Angioedema and contraception Dermatology 2003;206:106-9.

17. Cugno M, Cicardi M, Bottasso B, Coppola R, Paonessa R, Mannucci PM, et al. Activation of the coagulation cascade in C1-Inhibitor deficiencies. Blood 1997;89:3213-8.

18. Cugno M, Hack CE, de Boer JP, Eerenberg AJ, Agostini A, Cicardi M. Generation of plasmin during acute attacks of hereditary angioedema. J Lab Clin Med 1993;121:38-43.

19. Cugno M, Cicardi M, Coppola R, Agostini A. Activation of factor XII and cleavage of high molecular weight kininogen during acute attacks in hereditary and acquired C1-inhibitor deficiencies. Immunopharmacology 1996;33:361-4.

20. Han ED, MacFarlane RC, Mulligan AN, Scafadi J, Davis AE 3rd. Increased vascular permeability in C1 inhibitor-deficient mice mediated by the bradykinin type 2 receptor. J Clin Invest 2002;109:1057-63.

21. Nussberger J, Cugno M, Cicardi M. Bradykinin mediated angioedema. N Engl J Med 2002;347:621-2.

22. Lumry W, Ritchie B, Beck T, Morrison J. Interim results of EDEMA2, a multicenter, open-label, repeat-dosing study of intravenous and subcutaneous administration of ecallantide (DX-88) in hereditary angioedema. J Allergy Clin Immunol 2006;117:S179.

23. Farsatti A, Misiti S, Citarella F, Felici A, Andreoli M, Fantoni A, et al. Molecular basis of estrogen regulation of Hageman factor XII gene expression.Endocrinology 1995;136:5076-83.

24. Citarella F, Misiti S, Felici A, Farsetti A, Pontecorvi A, Fantoni A. Estrogen induction and contact phase activation of human factor XII. Steroids 1996;61:270-6.

25. Gordon EM, Johnson TR, Ramos LP, Scheimdler-Sapiro KT. Enhanced expression of factor XII (Hageman factor) in isolated livers of estrogen and prolactin treated rats. J Lab Clin Med 1991;117:353-8.

26. Gordon EM, Douglas JG, Ratnoff OD, Arafah BM. The influence of estrogen and prolactin on Hageman factor titer in ovariectomized and hypophysectomized rats. Blood 1985; 66:602-5.

27. Chen LM, Chung P, Chao S, Chao L, Chao J. Differential regulation of kininogen gene expression by estrogen and progesterone in vivo. Biochim Biophys Acta 1992;1131:145-51.

28. Madeddu P, Emanueli C, Song Q, Varoni MV, Demontis MP, Anania V, et al. Regulation of bradykinin B2-receptor expression by oestrogen. Br J Pharmacol 1997;121:1763-9.

29. Norris LA, Bonnar J. The effect of oestrogen dose and progesteron type on haemostatic changes in women taking low dose oral contraceptives. BJOG 1996;103:261-7.

30. Thiery M, Vermeulen A, Baele G, Deslypere JP. Effects of a very low estrogen oral contraceptive on clotting factors, carbohydrate metabolism and plasma lipids and lipoproteins. Med Sci Res 1987;15:1231-2.

31. Gordon EM, Williams SR, Frenchek B, Mazur CA, Speroff L. Dose dependant effects of postmenopausal estrogen and progestin on antithrombin III and factor XII. J Lab Clin Med 1988;111:52-6.

32. Gordon EM, Ratnoff OD, Saito H, Donaldson VH, Pensky J, Joes PK. Rapid fibrinolysis, augmented Hageman factor (factor XII) titers, and decreased C1 esterase inhibitor titers in women taking oral contraceptives. J Lab Clin Med 1980;96:762-9.

33. Hoem NO, Johannesen S, Hauge G, Rud AC, Sandem S, Briseid K. Contact activation factors in plasma from women using oral contraceptives increased levels of factor XII, kinin-free high molecular weight kininogen and acetone-activated kallikrein. Thromb Res 1991; 64:427-34.

34. Wessler S. Estrogen associated thromboembolism. Ann Epidemiol 1992;2:439-43.

35. Campbell SJ, Mackie IJ, Robinson GE, Machin SJ. Contact factor mediated fibrinolysis is increased by the combined oral contraceptive pill. BJOG 1993;100:79-84.

36. Luyer D, Khosla S, Owen WG, Miller VM. Prospective randomized study of effects of unopposed estrogen replacement therapy on markers of coagulation and inflammation in postmenopausal women. J Clin Endocrinol Metab 2001;86:3629-34.

37. Madsen JS, Kristensen SR, Gram J, Bladbjerg EM, Henriksen FL, Gram J, et al. Positive impact of hormone replacement therapy on the fibrinolysis system: a long term randomized controlled study in healthy postmenopausal women. J Thromb Haemost 2003;1:1984-91.

38. Teede HJ, McGrath BP, Smolich JJ, Malan E, Kotsopoulos D, Liang YL, et al. Postenopausal hormone replacement therapy increases coagulation activity and fibrinolysis. Arterioscler Thromb Vasc Biol 2000;20:1404-9.

39. Fossum S, Hoem NO, Gjonnaess H, Briseid K. Contact activation factors in plamsa from women on estrogen replacement therapy after ovariohysterectomy. Thromb Res 1999;93: 161-70.

40. Yilmazer M, Fencki V, Fencki S, Aktepe O, Sommerzer M, Kurtay G. Association of serum complement (C3, C4) and immunoglobulin (IgG, IgM) levels with hormone replacement therapy in healthy post-menopausal women. Hum Reprod 2003;18:1531-5.

41. Sumino H, Ichikawa S, Ohyama Y, Nakamura T, Kanda T, Sakamoto H, et al. Effects of hormone replacement therapy on serum angiotensin converting enzyme activity and plasma bradykinin in postmenopausal women according to angiotensin converting enzyme genotype. Hypertens Res 2003;26:53-8.

42. Nogawa N, Sumino H, Ichikawa S, Kumakura H, Takayama Y, Nakamura T, et al. Effect of long term hormone replacement therapy on angiotensin converting enzyme activity and bradykinin in postmenopausal women with essential hypertension and normotensive postmenopausal women. Menopause 2003;8: 210-5.

43. Gallagher PE, Li P, Lenhart JR, Chappell MC, Brosnihan KB. Estrogen regulation of angiotensin converting enzyme mRNA. Hypertension 1999;33:323-8.

44. Visy B, Fust G, Varga L, Szendei G, Takacs E, Karadi I, et al. Sex hormones in hereditary angioneurotic oedema. Clin Endocrinol 2004; 60:508-15.

CLINICAL PRACTICE

Hereditary Angioedema

Bruce L. Zuraw, M.D.

This Journal feature begins with a case vignette highlighting a common clinical problem.
Evidence supporting various strategies is then presented, followed by a review of formal guidelines,
when they exist. The article ends with the author's clinical recommendations.

A 19-year-old woman presents to the emergency department with light-headedness, severe abdominal pain, and intractable nausea and vomiting that began 12 hours earlier. The patient reports previous episodes of abdominal pain and swelling of her hands and feet that have been attributed possibly to food allergies, which have recently become more frequent. There is no associated urticaria. Her only medication is an oral contraceptive that was started 3 months earlier. She notes a history of similar episodes in her father. She is afebrile, with a blood pressure of 75/40 mm Hg, a pulse of 120 beats per minute, and diffuse abdominal tenderness with guarding and rebound tenderness. How should her case be evaluated and treated?

THE CLINICAL PROBLEM

Hereditary angioedema, initially described by Osler in 1888, is an autosomal dominant disease caused by a deficiency in functional C1 inhibitor.[1] Hereditary angioedema is characterized by recurrent episodes of nonpruritic, nonpitting, subcutaneous or submucosal edema typically involving the arms, legs, hands, feet, bowels, genitalia, trunk, face, tongue, or larynx (Fig. 1). Its prevalence is uncertain but is estimated to be approximately 1 case per 50,000 persons, without known differences among ethnic groups.[2] Symptoms typically begin in childhood (often as early as 2 or 3 years of age), worsen around puberty, and persist throughout life, with unpredictable severity. Untreated patients have attacks every 7 to 14 days on average, with the frequency ranging from virtually never to every 3 days.[3,4] There is considerable variation in the severity of hereditary angioedema, even within a kindred.[5] Results of observational studies suggest that minor trauma and stress are frequent precipitants of episodes of swelling, but many attacks occur without an apparent trigger.[6] Pregnancy has a variable effect on disease severity, but attacks are rare at the time of delivery. Patients with hereditary angioedema have an increased frequency of autoimmune diseases, especially glomerulonephritis.[7]

Attacks of hereditary angioedema usually follow a predictable course. Many attacks are preceded by a prodrome (usually a tingling sensation), and approximately a third are accompanied by erythema marginatum, a nonpruritic, serpiginous rash. The swelling classically worsens slowly but relentlessly over the first 24 hours, then gradually subsides over the subsequent 48 to 72 hours. The arms, legs, hands, feet, and abdomen are the most common sites of swelling.[4] Oropharyngeal swelling is less frequent, but over half of patients have had at least one episode of laryngeal angioedema during their lifetime.[4] Attacks may start in one location and then spread to another before resolving.

Hereditary angioedema affecting the abdomen or oropharynx can be associated with significant risk of illness and death.[2,6] Abdominal attacks can cause severe abdominal pain, nausea, and vomiting. Bowel sounds are often diminished or si-

From the University of California at San Diego and the Veterans Affairs Medical Center — both in San Diego. Address reprint requests to Dr. Zuraw at Mail Drop 0732, Department of Medicine, 9500 Gilman Dr., La Jolla, CA 92093-0732, or at bzuraw@ucsd.edu.

N Engl J Med 2008;359:1027-36.
Copyright © 2008 Massachusetts Medical Society.

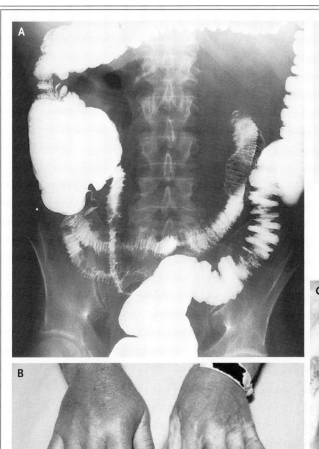

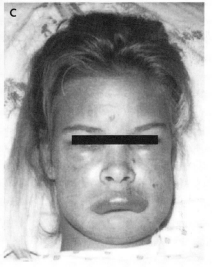

Figure 1. **Swelling in Patients with Hereditary Angioedema.**

Panel A shows the results of a barium study performed in a patient during an abdominal attack; there is clear evidence of submucosal swelling of the distal wall of the small intestine, with spiculation and thickening of intestinal folds. Panel B shows an example of asymmetric swelling of the hands. Another patient is shown during a facial attack (Panel C).

lent, and guarding and rebound tenderness may be present on physical examination, leading in some cases to unnecessary abdominal surgery. A shift of fluids into the interstitium or peritoneal cavity during abdominal attacks can cause clinically significant hypotension. Laryngeal edema poses the greatest risk for patients with hereditary angioedema; although proper diagnosis and treatment should protect them, historical data have suggested that asphyxiation caused over 30% of deaths among patients with this disease in the past.[6] Even today, patients occasionally die from asphyxiation, particularly in the absence of a proper diagnosis.

Hereditary angioedema results from a mutation in the C1-inhibitor gene.[8] According to the C1-inhibitor gene mutation database (HAEdb, http://hae.enzim.hu), over 150 different mutations have been identified in patients with hereditary angioedema.[9-11] There are two main types of hereditary angioedema: type I (accounting for 85% of cases) and type II (15% of cases). These are indistinguishable in clinical presentation but are caused by different mutations. C1-inhibitor mutations that cause type I hereditary angioedema occur throughout the gene and result in truncated or misfolded proteins that are not efficiently secreted, with decreases in both antigenic and functional levels of C1 inhibitor. Mutations that cause type II hereditary angioedema usually involve exon 8 at or near the active site, resulting in a mutant protein that is secreted but is dysfunctional; antigenic C1-inhibitor levels are normal but functional C1-inhibitor levels are low.

A third type of familial angioedema has also been described,[12,13] in which patients have normal antigenic and functional C1-inhibitor levels. The first description indicated a dependence on increased estrogen levels, with angioedema involving only women, particularly during pregnancy or treatment with exogenous estrogen. Subsequently, kindreds with some affected men have also been described. Clinically, patients with familial angioedema are virtually indistinguishable from those with hereditary angioedema, except that a higher percentage of their attacks are facial.[14] Several but not all kindreds have a gain-of-function mutation in coagulation factor XII that may predict enhanced generation of bradykinin.[15,16]

C1 inhibitor, a member of the serpin family of serine protease inhibitors, is the major inhibitor of several complement proteases (C1r, C1s, and mannose-binding lectin–associated serine protease [MASP] 1 and 2) and contact-system proteases (plasma kallikrein and coagulation factor XIIa) and a relatively minor inhibitor of the fibrinolytic protease plasmin and the coagulation protease factor XIa (Fig. 2).[8] During attacks of hereditary angioedema, these plasma proteolytic cascades are activated, and several vasoactive substances are generated. Studies have shown that bradykinin is the predominant mediator of enhanced vascular permeability in hereditary-angioedema attacks.[17] Bradykinin is a nanopeptide generated by activation of the contact system that can potently increase vascular permeability by binding to its cognate receptor (the bradykinin B2 receptor) on vascular endothelial cells. Consistent with these findings in humans is the demonstration that homozygous C1-inhibitor–knockout mice have a persistent defect in vascular permeability that is dependent on bradykinin.[18]

STRATEGIES AND EVIDENCE

DIAGNOSIS

Delays in diagnosis are common in patients with hereditary angioedema. The average time between the onset of symptoms and the diagnosis was 22 years as of 1977 and was still more than 10 years as of 2005.[6,19] The diagnosis should be suspected in any patient who presents with recurrent angioedema or abdominal pain in the absence of associated urticaria. Although most patients report a family history of angioedema, up to 25% have a

de novo C1-inhibitor mutation.[20] The differential diagnosis and major distinguishing features of hereditary angioedema are described in Table 1.

Laboratory testing is needed to confirm or rule out the diagnosis. Virtually all patients with hereditary angioedema have a persistently low antigenic C4 level with normal antigenic C1 and C3 levels.[20,21] Measurement of C4 levels is a cost-effective screening test to rule out hereditary angioedema, although in rare cases, the C4 level is normal between attacks.[21] Subsequent measurement of antigenic and functional C1-inhibitor levels confirms the diagnosis of hereditary angioedema and distinguishes between type I (low antigenic and functional C1-inhibitor levels) and type II (normal antigenic C1-inhibitor level but low functional C1-inhibitor activity).[22,23] In rare cases, patients with inherited angioedema have normal functional C1-inhibitor levels; some but not all of these patients are found to have a factor XII mutation.

MANAGEMENT

Optimal management of hereditary angioedema includes treatment of acute attacks, short-term prophylaxis to prevent an attack, and long-term prophylaxis to minimize the frequency and severity of recurrent attacks.

Short-Term Treatment

Purified C1-inhibitor replacement therapy has been shown to be highly effective and without serious adverse effects in randomized, controlled trials.[24,25] It is the main treatment for acute attacks of hereditary angioedema in many countries.[26-29] Attacks typically begin to resolve within 30 to 60 minutes after intravenous injection of C1 inhibitor (500 to 2000 U).[26-29] However, C1-inhibitor replacement therapy is not currently approved in the United States.

There are no other approved or well-studied treatments for acute attacks of hereditary angioedema, although various interventions have been suggested. Fresh-frozen plasma contains C1 inhibitor, and several uncontrolled studies have reported a benefit of its use in acute attacks of hereditary angioedema.[30] However, such use is controversial because fresh-frozen plasma also contains contact-system proteins that may provide substrate for additional generation of bradykinin, which could exacerbate attacks in some patients. This is a particular concern in patients

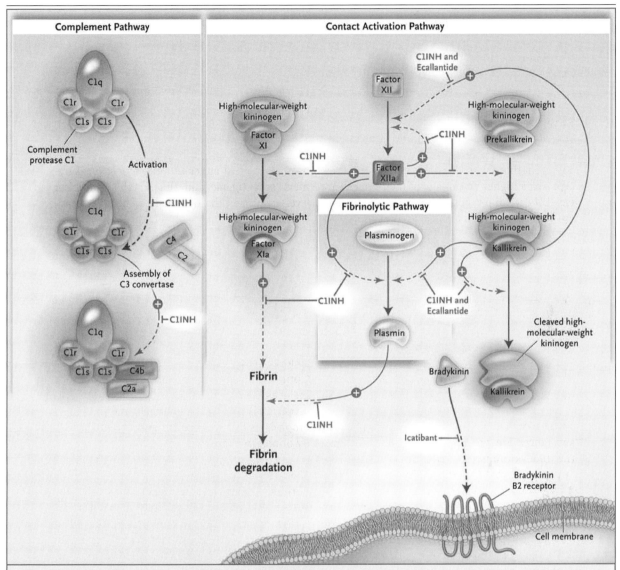

Figure 2. Pathways Inhibited by C1 Inhibitor (C1INH) and New Drugs.

In the classic complement pathway, the complement protease C1 is activated and then assembles the C3 convertase. (Activation is indicated by horizontal bars over the complement names.) In the contact activation pathway, trace amounts of factor XIIa activate additional factor XII, as well as prekallikrein. Activated factor XIIa activates factor XI to factor XIa, leading to enhanced fibrin formation. Activated factor XIIa and kallikrein activate each other, and then plasma kallikrein cleaves high-molecular-weight kininogen to release bradykinin. In the fibrinolytic pathway, plasminogen is activated to plasmin, which cleaves fibrin. Proteolytic activities are indicated with green arrows and point toward the steps they catalyze. Steps inhibited by C1INH, through conventional or new types of therapy, or by two other new drugs being investigated for the treatment of hereditary angioedema are shown with red T bars.

with laryngeal angioedema, who may require emergency intubation if the swelling worsens.

Clinical experience indicates that epinephrine may provide a transient benefit, occasionally (but not predictably) obviating the need for intubation.[31] Neither corticosteroids nor antihistamines have been shown to provide a meaningful benefit during attacks of hereditary angioedema and should not be used for this indication. Although 17α-alkylated androgens and antifibrinolytic drugs are efficacious in preventing attacks of hereditary angioedema, they do not become effective for several days, making them unsuitable for short-term treatment.

Symptomatic control is currently the cornerstone of therapy in the United States. Manage-

Table 1. Clinical and Laboratory Findings Associated with Angioedema of Various Causes.*

Type of Angioedema	Clinical Findings	Laboratory Findings				
		C4 Level	Antigenic C1-Inhibitor Level	Functional C1-Inhibitor Level	C1q Level	C3 Level
Hereditary angioedema	Recurrent angioedema and abdominal attacks without urticaria; attacks are episodic, with intervals between periods of swelling; onset in childhood or young adulthood, with worsening around the time of puberty; prolonged attacks (typically 72–96 hr in duration); family history in 75% of patients; attacks do not respond to antihistamines or corticosteroids	Decreased	Decreased (in type I) or normal (in type II)	Decreased	Normal	Normal
Acquired C1-inhibitor deficiency	Attacks similar to those in hereditary angioedema; onset in middle age or later; absence of family history; attacks do not respond to antihistamines or corticosteroids	Decreased	Decreased or normal	Decreased	Decreased	Normal or decreased
Inherited angioedema with normal C1-inhibitor levels	Family history of angioedema; possible preponderance of women among affected persons; may be estrogen-dependent; typically manifested after childhood; face, tongue, and extremities affected more than abdomen; attacks do not respond to antihistamines or corticosteroids	Normal	Normal	Normal	Normal	Normal
ACE-I–associated angioedema	History of ACE-I use; angioedema tends to affect face and tongue; more common in blacks and smokers than other subgroups; patients can usually tolerate angiotensin-receptor blockers	Normal	Normal	Normal	Normal	Normal
Idiopathic angioedema	Angioedema sometimes accompanied by urticaria; swelling typically lasts up to 48 hr; attacks may occur daily; attacks relieved with antihistamines or corticosteroids	Normal	Normal	Normal	Normal	Normal
Allergic angioedema	Angioedema usually accompanied by urticaria and sometimes anaphylaxis; may be pruritic; associated with exposure to food, venom, latex, drug or environmental allergen; attacks typically last 24–48 hr; attacks relieved with antihistamines or corticosteroids	Normal	Normal	Normal	Normal	Normal
NSAID-associated angioedema	Angioedema after ingestion of an NSAID; typically accompanied by urticaria; usually class-specific reaction due to pharmacologic effect of cyclooxygenase inhibition, but allergic in rare instances	Normal	Normal	Normal	Normal	Normal
Angioedema with urticarial vasculitis	Angioedema usually accompanied by urticaria; skin may show petechiae or purpura after resolution of swelling; often there are other symptoms that are consistent with underlying vasculitis	Decreased	Normal	Normal	Decreased	Decreased

* ACE-I denotes angiotensin-converting–enzyme inhibitor, and NSAID nonsteroidal antiinflammatory drug.

ment of abdominal attacks often requires the use of narcotic analgesics; addiction is a concern in patients with frequent attacks, and some patients are inappropriately considered to be "drug seeking." Antiemetic agents and aggressive fluid replacement are also mainstays of therapy.

Management of oropharyngeal attacks focuses on maintaining the patency of the airway. All patients with hereditary angioedema who have an oropharyngeal attack should be closely observed in a facility where rapid intubation or tracheotomy can be performed if necessary. Patients should be closely monitored for evidence of impending airway closure, including a change in voice, loss of the ability to swallow, and difficulty breathing; if any of these develop, elective intubation should be considered. The anatomy of the airway can be highly distorted by the angioedema, so immediate availability of backup tracheotomy is necessary. Direct visualization of the airway is discouraged if immediate airway support is not available, since the trauma of the procedure can worsen the angioedema.

Short-Term Prophylaxis

Short-term prophylactic treatment to prevent attacks of hereditary angioedema is useful in patients with planned exposure to a situation likely to trigger an attack, such as substantial dental work, invasive medical procedures, and surgical procedures. Consensus guidelines based on uncontrolled studies recommend that patients with hereditary angioedema be protected from severe swelling by means of prophylactic treatment with C1 inhibitor (500 to 1500 U given 1 hour before the provoking event) or, when C1 inhibitor is not available, by means of temporarily increasing plasma C1-inhibitor levels through treatment with high-dose 17α-alkylated androgens (e.g., danazol at a dose of 200 mg orally three times a day) for 5 to 10 days before the provoking event or through administration of 2 U of fresh-frozen plasma 1 to 12 hours before the event.[32,33] Although as compared with androgens, fresh-frozen plasma is more expensive and associated with a risk of infection, it is generally considered more effective in preventing or minimizing attacks (in contrast to its uncertain role in the treatment of acute attacks).

Long-Term Prophylaxis

For patients with hereditary angioedema who have frequent or severe attacks, long-term prophylaxis should be considered. Randomized trials

have shown that 17α-alkylated androgens and antifibrinolytic drugs significantly reduce the frequency of attacks; patients treated with either agent were attack-free 90% of the time during a 28-day period, as compared with little or none of the time among those receiving placebo. Although the two agents have not been compared head to head, 17α-alkylated androgens appear to be more effective.[34-37] Table 2 shows the drugs and doses commonly used for long-term prophylaxis against attacks of hereditary angioedema. In all patients, the dose should be slowly adjusted to the lowest that provides effective control of the hereditary angioedema, as measured by the clinical response; laboratory tests are not helpful in guiding decisions about the dosage.

Major side effects of 17α-alkylated androgens (cholestatic jaundice, peliosis hepatis, hepatocellular adenomas, and lipid abnormalities) and antifibrinolytic agents (muscle cramps, increased enzyme concentrations in muscle, and potential risk of thrombosis) are dose related and are reviewed in Table 2.[38-41] In patients treated with 17α-alkylated androgens, liver enzyme levels and serum lipid profiles should be monitored regularly (every 6 to 12 months). Because of reports of an association between the prolonged use of 17α-alkylated androgens and liver adenoma or carcinoma,[42,43] periodic liver ultrasonography is recommended for monitoring, particularly in patients with elevated hepatic enzyme levels who have been receiving therapy for more than 10 years. The risk of this complication is not well defined but is of greater concern with longer-term use.

The care of children and pregnant women with hereditary angioedema is complicated by concern about potential adverse effects of 17α-alkylated androgens on growth and development, particularly masculinization of the fetus, premature puberty, and premature closure of epiphyseal plates.[31,44] Antifibrinolytic drugs have therefore been recommended as the first choice in children and pregnant women who require long-term prophylaxis.[44] Nevertheless, there is evidence from uncontrolled trials that low-dose 17α-alkylated androgens can be safely used in children.[44] Oxandrolone has been approved for pediatric use and thus is the preferred 17α-alkylated androgen for the treatment of children.[45]

Patients with hereditary angioedema should be advised to avoid stimuli that may precipitate attacks. Because angiotensin-converting–enzyme inhibitors slow the catabolism of bradykinin,

Table 2. Drugs Commonly Used as Long-Term Prophylaxis for Hereditary Angioedema.*

Drug Class and Name	Usual Adult Dose (Range)	Usual Pediatric Dose (Range)	FDA-Approved for Hereditary Angioedema		Side Effects
			Adults	Children	
17α-Alkylated androgens					
Danazol (Danocrine, Sanofi–Synthelabo)	200 mg/day (100 mg every 3 days–600 mg/day)	50 mg/day (50 mg/wk–200 mg/day)	Yes	No	Common: weight gain, virilization, acne, altered libido, muscle pains and cramps, headaches, depression, fatigue, nausea, constipation, menstrual abnormalities, increase in liver enzymes, hypertension, and alterations in lipid profile
Stanozolol (Winstrol, Winthrop)	2 mg/day (1 mg every 3 days–6 mg/day)	0.5–1 mg/day for children <6 yr; 0.5–2 mg/day for children 6–12 yr	Yes	Yes	Uncommon: decreased growth rate in children, masculinization of the female fetus, cholestatic jaundice, peliosis hepatis, and hepatocellular adenoma
Oxandrolone (Oxandrin, Savient Pharmaceuticals)	10 mg/day (2.5 mg every 3 days–20 mg/day)	0.1 mg/kg/day	No	No	
Methyltestosterone (Android, Valeant Pharmaceuticals)	In men only, 10 mg/day (5 mg every 3 days–30 mg/day)	Not recommended for use in children	No	No	
Antifibrinolytic agents					
Epsilon aminocaproic acid (Amicar, Xanodyne Pharmaceuticals)	2 g thrice daily (1 g twice daily–4 g thrice daily)	0.05 g/kg twice daily (0.025 g/kg twice daily–0.1 g/kg twice daily)	No	No	Common: nausea, vertigo, diarrhea, postural hypotension, fatigue, muscle cramps with increased muscle enzymes
Tranexamic acid (Cyklokapron, Pfizer)	1 g twice daily (0.25 g twice daily–1.5 g thrice daily)	20 mg/kg twice daily (10 mg/kg twice daily–25 mg/kg thrice daily)	No	No	Uncommon: thrombosis

* All the listed drugs are approved by the Food and Drug Administration (FDA) but not necessarily for the indication of hereditary angioedema. Dosage information for danazol is from Farkas et al.[44] and Gompels et al.[53] and for epsilon aminocaproic acid and tranexamic acid is from Agostoni et al.,[31] Farkas et al.,[44] and Gompels et al.[53]

their use is contraindicated in such patients.[46] Similarly, exogenous estrogens (oral contraceptive pills or hormone-replacement therapy) may exacerbate hereditary angioedema as well as familial angioedema with normal C1-inhibitor levels,[6,47] and caution should be exercised in their use. A recent observational study of oral contraceptive use in patients with hereditary angioedema showed that progestin-only oral contraceptives did not worsen the symptoms of hereditary angioedema and might even improve them.[48] Stress is a known precipitant of attacks of hereditary angioedema, and although there is no direct evidence, stress reduction may substantively improve disease control.

AREAS OF UNCERTAINTY

Despite progress in elucidating the biochemical and molecular characteristics of hereditary angioedema, the mechanisms underlying the initiation and resolution of attacks remain unknown. The severity of symptoms of hereditary angio-edema is highly variable and does not correlate well with plasma C1-inhibitor levels. Other factors, such as polymorphisms in the bradykinin receptor or contact-system proteins or variations in the level or function of kininases,[49,50] probably modify the severity of the disease, but these factors remain incompletely understood.

Optimal strategies for managing acute attacks still need to be defined. Five new drugs (Table 3) have been studied in phase 3 clinical trials for the treatment of hereditary angioedema,[51] although none are currently approved by the Food and Drug Administration. All have shown significant efficacy in the treatment of acute attacks, and one (nanofiltered C1 inhibitor) also provided a significant benefit as long-term prophylaxis. Further data are needed to inform the role of these agents in practice. Questions include whether drugs targeting the bradykinin pathway alone (ecallantide and icatibant) are as effective as C1-inhibitor replacement therapy, whether recombinant C1 inhibitor is as effective as plasma-derived C1 inhibitor, whether there

Table 3. New Drugs under Investigation for Treatment of Hereditary Angioedema.

Drug	Potential Indications	Dose	Mechanism*	Anticipated Potential Side Effects
Plasma-derived nanofiltered C1 inhibitor (Cinryze, Lev Pharmaceuticals)	Acute attacks, short-term prophylaxis, long-term prophylaxis	1000 U intravenously	Inhibits plasma kallikrein, coagulation factors XIIa and XIa, C1s, C1r, MASP-1, MASP-2, and plasmin	Rare: anaphylaxis Theoretical: transmission of infectious agent
Plasma-derived C1 inhibitor (Berinert-P, CSL Behring)	Acute attacks, short-term prophylaxis, long-term prophylaxis	20 U per kg intravenously	Inhibits plasma kallikrein, coagulation factors XIIa and XIa, C1s, C1r, MASP-1, MASP-2, and plasmin	Rare: anaphylaxis Theoretical: transmission of infectious agent
Recombinant human C1 inhibitor (Rhucin, Pharming)	Acute attacks, short-term prophylaxis	50–100 U per kg intravenously	Inhibits plasma kallikrein, coagulation factors XIIa and XIa, C1s, C1r, MASP-1, MASP-2, and plasmin	Uncommon: anaphylaxis
Ecallantide (Dyax)†	Acute attacks	30 mg subcutaneously	Inhibits plasma kallikrein	Common: prolonged partial-thromboplastin time Uncommon: development of antidrug antibodies, anaphylaxis
Icatibant (Firazyr, Jerini)	Acute attacks	30 mg subcutaneously	Bradykinin B2 receptor antagonist	Common: discomfort at injection site

* MASP denotes mannose-binding lectin–associated serine protease.
† There is currently no trade name for ecallantide.

are clinically relevant differences in the responses to these drugs, and which patients would benefit from long-term prophylaxis with C1 inhibitor. Additional studies are needed to determine the value of prophylactic treatment as compared with on-demand treatment for acute attacks as well as to assess the benefits and risks of allowing patients to use these new drugs at home to treat attacks at an early point in their course.[52] The optimal approach to the diagnosis and treatment of inherited angioedema with normal C1 inhibitor levels remains unknown.

GUIDELINES

Consensus guidelines regarding the diagnosis and management of hereditary angioedema have recently been published.[53] The recommendations in this article are generally consistent with these guidelines, except that plasma-derived C1 inhibitor is unavailable in the United States.

CONCLUSIONS AND RECOMMENDATIONS

The presentation of the young woman described in the vignette is consistent with an abdominal attack of hereditary angioedema. The escalation

in attack frequency may be related to the use of an oral contraceptive. A detailed family and personal history generally suggests the diagnosis of hereditary angioedema and reduces the likelihood of inappropriate surgical intervention for abdominal pain. Measurement of the C4 level is an effective screening test for hereditary angioedema; documentation of a low level should be followed by measurement of the C1-inhibitor level and the C1 level to confirm the clinical diagnosis and rule out acquired C1-inhibitor deficiency. Patients with hypotension and severe abdominal pain, like the woman in the vignette, need to be hospitalized and treated with aggressive intravenous hydration to restore vascular volume, pain medications (including narcotics if necessary), and antiemetic agents. I would advise this patient to discontinue her oral contraceptive pills and use nonhormonal means of contraception or possibly a progestin-only oral contraceptive. Given the severity of her attacks, I would prescribe a medication to reduce the frequency of attacks; I generally start with low-dose danazol, typically 100 mg per day in young women, with an increase or decrease in the dose after 1 month, depending on the initial response. The course of hereditary angioedema is unpredictable; the danazol dose may need to be increased (to 200 mg per day) or slowly tapered and stopped. Finally, the patient should be given a card to keep with her that identifies her as having hereditary angioedema and contains information about appropriate emergency treatment.

Dr. Zuraw reports receiving consulting fees from Lev Pharmaceuticals, Jerini, CSL Behring, and Dyax and grant support from Lev Pharmaceuticals and Pharming. No other potential conflict of interest relevant to this article was reported.

REFERENCES

1. Donaldson VH, Evans RR. A biochemical abnormality in hereditary angioneurotic edema: absence of serum inhibitor of C' 1-esterase. Am J Med 1963;35:37-44.
2. Nzeako UC, Frigas E, Tremaine WJ. Hereditary angioedema: a broad review for clinicians. Arch Intern Med 2001;161: 2417-29.
3. Agostoni A, Cicardi M. Hereditary and acquired C1-inhibitor deficiency: biological and clinical characteristics in 235 patients. Medicine (Baltimore) 1992;71: 206-15.
4. Bork K, Meng G, Staubach P, Hardt J. Hereditary angioedema: new findings concerning symptoms, affected organs, and course. Am J Med 2006;119:267-74.
5. Winnewisser J, Rossi M, Späth P, Bürgi H. Type I hereditary angio-oedema: variability of clinical presentation and course within two large kindreds. J Intern Med 1997;241:39-46.
6. Frank MM, Gelfand JA, Atkinson JP. Hereditary angioedema: the clinical syndrome and its management. Ann Intern Med 1976;84:580-93.
7. Brickman CM, Tsokos GC, Balow JE, et al. Immunoregulatory disorders associated with hereditary angioedema. I. Clinical manifestations of autoimmune disease. J Allergy Clin Immunol 1986;77: 749-57.
8. Davis AE III. C1 inhibitor and hereditary angioneurotic edema. Annu Rev Immunol 1988;6:595-628.
9. Bissler JJ, Aulak KS, Donaldson VH, et al. Molecular defects in hereditary angioneurotic edema. Proc Assoc Am Physicians 1997;109:164-73.
10. Verpy E, Biasotto M, Brai M, Misiano G, Meo T, Tosi M. Exhaustive mutation scanning by fluorescence-assisted mismatch analysis discloses new genotype-phenotype correlations in angioedema. Am J Hum Genet 1996;59:308-19.
11. Zuraw BL, Herschbach J. Detection of C1 inhibitor mutations in patients with hereditary angioedema. J Allergy Clin Immunol 2000;105:541-6.
12. Binkley KE, Davis A III. Clinical, biochemical, and genetic characterization of a novel estrogen-dependent inherited form of angioedema. J Allergy Clin Immunol 2000;106:546-50.
13. Bork K, Barnstedt SE, Koch P, Traupe H. Hereditary angioedema with normal C1-inhibitor activity in women. Lancet 2000;356:213-7.
14. Bork K, Gül D, Hardt J, Dewald G. Hereditary angioedema with normal C1 inhibitor: clinical symptoms and course. Am J Med 2007;120:987-92.
15. Cichon S, Martin L, Hennies HC, et al. Increased activity of coagulation factor XII (Hageman factor) causes hereditary angioedema type III. Am J Hum Genet 2006;79:1098-104.
16. Dewald G, Bork K. Missense mutations in the coagulation factor XII (Hageman factor) gene in hereditary angioedema with normal C1 inhibitor. Biochem Biophys Res Commun 2006;343:1286-9.
17. Davis AE III. Mechanism of angioedema in first complement component inhibitor deficiency. Immunol Allergy Clin North Am 2006;26:633-51.
18. Han ED, MacFarlane RC, Mulligan AN, Scafidi J, Davis AE III. Increased vascular permeability in C1 inhibitor-deficient mice mediated by the bradykinin type 2 receptor. J Clin Invest 2002;109:1057-63.
19. Roche O, Blanch A, Caballero T, Sastre N, Callejo D, López-Trascasa M. Hereditary angioedema due to C1 inhibitor deficiency: patient registry and approach to the prevalence in Spain. Ann Allergy Asthma Immunol 2005;94:498-503.
20. Pappalardo E, Cicardi M, Duponchel C, et al. Frequent de novo mutations and exon deletions in the C1 inhibitor gene of patients with angioedema. J Allergy Clin Immunol 2000;106:1147-54.
21. Zuraw BL, Sugimoto S, Curd JG. The value of rocket immunoelectrophoresis for C4 activation in the evaluation of patients with angioedema or C1-inhibitor deficiency. J Allergy Clin Immunol 1986; 78:1115-20.
22. Rosen FS, Alper CA, Pensky J, Klemperer MR, Donaldson VH. Genetically determined heterogeneity of the C1 esterase inhibitor in patients with hereditary angioneurotic edema. J Clin Invest 1971;50: 2143-9.
23. Rosen FS, Pensky J, Donaldson VH, Charache P. Hereditary angioneurotic edema: two genetic variants. Science 1965; 148:957-8.
24. Waytes AT, Rosen FS, Frank MM. Treatment of hereditary angioedema with a vapor-heated C1 inhibitor concentrate. N Engl J Med 1996;334:1630-4.
25. Kunschak M, Engl W, Maritsch F, et al. A randomized, controlled trial to study the efficacy and safety of C1 inhibitor concentrate in treating hereditary angioedema. Transfusion 1998;38:540-9.
26. Bork K, Barnstedt SE. Treatment of 193 episodes of laryngeal edema with C1 inhibitor concentrate in patients with hereditary angioedema. Arch Intern Med 2001;161:714-8.
27. Cicardi M, Zingale L. How do we treat patients with hereditary angioedema. Transfus Apher Sci 2003;29:221-7.
28. Farkas H, Jakab L, Temesszentandrási G, et al. Hereditary angioedema: a decade of human C1-inhibitor concentrate therapy. J Allergy Clin Immunol 2007;120:941-7.
29. Bork K, Meng G, Staubach P, Hardt J. Treatment with C1 inhibitor concentrate in abdominal pain attacks of patients with hereditary angioedema. Transfusion 2005; 45:1774-84.
30. Prematta M, Gibbs JG, Pratt EL, Stoughton TR, Craig TJ. Fresh frozen plasma for the treatment of hereditary angioedema. Ann Allergy Asthma Immunol 2007;98:383-8.
31. Agostoni A, Aygören-Pürsün E, Binkley KE, et al. Hereditary and acquired angioedema: problems and progress: proceedings of the third C1 Esterase Inhibitor Deficiency Workshop and beyond. J Allergy Clin Immunol 2004;114:Suppl:S51-S131.
32. Jaffe CJ, Atkinson JP, Gelfand JA, Frank MM. Hereditary angioedema: the use of fresh frozen plasma for prophylaxis in patients undergoing oral surgery. J Allergy Clin Immunol 1975;55:386-93.
33. Bowen T, Cicardi M, Bork K, et al. Hereditary angioedema: a current state-of-the-art review. VII. Canadian Hungarian 2007 International Consensus Algorithm for the Diagnosis, Therapy, and Management of Hereditary Angioedema. Ann Allergy Asthma Immunol 2008;100:Suppl 2: S30-S40.
34. Frank MM, Sergent JS, Kane MA, Alling DW. Epsilon aminocaproic acid therapy of hereditary angioneurotic edema: a double-blind study. N Engl J Med 1972; 286:808-12.
35. Gelfand JA, Sherins RJ, Alling DW, Frank MM. Treatment of hereditary angioedema with danazol: reversal of clinical and biochemical abnormalities. N Engl J Med 1976;295:1444-8.
36. Frank MM. Hereditary angioedema: the clinical syndrome and its management in the United States. Immunol Allergy Clin North Am 2006;26:653-68.
37. Sheffer AL, Austen KF, Rosen FS. Tranexamic acid therapy in hereditary angioneurotic edema. N Engl J Med 1972;287: 452-4.
38. Cicardi M, Castelli R, Zingale LC, Agostoni A. Side effects of long-term prophylaxis with attenuated androgens in hereditary angioedema: comparison of

treated and untreated patients. J Allergy Clin Immunol 1997;99:194-6.

39. Széplaki G, Varga L, Valentin S, et al. Adverse effects of danazol prophylaxis on the lipid profiles of patients with hereditary angioedema. J Allergy Clin Immunol 2005;115:864-9.

40. Sloane DE, Lee CW, Sheffer AL. Hereditary angioedema: safety of long-term stanozolol therapy. J Allergy Clin Immunol 2007;120:654-8.

41. Bork K, Bygum A, Hardt J. Benefits and risks of danazol in hereditary angioedema: a long-term survey of 118 patients. Ann Allergy Asthma Immunol 2008;100: 153-61.

42. Bork K, Pitton M, Harten P, Koch P. Hepatocellular adenomas in patients taking danazol for hereditary angio-oedema. Lancet 1999;353:1066-7.

43. Monnier N, Ponard D, Duponchel C, et al. Characterisation of a new C1 inhibitor mutant in a patient with hepatocellular carcinoma. Mol Immunol 2006;43: 2161-8.

44. Farkas H, Varga L, Széplaki G, Visy B, Harmat G, Bowen T. Management of hereditary angioedema in pediatric patients. Pediatrics 2007;120(3):e713-e722.

45. Church JA. Oxandrolone treatment of childhood hereditary angioedema. Ann Allergy Asthma Immunol 2004;92:377-8.

46. Byrd JB, Adam A, Brown NJ. Angiotensin-converting enzyme inhibitor-associated angioedema. Immunol Allergy Clin North Am 2006;26:725-37.

47. Frank MM. Effect of sex hormones on the complement-related clinical disorder of hereditary angioedema. Arthritis Rheum 1979;22:1295-9.

48. Bouillet L, Longhurst H, Boccon-Gibod I, et al. Disease expression in women with hereditary angioedema. Am J Obstet Gynecol 2008 June 11 (Epub ahead of print).

49. Lung CC, Chan EKL, Zuraw BL. Analysis of an exon 1 polymorphism of the B2 bradykinin receptor gene and its transcript in normal subjects and patients with C1 inhibitor deficiency. J Allergy Clin Immunol 1997;99:134-46.

50. Drouet C, Désormeaux A, Robillard J, et al. Metallopeptidase activities in hereditary angioedema: effect of androgen prophylaxis on plasma aminopeptidase P. J Allergy Clin Immunol 2008;121:429-33.

51. Zuraw BL, Christiansen SC. New promise and hope for treating hereditary angioedema. Expert Opin Investig Drugs 2008;17:697-706.

52. Levi M, Choi G, Picavet C, Hack CE. Self-administration of C1-inhibitor concentrate in patients with hereditary or acquired angioedema caused by C1-inhibitor deficiency. J Allergy Clin Immunol 2006; 117:904-8.

53. Gompels MM, Lock RJ, Abinun M, et al. C1 inhibitor deficiency: consensus document. Clin Exp Immunol 2005;139:379-94. [Erratum, Clin Exp Immunol 2005;141: 189-90.]

AUTHOR INDEX